THE PHYSIOLOGY OF INSECTA

Second Edition

VOLUME I

CONTRIBUTORS

IVAR P. S. AGRELL

ARNOLD DE LOOF

JAN DE WILDE

LAWRENCE I. GILBERT

ANDERS M. LUNDQUIST

JAIME MIQUEL

MORRIS ROCKSTEIN

DAVID SHAW KING

THE PHYSIOLOGY OF INSECTA

Second Edition

Edited by *MORRIS ROCKSTEIN*

Department of Physiology and Biophysics
University of Miami School of Medicine
Miami, Florida

Volume I

1973

ACADEMIC PRESS   New York and London

A Subsidiary of Harcourt Brace Jovanovich, Publishers

ACADEMIC PRESS, INC.
111 Fifth Avenue, New York, New York 10003

United Kingdom Edition published by
ACADEMIC PRESS, INC. (LONDON) LTD.
24/28 Oval Road, London NW1

Library of Congress Cataloging in Publication Data

Rockstein, Morris, ed.
    The physiology of Insecta.

    Includes bibliographies.
    1. Insects—Physiology.   I.   Title.
QL495.R58   1973   595.7'01   72-9986
ISBN 0-12-591601-9

CONTENTS

LIST OF CONTRIBUTORS   vii

PREFACE   ix

PREFACE TO FIRST EDITION   xi

CONTENTS OF OTHER VOLUMES   xiii

Physiology of Ontogeny—Biology, Development, and Aging

Chapter 1. BIOLOGY OF THE INSECTA

Morris Rockstein

Biology of the Insecta   3

References   8

Chapter 2. REPRODUCTION

Jan de Wilde and Arnold de Loof

I. Structure and Origin of the Female Reproductive System   12

II. Oogenesis   17

III. Oviposition: Accessory Glands   54

IV. Fertility and Sterility   57

V. Structure and Origin of the Male Reproductive System   61

VI. Formation of Sperm and Semen   64

VII. Courtship and the Role of Pheromones   70

VIII. Insemination: The Copulatory Act   72

IX. Determination of Sex and Sexual Characters: Parthenogenesis   78

References   85

Chapter 3. REPRODUCTION—ENDOCRINE CONTROL

Jan de Wilde and Arnold de Loof

I.	Control of Oogenesis	97
II.	Control of Semen Production	136
III.	Control of Sexual Behavior and Oviposition	141
IV.	Social Relations in Control of Reproduction	144
	References	150

Chapter 4. PHYSIOLOGICAL AND BIOCHEMICAL CHANGES
DURING INSECT DEVELOPMENT

Ivar P. S. Agrell and Anders M. Lundquist

I.	Introduction	159
II.	Embryonic Development	160
III.	Postembryonic Development	208
IV.	Prospects for Future Work in the Physiology and Biochemistry of Insect Development	231
	References	233

Chapter 5. PHYSIOLOGY OF GROWTH AND DEVELOPMENT:
ENDOCRINE ASPECTS

Lawrence I. Gilbert and David Shaw King

I.	Introduction	250
II.	The Endocrine Glands: Structure and General Functions	252
III.	Endocrine Gland Interactions	262
IV.	The Molting Hormone—Chemistry and Metabolism	271
V.	The Juvenile Hormone—Chemistry and Metabolism	288
VI.	The Action of Insect Hormones	299
VII.	Conclusions	352
	References	354
	Supplementary References	368

Chapter 6. AGING IN INSECTS

Morris Rockstein and Jaime Miquel

I.	Insects in the Study of Aging	371
II.	Adult Life Span of Insects	377
III.	Factors Influencing Life Span	391
IV.	Manifestations of Senescence	424
V.	Evolution of Aging	468
VI.	Summary	470
	References	471

AUTHOR INDEX	479
SUBJECT INDEX	502

LIST OF CONTRIBUTORS

Numbers in parentheses indicate the pages on which the authors' contributions begin.

IVAR P. S. AGRELL (159), Zoophysiological Institute at the University of Lund, Lund, Sweden

ARNOLD DE LOOF (11, 97), Faculteit der Landbouwwetenschappen, Rijksuniversiteit Ghent, Belgium

JAN DE WILDE (11, 97), Laboratorium voor Entomologie, Landbouwhogeschool, Wageningen, The Netherlands

LAWRENCE I. GILBERT (249), Department of Biological Sciences, Northwestern University, Evanston, Illinois

ANDERS M. LUNDQUIST (159), Zoophysiological Institute at the University of Lund, Lund, Sweden

JAIME MIQUEL (371), NASA, Ames Research Center, Moffett Field, California

MORRIS ROCKSTEIN (3, 371), Department of Physiology and Biophysics, University of Miami School of Medicine, Miami, Florida

DAVID SHAW KING (249), Zoëcon Corporation, Palo Alto, California

PREFACE

Since the first edition of this multivolume treatise appeared, well over eight years ago, there has been a notable expansion of scientific endeavor in each of the various aspects of insect physiology. Accordingly, revising this major reference work has been a challenging undertaking both to the original authors as well as to the several new contributors in areas in which growth of research and, therefore, the revelant body of knowledge has grown so much as to warrant such additional coverage. Consequently, the original three-volume work has now grown "like Topsy" to a thoroughly revised six-volume treatise.

In this first volume, specifically, the chapter on aging now includes both physiological as well as histological and microanatomical manifestations of the aging process in insects.

Volume II includes two entirely new and distinct chapters: Radiation by Dr. D. S. Grosch and Circadian Rhythms and Photoperiodism in Insects by Dr. D. S. Saunders. Subsequent volumes will similarly include new chapters: Insect Pheromones by Dr. M. Jacobson, The Pharmacology of the Insect Nervous System by Dr. Y. Pichon, Protein Synthesis in Insects by Drs. Joseph and Judith Ilan, and Microsomal Mixed Function Oxidases by Drs. A. S. Perry and M. Agosin. The Physiology of Insect Behavior, originally a single chapter by Professors Markl and Lindauer, has now been expanded and appears as two separate chapters: one on the physiology of insect behavior by Professor Markl and the second on social behavior and mutual communication by Professor Lindauer. Similarly the Circulatory System of Insects, formerly covered in one chapter by Dr. Jack Jones, has now been subdivided into three chapters: Circulation by Dr.

Jack Jones, Electrophysiology of the Insect Heart by Dr. T. A. Miller, and Hemocytes by Dr. J. W. Arnold. These chapters appear in Volume V. Likewise the original chapter on respiration: Aerial Gas Transport by Dr. P. L. Miller has been expanded into two chapters: Respiration: Aerial Gas Transport by Dr. P. L. Miller and Respiration: Aquatic Insects by Dr. P. J. Mill. Some additional new contributors have been added to the roster of authors as co-authors, namely, Drs. Arnold de Loof, Anders M. Lunquist, David S. King, and Jaime Miquel in this volume and Drs. G. Bernard, H. H. Seliger, and M. DeLuca in Volume II.

Once again I am deeply indebted to my former teacher and mentor, Professor A. Glenn Richards, whose criticism and suggestions concerning the first edition have assisted immeasurably in my endeavor to improve both the content and scope of this, the second edition. Once more, also, the cooperation and concern for quality of content and accuracy by each of the authors of this volume must be recognized with appreciation. I am especially grateful to Mrs. Estella Cooney, Ricki Davidson, and to my daughter Susan, without whose technical and editorial assistance (under the stress of exacting technical standards which a work of this nature demands) the completion of this volume would have been impossible. Finally, I must once again emphasize the important role played by the staff of Academic Press. Their unfailing encouragement, cooperation, and tactical assistance throughout the planning and the ultimate completion of the collation of the various components of this, the first volume of the second edition of "The Physiology of Insecta" are gratefully acknowledged.

MORRIS ROCKSTEIN

PREFACE TO FIRST EDITION

This multivolume treatise brings together the known facts, the controversial material, and the many still unsolved and unsettled problems of insect physiology in chapters written by the outstanding workers in each of a wide range of areas of insect function.

It is designed to meet a manifest need which has arisen from the phenomenal increase in research activity on insects (during the past two decades, especially) for an authoritative, comprehensive reference work in insect physiology.

Although the insect physiologist usually considers himself either a comparative physiologist or a general physiologist studying a particular process in insects, the fact is that each is a biologist whose primary interest is in the *total organism* in relation to a specific function. This viewpoint is reflected in the organization and arrangement of the chapters by sections and volumes. Thus, instead of that classic arrangement of chapters which emphasizes organ or systemic physiology, this treatise has been organized into three main sections, each covering a major division of insect biology: the ontogeny of insects from reproduction to senescence of the individual; the insect's perception of and reaction to its external environment; and the mechanisms by which the internal homeostatic state is maintained. The last-mentioned division, especially, includes many classic functions—from the role of the nervous system to nutrition, metabolism, respiration, circulation, maintenance of salt and water balance, and cuticular functions. In addition, under this major division the heretofore unemphasized areas of immunological responses and mechanisms of insect resistance to insecticides have been included, since the contributions of research investigators to these fields in recent times are widely recognized.

I hope that this diversified subject matter will serve an equally varied group of students of biology. To the student of comparative physiology as well as to the entomologist, the organization of the now extensive literature on insect physiology into one large work should be especially useful. To the applied entomologist, the chapters concerned with insect functions in relation to the external environment should prove especially interesting; they provide a basis for understanding the distribution, epidemiology, and bionomics of insects in general, but especially of those insects of medical and economic importance. Those chapters concerned with the maintenance of the constancy of the internal environment should be equally helpful, forming a rational basis for control of insect pests. Finally, the details of structure, both gross and histological, necessarily included in those chapters covering neurophysiology, circulation, respiration, digestion, and cuticular functions, should be of special interest to the anatomist or taxonomist concerned with the physiological implications of his own research interests in insects.

The responsibilities of editing an opus of this size include securing the complete cooperation and sustained efforts of one's co-authors. To this I can attest without qualification. I must also acknowledge the critical, but always helpful suggestions—especially in the early planning and in the reading of some of the manuscripts—of my many colleagues, namely, Dr. A. Glenn Richards, Dr. V. B. Wigglesworth, Dr. Carroll M. Williams, Dr. Leigh E. Chadwick, Dr. Vincent G. Dethier, Dr. Herbert H. Ross, Dr. Curtis W. Sabrosky, and the late Dr. R. N. Snodgrass.

To Miss Norma Moskovitz, special expression of appreciation is due for her untiring efforts and sustained dedication to achieving a final product of exacting technical standards.

On a more personal level, the early encouragement of the late Elaine S. Rockstein and the patience and forbearance of my oftimes neglected daughters Susan and Madelaine, especially during the past year, must be gratefully acknowledged as well.

MORRIS ROCKSTEIN

CONTENTS OF OTHER VOLUMES

Volume II

PART A
The Insect and the External Environment. I. Environmental Aspects

ENVIRONMENTAL ASPECTS—TEMPERATURE
  E. Bursell

ENVIRONMENTAL ASPECTS—HUMIDITY
  E. Bursell

ENVIRONMENTAL ASPECTS—RADIATION
  Daniel S. Grosch

PART B
The Insect and the External Environment. II. Reaction and Interaction

CHEMORECEPTION
  E. S. Hodgson

THE VISUAL SYSTEM OF INSECTS
  Timothy H. Goldsmith and Gary D. Bernard

MECHANORECEPTION
  J. Schwartzkopff

SOUND PRODUCTION
  P. T. Haskell

INSECT BIOLUMINESCENCE
  W. D. McElroy, H. H. Seliger, and M. DeLuca

CIRCADIAN RHYTHMS AND PHOTOPERIODISM IN INSECTS
  D. S. Saunders

AUTHOR INDEX—SUBJECT INDEX

Volume III

PART A
The Insect and the External Environment. II. Reaction and Interaction

INSECT BEHAVIOR: FUNCTIONS AND MECHANISMS
Hubert Markl

SOCIAL BEHAVIOR AND MUTUAL COMMUNICATION
Martin Lindauer

INSECT PHEROMONES
Martin Jacobson

PART B
The Insect and the External Environment. II. Locomotion

INSECT MIGRATION ASPECTS OF ITS PHYSIOLOGY
C. G. Johnson

LOCOMOTION: TERRESTRIAL
G. M. Hughes and P. J. Mill

LOCOMOTION MECHANICS AND HYDRODYNAMICS OF SWIMMING IN AQUATIC INSECTS
Werner Nachtigall

LOCOMOTION: FLIGHT
J. W. S. Pringle

AUTHOR INDEX—SUBJECT INDEX

Volume IV

The Insect and the Internal Environment—Homeostasis I

NEURAL INTERGRATION (CENTRAL NERVOUS SYSTEM)
F. Huber

THE PHARMACOLOGY OF THE INSECT NERVOUS SYSTEM
Yves Pichon

NEURAL CONTROL OF SKELETAL MUSCLE
G. Hoyle

THE BIOCHEMISTRY OF THE CONTRACTILE ELEMENTS OF INSECT MUSCLE
K. Maruyama

BIOLOGICAL OXIDATIONS AND ENERGETICS IN INSECT MILTOCHONDRIA
B. Sacktor

PROTEIN SYNTHESIS IN INSECTS
J. Ilan and J. Ilan

AUTHOR INDEX—SUBJECT INDEX

Volume V

The Insect and the Internal Environment—Homeostasis II

NUTRITION
H. L. House

DIGESTION
H. L. House

FACTORS AFFECTING HEART RATES IN INSECTS
Jack Colvard Jones

ELECTROPHYSIOLOGY OF THE INSECT HEART
Thomas A. Miller

THE HEMOCYTES OF INSECTS
John W. Arnold

HEMOLYMPH: COMPOSITION
Marcel Florkin and Charles Jeuniaux

HEMOLYMPH COAGULATION
Ch. Gregoire

SALT AND WATER BALANCE EXCRETION
R. H. Stobbart and J. Shaw

INSECT DEFENSE MECHANISMS AGAINST MICROORGANISMS AND PARASITOIDS
Robert F. Whitcomb, Martin Shapiro, and Robert R. Granados

MICROSOMAL MIXED-FUNCTION OXIDASES
Moises Agosin and Albert S. Perry

AUTHOR INDEX—SUBJECT INDEX

Volume VI (tentative)

The Insect and the Internal Environment—Homeostasis III

THE PHYSIOLOGY OF INSECTICIDE RESISTANCE BY INSECTS
Albert S. Perry and Moises Agosin

THE STRUCTURE AND FORMATION OF THE INTEGUMENT IN INSECTS
    Michael Locke

CHEMISTRY OF THE INSECT CUTICLE
    R. H. Hackman

PERMEABILITY OF INSECT CUTICLE
    W. Ebling

RESPIRATION: AERIAL GAS TRANSPORT
    P. L. Miller

RESPIRATION IN AQUATIC INSECTS
    P. J. Mill

RESPIRATION: SOME EXOGENOUS AND ENDOGENOUS EFFECTS ON RATE OF RESPIRATION
    Margaret Keister and John Buck

AUTHOR INDEX—SUBJECT INDEX

Physiology of Ontogeny—
Biology, Development, and Aging

Chapter 1

BIOLOGY OF THE INSECTA

Morris Rockstein

Biology of the Insecta 3
  A. Distribution 4
  B. General Characteristics 5
  C. Insects in Physiological Studies 6
References 8

Biology of the Insecta

Physiology is most simply defined as being concerned with the functions of the organism and its parts. Nevertheless, as a science, physiology cannot be isolated or distinquished from biophysics, biochemistry, anatomy, embryology, or even systematics. Indeed, the late R. E. Snodgrass applied his elegant anatomical observations to the deduction of function, particularly as regards the mouth parts and feeding habits of a considerable range of insect forms. Moreover, as the complete biologist, Snodgrass (1935, 1950, 1954, 1958) was able to derive important concepts concerning the phylogeny and evolution of insect structures in relation to functional adaptation implicit in such structural evolution. Thus, the functioning of an organism is best described in terms of total organization of its parts, from which its basic anatomical features obviously cannot be separated as a biological property distinct from the functioning of the parts concerned.

3

By the same token, the now rapidly growing population of "insect phys-iologists" are not, as Richards (1961) has stressed, working solely in "insect physiology," per se, but rather are biologists interested in some phase of insect function at any one level (i.e., from the gross organismic to the most intimate subcellular or molecular level within the cell). In-deed, it is the biochemist or biophysicist and, more recently, the molecu-lar geneticist, who have discovered in the Insecta a highly diversified group of organisms admirably suited to a wide variety of experimental in-vestigations from virtually every standpoint (including their ecology, their food habits, and their means of reproduction and development). The classical works of Snodgrass (1935), Comstock (1940), Folsom and Wardle (1934), Weber (1933, 1954), and Ross (1948) are recom-mended to that group of investigators who may be interested in studies in-volving insects and, accordingly, in obtaining basic information on the general features of this highly diversified and successful group of animals. To the entomologist himself who will have the opportunity to peruse cri-tically the contents of this introductory chapter, the author agrees that such coverage can only be described as too little. However, its function is to serve as a jumping-off point, both as regards the general characteris-tics of insects, on the one hand, and the pursuit in any dimension by non-entomologists of further insight into the more intimate biology of the Insecta in greater depth.

A. DISTRIBUTION

The actual number of insect species described to date number approxi-mately three-quarters of a million; however, Sabrosky (1952) has esti-mated the actual total number to be well over one and a half-million species, if all the extant species were properly identified and described. However, this vast number of species, belonging to one group of arthro-pods alone, represents the successful evolution as regards both their life habits and the variety of ecological niches which they can occupy. Thus, insects inhabit not only the surface and subsurface of the earth, the fresh waters and the shoreline of the sea, but also the exterior or interior of other living organisms, both plant and animal. Moreover, one finds in-sects adapted to living at the snow line of alpine heights (*Grylloblatta*) or at temperatures of close to 120°F in the mud of the hot springs of Yel-lowstone Park (chironomid larvae), on the marine shores (*Anurida maritima*), in the beds of swift-flowing streams, on the hot sand dunes, in the interior of living and dead plants or animals, and in desiccated stored food products. Thus, insects have structural and physiological adapta-tions to virtually every ecological situation, such as food sources, temperature, humidity, and radiant energy, in which at least some form of life can exist. Concomitantly, beginning with the primitive silverfishlike insect ancestor in the Devonian, evolutionary radiation over a period of more than 350 million years has resulted in this tremendous number of species of animals using every type of locomotion from crawling, to burrowing, to walking, to running, to jumping, to flying, and even to swimming.

B. General Characteristics

A distinguishing characteristic of the arthropods is the possession of an annulate body bearing segmentally placed, jointed appendages. Each of the limb segments is capable of independent movement by virtue of the fact that it possesses individual muscles. The body segments are arranged typically in aggregates or distinct sections called "tagmata." The body covering, a proteinaceous–chitinous exoskeleton, is characteristically rigidified or sclerotized owing to tanning of the protein and/or by the deposition of a hardening substance (calcification in the Crustacea), but only in distinct regions or sclerites which are demarcated from one another by membranous regions. This alternation of sclerotized and membranous regions, with attachment of muscles on the sclerites, permits freedom of movement.

The arrangement of the tagmata among the arthropods includes a distinct head followed by a body region consisting typically of a succession of uniform body segments.

Like the Annelida, the Arthropoda possess a blood-vascular system, a distinct alimentary tract with oral and anal openings, and a nervous system consisting, in the primitive form, of the dorsally located brain (composed of three primitive lobes), subesophageal ganglia, and the ladder-like, ventral nerve cord with segmentally arranged, paired ganglia; various degrees of ganglionic fusion are common. The compound lateral eyes, innervated by the primary brain lobe or protocerebrum, represent a morphological adaptation, typical of the Arthropoda in general, with dorsal (and lateral) simple eyes or ocelli usually present, as well. Unlike the Annelida, segmental nephridia are typically absent.

The Insecta (Hexapoda), with a distinct head, thorax, and abdomen, possess, at least in the adult stage, three pairs of jointed appendages or legs, borne by its three body segments which are usually combined as a tagma, called the thorax. The abdomen consists of eleven primitive, true segments plus a terminal periproct, although this number can seldom be recognized in the adult form.

It is generally accepted that the insect head is made up of a primary blastocephalon to which have been added four postoral segments. The

head bears a pair of antennules (procephalic antennae), embryologically
a pair of second antennae, one pair of mandibles, and two pairs of maxil-
lae, the second pair of which is modified into a composite structure, the
labium. Unlike the Crustacea, appendages are never biramous in the
strict sense of the term. The typical lateral, compound eyes are present in
most adults and nymphs, but absent in larval forms. The simple eyes of
the adult insect head, when present, include one median and two more
laterally placed dorsal ocelli. The primitive divisions of the hexapod
brain include the protocerebrum, the deutocerebrum, and the tritocere-
brum.

The Insecta are divisible on the basis of possession of wings into two
major groups, the alate Apterygota and winged Pterygota. The development of this, the highest level of mechanical achievement, occurred as
early as the Carboniferous period.

However, most striking of all of the adaptations of insects is the re-
striction by form, intimate structure, and biochemical makeup of the immature stages of most insects to general feeding and growth and of the
adult to specialized (usually more restricted) feeding, mating, and egg
laying. This dichotomy of function between immature and adult individuals attains its peak in the Holometabola, i.e., those insects which undergo
a complete metamorphosis from a true (wingless) larva, such as the
creeping caterpillar or maggot, to a winged adult, such as the moth or fly,
respectively. This characteristic of the higher orders of insects, one of relatively recent origin, is generally accepted as being unrelated to the typical metamorphic changes observed in developing Annelida and Crustacea
(see Poyarkoff, 1910, 1914; Hinton, 1948; Snodgrass, 1954; Rockstein,
1959).

C. Insects in Physiological Studies

Because of their large numbers and diversity, insects can be found suited to practically every kind of research problem.

To the modern physiologist, especially, the study of insects has proven
a most fertile, hitherto virtually unexplored area of research investigation
from biochemistry to electrophysiology, both because of their wide ecological versatility, on one hand, and their several distinctive features, on
the other.

Thus, the small size of insects is often an advantage rather than a
hindrance. For example, it permitted an early localization, by total body
ligation, of the time and site of activity of hormones, in a simple and yet
elegant pioneer experiment by Fraenkel (1935). Moreover, despite the

diminutive size of the total animal, the individual cells of insects are of the same order of magnitude as those of higher vertebrates. Indeed, this means a smaller number of cells per organism, with obviously attendant advantages from the standpoint of quantitative and qualitative histological determinations. As A. G. Richards (personal communication) has observed, the size of insects is intermediate between that of the more diminutive bacteria, on one hand, and the larger vertebrates, on the other. Depending on his research interests, this permits the experimental entomologist to use either entire populations of insects, like the microbiologist, or the individual animal (or its parts), like the vertebrate biologist.

Despite their small size, ultramicroanalytical procedures in the isolation and characterization of biochemical components of insects from enzymes to hormones may not be necessary in many cases. That is because the high level of fecundity of some species permits one to use large numbers of insects instead. Indeed, the important recent work on isolation and purification of insect hormones by workers like Karlson, Butenandt, Williams, and Schneiderman (see Chapter 5 of this volume) was possible through the use of large numbers of two species of insects of high reproductive potential. This characteristic of insects also means the possibility of high levels of replication which, in turn, means adequate data of statistical validity in studies such as longevity and aging, radiation studies, and toxicology–pharmacology experiments.

Because of their short life spans and (therefore) rapid turnover of generations, replicate physiological studies of successive generations of individuals within one species of insects are possible over relatively short periods of time. Indeed, current investigations on the effects of radiation on the duration of the various stages of insect life histories, on longevity, on parental fertility and fecundity, as well as on the viability and normal functions of offspring of irradiated parents, have been especially possible in insects because of their short life spans.

The relatively simple, yet technically readily manipulable and accessible, Malpighian tubules of insects similarly permit comparative studies of excretion, ion transport, and permeability. Permeability and absorption studies have also been possible in insects, as have been investigations of the chemistry of digestion, because of the relatively clear-cut demarcation of the alimentary canal and accessory digestive glands in the typical insect alimentary tract.

The unique possession of an exoskeleton has likewise permitted clarification of the functional anatomy, i.e., the morphology of movement, of the appendages in insects as a model of limb and gnathal movement (see the many scholarly studies of Snodgrass, 1935, 1950, 1954, 1958). The cuticle itself, because of its protein–chitin composition, also represents unusual biological material for the physical chemist, the biochemist, and the biophysicist to investigate.

The high degree of social organization typical of the termites (Isoptera) and of bees and ants (Hymenoptera) similarly provides an excellent closed biological system for developmental, endocrine, nutritional, and pheromonal studies. That is, the bee or ant colony represents an ideal laboratory "organism" for the endocrinologist or the experimental embryologist concerned with intimate details of the (biochemical) basis for development and organ differentiation, especially in relation to caste differentiation.

With the attainment of the status of a full-fledged discipline in the still broadening horizons of biological investigation, the field of insect physiology needs no apologia; nevertheless, for the nonentomologist, one can do no better than quote from the Croonian lecture by the foremost insect physiologist of the recent past and present, V. B. Wigglesworth (1948) :

> Insects live and feed, move, grow and multiply like other animals; but they are so varied in form, so rich in species, and adapted to such diverse conditions of life that they afford unrivalled opportunities for physiological study. The general problems of physiology are much the same in all groups of animals; and this lecture, which represents, in effect, an apology for the study of insect physiology, is an attempt to show that among the insects may be found material well suited for the solution of many of these problems.
>
> By human standards most insects are small in size, and this brings with it certain features which dominate their physiology. There is the same degree of functional specialization in their organs as there is in mammals; but they are made up of cells of the same dimensions as those in other animals—often, indeed, of cells which are larger than most. Each organ, therefore, contains far fewer cells, and the organization of their bodies must of necessity appear more simple. It is, however, a deceptive simplicity; for the range of physiological activities of which the single cell is capable is no less and may indeed be greater than it is in larger animals. . . .
>
> Clearly, insects present some very desirable properties as objects for experiment. They are extremely tolerant of operation; they are so varied in form and habit that some species suited to the problem in hand can surely be found; and their small size makes it possible for the observer to be constantly aware of the whole while focusing his attention upon the part.

References

Comstock, J. H. (1940). "An Introduction to Entomology." Cornell Univ. Press (Comstock), Ithaca, New York.

Folsom, J. W., and Wardle, R. A. (1934). "Entomology." McGraw-Hill (Blakiston), New York.

Fraenkel, G. (1935). *Proc. Roy. Soc., Ser. B* **118**, 1.

Hinton, H. E. (1948). *Trans. Roy. Entomol. Soc.* **99**, 395.

Poyarkoff, E. (1910). *Arch. Anat. Microsc.* **12**, 333.

Poyarkoff, E. (1914). *Arch. Zool. Exp. Gen.* **54**, 221.

Richards, A. G. (1961). *Bull. Entomol. Soc. Amer.* **7**, 20.

Rockstein, M. (1959). *Smithson. Misc. Collect.* **137**, 263.

Ross, H. H. (1948). "A Textbook of Entomology." Wiley, New York.

Sabrosky, C. W. (1952). *In* "Insects, The Yearbook of Agriculture" (A. Stefferud, ed.), pp. 1–7. U. S. Govt. Printing Office, Washington, D.C.

Snodgrass, R. E. (1935). "Principles of Insect Morphology." McGraw-Hill, New York.

Snodgrass, R. E. (1950). *Smithson. Misc. Collect.* **116**.

Snodgrass, R. E. (1954). *Smithson. Misc. Collect.* **122**.

Snodgrass, R. E. (1958). *Smithson. Misc. Collect.* **138**.

Weber, H. (1933). "Lehrbuch der Entomologie." Fischer, Jena.

Weber, H. (1954). "Grundriss der Insektenkunde," 3rd ed. Fisher, Stuttgart.

Wigglesworth, V. B. (1948). *Proc. Roy. Soc., Ser. B* **135**, 430.

Chapter 2

REPRODUCTION

Jan de Wilde and Arnold de Loof

I.	Structure and Origin of the Female Reproductive System	12
	A. Internal Apparatus	12
	B. External Appendages	14
	C. The Ovariole	14
II.	Oogenesis	17
	A. The Formation of Oocytes and Nurse Cells	17
	B. The Follicle Cells	25
	C. Alimentary aspects of Oogenesis	26
	D. Polarity of the Oocyte	39
	E. Formation of Egg Membranes and Specialized Chorionic Structures	41
	F. Oosorption	47
	G. Transfer of Symbionts during Oogenesis	48
	H. Oogenesis in Postembryonic Development	50
	I. Fecundity	53
III.	Oviposition: Accessory Glands	54
IV.	Fertility and Sterility	57
	A. Fertility	57
	B. Sterility	57
V.	Structure and Origin of the Male Reproductive System	61
	A. Gonads and Gonoducts	61
	B. Phallus, Parameres, and Terminalia	62
VI.	Formation of Sperm and Semen	63
	A. The Testis: Spermatogenesis	63
	B. Accessory Glands	67
	C. Chemical Composition of Semen	69
VII.	Courtship and the Role of Pheromones	70

VIII.   Insemination: The Copulatory Act **73**
        A. Impregnation **73**
        B. Spermatophores 75
        C. Traumatic Insemination 78
IX.   Determination of Sex and Sexual Characters. Parthenogenesis **79**
        A. Bisexual Reproduction **79**
        B. Parthenogenesis 79
        C. Parthenogenesis and Polyploidy 81
        D. Gynandromorphs **82**
        E. Intersexes 82
        References 85

Reproduction is a function of the organism which serves the maintenance of the species rather than that of the organism itself. Reproduction,
therefore, may be damaging or even detrimental to the individual, as is
demonstrated so clearly by paedogenesis. Reproduction involves the re-
shuffeling and storage of developmental information in such a way that
natural selection can play its role in fitting the organism into its environment. Every single act or process in reproduction, however bizarre and
seemingly endless in variation, has to be understood in this context.

Reproductive processes involve three levels of integration: the population, the organism, and the cellular and subcellular processes. In this and
the following chapter our discussions will range from the ultrastructural
up to the ecophysiological level.

I. Structure and Origin of the Female Reproductive System

A. INTERNAL APPARATUS

The internal reproductive system comprises the paired ovaria and mesodermal oviducts, and the ectodermal medial oviduct and vagina. The
ovaria usually are composite structures, consisting of a variable number
of tubular ovarioles in which oogenesis takes place. The medial oviduct
usually carries one or more spermathecae, in which sperm is stored after
copulation. Bursae copulatrices may be diverticulae either of the medial
oviduct or of the vagina. They serve as primary organs of sperm deposition and are often fitted to receive special structures of the male organ
during copulation. Accessory glands usually open into the vaginal cavity
(Fig. 1).

The ovarium emerges from segmentally arranged ridges in the mesodermal coelomic wall, taking up groups of germ cells. These ridges are
subsequently united by a mesodermal genital strand, differentiating into
a paired genital duct. Its widened caudal end, the ampulla, attaches itself

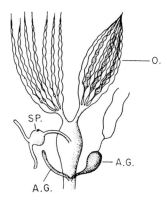

Fig. 1. Female reproductive system, diagrammatic (after Weber, 1938). O., ovarium; A.G., accessory gland; SP., spermatheca.

to an ectodermal invagination of the seventh abdominal sternum, forming the gonoporus. The paired condition of this gonoporus is retained only in Ephemeroptera. Unpaired invaginations of the eighth and ninth sternum form the vagina, spermatheca, bursa copulatrix, and accessory glands. In the majority of cases, the structures are united and open into the vulva at the posterior end of the eighth or ninth sternum, sometimes widened to form a vestibulum (Fig. 2). In Lepidoptera and some Coleoptera, the bursa may retain its separate external orifice (Fig. 3).

As follows from their mesodermal origin, ovaria and paired oviducts have an endothelial sheath and may be provided with muscle cells. A connective tissue sheath probably formed by the hemocytes (Ochsé, 1946) serves as a basement membrane to the endothelium. The muscle

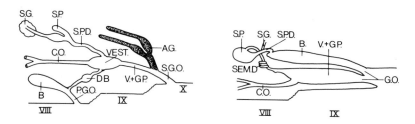

Fig. 2. Gonoducts in Lepidoptera (left) and *Hydroporus* (Coleoptera) with retained bursal duct system (redrawn from Weber, 1938). A.G., accessory gland; C.O., common oviduct; D.B., ductus bursae; SEM. D., seminal duct; S.G.O., secondary genital orifice; S.P.D., spermathecal duct; V. + G.P., vagina + genital pouch; B., bursa copulatrix; G.O., genital orifice; P.G.O., primary genital orifice; S.G., spermathecal gland; S.P., spermatheca, and VEST., vestibulum.

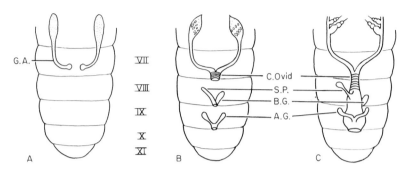

Fig. 3. Schematic representation of ontogenetic development of female reproductive system (modified after Imms, 1957). G.A., genital ampulla; C. Ovid., common oviduct; A.G., accessory glands; S.P., spermatheca.

cells vary greatly in structure and density. They generally perform peristaltic contractions which assist in ovulation as well as in the removal of waste products produced during oogenesis and oosorption.

Being of ectodermal origin, the vagina, bursa copulatrix, and spermatheca have a cuticular inner lining.

B. External Appendages

The genital appendages or gonopods belonging to the eighth and ninth abdominal segments may be developed to a varying degree. In some cases the vulva merely is located on a telescopic extension of the genital segments, the ovitubus (Fig. 14b). In most cases, however, the gonopods take part in the formation of both the copulatory apparatus and the ovipositor. Each gonopod consists of a basal valvifer, a mobile element provided with muscles, and a gonapophysis (valvula). The bases of the second gonopods, which may carry the gonostyli, occasionally extend to form a third pair of valvulae (Fig. 14a).

C. The Ovariole

The number of ovarioles may vary greatly. One paired ovariole is present in *Eosentomon, Campodea, Glossina,* and some Hemiptera. Secondary reduction to a single ovariole occurs in several aphid families, and in some scarabaeid beetles. Honey bee queens have 160–180, while some termite queens have more than 2000 ovarioles in each ovary.

The ovariole is divided into three regions:

1. Germarium, containing the oogonia, enveloped in a layer of mesodermal cells. In certain types of ovarioles, oogonia differentiate into pri-

mary oocytes and nutritive cells (trophocytes). Somatic mesodermal cells, located at the base of the germarium, form the prefollicular tissue.

2. Vitellarium, a very extensible region, the size of which strongly depends upon reproductive activity. In this region, one or more oocytes are each enveloped in an epithelial follicle. In most cases, they are arranged in a single row. They gradually develop into eggs, and increase in size accordingly. At the anterior end of each follicle, one or more trophocytes may be present.

3. Ovariole stalk, in which the mature eggs pass to the oviduct, after the epithelial plug separating them from the lumen has been ruptured.

Each ovariole is enveloped in a double sheath of endothelium and connective tissue (Bonhag, 1961) which continues into the terminal filament, attaching the ovary to the sclerites of the body wall.

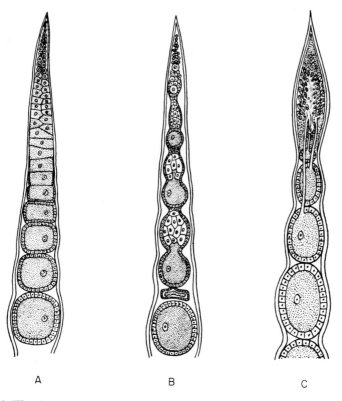

A   B   C

Fig. 4. The 3 main types of ovarioles. A, panoistic type; B, polytrophic type; C, teleotrophic type (modified from Imms, 1957).

The following types of ovarioles are recognized (Fig. 4).

1. In Panoistic ovarioles (Brandt, 1874), the germarium merely contains oogonia, primary oocytes, and mesodermal prefollicular tissue. The follicle is the only trophic tissue of the vitellarium. This type occurs in Apterygota, Orthoptera, Aphaniptera, and in some of the Coleoptera.

2. In Meroistic ovarioles (Brandt, 1874), the germarium contains oogonia, oocytes, nutritive cells, and prefollicular tissue. This group is again subdivided.

  a. Polytrophic ovarioles (Grosz, 1903), in which nutritive cells migrate into the vitellarium, alternating with the oocytes enveloped in

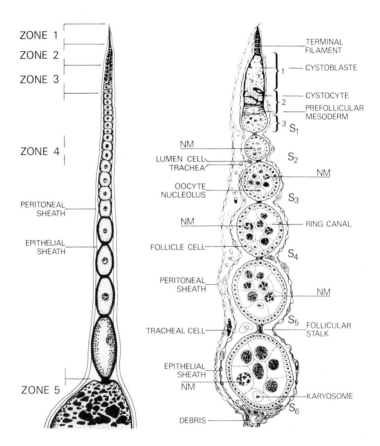

Fig. 5. Zonation in panoistic ovariole *Periplaneta*, left (redrawn from Anderson, 1964); and in polytrophic ovariole *Drosophila*, right (redrawn from Koch *et al.*, 1967). NM, nuclear material shown with special staining method.

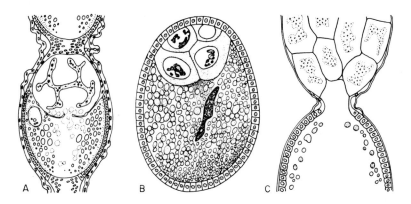

Fig. 6. Endofollicular (A, B) and exofollicular (C) trophocytes. A, *Anisolabis mariti-ma* (Bonhag, 1958); B, *Anopheles maculipennis* (Nicholson, 1921); C, *Apis mellifera* (Bonhag, 1958).

their follicles. Both trophic elements take part in vitellogenesis. This is found in Neuroptera, Lepidoptera, Hymenoptera, Diptera, and some Coleoptera.

b. Telotrophic ovarioles (Grosz, 1903), in which the trophocytes remain concentrated in the germarium. They may be connected to the descending oocytes by cytoplasmic strands and exert their trophic function by way of these. This occuds in Hemiptera. In some Coleoptera, similar conditions prevail, the oocyte loosing its connecting cord upon entering into the vitellarium.

3. In Dieroistic ovarioles (Berlese, 1909) occurring in some Collembola and Microhymenoptera, the follicles are united in a common sac, the ovarioles lacking their separate envelopes.

II. Oogenesis

In oogenesis, biophysical and biochemical problems merge to provide a field of general zoophysiology rather than a chapter of special physiology of an animal group. As a consequence, the study of this field profits greatly from a more generalized zoological approach (Raven, 1961). Nevertheless, insect oogenesis provides many characteristic structures and processes, some of which are being reviewed periodically (Bonhag, 1958; Telfer, 1965; Engelmann, 1968, 1970).

A. THE FORMATION OF OOCYTES AND NURSE CELLS

Oogonial differentiation takes place in the germarium.

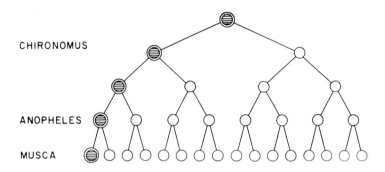

CHIRONOMUS

ANOPHELES

MUSCA

Fig. 7. Diagrammatic representation of oogonial divisions in some Diptera, resulting in different numbers of trophocytes in each nutritive cluster (after Schröder, 1928).

1. Panoistic Ovarioles

It is believed that in an ovariole of the panoistic type, all germ cells differentiate into oocytes which are subsequently enveloped by epithelial cells derived from the actively dividing prefollicular tissue. It is not possible to differentiate between primary and secondary oogonia. The best studied germarium in panoistic ovarioles is that of *Periplaneta* (Bonhag, 1959; Anderson, 1964). Five zones are recognized in each ovariole (Fig. 5, left).

2. Polytrophic Ovarioles

Polytrophic ovarioles are characterized by follicles consisting of one oocyte together with a well-defined number of trophocytes or nurse cells, the whole complex being surrounded by a sheath of follicle cells (Fig. 5, right). Oocyte differentiation in this type of ovariole has been extensively studied in *Drosophila* by R. C. King and associates. In this insect, a primary oogonium "stem cell" occurs in the apical region of each germarium, close to the cells of the terminal filaments (Fig. 8). The primary oogonium divides into a cystoblast and another primary oogonium (Brown and King, 1964). As the cystoblast moves down the germarium it undergoes four mitoses giving rise to a cyst of sixteen cells (cystocytes) which form an egg–nurse-cell complex. One of the cystocytes will be the oocyte, the others the trophocytes. Subsequently, this complex is enveloped within a sheath of follicle cells, originating from the mesodermal prefollicular tissue. As the oocyte grows, the follicle cells undergo divisions. They will not only alter in shape and size but their function will also change. Finally the cysts pinch off from the germarium and thus become a follicle. The oocyte and trophocytes are interconnected by fifteen

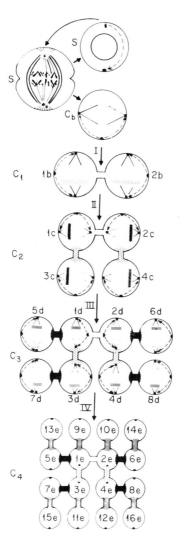

Fig. 8. Schematic drawing of the successive divisions leading to a cluster of 16 interconnected cystocytes in *Drosophila* (from Koch *et al.,* 1967).

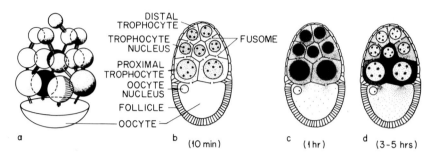

Fig. 9. Schematic drawing of the composition of an endofollicular cluster in a Dipteran (redrawn from Bier, 1970). a, Only 4 trophocytes are in direct contact with the oocyte. One of these (shaded) is in contact with 7 other trophocytes, one (white) with 3, one (black) with only 1, and one (striped) is without contact with trophocytes. b–d, Upon incubation with radiolabeled nucleotides, marking is at first evenly distributed, but after 3–5 hours, intensity of marking correlates with the number of intertrophocyte contacts, suggesting RNA transport between the trophocytes.

canals (Fig. 9) each surrounded by a protein-rich ring (Koch and King, 1966; 1969; Koch *et al.*, 1967) which will allow the transport of RNA (ribosomes) and mitochondria to the oocyte during vitellogenesis. Trophocyte nuclei usually become polyploid through endomitosis, but the oocyte nucleus remains diploid.

This mechanism of oocyte differentiation is probably applicable to the greater part of insects with polytrophic ovarioles. The number of trophocytes is variable from species to species but is always constant in the same species (Fig. 7). The numerical relation between trophocytes and oocytes is 1:1 in Dermaptera and *Chironomus,* 5:1 in Mallophaga and Siphunculata, 7:1 in *Anopheles* and *Gyrinus,* 15:1 in *Drosophila* and *Musca,* and 48:1 in *Apis.* Descending into the germarium, each oocyte is followed by its trophocytes (Fig. 5).

Except in Dermaptera, Mallophaga, and Siphunculata, where trophocytes and oocytes are found enveloped in the same follicle, both cellular elements are usually found in separate follicles, with only the oocyte follicle showing secretory activity. A nipplelike oocyte process usually extends into the nutritive follice (Fig. 6). Panelius (1968) found that in the paedogenetic larva of the Dipteran *Heteropeza pygmaea*, the trophocytes do not originate from the oogonium but are of somatic origin.

3. Telotrophic Ovarioles

In telotrophic ovarioles different conditions may prevail. In *Oncopeltus,* and probably other Hemiptera–Heteroptera, the trophocyte nuclei partly fuse to form giant nuclei arranged in the periphery of the germarium. The central part is occupied by the cytoplasmic nutritive chamber or trophic core, into which the nuclei eventually release their contents. The oocyte remains connected to this trophic core by means of a cytoplasmic strand serving as a "feeding channel." Alimentary egg formation is realized both by way of this "trophic strand" and by the follicle (Fig. 10).

In *Tenebrio* and probably other Coleoptera Polyphaga, the situation is different. The trophic core is absent, nutritive cells being scattered throughout the germarium. They break down individually into trophic strands, but these may often disappear as the follicle is completed (Bryan, 1954; Bonhag, 1955b; de Wilde *et al.*, 1959).

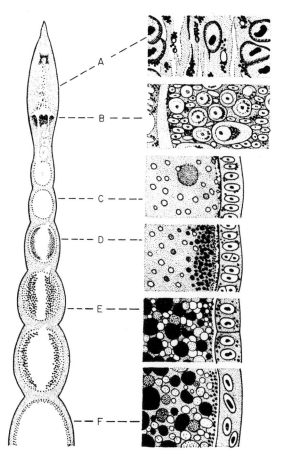

Fig. 10. Distribution of phospholipids during oogenesis (represented as black dots) in *Oncopeltus fasciatus* (after Bonhag, 1955a).

4. Oocyte Determination in Polytrophic Ovarioles

Only in a few species has the question of how the oocyte is determined from among the cystocytes been studied. In *Dytiscus marginalis,* extrachromosomal DNA, which forms a ring about the spindle at metaphase, occurs in the prophase of the first cystocyte division (Günthart, 1910). An unequal cytokinesis then takes place during which the extrachromosomal DNA enters the larger cell. This is repeated during the three following divisions. The small cell, arising after each division, which is destined to become a trophocyte, also cleaves at the next mitosis, giving rise to two small sister cells of similar size. Thus after the four cystocyte divisions, fifteen small nurse cells are produced in addition to one large cell which

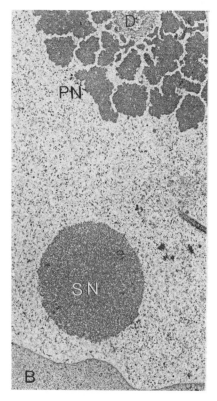

Fig. 11. Part of panoistic ovariole of *Acheta domesticus.* Note extrachromosomal DNA in oocyte (from Allen and Cave, 1969). PN, primary nucleolus; SN, secondary nucleolus.

contains the extrachromosomal DNA and becomes the oocyte. It is interesting to note that a large extrachromosomal DNA body is found in oogonial and oocyte nuclei, but not in the somatic cells within the panoistic ovary of *Acheta domesticus* (Cave and Allen, 1969, 1970; Allen and Cave, 1969; Hansen-Delkeskamp, 1969) (Fig. 11).

In *Tipula lateralis* (Bayreuther, 1956), in both of the two cystocytes cleaved from the cytoblast, an amorphous Feulgen-positive mass is formed in association with the X chromosomes during mitotic prophase. The body is passed in a specific way during the following three divisions, so that in a sixteen-cell cyst only two adjacent cystocytes contain the body and only these two cystocytes enter into the phase of pachynema. Subsequently, in the cell destined to become the oocyte, the Feulgen-positive body breaks down and the oocyte nucleus becomes Feulgen-negative. In both *Tipula* and *Dytiscus,* the cell which becomes the oocyte seems to be determined by some sort of cortical polarity (Highnam, 1964).

In *Drosophila,* the cystoblast divides four times to give rise to sixteen cystocytes which are interconnected by canals (Fig. 8). Only the two cystocytes, which arise from the first division, will finally have four ring canals in contrast to the other cystocytes which have only one or two canals (Koch and King, 1966; 1969; Koch *et al.,* 1967). Only the two cells with four ring canals enter meiotic prophase and they are the only ones which form synaptonemal complexes during this period (Smith and King, 1968). One of the pro-oocytes becomes endopolyploid like the other nurse cells and from then on behaves as a nurse cell. Koch and King (1968) also observed that the definite oocyte has seven times more plasmalemma in contact with the follicle cells than does the other pro-oocyte. This fact may be related to the determination of the oocyte, but the mechanism is still obscure.

After differentiation is completed, the oocyte enters into its vegetative phase, during which vitellogenesis takes place. Its nucleus, swelling by virtue of the abundance of caryolymph, transforms into the germinal vesicle. Its cell volume undergoes a rapid increase, resulting from a constant flow of nutritive material. In *Drosophila,* oocyte volume increases in 3 days by 100,000 times (King *et al.,* 1956). In *Periplaneta,* the oocyte, while in the follicle, increases in volume more than 2.5 million times (Bonhag, 1959).

By the end of the yolk-forming period, the limiting membrane of the germinal vesicle breaks down, its nucleus being ready to complete maturation divisions.

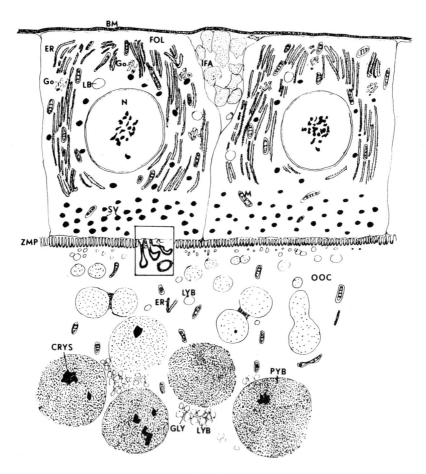

Fig. 12. Follicle cells and periphery of oocyte in relation to proteid yolk formation in the Colorado beetle (from de Loof, 1972) FOL, follicle, ER, endoplasmatic reticulum; LB, lysosomelike body; PYB, protein yolk body; CRYS, protein crystal; M, mitochondrion; ZMP, zone of microvilli and pinocytotic vesicles; OOC, oocyte; Go, Golgi body; LYB, lipid yolk body; GLY, glycogen granules; SV, secretion vesicles; BM, basal membrane of follicle. It is supposed that mucopolysaccharide material is secreted into the interspace between follicle and oocyte and is precipitated upon the oocyte surface, together with the vitellogenic blood proteins which pass through the interfollicular space (IFA). This material is taken up pinocytotically and is gradually condensed to form the proteid yolk bodies.

B. The Follicle Cells

As the oocyte, moving down the germarium, passes through the mesodermal prefollicular tissue (Fig. 10), it is enveloped by a layer of follicle cells, which still have a primitive subcellular cytoarchitecture at this time.

Upon descending into the vitellarium, the follicle cells increase in number by mitotic divisions and form a monolayer. Soon their number remains stationary and the steady increase in volume of the oocyte merely results in a tangential stretch of the follicle cells. Consequently, these cells are first columnar, then cuboidal, and at last flattened. They often become binucleate by amitotic divisions (Schlottmann and Bonhag, 1956). The posteriad movement of the follicles in the ovarian envelopes may be effected by "crowding" (Raven, 1961), but may be assisted by peristaltic contraction waves of the myoepithelial cells of the outer envelope (Grosz, 1903, King and Aggarwal, 1965).

At the onset of proteid yolk formation, both the follicle and the terminal oocyte may develop microvilli. During this stage of vitellogenesis, the follicle cells play a role in the selective absorption of vitellogenic blood proteins by the oocyte (Fig. 12). After vitellogenesis is complete,

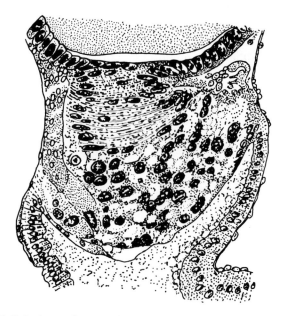

Fig. 13. Epithelial plug and corpus luteum in the ovarial stalk of *Tenebrio* (after Schlottmann and Bonhag, 1956).

the follicle cells secrete the vitelline membrane (in most insects, see p.
42) and the chorion, which in many cases may show impressions of follicle folds and villi. Finally, the egg leaves the vitellarium by rupturing the
follicle and the epithelial plug separating it from the ovarial stalk. The
follicle cells, remaining in the ovariole, degenerate. In some cases they
form a corpus luteum, which, however, does not show progressive development and secretory activity (Fig. 13).

C. Alimentary Aspects of Oogenesis

Yolk is deposited in the ooplasm in the form of globules or platelets,
consisting of proteins or lipids. Glycogen occurs in a typical particulate
form. The yolk-precursor substances are provided by the trophyocytes,
the follicle cells, the oocyte itself, or are absorbed from the hemolymph.
Proteid bodies account for most of the oocyte volume. Lipid yolk globules are distributed in between while free glycogen, when present, is either
dispersed throughout the ooplasm or in spaces between the proteid yolk
bodies.

1. The Origin of Proteid Yolk

At this time it is still too early to derive a general mechanism of proteid yolk formation from the few relatively well-studied cases. Our knowledge of the subtle processes involved in vitellogenesis is still very limited
and remarkable differences among different insect species, which at present we consider as very important, in the future may prove to be merely
secondary phenomena. It is evident that the relative importance of proteid yolk synthesis by the oocyte, the trophocytes, or follicle cells, on one
hand, and the uptake by pinocytosis of proteid yolk precursors from the
hemolymph, on the other hand, may vary from one species to another, depending upon the peculiarities of its life cycle and habitat. For this reason, it seems better to consider the mechanism of yolk formation in each
separate case and to avoid generalizing until more data will be available.

We will present here the main results of research performed in four insect species. It will become clear that there are similarities in all cases but
that also important differences, even between species with the same type
of ovariole, may occur.

a. *Proteid Yolk Formation in Hyalophora cecropia (Polytrophic
Ovariole).* Telfer and associates have demonstrated that the exogenous
supply by the hemolymph is the most important source of proteid yolk
precursors in *Hyalophora*. Proteins enter into the vitellogenic oocyte
from four sources: (1) As can be demonstrated by autoradiographic ex-

periments, the oocyte itself synthesizes proteins, presumably in the oocyte cortex, which are deposited in the yolk spheres along with the blood proteins. Little of the labeled proteins enter into yolk spheres (Melius and Telfer, 1969). (2) The nurse cells or trophocytes deliver part of their cytoplasm, including proteins, to the oocyte (King and Aggarwal, 1965). (3) The follicle cells release a nondialyzable product, believed to be at least partly protein in nature (Anderson and Telfer, 1969), into the intercellular space between the follicle cells and the oocyte. This material seems to be necessary to enhance pinocytotic activity in the oolemma. Maybe it stimulates membrane turnover here. Isolated oocytes incorporate this follicle cell product in small cortical yolk bodies, presumably by pinocytosis (Anderson, 1971). (4) By far the most important source of vitellogenic proteins is the hemolymph. Telfer (1954, 1960) demonstrated in the hemolymph of *Hyalophora cecropia,* a sex-limited protein (female protein, vitellogenin) which is about 1000 times more abundant in the hemolymph of females than of males and about 20–30 times more concentrated in eggs than in hemolymph. It is synthesized in the fat body (Pan *et al.,* 1969) and selectively absorbed and accumulated by the terminal oocytes. The other blood proteins can also be demonstrated in the eggs, but are not accumulated to a comparable degree. Exogenous blood proteins are incorporated into the oocyte by pinocytosis through the oolemma (Stay, 1965). The hemolymph reaches the oocyte surface through spaces between adjacent follicle cells. Moreover, at the time when yolk deposition starts, the follicular epithelium retracts from the oocyte surface, giving rise to an intercellular space, which greatly improves the contact between the hemolymph and the oocyte (Stay, 1965; King and Aggarwal, 1965. In this space, the female protein is concentrated (Anderson and Telfer, 1970).

In accordance with the findings of Hausman *et al.* (1971), based upon *in vitro* experiments with intact ovaries, Anderson (1971) found that isolated oocytes absorb male blood proteins to a lesser extent than female proteins. As a result, the preferential uptake of female protein seems to be localized in the oocyte surface rather than in the ovariole wall. In *Aedes aegypti,* Anderson and Spielman (1971) demonstrated that the basement lamina is freely permeable to particles with a molecular weight ranging from 12,000 to 50,000. In *H. cecropia,* the oocyte itself may participate in the selection of blood-borne proteins for incorporation into yolk platelets, but apparently requires the presence of an intact follicular epithelium to collect and concentrate these proteins.

b. *Proteid Yolk Formation in Drosophila melanogaster (Polytrophic Ovariole).* The mechanism described above for *H. cecropia* is not applicable to *Drosophila,* an insect also with a polytrophic ovary (Cummings and King, 1970). Possibly, the considerable difference in reproductive biology is involved here. In *H. cecropia,* cystoblast formation takes place in the penultimate larval instar (King and Aggarwal, 1965), proteid yolk is deposited during late pupal development, and adult life is devoted exclusively to reproduction. The adult female cannot ingest food and dies already after a few days. On the contrary, the ovaries of *Drosophila* start developing after emergence. Eggs are produced almost daily during about 1 month and they are formed almost exclusively on the basis of nutrients ingested during adult life.

The insect being almost too small to investigate the relation between hemolymph proteins and vitellogenesis, the conclusions derived by King and associates are mainly based on histological observations. It is assumed that in *Drosophila,* unlike *H. cecropia,* the exogenous supply of yolk proteins is only of minor importance, but that the nurse cells, and presumably the oocyte itself, synthesize these proteins.

Cessation of growth of the oocyte after nurse-cell degeneration, absence of formation of an intercellular space between follicle cells and oocyte at the onset of yolk deposition, absence of extensive pinocytotic activity at the oocyte surface, the presence of a very well-developed machinery for protein synthesis in the oocyte itself are arguments to assume that the exogenous supply of proteid yolk precursors is probably very limited. Cummings and King (1970), calculating that the number of pinosomes needed to provide the membranes surrounding the yolk spheres is more than ten thousand times the number actually found, suppose that the activity of the oolemma must be interpreted rather as proliferation of cytoplasmic membranes than as pinocytosis. Histological data, however, can never be a substitute for but rather are a complement to physiological evidence. In this respect, it is important to note that in the flies *Phormia regina, Musca domestica,* and *Sarcophaga bullata,* the presence of vitellogenic hemolymph proteins has been established (Orr, 1964; Bodnaryk and Morrison, 1966; Wilkens, 1969).

c. Proteid Yolk Formation in Leptinotarsa decemlineata (Telotrophic Ovariole). The ovaries develop immediately after pupal–adult ecdysis and the eggs are formed exclusively on the basis of nutrients ingested during adult life. The mechanism of proteid yolk formation resembles closely that described in *H. cecropia.* The trophic tissues in the germarium do not take part in proteid yolk formation. The oocytes selectively absorb and accumulate a hemolymph-borne female protein which is a glycoprotein with a molecular weight of about 250,000 (de Loof and de Wilde, 1970). At the onset of proteid yolk deposition, an intercellular space arises between follicle cells and oocyte. Hemolymph proteins are taken up in the oolemma by pinocytosis. The follicle cells, being highly specialized for protein synthesis, release a mucopolysaccharide–protein complex. A selective reaction between this product and the female protein, leading to the precipitation or crystallization of the female protein, is supposed. Bringing the female protein in an insoluble form has several advantages:

1. It enables the oocyte to accumulate globulins to concentrations as high as 17% without disturbing the osmotic pressure in the cell.

2. This high protein concentration will favor the formation of protein crystals inside the proteid yolk bodies.

3. The preservation of proteins will be enhanced (de Loof et al., 1972).

In all insects so far studied, the ingested hemolymph proteins are never set free in the cytoplasm of the oocyte after pinocytosis but they remain permanently surrounded by a membrane pinched off from the oolemma. There would only seem to be a necessity to do so when the ingested products, after being set free in the oocyte cytoplasm, would be harmful to normal cell functions, or when their half-life time should become too much reduced (de Loof et al., 1972).

d. *Proteid Yolk Formation in Periplaneta americana (Panoistic Ovariole).* Trophocytes being absent (Fig. 5), the possible sources of vitellogenic proteins are the oocyte, the follicle cells, and the hemolymph. A striking feature of the cytoplasm of all oocytes, regardless of their position within the ovariole, is the absence of an organized endoplasmic reticulum. Instead, the cytoplasmic matrix is filled with a host of free ribosomes. During active yolk deposition, the follicle cells are even highly specialized for protein synthesis as can be deduced from the very extensive endoplasmic reticulum and the numerous Golgi systems. Just as in *H. cecropia,* the follicular epithelium retracts from the oocyte surface at the time when proteid yolk deposition starts. The resulting space is filled with intensively periodic acid–Schiff-positive (PAS-positive) and salivary amylase–resistant material. At the oocyte surface, numerous pinocytotic vesicles are pinched off, suggesting the absorption of extraovarian proteins (Anderson, 1964).

Thomas and Nation (1966) and Bell (1970) detected a female protein in the hemolymph of *Periplaneta* and Menon (1966) found changes in the blood protein pattern, correlated with oogenesis. The proteid yolk bodies are composed of at least two components, protein and polysaccharide, the latter being salivary amylase–resistant.

e. *Proteid Yolk Formation in Other Insects.* In addition to the insects cited above, sex-specific vitellogenic hemolymph proteins are also found in *Philosamia cynthia* (Laufer, 1960), *Antheraea polyphemus* (Telfer, 1960; Blumenfeld and Schneiderman, 1969), *Schistocerca gregaria* (Hill, 1962; Dufour *et al.*, 1970), *Phormia regina* (Orr, 1964), *Rhodnius prolixus* (Coles, 1965), *Leucophaea maderae* (Engelmann and Penney, 1966; Dejmal and Brookes, 1968; Engelmann, 1969), *Nauphaeta cinerea* (Adiyodi, 1967), *Pieris brassicae* (Lamy, 1967a), *Musca domestica* (Bodnaryk and Morrison, 1966), *Apis mellifera* (Lensky and Alumot, 1969), *Tenebrio molitor* (Laverdure, 1969), *Locusta* (Bentz, 1969), *Gryllus domesticus* (Kunz and Petzelt, 1970), and *Dysdercus* (Hollweg, 1970). In other insects, such as *Lymantria dispar* (Lamy, 1967b), *Bombyx mori* (Groulade *et al.*, 1961), *Anthonomus grandis* (Mitlin *et al.*, 1967), and *Oncopeltus fasciatus* (Terando and Feir, 1967a,b), distinct vitellogenins do not seem to occur.

In recent years also many descriptive histological and electron microscopic studies, all dealing with some aspects of oogenesis, appeared and some will be cited.

Patchin and Davey (1968) used the intensity of staining of the follicular epithelium with mercury-2-bromphenol blue as an index of the intensity of protein transfer in *Rhodnius*. Vitellogenesis begins the second day after feeding and continues until the ninth day when it gradually decreases. Ramamurthy (1968) found a system of channels and lacunes in the peritoneal epithelium which may represent pathways through which hemolymph proteins penetrate to the surface of the tunica propria, which is at this stage greatly attenuated to aid diffusion of the protein molecules.

Louis *et al.* (1969) have observed that the trophocytes of the telotrophic ovary of the beetle *Oryzaephilus surinamensis* form a kind of syncytium. The trophocytes extend pseudopods, orienting themselves towards the young oocytes and forming in this way the trophic strands of the follicles.

Hamon (1969) only rarely observed mitotic divisions in the prefollicular cells of *Ulogra reticulata*. The nuclei showed hypertrophy which could not be fully explained by their polyploidy.

During the longitudinal growth of the oocyte of *Pimpla turionella* (Ichneumonidae), the oocyte itself synthesizes proteins but does not as yet receive proteins from the trophocytes. Later on, the trophocytes supply stable and unstable RNA from the nurse-cell chamber and yolk proteins are absorbed from the hemolymph (Meng, 1970). Truckenbrodt (1970) has described the fine structure of the terminal filament, the germarium, and the prophase region of the ovary of the termite *Kalotermes flavicollis*. Transport of substance into the oocytes has to occur through the follicular cells or at least by their mediation. Royer (1970) investigated the ultrastructure of the telotrophic ovariole of *Icerya purchasi* and observed that every oocyte is in cytoplasmic connection with the trophocytes. As in all other insects so far studied, microvilli occur between follicle cells and oocytes. The ultrastructure of the ovary of *Chironomus* was described by Wülker and Winter (1970). The ovary does not differ functionally from other polytrophic meroistic insect ovarioles in spite of the extremely small number of nurse cells within the follicle.

In *Apanteles glomeratus,* the mechanisms involved are similar to those in other hymenopteran species, except that no uptake of protein and associated configurations in the follicle cells and the periphery of the oocyte are observed (King *et al.,* 1971).

A cytological study of Palévody (1971) showed that the anatomy of the simple ovariole of some Collembola is rather different from all other types of ovarioles: the germarium is located mediodorsally and not apically of the vitellarium. The cellular chaplets are disseminated in the cavity of the vitellarium before vitellogenesis starts. A well-differentiated ovarian follicle, and especially well-differentiated follicle cells, are not present. Vitellogenesis takes place simultaneously in all oocytes. There is no real chorion; only a vitelline membrane, synthesized by the oocyte, is found.

Cruikshank (1971), working with *Anagasta kühniella,* used pulse-chase experiments to examine the movements of proteins between follicle cells and yolk. The follicle cells produce proteins which are incorporated into the yolk in some stages of vitellogenesis. These cells, however, are the most active sites of protein synthesis in the entire ovary during chorion formation. Proteins are synthesized in the yolk. The oocyte cortex synthesizes proteins which are incorporated into the vitelline membrane.

2. RNA Supply

The oocyte nucleus of polytrophic and telotrophic ovarioles, apart from a few exceptions (Bier, 1965), is inactive and does not participate in the supply of ribonucleic acids to the oocyte. With histological, autoradiographic, and electron microscopic methods, many authors have demonstrated that presumably the trophocytes deliver RNA to the oocyte. In telotrophic ovarioles, a stream of RNA material is transported from the trophic tissues to the oocyte via the trophic core [in *Rhodnius,* Vanderberg (1963); in *Oncopeltus,* Bonhag (1955a); in *Notonecta glauca,* McGregor and Stebblings (1970)]. According to McGregor and Stebblings (1970), the massive system of microtubules probably facilitates the movement of ribosomes. Bier's autoradiographic experiments with *Musca* and *Calliphora* (Bier, 1963a,b) clearly demonstrated that in these poly-trophic ovarioles a directed flow of RNA proceeds from the more anterior nurse cells through the posterior ones into the oocyte. The injected [³H]uridine was first observed in the nuclei of the nurse cells, subsequently in their cytoplasm, and later in a distinct stream entering into the oocyte while the nurse cells became emptied (Fig. 9). Similar results are described in mosquitoes (Roth *et al.*, 1968), in *Dytiscus marginalis* (Ficq, 1969), *Rynchosciara angelae* (Basile, 1969), in Dermaptera (Engels, 1970), and in the collembole, *Tetradontophora bielanensis* (Krzystofowicz, 1971). In Diptera, RNA emission starts within 1 hour after injection, while in Dermaptera a directed immigration into the ooplasm is at first observed 17–20 hours after [³H] uridine administration. According to Engels (1970), it can be concluded that in the evolution of meroistic Holo-metabola efficiency of oocyte growth developed mainly by increase in RNA transport.

Electron microscopic studies revealed that RNA was delivered from the trophocytes to the oocyte as ribosomes. Oocytes receiving ribosomes are described in *Drosophila* (Dapples and King, 1970), *Hyalophora* (King and Aggarwal, 1965), *Bombyx* (Miya *et al.*, 1969), *Oryzaephilus surinamensis* (Louis *et al.*, 1969), in *Notonecta glauca* (McGregor and Stebblings, 1970), *Nasonia vitripennis* (King and Richards, 1969), *Antheraea polyphemus* (Hughes and Berry, 1970). It is evident however, that soluble RNA fractions also can be delivered to the oocyte together with ribosomes. The primary function of trophocytes may well be the delivery to the oocyte of a great bulk of ribosomes which will serve as the machinery for protein synthesis during early stages of embryogenesis, or maybe even for proteid yolk synthesis in insects like *Drosophila* (Telfer, 1965; Roth *et al.*, 1968; Cummings and King, 1970).

In pre-yolk oocytes of panoistic ovarioles, e.g., in *Periplaneta* (Anderson, 1964), millions of ribosomes can be found which are synthesized by the oocyte nucleus. Presumably in this type of ovariole, the nucleolus or nucleoli of the oocyte nucleus can emit small masses of material (Bonhag, 1959). Often the transfer of nuclear products into the ooplasm is visible microscopically, either as fluids or as corpuscular elements. In this respect, we may briefly deal with the emission of nucleolar extrusion bodies, as described by Hogben (1920), Nath and Mohan (1929), Gresson (1930, 1931), Gresson and Threadgold (1962), Mulnard (1950, 1954), and Bonhag (1955a,b, 1959, 1961). The nucleolus may extrude material originating from internal vacuoles, or from its surface. In *Periplaneta* and *Acanthoscelides*, both ways are successively followed in different stages of oogenesis. In *Periplaneta* the nucleolar extrusions move

TABLE I

DNA CONTENT, EGG TYPE AND RATE OF DEVELOPMENT DURING OOGENESIS AND EMBRYOGENESIS OF SEVERAL INSECT SPECIES[a]

	DNA content during oogenesis (pg)		Egg type	Temp. (°C)	Duration of oogenesis (days)	Duration of vitellogenesis (days)	Duration of embryogenesis (days)	
							Until first blastoderm formation	Until hatching
	n[b]	X × n[c]	total						
Gryllus domesticus	2.3	4[d]	9.2	polyplasmatic, polylecithal	23	100	6	30	30
Locusta migratoria	6.18	4	24.7	id.	33	42	4	23	13
Musca domestica	1.04	15 × 256[d]	3994	polyplasmatic	21	6-7	4	1½	1½
Drosophila melanogaster	0.09	15 × 128	173	id.	23	4-8	3	1½	1

[a] After Bier (1970).
[b] In haploid set of chromosomes.
[c] Number of sets of chromosomes.
[d] Growth takes place in g_2 phase.
[e] Stage of polyploidy of the 15 trophocytes in the middle phase of oogenesis.

into the nucleoplasm and become randomly distributed (Nath and Mohan, 1929; Anderson, 1964). In dragonflies and damselflies, oocytes regularly contain two nucleoluslike bodies of different size, a primary and a secondary nucleolus. This is also found in *Acheta* (Fig. 11). The primary nucleolus probably produces ribosomal RNA while the secondary one, which is active in protein synthesis and in the synthesis, accumulation, or transitory coupling of soluble RNA, has still an enigmatic role in cellular metabolism (Halkka and Halkka, 1968). Another characteristic feature of panoistic ovarioles is the occurrence of giant lampbrush chromosomes which appear to be very active in RNA synthesis as was demonstrated in *Schistocerca* (Kunz, 1967). At any event, with disregard of the question whether or not the nuclear RNA synthesis reflects the involvement of the oocyte in proteid yolk synthesis, in earlier stages of oogenesis in *Periplaneta*, however, oocytes participate in protein synthesis (Zinsmeister and Davenport, 1971).

That the genome of auxiliary cells, as well as of the trophocytes, would deliver RNA to the oocyte is, in fact, not in agreement with a basic principle of cell metabolism: regulation of protein synthesis in a cell by its own genome. Another principle is respected: the RNA is not transported through the cell membrane but via cytoplasmic bridges (ring canals, Fig. 9). In meroistic ovaries, the capacity of RNA-transcription, which is at the disposal of the growing oocyte, is seemingly increased by the involvement of polyploid trophocytes (Table I). As can be expected, this capacity of increased RNA synthesis in meroistic ovarioles will not only shorten the period needed for oocyte maturation in the ovary, but will presumably result in much larger germ-anlagen and, as a result, also a shorter duration of embryogenesis (Bier, 1970).

Vesicle-enclosed bodies budded from the nuclear membrane, described by many authors as accessory nuclei are Feulgen-negative (Mukerji, 1930). In *Nasonia vitripennis,* the accessory nuclei are rich in RNA. They are found at the periphery of the oocyte where they probably play a role in the formation of yolk bodies from pinocytotic vesicles (King and Richards, 1969). In *Ophion luteus* and *Apanteles glomeratus,* the accessory nuclei are produced by folding of annulate lamellae produced from the nuclear envelope. The nucleus and accessory nuclei give rise to other annulate lamellae by two distinct modes of budding. Electron microscopic studies have also revealed the presence of annulate lamellae in the periphery of the oocyte (Fig. 14). These structures are produced by the nuclear envelope and appear to be involved in the formation of membranes (King and Richards, 1969; Kessel and Beams, 1969; King and Fordy, 1970).

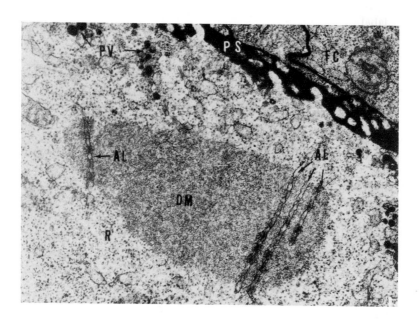

Fig. 14. Annulate lamellae (AL) in the periphery of the terminal oocyte in *Aeschna* (from Kessel and Beams, 1969). PV, pinocytotic vesicles; PS, perivitelline space; FC, follicle cell; R, ribosomes; DM, basophilic mass.

3. *The Occurrence of DNA in the Ooplasm*

The presence of DNA in the cytoplasm of the oocyte has been reported in several insects. In *Acanthocephala* and *Oncopeltus,* nuclei and Feulgen-positive droplets enter the trophic core where they become Feulgen-negative, only to become positive again after being transported to the oocyte (Bonhag, 1955a). However, by means of autoradiography and ligation of the trophic core, Zinsmeister and Davenport (1971) demonstrated that neither DNA nor protein enter the oocyte from external sources in *Oncopeltus.* In *Rhodnius,* there appeared to be a transfer of some of the DNA in a partially depolymerized form from the trophic tissues of the ovary to the growing oocytes (Vanderberg, 1963). Favard-Séréno and Durand (1963) injected [³H]thymidine into the hemocoel of *Gryllus* and observed that not only the nuclei of some of the follicle cells but also the cytoplasm and the adjacent ooplasm were labeled. Digestion with DNase removed the label from each of these sites.

A reservoir of DNA seems to exist in the cytoplasm of the oocyte of *Drosophila* (Nigon and Gillot, 1964; Nigon and Nonnenmacher, 1961). An acceptable explanation could be that the DNA originates from the disintegrating endopolyploid nurse cells (Jacob and Sirlin, 1959). We must keep in mind, however, that the nurse cells, including their nuclei, remain outside the oocyte when the chorionic layers are formed. Nigon and Gillot (1964) injected [³H]thymidine into *Drosophila* and found that the label, which was incorporated in the cytoplasm of both the oocyte and nurse cells, could not be removed by DNase or other procedures designed to extract DNA. However, Muckenthaler and Mahowald (1966) found that this ooplasmic label is sensitive to hydrolysis with DNase when the hydrolysis is preceded by removal of proteins by proteases, and they also observed that most of this cytoplasmic label (65%) is localized in the mitochondria.

In *Dytiscus marginalis*, Ficq (1969) observed that, in early stages of oogenesis, the Giardina body and the nurse cells incorporate labeled DNA precursor. In more advanced stages, some labeled granules could be seen in the ooplasm. Basile (1969) found that in the nurse cells of *Rhynchosciara angelae*, DNA synthesis is restricted to the polyploidization process.

The results of the above cited studies indicate that we must be very careful in the interpretation of the data. Ooplasmic DNA seems to be partly localized in the mitochondria. The nonmitochondrial DNA may be a "storage" DNA necessary to provide precursors for the rapid nuclear proliferation in early embryogenesis (Muckenthaler and Mahowald, 1966).

4. Origin of Carbohydrate Yolk

Carbohydrate yolk occurs in the oocyte as glycogen and mucopolysaccharide–protein complexes in the proteid yolk bodies. Glycogen is synthesized in the ovary itself. Glycogen synthetases are formed early in vitellogenesis and are multiplied during the growth of the oocyte (Engels and Bier, 1967). Only at the end of vitellogenesis is glycogen very quickly condensed from glucose (Engels and Drescher, 1964; Engels, 1966). The late synthesis of glycogen seems to be characteristic of oogenesis in the whole animal kingdom (Raven, 1961). However, in *Anisolobis maritima* (Bonhag, 1956) and *Drosophila* (King and Aggarwal, 1965; Cummings and King, 1970), some glycogen appears first in the trophocyte and is discharged through the fusosomes (ring canals) into the oocyte lumen. Glycogen is lacking in the ooplasm of *Oncopeltus* (Bonhag, 1956) and *Periplaneta* (Bonhag, 1959). In almost all insects so far studied, proteid yolk bodies are PAS-reactive and salivary amylase-resistant, suggesting incorporation of carbohydrates in glycoproteids or mucoproteids. Favard-Séréno (1969) demonstrated that, in *Gryllus*

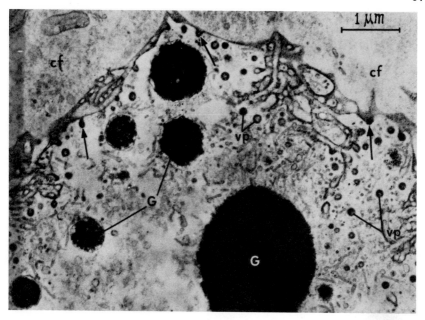

Fig. 15. Inner region of follicle cells (cf) and peripheral ooplasm in *Acheta domesticus,* with pinocytotic vesicles (vp) and invaginations (arrows) ; g., yolk body. Black
regions contain polysaccharides (from Favard-Séréno, 1969).

capitatus, the carbohydrates in the proteid yolk bodies are polysaccharides or more likely of a glycoproteid nature and of exogenous origin. They enter into the oocyte via pinocytosis (Fig. 15) . In *Hyalophora
cecropia* (Anderson and Telfer, 1969; Anderson, 1971) and in the Colorado beetle (de Loof *et al.,* 1972) the follicle cells release a product,
probably of a glycoproteid nature, which is necessary to induce pinocytotic activity in the oocyte surface and which is absorbed by the oocyte. The
vitellogenic female protein, the most important proteid yolk precursor in
the hemolymph, is also a glycoproteid in the Colorado beetle (de Loof
and de Wilde, 1970) and in Gryllus (Kunz and Petzelt, 1970) . This fact
may be responsible for the PAS-positive reaction of proteid yolk. Ramamurthy (1968) found that in the polytrophic ovary of *Panorpa communis*
the carbohydrate component of the yolk is synthesized in the egg cortex from precursors derived from the blood, but there was no evidence
that the follicle cells or trophocytes were involved in carbohydrate yolk
synthesis.

Apart from the real carbohydrate yolk components, soluble sugars
such as mannose, glucose, fructose, and trehalose have been identified in

eggs of *Aulacara elliotti* (Quickenden, 1969). Trehalose had already been detected in ovaries of *Antheraea* (Egarov and Smolin, 1962).

5. The Origin of Lipid Yolk

Before the introduction of the electron microscope, many papers on vitellogenesis concentrated on the origin of lipid yolk. Usually, lipid yolk bodies were thought to be formed by Golgi bodies and mitochondria. The formation by Golgi bodies has generally been observed: *Periplaneta* (Nath and Mohan, 1929; Gresson, 1931), *Gryllotalpa* (Voinov, 1925), *Dysdercus* (Bhandari and Nath, 1930), *Pediculus* (Ries and Weel, 1934), *Luciola* (Nath and Mehta, 1930), *Culex* (Nath, 1929), *Dytiscus* (Nussbaum-Hilarowicz, 1917), and *Gelastocoris* (Payne, 1932).

In *Oncopeltus*, lipid yolk bodies are first formed in the oocyte from precursor bodies near the entrance of the trophic strand. In later stages of oogenesis they occur near the follicle epithelium, suggesting their origin

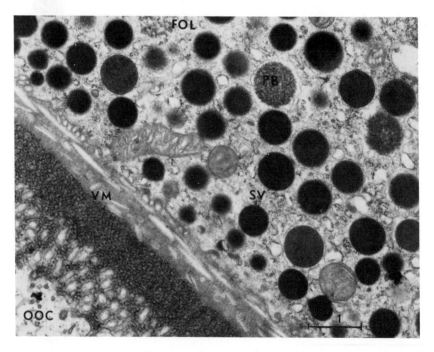

Fig. 16. Formation of vitelline membrane (VM) by the follicle cells (FOL) in the Colorado beetle. The flocculated dense material fills the microvilli and is covered by a less dense layer in which most of the needlelike crystals are oriented in a longitudinal direction. Two types of secretion vesicles (SV) can be recognized in the follicle cell: electron dense (SV) and more granulate (PB) (from de Loof, 1971).

from this source (Bonhag, 1955a, Fig. 10). The precursor bodies are "Golgi vacuoles" (Nath, 1929) or "lipochondria" (Ries and Weel, 1934).

Nath *et al.* (1958) have described three kinds of lipid bodies in the cockroach: (1) L1 bodies, present in the earliest oocyte, which persist until the oocyte measures approximately 0.5 mm and which contain phospholipids only, possibly having more lecithins than cephalins; (2) L2 bodies, which first arise in the oocyte measuring 0.4 mm and have a complete or incomplete sheath of phospholipids surrounding a medulla of triglycerides, and which are rather highly saturated; and (3) L3 bodies, which are the only types of lipids in the oocytes measuring more than 0.65 mm and consist of rather highly saturated triglycerides. The L1 bodies of these authors correspond to the "Golgi bodies" of Nath and Mohan (1929).

In *Chrotogonus, Gryllodes, Culex fatigans* and *Labidura* species, three types of lipid bodies are also found (see review by Nath, 1966).

Electron microscopic studies have demonstrated that Golgi complexes or mitochondria do not take part in lipid yolk formation, but no studies have been performed to elucidate their way of origin. Przelecka and Dutkowski (1965) observed that during vitellogensis [^{14}C]palmitate is most readily incorporated in the follicular epithelium of *Galleria mellonella* and much less into the ooplasm and trophocytes. In the panoistic ovariole of *Carausius morosus,* the most intensive radioactivity was found in the peripheral region of the ooplasm, while the follicular epithelium and the other regions of the ooplasm were only weakly labeled. In *Hyalophora* (King and Aggarwal, 1965) and *Drosophila* (Cummings and King, 1970) part of the lipid yolk bodies is transported from the trophocytes to the oocyte.

D. POLARITY OF THE OOCYTE

Longitudinal polarity is determined by the position of the oocyte in the ovariole, the animal pole being oriented anteriad, the vegetative pole posteriad. Mostly, the oocyte is elongated during the period preceding vitellogenesis. Its long axis corresponds to the future craniocaudal axis of the embryo. Within the ovariole, the orientation of the eggs is the same as that of the mother, craniocaudally as well as laterally. This general law of orientation was first formulated by Hallez (1885, 1886) and has repeatedly been confirmed by subsequent observers. In cases where the polarity of the deposited egg would seem to deviate from this rule, typical features of oviposition such as forward syringing and/or rotation of the egg may be involved.

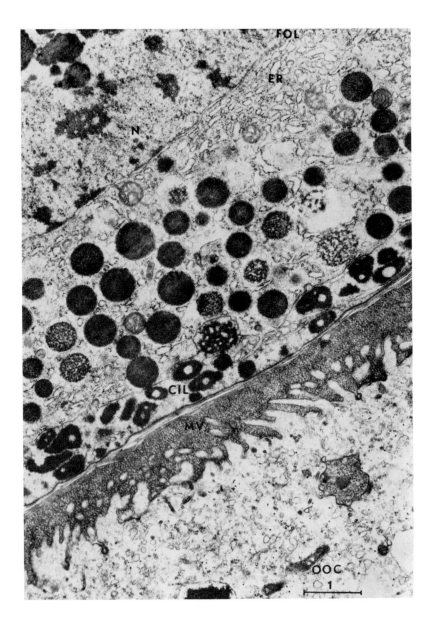

Fig. 17. Deposition of inner chorionic layer (CIL) in the Colorado beetle. The follicle cell retracts from the vitelline membrane (MV). In the resulting space, follicular secretion vesicles (SV) disintegrate in a manner different from vitelline membrane formation (cf. Fig. 16) (from de Loof, 1971).

Bilateral symmetry is soon indicated by the position of the germinal vesicle. The nuclear pole, at which the germinal vesicle lies closest to the surface, either becomes the dorsal *(Tachycines:* von Kraft, 1960; *Acanthoscelides:* Mulnard, 1954) or the ventral side *(Apis:* Kaufmann *et al.,* 1953; Morgenthaler, 1952; Bier, 1952; *Tenebrio:* Bonhag, 1956). At the same time, the dorsoventral polarity may be reflected in the structure of the egg follicle. In *Acanthoscelides,* the contact between follicle and oocyte is strongest at the side of the germinal vesicle, where the follicle cells are more basophilic, due to accumulation of RNA (Mulnard, 1954). It has been suggested that the follicle cells "imprint" the cortical field upon the egg, determining polarity and symmetry and possibly other "blueprint" characteristics of the cortical ooplasm (Raven, 1961).

E. FORMATION OF EGG MEMBRANES AND SPECIALIZED CHORIONIC STRUCTURES

After termination of yolk deposition, the oocyte becomes surrounded by two protective layers, the vitelline membrane and the chorion. The structure of these layers is such that respiration remains possible while water evaporation is kept to a minimum.

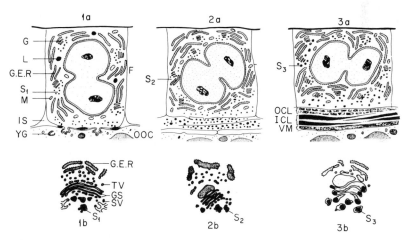

Fig. 18. Synthesis of egg envelope precursors in 3 successive secretory cycles (S_1–S_3) in *Acheta domesticus* (redrawn from Favard-Séréno, 1971). 1a and 2b, secretion of vitelline membrane material (VM); 2a and 2b, secretion of inner chorionic material (ICL); 3a and 3b, secretion of outer chorionic material (OCL). G, Golgi body; G.E.R. granulated endoplasmic recticulum; IS, intercellular space; M, mitochondrion; TV, transition vesicle; GS, Golgi saccule; L, lipid inclusions; SV, secretion vesicle; YG, yolk granule.

Much debate has been raised around the question whether the oocyte itself or the follicle cells secrete the vitelline membrane. Recent ultrastructural investigations in *Gryllus* (Favard-Séréno, 1971), *Leptinotarsa* (de Loof, 1971), *Drosophila* (King, 1964; Quatropiani and Anderson, 1969; Cummings *et al.*, 1971), *Nasonia* (King *et al.*, 1971), and *Aeschna* (Beams and Kessel, 1969) clearly demonstrated that the follicle cells synthesize the precursor material for the vitelline membrane. The precursor material is synthesized in the Golgi complexes and is a polysaccharide–protein complex (Favard-Séréno, 1971; de Loof, 1971) (Fig. 16). In *Lytta viridana* (Gerrity *et al.*, 1967) and in *Acheta domes-*

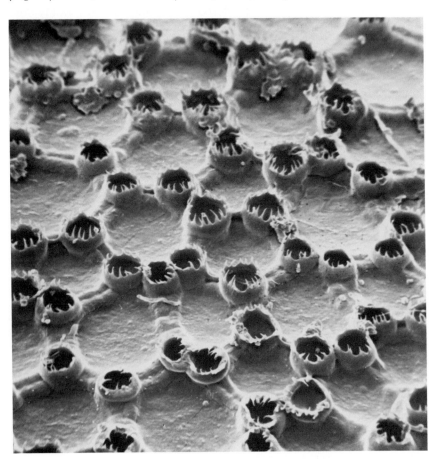

Fig. 19. Outer surface of the eggshell of the silkworm *Antheraea pernyi* with respiratory tubes and irregular ridges (from Hinton, 1970).

ticus (McFarlane, 1970), the vitelline membrane seems to be synthesized by the oocyte. The practice of designating an outer layer of the chorion as "exochorion" and an inner layer as "endochorion" suggests homologies that do not always exist. Because there is no strict correspondence between these layers in different insects, it is perhaps best merely to speak of the outer and inner layers of the chorion (Hinton, 1969). The chorionic layers are synthesized by the follicle cells (Slifer, 1937; Beament, 1946; King, 1960; Wigglesworth and Salpeter, 1962; de Loof, 1971; and many others) (Fig. 17). Favard-Séréno (1971) found that the precursors of the two egg envelopes are synthesized within the follicle cells through three successive secretory cycles and that at last they are released in the intercellular space between follicle cells and oocyte (Fig. 18). The hexagonal lining of the follicle produces a pattern on the chorion surface of many species.

This activity of the follicle cells is undoubtedly one of the most remarkable and complicated features of oogenesis. If we consider the vast variety of forms and structures of insect eggs, adapted to a great many oviposition media and substrates, their micropylar apparatus, ridges and caps, their finely sculptured outer surface, it is difficult to realize that this is accomplished by one layer of cells (Fig. 19). However, no less remarkable is the ability of these cells to secrete subsequently and synchronously a variety of substances, together forming the several layers of the chorion.

Most authors, following Korschelt (1887), recognize two main groups of layers, secreted during two distinct phases: the more or less rigid chorionic outer layers and the finely structured chorionic inner layers.

The composition of the these layers in *Rhodnius prolixus,* according to Beament (1946), is as follows:

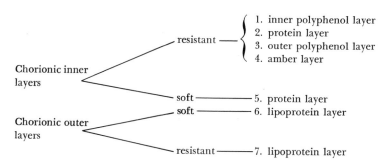

In the first secretory phase, the follicle cells produce the inner layers and the soft outer layer. In the second secretory phase, they produce the

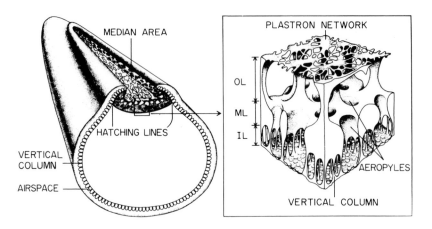

Fig. 20. Egg of the blowfly *Calliphora erythrocephala* with plastron confined to medial strip between 2 hatching lines (left). Square section of the structure enlarged (right) showing the 3 chorionic layers, OL (outer layer), ML (middle layer), IL (inner layer) ; the vertical columns; and aeropyles (redrawn from Hinton, 1970).

resistant outer layers not very permeable to water, and possessing mechanical rigidity.

In some phasmids (*Carausius* and *Phobaeticus*) after the first secretory phase, the follicle cells divide by amitosis, the follicle as a whole becoming folded. These folds subsequently stretch and secrete a second chorionic layer, loosely surrounding the first one (Cappe de Baillon, 1933).

Studies by means of the transmission and scanning electron microscope have shown architectural features in the eggshell related to its permeability to respiratory gases, water, and sperm. The crucial problem for eggs laid in dry environments is how to minimize water evaporation and at the same time allow the free exchange of O_2 and CO_2. Specialized areas of the chorion are aeropylar, hydropylar, and micropylar structures. The unspecialized region of the shell may be thin and entirely solid in eggs regularly deposited within plants or animals. In most cases the shell is made up of one or more layers of fine meshwork, filled with gas (Fig. 20). This gas store is in exchange either with the ambient air or, when the egg is immersed in water, with the gases dissolved in this medium. In the latter case, the respiratory system functions as a plastron, "a gas layer of constant volume and extensive water–air interface. Such layers are held in position by a system of hydrofuge structures that resist the entry of water under pressure" (Hinton, 1962). In dipteran eggs, the whole surface or a more restricted area may function as a plastron (Hinton,

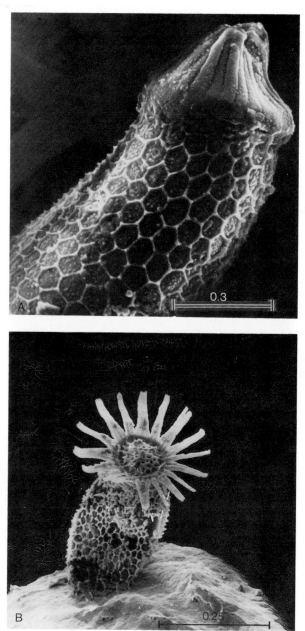

Fig. 21. Aeropylar filaments of *Loricula* eggs (Heteroptera) under different humidity conditions. A, *L. elegantula,* humid environment, B, *L. Pselaphiforinis,* dry environment. Filaments spread out in latter case (from Cobben, 1968).

1960) (Fig. 20). In *Calliphora* the vacuolar shell of the egg has a plastron at its waist, the functioning of which is vital to the egg (Anderson,
1960). In other cases, respiratory horns with aeropylar filaments are present. The structure and function of the respiratory system of the chorion
proper, and of the plastron-bearing horns in Hemiptera, in many Diptera,
and in the Encyrtidae (Hymenoptera), all of which have predominantly
terrestrial eggs, have been discussed in detail (Hinton, 1960, 1961, 1962;
Cobben, 1968).

When the eggs are not immersed, respiratory horns with a plastron
merely function as aeropyles. In Microphysidae (Heteroptera) the aeropylar filaments alternately radiate out and close again with humidity
changes, undoubtedly affecting the rate of gas exchange (Cobben, 1968)
(Fig. 21).

Hydropyles are chorionic structures with a coarse meshwork conducting fluid to the embryonic system. In *Nepa,* the inner surface of the
hydropyle has openings large enough to permit the passage of water, although these ducts could not be distinguished optically (Hinton, 1961).

The micropylar apparatus, situated at the anterior pole of the egg, is a
system of canaliculae serving the entrance of sperm. At these places, the
chorion is secreted around long protoplasmic projections of the follicle
cells. In *Rhodnius,* all seven layers of the chorion are represented in the
micropylar complex. In this region, the cells start to secrete at various
stages in the seven-phase cycle. The rim of the characteristic cap of the
anterior pole is produced by four rings of follicle cells. Thickness is
achieved by increase of exochorion layers, secreted around long follicular
villi, and forming pits. The sealing bar, produced by one ring of follicle
cells, is composed of the inner four layers of the chorion only. Three
rings of pits become closed, the fourth row remains. Its pits become micropylae and associated structures. The micropyle-forming cells are determined in the earliest stages of secretion, being pressed out of their
ring. There are 200 pits, about 10–20 of which become micropylae. The
remainder, closed at both ends, are pseudomicropylae (Beament, 1947).
No less complex phenomena are involved in micropyle formation in *Anopheles* (Nicholson, 1921). The number of micropylae may vary greatly,
within a species as well as between species. In *Locusta migratoria* the
number is 35–43 (Roonwal, 1936). Tettigoniids have from 1–23 micropylae (Cappe de Baillon, 1920). In the book louse, *Liposcelis divergens,*
micropylae are reported absent (Goss, 1954).

In Diptera, the micropyle is often complex and consists of an ectomi-
cropyle in the chorion proper and an endomicropyle penetrating the vitelline membrane (King, 1964). In the newly laid egg of the meloid *Lytta*

viridana, the vitelline membrane is at first porous, but becomes continuous several hours after sperm penetration (Rempel and Church, 1965). A survey of the number of micropylae per insect order has been given by Cobben (1968).

F. OOSORPTION

Under the influence of a variety of factors, most of which might possibly result in "pseudo-allatectomy" (Johansson, 1958) vitellogenesis may be interrupted and the oocyte, wholly enveloped in its follicle, may die. Resorption of oocytes can be triggered by starvation (Johansson, 1955, 1958; Bell, 1971), short photoperiod (de Wilde *et al.*, 1959; de Wilde and de Boer, 1961), failure to mate (Roth and Stay, 1962), absence of adult males (Highnam and Lusis, 1962), unavailability of a parasitic host (Flanders, 1942, 1950), or abnormally long retention of a spermatophore (Roth, 1964).

Oosorption may also be induced by allatectomy (Chapter 3). In *Labidura riparia* (Dermaptera), the penultimate follicle degenerates just before oviposition and in the period during which the female tenders the egg (Cassaunel, 1971). In nonreproductive female castes of social insects (Weyer, 1928; Pardi, 1946) oosorption is also observed. In normal females of *Schistocerca*, there is always a limited number of degenerating ovarioles. Partial ovariectomy results in less resorbed oocytes in the remaining ovary, indicating that the concentration of yolk precursors in the hemolymph may be an important factor (Highnam and Haskell, 1964).

The follicle cells cease to participate in alimentary egg formation. They sometimes divide amitotically and absorb the dead oocyte. Their nuclei subsequently become pycnotic and the cells break down and are absorbed through the ovarian sheaths. After this phenomenon was first observed by Wigglesworth (1936) in *Rhodnius*, it has been described in many other insects, e.g., in *Oncopeltus* (Johansson, 1958), *Calliphora* (Thomsen, 1952), Hymenoptera (Flanders, 1942; Thompson and Parker, 1928; Medler, 1962; Maeta and Kurihara, 1971), and *Schistocerca* (Lusis, 1963).

In *Rhodnius* and *Oncopeltus*, both with telotrophic ovarioles in which the oocyte remains connected to "trophic strands" for some distance along its passage through the vitellarium, oosorption only occurs after this phase of oogenesis has finished (Wigglesworth, 1936; Johansson, 1958). As a consequence, one may observe alimentary egg formation as well as oosorption occurring in one ovariole.

Ultrastructural observations have recently shown that oosorption may be another instance of "controlled cell death."

Following allatectomy, the follicle cells of the Colorado beetle ovary do not divide amitotically and do not take part in the resorption of the oocyte. The proteid yolk bodies are dissolved by lysosomelike bodies, which are numerous in the degenerating oocyte. All products which resist this enzymic digestion, such as the crystals in the protein yolk bodies, degenerating nuclei of the follicle cells, lipid yolk droplets and numerous myelin figures, will form the plug with autolyzing residues (corpus luteum). As oosorption advances, the volume of the oocyte gradually diminishes so that the follicular epithelium becomes too large. As a result the follicle cells glide along each other, giving the faulty impression of multiplication. Absence of juvenile hormone not only induces lysosomal breakdown of the oocyte, but also arrests the uptake of proteid yolk precursors from the hemolymph, which are nevertheless available in large quantities, and the synthesis of mucopolysaccharide–protein complexes by the follicle cells (de Loof and Lagasse, 1970). It is not excluded that conditions like the above may be the rule rather than the exception.

G. Transfer of Symbionts during Oogenesis

Endosymbiontic microorganisms—a common feature in insects—may be transferred from parent to offspring in a variety of ways. We will treat here the transmission by way of the ovaries, as this is in many insect species an essential element of oogenesis.

1. Infection without Specialized Organs of Transmission

a. Embryonic Infection. In *Ischnodemus sabuleti* (Lygaeidae) a paired mycetome primordium is present in the embryonic fat body and is situated close to the mesodermal ovarian primordium. The symbionts penetrate the ovarium and multiply between the primordial germ cells. When the germarium differentiates, the symbionts penetrate into the trophocytes and enter the oocytes by way of the trophic strands (Schneider, 1940). The same is found in *Cimex lectularius* (Buchner, 1923).

In several Curculionidae *(Apion, Sabinia, Sitophila)* the primordial germ cells of both sexes are already infected in the blastoderm stage of the embryo. The symbionts multiply in the female, but gradually disappear in the male during further differentiation (Scheinert, 1933; Nolte, 1937).

b. Adult Infection. In *Lyctus linearis* (Col.) mycetomes located in the fat body periodically release the infective symbiont stages. They migrate toward the vitellarium. The follicle cells, normally forming a continuous layer, partly disconnect, openings being left in between through which the bacteria pass. When they have reached the oocyte, the pores are closed again (Koch, 1936).

In ants *(Camponotus, Formica)* symbionts pass through the bodies of the follicle cells, penetrate into the oocyte, and multiply in the ooplasm (Buchner, 1928; Lilienstern, 1932). In Dictyoptera (Gier, 1936; Koch, 1949) and some primitive termites (Koch, 1938), bacteriocytes, not incorporated in the fat body, become located against the ovarioles. Bacteria pass through the follicle cell bodies to the surface of the early oocyte stages. They multiply at this surface, and collect in the neighborhood of the egg poles. Infection of the yolk cavity occurs much later.

2. Infections by Way of Specialized Structures of the Ovary

This occurs in a variety of Homoptera. Infectious forms of symbionts are produced in the mycetomes, which often form "infective protrusions." They are transported in the hemolymph, either free or within wandering mycetocytes (Membracidea: many Coccidae). They subsequently penetrate the ovary. The follicle has a specialized region, the "receptive cells," which are either passed in between or penetrated. In Aphididae, Membracidae, Fulgoridae, Cicadidae, Psyllidae, and some Coccidae, this region is located near the caudal egg pole. In Coccidae the symbionts pass in between the follicle and the trophic strands to the cranial egg pole, and collect in a depression at the egg surface. Penetration into the interior of the egg occurs only in the first cleavage stages. In Cicadinae and Psyllidae, the symbionts are located in a depression at the posterior end of the oocyte and are released into the yolk cavity with the nutritive stream (Buchner, 1925; Müller, 1940; Rau, 1942; Carayon, 1952a).

3. Infection by Means of Auxiliary Mycetomes

In this, the most complicated category, embryonic and larval mycetomes produce first-order infectious forms, which penetrate into a secondary or auxiliary mycetome. In the adult stage this mycetome produces second-order infectious forms, entering the oocyte lumen. The following types of auxiliary mycetomes are recognized.

a. Ovarial Mycetomes. These are located between germarium and vitellarium (Fulgoridae, Lygaedia). The symbiotic bacteria pass into the oocyte by way of the trophic strands (Buchner, 1953; Müller, 1940).

b. Rectal Mycetomes (Rectal Organs). This is found in many Fulgoridae. Migratory symbiont stages enter the intestinal lumen and collect in a provisional intestinal mycetome. Liberated from this mycetome, they are again collected by a "symbiont filter" in the hindgut. Near to this filter is a "rectal organ." Here, the symbionts collect in mycetocytes, and give rise to infective stages. These move into the ovaries and collect in the oocytes. During the embryonic development, further differentiations occur (Müller, 1940).

c. *Ovarial Ampullae*. In Anoplura and Mallophaga, the ovarial stalk differentiates in a specialized way. The wall increases in thickness and forms a fixed number of cellular layers, one of which contains the symbiont. Infection is performed from this layer, as the caudal pole of the oocyte comes into contact with the ampulla. In embryonic stages of *Pediculus capitis* and *Pediculus vestimenti*, the symbionts form a primordial mycetome, which enters into the differentiating genital tract (Fig. 22). From this source, the symbionts reach the ovarial ampulla (Ries, 1931). For further details reference is made to the review by Carayon (1952a) and the classical work of Buchner (1953).

H. OOGENESIS IN POSTEMBRYONIC DEVELOPMENT

1. Imaginal Reproduction

Generally, oogonial mitoses have ended before the adult molt. In *Oncopeltus* at the time of hatching the first larval instar has only approximately 24 oogenia in the telotrophic ovariole. During the first three larval instars the number increases considerably as a result of further mitoses. In the latter part of the fourth instar some oogenia differentiate into trophocytes and oocytes. The trophocytes undergo further mitotic divisions at the end of the fourth and fifth instar. The oocytes accumulate during the fifth and last instar at the posterior end of the germarium. Some of these oocytes are not retained; they migrate into the prefollicular tissue and disappear. As a result, there are fewer oocytes in the young adult than in the early fifth instar larva (Wick and Bonhag, 1955). Follicle formation takes place only in the adult stage.

In *Dytiscus,* oogonial differentiation is known to occur during adult life, oocytes virtually being absent at the time of adult molt (Günthart, 1910). The degree of completion of oogenesis at the adult molt may vary greatly between species. In Lepidoptera, three categories are recognized (Eidmann, 1931).

1. Oogenesis is complete and the full number of ripe eggs present in species with a very short adult life such as many Bombycidae.

2. Part of the eggs are formed before metamorphosis, and part are formed during adult life in Sphingidae, *Panolis, Bupalus*. Adult life is longer in these cases.

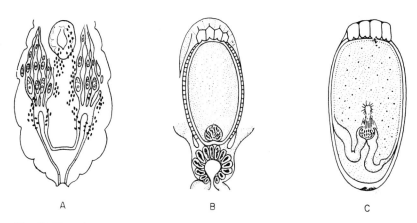

Fig. 22. Transfer of symbionts during oogenesis in *Pediculus capitis.* A, Release from stomacal mycetome to form ovarial ampulla. B, Penetration from ovarial ampulla into the yolk cavity of the egg. C, Perforation of the embryonic enteric to form stomacal mycetome (after Ries, 1931).

3. The formation of ripe eggs occurs exclusively in the adult stage in Rhopalocera, where adult life is longest and adult feeding regularly occurs.

Oogenesis is completed before the adult molt in Ephemeroptera, Plecoptera, Cicadina. It takes place during adult life in most Orthoptera, Dictyoptera, Isoptera, Diptera (Weber, 1954), and many Hemiptera Heteroptera *(Rhodnius, Cimex),* Coleoptera, and Hymenoptera.

2. Paedogenesis

The most extreme case of early oogenesis is found in paedogenetic insects, in which ova not only are formed during the immature stages, but even start, and sometimes complete, embryonic development.

a. Hemiptera. In parthenogenetic, viviparous aphids, paedogenetic development occurs in the elongated vitellarium of the ovariole, a structure already fully developed at the end of embryonic life. In *Macrosiphum tanaceti,* according to Uichanco (1924), about 80 ova, varying in development from newly ovulated egg to fully developed embryos, may be found in the vitellarium before the mother has performed the adult molt. Only one-third of this number is ovulated during adult life. One or two eggs are ovulated while the female is in the embryonic stage (Metchnikoff, 1866).

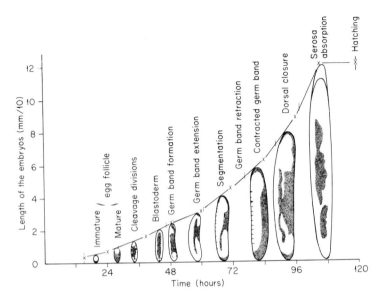

Fig. 23. Continuous oogenesis and embryogenesis within the follicles of the paedogenetic gall midge *Heteropeza pygmaea* (redrawn from Went, 1971).

In the parasitic family Polyctenidae, paedogenesis has been described in the bisexual species *Hesperoctenes fumarius*. Ovulation, fertilization, and embryonic development take place in the ovariole and may start while the mother is in the nymphal stage (Hagan, 1931).

b. Coleoptera. In the larva of *Micromalthus debilis*, eggs and larvae develop in large follicles within the vitellarium. Imaginal males and females are formed but apparently do not take part in reproduction (Scott, 1936, 1938; Pringle, 1938).

c. Strepsiptera. In this parasitic order, the sexually mature female is neotenic and remains located inside the abdomen of its host. Two or three ovarial strands are found on each side of the intestine. Oviducts are absent, ovulation taking place into the hemocoel (Hughes-Schräder, 1924).

d. Diptera. In the family Cecidomyidae, species of the genera *Miastor, Oligarces,* and *Tanytarsus* have paedogenetic larvae although functional adults of both sexes may also be produced. In *Miastor metroloas* and *Heteropeza pygmaea,* the larval ovary merely consists of the germarium. After oocyte differentiation, the mature oocyte, together with its cluster of trophocytes, is enclosed in the mesodermal follicle. The follicles collect in an epithelial sac which subsequently bursts and releases its contents in the hemocoel. Here, oogenesis is completed and immediately followed by parthenogenetic development. Since no chorion is present the embryos can take up nutrients from the maternal hemolymph and grow continuously (Fig. 23).

Upon eclosion, the larvae disrupt the cuticle of the mother and assume a phytophagous way of life (Kahle, 1908; Ulrich, 1936, 1962; Camenzind, 1962; Went, 1971).

I. FECUNDITY

Fecundity is a function of so many intrinsic and extrinsic factors (see Chapter 3 of this volume) that any attempt at generalization must necessarily be questionable. Data mentioned in literature have been obtained under various and often far from optimal conditions. Fecundity often parallels the risk of preimaginal mortality in relation to the ecological peculiarities of the life cycle. Even between related species, therefore, fecundity may vary widely.

Engelmann (1970) has compiled a vast number of data on fecundity from the literature. Some examples are quoted here.

In a rather homogeneous group such as the Orthoptera, average fecundity shows a moderate variation between species ($\pm$ 100–1000 eggs/ female), and the same is true for Lepidoptera (100–2500 with maxima for the genus *Agrotis*). In a very heterogeneous group such as the Homoptera, limits are 4–6 *(Pineus pineoides)* to 1250 *(Icerya purchasi)*. The Diptera show a similar picture (4–5 for *Hippobosca* to 1500–1800 for *Drosophila*). Also the Coleoptera, a biologically very diversified group vary greatly in fecundity (15 in *Phyllopertha horticola*, 3–4000 in *Meloë*). Extremes are reached in the queens of social insects. The honeybee queen deposits 120,000 eggs per year (and may oviposit during three or more successive years), while the large termite queens reportedly lay several million eggs during their life span.

Body size is by no means a measure of fecundity *(Calandra granaria, 190; Rhynchophorus palmarius, 245)*.

The fecundity of univoltine species does not differ systematically from multivoltine species *(Dendrolimus pini, 255; Bombyx mori, 750; Lampetia equestris, 80; Musca domestica, 920; Sitona lineata, 1800; Calandra granaria, 190)*.

The number of ovarioles appears to be related to fecundity. Termite queens may have more than 2000, honey bee queens 160–180 ovarioles in each of the two ovaries (p. 14). In the extremely fecund *Meloë* species, more than 200 ovarioles are found in both ovaries while in the Coprinae, with a very low reproductive potential, there is only one ovary and one ovariole (Robertson, 1961).

III. Oviposition: Accessory Glands

After ovulation, the eggs either descend into the oviposition apparatus, or are collected in a common egg chamber in which both lateral oviducts unite. In the first case, a covering of the egg may be secreted by a glandular section of the ovariole, as in *Steraspis* (Martoja, 1964), or by mesodermal glands opening in the oviduct. In the latter case, the eggs are laid in batches, which may be enveloped in an ootheca, covered by a foamy secretion, or embedded in an egg cocoon. The substances involved are products of the accessory glands.

The accessory glands may vary greatly in structure, location, and secretory products. Glandulae sebaceae may either be paired or reduced to one medial (Odonata, Thysanoptera, Mecoptera, Culicidae) or lateral (Psocidae) glandular tube or sac. They may open into the unpaired oviduct, the vagina, or the bursa copulatrix. Their substance generally coats the egg surface and promotes adhesion to the substratum on which the eggs are deposited (Hemiptera, Neuroptera, Lepidoptera, Hymenoptera aculeata), or provides a gelatinous coating swelling in water. In Plecoptera, Ephemeroptera, Trichoptera, Chironomidae, and some Odonata, the eggs are deposited in water in a gelatinous sheath, secreted by vestibular "mucous glands" (Wesenberg-Lund, 1913). In Delphacidae, glandular epithelium of the oviduct secretes foamy mucus, varying remarkably in color. Most species have white, some blue, and others red secretions (Strübing, 1956). In Mantidae, a spongious ootheca is formed by the secretion of a viscous fluid, vacuolated by air bubbles, and hardening upon contact with the air (Williams and Buxton, 1916). This fluid is a product of paired accessory glands opening into the medial oviduct.

In *Locusta,* the eggs are embedded in a secretion produced by glandular tissue in the wall of the lateral oviduct but are covered by a foamy ootheca formed by the accessory glands opening into the anterior part of the oviducts (Lauverjat, 1964). The secretion of these glands is vacuolated with air by means of characteristic "beating" movements of the genital appendages. In Dictyoptera, the vagina and part of the medial oviduct form a molding cavity (vestibulum and atrium) surrounded by a multitude of secretory tissues all contributing to the formation of the

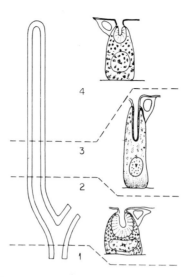

Fig. 24. A tubule of the left collaterial gland in *Periplaneta,* showing distribution of the 4 types of glandular cells; 1, presecretory; 2, secreting structural protein; 3, secreting oxidase; 4, secreting structural protein and calcium oxalate (after Brunet, 1952).

complex ootheca. The following account illustrates the complexity of the situation as found in *Periplaneta americana* L. In the dorsal wall of the vestibulum, the paired collaterial glands are present as invaginations formed by glandular epithelium (Fig. 24). The left collaterial gland branches into tubules and contains a white substance consisting of protein and calcium oxalate. Each tubule contains four types of cells:

1. Basal, presecretory, epidermal
2. Glandular, secreting structural protein
3. Glandular, secreting oxidase
4. Glandular, secreting structural protein + calcium oxalate

The right collaterial gland contains a more transparent secretion, and is composed of three cell types:

1. Presecretory, epidermal
2. Glandular, secreting structural protein
3. Glandular, secreting protocatechuic acid

Simultaneous activity of both glands results in enzymic conversion of protocatechuic acid into a quinone which cross-links the protein molecules to form a stable microphysical structure. This tanned protein has a resilient

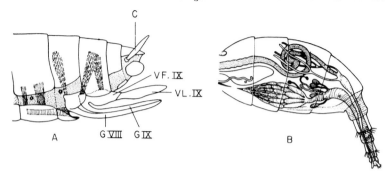

Fig. 25. Diagrammatic representation of orthopteran ovipositor (A) and dipteran ovitubus (B). G, gonapophysis; VF, valvifer; VL, valvula (after Weber, 1938).

nature (Hallez, 1909; Pryor, 1940; Brunet, 1951, 1952). Other epithelial oothecal glands in *Periplaneta* are located on the valvifer, the third valvula, the posterior apophysis, and scattered in the form of patches. The surface of the third valvula is perforated by the ducts of glands located in the second valvula. Some of these glands contribute to the formation of oothecal sclerotin, others to its molding into a distinct shape, and again others to its smooth release from the vestibulum. In Psocoptera and *Hydrophilus,* accessory glands are transformed into silk glands forming the egg cocoon. In Psocoptera, this is merely a silken covering of the eggs laid on a solid substratum. Some tropical Psocoptera live in social communities and spin elaborate cobwebs covering whole trees, apparently with a protective function. In *Hydrophilus,* the egg cocoon, swimming on the water surface, is provided with a vertical mast, the respiratory function of which has been proven (Laabs, 1939; Vlasblom and Wolvekamp, 1954).

Oviposition involves the function of the ovitubus, a simple telescopic extrusion of the last abdominal segments (*Thysanoptera tubulifera,* Diptera) or of the ovipositor, in which the gonapophyses participate (Fig. 25). In Gryllidae and Tettigoniidae, the function of the ovipositor has been thoroughly studied. It performs remarkable functions in Hymenoptera parasitica, notably cynipids (Beyerinck, 1876–1877; Frühauf, 1924) and ichneumonids, as an injection apparatus placing the egg in deep crevices and through the depth of plant tissues. In *Rhyssa,* the ovipositor is capable of penetrating 5 cm of healthy wood to reach its siricid host.

During oviposition, the eggs may be rotated in the genital tract or ovipositor, depending on the mode of placement upon the substrate. In Heteroptera, rotation is through 180° in Saldidae and Mesoveliidae and through 90° in some pentatomids. This seems to be correlated with a concave or downward bent ovipositor (Cobben, 1968). In Hymenoptera aculeata, the ovipositor has been transformed into the sting apparatus. One of the accessory glands opening into the vestibulum has retained a lubricating and adhesive function (Dufour's gland, alkaline gland). The other has been transformed into the acid gland, secreting bee venom (Hesselhaus, 1922). The choice of oviposition substratum is greatly aided by the presence of tactile and chemosensory organs on the ovipositor, as in *Gryllus domesticus, Phormia reginae* (Browne, 1960; Wallis, 1962), and parasitic Hymenoptera (Dethier, 1947). In other cases, chemosensory perception in oviposition is merely effected by the antennae *(Achroia grisella:* Makings, 1958) or the tarsi *(Pieris brassicae:* David and Gardiner, 1962; *Anopheles:* Hudson, 1956).

IV. Fertility and Sterility

A. FERTILITY

For physiological purposes, it seems most suitable to define fertility as the percentage of eggs deposited that develops to produce a viable larva (Hyde, 1914). In species without parthenogenesis, fertility in the first place depends upon successful fertilization of the eggs; senescence in many insect species is characterized by decreasing fertility. In *Drosophila* (Hadorn and Zeller, 1943) it has been shown that the spermathecae of such senescent females still may retain a sufficient quantity of viable sperm. In *Rhodnius* (Beament, 1946) it has been shown that the number of functional micropylae in the chorion diminishes with increasing age, thus decreasing the probability of fertilization. Other factors influencing fertility are temperature and food. In *Drosophila melanogaster* reared at 31°C, 96% of males and 50% of females are sterile (Young and Plough, 1926). In *Ephestia,* sexual activity is normal in adults grown at 31°C, but no viable eggs are produced (Norris, 1933).

B. STERILITY

Next to the factors mentioned above, sterility may be caused by a variety of factors and may result from defects ranging from ovarian atrophy in the female adult to the deposition of nonviable eggs. In forms with bisexual reproduction, sterility may be the consequence of defective maternal physiology as well as of paternal factors, e.g., dominant lethal factors in the sperm.

1. Castration

Exogenous sterility due to ovarian atrophy or defective oogenesis has been named castration. The following types are recognized (Wheeler, 1910) :

a. *Alimentary Castration.* This is ovarian atrophy and insufficiency as a consequence of deficient larval feeding, be it quantitative as in the case of ants (Wheeler, 1910) or qualitative as in the honey bee, where royal jelly is involved in morphogenetic differentiation of the female sexual apparatus. It has been suggested that a dialyzable substance from the mandibular glands is the active principle (Rembold, 1967).

b. *Phase Castration.* This is a periodic state of insufficiency of the reproductive glands, as occurring in parasitic Hymenoptera (Flanders, 1942) or in some species of mosquitoes, where it is known as gonotrophic dissociation (Beklemishev, 1934). Seasonal "token" stimuli are involved (Chapter 3).

c. *Nutrimentary Castration.* This is known to occur in many insects as a consequence of lack of food in the adult *(Rhodnius,* Wigglesworth, 1948; *Oncopeltus,* Johansson, 1958), or of deficiency of a specific nutritional element *(Leptinotarsa,* Grison, 1957). This is not necessarily a matter of body reserves, but rather one of induced hormonal deficiency (Johansson, 1958).

d. *Parasitic Castration.* This occurs when the function of the gonads is suppressed by the presence of parasites, as in stylopization of Hymenoptera aculeata and Hemiptera, caused by Strepsiptera. Another example is presented by Nematodes *(Mermis* sp.) castrating bumblebee queens. There are indications that in both cases endocrine deficiency is involved (Brandenburg, 1956; Palm, 1948).

Sterility may be the result of inbreeding, as in the honey bee (Mackensen, 1951) where eggs homozygous for one of the sex alleles are nonviable. It generally occurs in interspecific hybrids, as in Pieridae (Lorkovic, 1953).

2. Sterilization

Induced sterility by radiation or the application of chemosterilants usually involves the production of chromosomal defects.

a. *Sterilization by Radiation.* The physiological effects of irradiation have been studied in an increasing number of insect species of economic and medical importance (Grosch, 1962; Proverbs, 1969). Radiation effects are mostly judged by two groups of criteria: genetic and physiological. The application of X-rays and gamma rays, both of which have great penetrating power, has been especially successful in inducing lethal mutations during spermatogenesis and oocyte formation. Much of the mutagenic effect of this radiation is due to chemical changes in DNA within the chromosomes before or during cellular divisions (LaChance, 1967). These changes may not only involve the chemical structure of individual genes, but also their linkage within the chromosomes. As a result, the chromosomes may break or stick together during the anaphase of mitosis, the genetic material being distributed in an uneven way between the daughter cells (LaChance and Riemann, 1964). Also parts of chromosomes may become exchanged (translocations). At the same time, the cytoplasmic constitution of the gametes, in which these lethal mutations have been produced, may remain normal, resulting in normal viability and vigor. Spermatozoids thus treated may fertilize normal eggs and produce lethal zygotes (Fig. 26). Dominant lethal factors are among the most serious genetic effects of radiation, leading to the death of the zygote at an early stage of development.

Normal viability of the adults carrying lethal gametes is only obtained

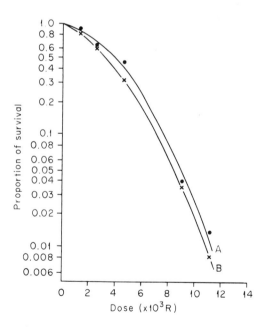

Fig. 26. Proportion of *Drosophila* eggs fertilized by irradiated sperm, which attain the stage of A, larva; B, adult.

if the sensitivity of the somatic cells in the radiated stage is much less than that of the dividing germ cells (Sobels, 1963; Mandl, 1964). Following the discovery of these effects in *Drosophila* (Müller, 1927, 1938), they have subsequently been studied in a variety of insects (La-Chance, 1967). The sensitivity to irradiation may vary between species as well as between developmental stages and both sexes of the same species. Thus, in the screwworm fly, *Cochliomyia hominivorax,* by radiating the pupa before the initiation of the adult molt, males are sterilized by a dose of 2500 R, while in the female, oogenesis becomes deficient at 5000 R, and is completely prevented by 7500 R. Sterilizing adults by irradiation of the flies requires 5000–7000 R (La-Chance and Chrystal, 1965). The life span of the adults emerging from irradiated pupae is slightly shortened, but they survive doses as high as 20,000 R (Bushland and Hopkins, 1951, 1953).

Physiological criteria of radiation effects are (a) infecundity in females, (b) sperm inactivation, (c) aspermia, (d) inability to mate, (e) reduced life span, (f) malformations and (g) inactivity of the individual. Several of these effects are discussed by LaChance (1967). As genetic effects are manifest at relatively low doses and physiological effects at high doses, histological effects, already apparent at intermediate doses, have recently obtained attention (Theunissen, 1971). Symptoms are degeneration, hypertrophy, metaplasia, dysplasia, anaplasia, characteristic cellular deformations, and shifts in cellular populations.

Eradication programs of the screwworm fly, carried out on the basis of mass release of irradiated males carrying dominant lethal sperm, have met with a great deal of success (Bushland, 1971). In *Ceratitis capitata, Dacus cucurbitae, D. dorsalis, D. oleae, D. tryoni,* and other fruitflies, for complete sterilization of both sexes doses of 3,000–18,000 R are needed (Anonymus, 1970; LaChance *et al.,* 1967). Often these doses affect very much the vigor of the males (Steiner and Christenson, 1956).

Radiation-induced translocations have been used by Laven (1968) Laven *et al.,* (1971) to induce semisterility in heterozygotes of *Culex pipiens*. This is a purely genetic form of control, which has also been proposed for the control of the tsetse fly, *Glossina* sp. (Curtis, 1968). The extent to which this method is applicable is still under discussion (Whitten, 1971). Another type of genetic control makes use of cytoplasmic incompatability between different strains of one species (Laven, 1967).

b. Sterilization by Chemicals. Chemicals may cause the same genetic, pathological, and physiological effects as ionizing radiations (La Brecque and Smith, 1968; Stüben, 1969). This is especially true in the aziridines with alkylating proporties: aphoxide, aphomide, apholate, Tepa, and Metepa, are rariomimetic chemosterilants (La Brecque, 1961, 1962; LaChance *et al.,* 1967; LaChance and Leopold, 1969; LaChance and Leverich, 1968, 1969). The effect on the spermatogonia in the testis of *Anthonomus grandis* proved to be reversible (Reinecke *et al.,* 1969). Application is hampered by general toxic effects.

Very interesting sterilizing and ovicidal effects have recently been obtained with the juvenile hormone (Chapter 3) and its analogues. External applications of the "paper factor" juvabione (Slăma and Williams, 1966) and of a synthetic mixture containing methyl farnesoate dihydrochloride (Riddiford and Williams, 1967) induced sterility when applied to females of *Pyrrhocoris* and *H. cecropia,* respectively. This effect may even be transmitted by treated males during copulations (Masner *et al.,* 1968).

V. Structure and Origin of the Male Reproductive System

A. GONADS AND GONODUCTS

The internal male genitalia comprise the paired testes, mesodermal vasa deferentia, vesculae seminales, and the ectodermal, unpaired ductus ejaculatorius (Fig. 27).

The testes are composed of a varying number of follicles, each opening into the vas deferens. Only a single follicle is found in many Heteroptera (Cobben, 1968). In these follicles, spermatogenesis takes place. Depend-

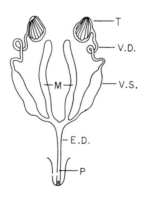

Fig. 27. Diagrammatic representation of the male gonads and gonoducts (after Wigglesworth, 1972). T, testis; V.D., vas deferens; V.S., vesicula seminalis; M, mesadenia; E.D., ejaculatory duct; P, penis.

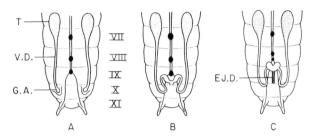

Fig. 28. Ontogenetic development of male reproductive system (after Imms, 1957). T, testis; V.D., vas deferens; G.A., genital ampulla; EJ.D., ejaculatory duct.

ing upon number, shape, and arrangement of the follicles, the testes may have a tubular, racemose, or globular form. The upper part of the vas deferens widens into the seminal vesicle, in which the spermatozoa accumulate. The vasa deferentia leaving the vesicle are usually of a mixed ecto- and mesodermal origin and bear the accessory glands (mesadenia). The seminal vesicles, mesadenia, and the ejaculatory duct are usually provided with layers of striated muscle which aid in the propulsion of semen.

The mesodermal part of the male genitalia develops, as in the female, from coelomic ridges united by a genital strand provided with a terminal ampulla. These ridges take up groups of germinal cells, but will develop perfectly normally without these.

Geigy and Aboim (1944) have irradiated the lower egg pole in *Drosophila* during the earliest development of the embryonic germ cells by means of a narrow beam of ultraviolet light. While the germ cells degenerate, gonads may develop in the normal way.

The ejaculatory duct develops during postembryonic growth from a pair of primary phallic lobes of ectodermal origin, usually arising from the posterior part of the ninth larval abdominal segment (Fig. 28). In the adults, the gonoporus is situated behind the sternal plate of this segment.

The terminal ampullae of the mesodermal vasa deferentia fuse with these lobes (Snodgrass, 1957).

B. PHALLUS, PARAMERES, AND TERMINALIA

The phallus comprises the aedeagus and the parameres, serving the dual functions of copulation and insemination. In the higher orders, the parameres may have two segments and comprise a proximal basimere and a distal harpagon (Snodgrass, 1957; Fig. 29).

Secondary structures provided by the eighth, ninth, and tenth abdominal segments, the terminalia, usually serve some function in copulation.

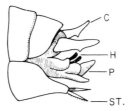

Fig. 29. External appendages of male sexual apparatus (Acridiidae). P, penis; ST., stylus; C, cercus; H, harpagon.

The wealth of morphological variation of all these structures is "the delight of taxonomists, the despair of morphologists" (Snodgrass, 1957, p. 11). The study of their function clearly surpasses the limits of this treatise.

In the Ephemeroptera, the genital outlet retains a paired character, the primary lobes becoming a pair of penes. In the higher insect orders, each primary lobe divides into two secondary phallomeres. Between their bases, an ectodermal ingrowth forms the gonopore, into which the ductus ejaculatorius opens.

With further development, the genital ampullae are carried inward to form the bursa genitalis.

Two of the phallomeres, by fusion of a lateral pair, form the medial aedeagus; the others develop into the parameres, the genital claspers of the male (Snodgrass, 1957).

VI. Formation of Sperm and Semen

A. THE TESTIS: SPERMATOGENESIS

1. Spermatid Formation

In Fig. 30 testicular follicles in Acridiidae are shown in different degrees of enlargement. Each follicle is an epithelial pouch, in the upper end of which the germ cells are contained. It would seem as if (as in some types of oogenesis) the germ cells differentiate to form a secretory cell (apical cell) and a number of spermatogonia which surround the nurse cell while in the process of multiplication. Each spermatogonium performs 6–8 equation divisions, and thus forms a cluster of 64–256 diploid spermatocytes, united in a "spermatocyst." These spermatocysts gradually move in proximal direction, the most advanced being located most proximally to the meiotic stages. In *Oncopeltus* (Bonhag and Wick,

1953), the terminal spermatogonia surround a trophic syncytium, the "apical complex," containing 9–11 nuclei. Darkly staining strands radiate from these nuclei to the surrounding spermatogonia. In *Adelphocoris lineolatus*, Masner (1965) found merely one apical cell, surrounded by spermatogonia to form an "apical organ." In *Tenebrio molitor* and *Zophobas rugipes*, Menon (1969) found the multinucleate, apical complex to have a secretory function. In *Hylemya antiqua*, the syncytial apical complex has a varying number (9–20) of nuclei (J. Theunissen, personal communication) (Fig. 31). Other trophic cells are present in *Oncopeltus* as irregular-shaped cells, located between adjacent cysts (Bonhag and Wick, 1953). Histochemical data on nutrimentary sperm formation, however, are almost entirely lacking.

The spermatocytes subsequently perform two maturation divisions, resulting in four haploid spermatids. In haploid parthenogenesis as occurs in the Apidae, meiosis is lacking during maturation divisions. From the resulting two spermatids, one is rudimentary. Each spermatocyte, therefore, produces one spermatozoon.

In *Pediculus* the first maturation division is lacking, but otherwise similar conditions prevail (Doncaster and Cannon, 1920).

The rate of development in spermatogenetic processes can be followed by means of autoradiographic techniques. In *Anthonomus grandis*, development from spermatogonium to spermatozoid takes 10 days (Chang

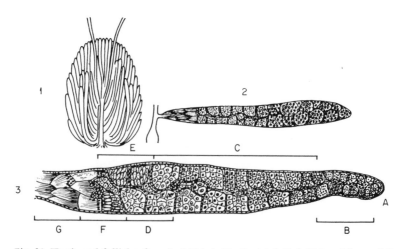

Fig. 30. Testis and follicle of an Acridiid. 1, Testis, total; 2, follicle with vas defferens; 3, Follicle, enlarged. A, apical cells; B, spermatogonia; C, spermatocytes; D, first maturation division; E, second maturation division; F. spermatids; G, spermatozoa (after Schröder, 1928).

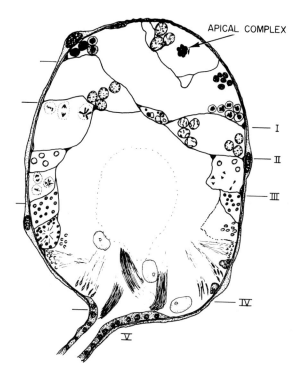

APICAL COMPLEX

I

II

III

IV

V

Fig. 31. Schematic drawing of testis of just emerged onion fly, *Hylemya antiqua* (Meigen). General sequence of germ cell types during spermatogenesis. I, different types of spermatogonia; II, primary spermatocytes; III, meiotic divisions and secondary spermatocytes; IV, spermatids; V, sperm cells in central cavity and dorsal part of testis (courtesy of J. Theunissen).

and Riemann, 1967), and the same is valid for *Culex pipiens* (Sharma *et al.,* 1970) and *Hylemya antiqua* (J. Theunissen, personal communication). Recently, spermiogenesis in *Drosophila melanogaster* has been reviewed extensively by Tokuyasu *et al.* (1972a,b).

Ultrastructural studies on spermatogenesis in *D. melanogaster* have been carried out by Tates (1971). The ultrastructure of the spermatids in different insect species has been described by Breland *et al.* (1966, 1967, 1968) and by Gassner (1967).

2. *Sperm Differentiation*

The subsequent differentiation of spermatids into flagellated spermatozoa takes place in the basal part of the follicle, and may even be completed in the seminal vesicle. It involves the concentration of nuclear material

in the head of the sperm, and the characteristic distribution of spermio-
plasma to form the acroblast, the middle plasmatic zone containing the
cytocenter, and the flagellum.

The spermatozoa, while in their cysts, may remain united by a gelatinous cap to form *spermiodesms* (Cantacuzène, 1968). These may dissolve in the seminal vesicles, probably by their characteristic secretions
(enzymes?) and sometimes even while already in the seminal receptacle
of the female (Payne, 1933). In most cases, however, the spermatozoa
are already separated while leaving the testes.

The number of sperm produced is a function of reproductive biology
of the species and especially, of female fecundity. Mackensen and Roberts (1948), Woyke (1955), and Ruttner (1957) have determined the
number of sperm produced by male honeybees. According to Ruttner
(1957), the vesiculae seminales of mature drones contain 11.9×10^6
spermatozoa, weighing 0.43 mg. The queen may produce 300,000 or
more fertilized eggs during her life span. In contrast, in the parasitic dipteran *Miastor,* the male produces only 512 spermatozoids per testis, in
total 1024. The female produces about 56 eggs (White, 1946). It follows
that the efficiency of fertilization is of a high order.

3. Active Movements of Sperm

The spermatozoa migrate to the seminal vesicles where they become
remarkably immobile. They gradually become densely packed, their heads
attached to the vesicle wall. Their reduced motility may be attributed to
the scarcity of seminal plasm or to inhibiting substances secreted by the
vesicle wall (Payne, 1933). When diluted with saline or male ejaculate
fluids, the motility of spermatozoa in *Apis* is greatly increased (Bishop,
1920; Blum *et al.,* 1962).

Ruttner (1956a,b, 1957) suggests that in *Apis mellifera* an alkaline
medium promotes thigmotactic behavior of the spermatozoa, causing
them to attach themselves to the walls of the gonoducts, or to each other.
Though, in some cases, semen is directly deposited in the female spermatheca by the male, in most instances the spermatozoa enter the spermatheca after copulation. Much has been written on the active or passive
transport to this organ.

As the sperm becomes mobilized on insemination, it has been supposed to enter the spermathecal duct chemotactically, guided by secretions of the spermathecal glands.

In species where the female lacks the apparatus for mechanical filling
of the spermatheca, as in *Drosophila,* the spematozoa swim actively to the
seminal receptacles (Nonidez, 1920). In Lepidoptera, where the sperm is

deposited in a separate bursa copulatrix, the sperm moves through a narrow seminal duct toward the spermatheca. The spermatozoa of *Bombyx mori* have been observed to swim chemotactically in saline through a capillary glass tube provided with a receptacular gland (Weidner, 1934). After being deposited in the female reproductive tract, the spermatozoa of *Periplaneta* change in two respects: the rate of beating frequency of the tail is increased and the capacious sac around the aerosome is reduced (Hughes and Davey, 1969).

But information is lacking on the substances involved, and there is little experimental evidence as to their site of production. The same is true for the factors determining the subsequent release of spermatozoa from the receptacle and their active passage through the micropyle of the egg. In many cases, the spermatozoa appear to be injected directly into the micropyle of the egg by the spermathecal apparatus (Davey, 1965).

4. Spermatogenesis in Postembryonic Development

In most cases, spermatogenesis is completed at the time of the adult molt. In the early days of adult life, the spermatozoa have migrated to the vesiculae seminales in full number and the testes gradually atrophy. In species in which copulations are frequently repeated throughout adult life and in which the males are even active in successive years, e.g., in many Chrysomelids, the testes remain active until the end of the adult life span. The following examples may be given.

In *Pediculus corporis,* throughout the first larval instar the testes merely contain spermatogonia. In the second instar the formation of spermatocytes begins. At the end of the third instar all stages of spermatogenesis are present in the follicle (Doncaster and Cannon, 1920).

In *Melanoplus differentialis* (Acridiidae), secondary spermatogonia are formed in the beginning of the second larval instar. Gonial divisions take place throughout the second, third, and fourth instars. Maturation divisions begin in the sixth (last) instar, and spermatids complete their metamorphosis shortly after the adult molt (Nelsen, 1931).

In the honey bee drone, spermatid formation is completed during the pupal stage. Sperm differentiation begins 4 days before emergence. Sperm begins to descend to the vesiculae seminales 2 days before emergence, and completes migration during the first 3 days of adult life. By this time, the testes start degenerating (Bishop, 1920).

B. Accessory Glands

The glandular apparatus of the male organ comprises the glandular elements of the walls of the vasa deferentia and seminal vesicle, and the mesadenia opening into the vasa deferentia. The gross anatomy of the mesadenia is most variable from species to species, and reflects the very varied functions of these glands. In some species they merely form a plug occluding the female gonoduct after insemination. In *Oncopeltus* (Bonhag and Wick, 1953) this is a "granular," in *Apis* (Bishop, 1920) a "mucous white" material.

In *Apis,* a clear fluid secreted by the gonoduct walls collects at the base of the mucus-gland reservoir and in the penis bulb. Upon ejaculation, these secretions are mixed with the sperm, thus constituting the bulk of seminal plasma (1.1 μl in a total quantity of 1.25 μl; Blum *et al.,* 1962). The mucous material, coagulating on contact with air and water, is probably mucoproteid in nature. In the mesadenia of *Chortophaga* (Acridiidae), where both types of secretion are produced separately by different follicles, the white secretion stains with Sudan III and osmium, suggesting the presence of lipoproteins. In *Apis,* the accessory glands are forming reservoirs provided with three layers of striated muscle. During ejaculation, contraction of these fibers is coordinated with the contraction of the seminal vesicles. This is performed by a nervous reflex, assuring the discharge of mucus immediately following the release of sperm (Bishop, 1920, and personal observations).

In other species, the mesadenia produce the material for the often complex spermatophores (p. 75). In several *Plodia* and *Ephestia* species (Norris, 1932), as for example in *Ephestia kuehniella* (Musgrave, 1937), one pair of tubular accessory glands is found.

The question of whether the different types of secretory granules in the glandular lumen are indeed chemically different or whether they represent a sequence in the maturation process of the granules (Callahan and Cascio, 1963) is controversial. Contrary to the rather simple anatomy of the mesadenia in *Ephestia* species, that of *Locusta migratoria* is

TABLE II

DNA QUANTITY (PHOTOMETRIC FEULGEN DETERMINATION) AS COMPARED WITH CHROMOSOME PLOIDY DURING SPERMATOGENESIS IN *Melanoplus*[a]

Stadium	DNA class	DNA quantity	S. E.	No of determinations
Spermatogonia	2c-4c	6.9	0.46	18
Primary spermatocytes	4c	9.5	0.12	59
Secondary spermatocytes	2c	5.1	0.11	14
Spermatids	c	2.56	0.06	25

[a] Data from Swift and Kleinfeld (1953).

very complex. A very detailed description of the mesadenia of *Locusta* is given by Odhiambo (1969a,b,c, 1970, 1971). In this species both mesadenia contain as many as sixteen tubular glands, which can be grouped into nine different types. Each type has a characteristic anatomy and secretes a product with distinctive morphological and (or) histochemical properties. The sixteen glands together form the spermatophore. In the Colorado beetle both mesadenia are simple tubular glands. No regional differences can be observed in the secretory product present in the lumen (de Loof and Lagasse, 1972).

C. CHEMICAL COMPOSITION OF SEMEN

The semen, as composed of sperm and seminal plasma, is generally a cream-colored fluid. In the honey bee the volumetric ratio of sperm to seminal plasm varies from 1:1 to 1:2, depending upon the season. The pH of ejaculated semen is 6.8–7.0 (Blum *et al.,* 1962).

1. *Deoxyribonucleic Acid*

As might be expected, nuclear DNA quantity during spermatogenesis corresponds with the quantity of chromosome material. Spermatogonia are diploid cells, but during formation of spermatocytes each cell has to accumulate two times the diploid quantity of chromosome material, which is subsequently distributed over four haploid spermatids. As Swift and Kleinfeld (1953) have found in *Melanoplus differentialis* (Acrididae), this is reflected in DNA quantity (Table II).

2. *Proteins and Amino Acids*

Novak *et al.* (1960) have determined the amino acid composition of the semen of mature honey bee drones (Table III). As might be anticipated, protein content of sperm is highest, and moreover differs qualitatively from seminal plasm. Regarding the presence of free amino acids in seminal plasm, it should be mentioned that these acids abound in insect hemolymph (Volume III). The high arginine content of sperm undoubtedly bears relation to the fact that in energy metabolism of arthropods arginine takes the place of creatine in the vertebrates. Leucine content of seminal plasm is lower than that of lysine and glutamic acid, but in sperm the quantities are equal.

3. *Carbohydrates*

Humphrey and Robertson (1949) observed a high content of fructose in the male reproductive organs of *Locusta migratoria.*

Blum *et al.* (1962) have determined the quantity and composition of sugars in different anatomical parts of the male reproductive system in *Apis mellifera*. Their results are shown in Table IV.

In semen, the sugars are almost exclusively found in the plasm. As the penis bulb contributes the bulk of this fluid, it is concluded that during ejaculation most of the carbohydrates are transferred to the sperm by this organ.

From the quantities observed before and after flight (Table IV) it follows that the sugar content of the drone reproductive system reflects the level of these sugars in the hemolymph.

In view of the rapid fructolysis by honey bee semen (50% of the initial quantity is decomposed within 30 minutes after ejaculation) it is concluded improbable that this hexose as provided by the ejaculate plays a critical role in the long-term storage of sperm, as performed within the female spermatheca (Blum *et al.*, 1962).

VII. Courtship and the Role of Pheromones

Coincidence and synchronization of the partners are a necessity in any type of bisexual reproduction. In most cases this involves communication mechanisms in which physical and chemical stimuli may participate.

In long-distance attraction between males and females, as well as in aggregation of individuals of both sexes, chemical messengers are often involved: sex pheromones and aggregation pheromones.

The term pheromone (Karlson and Lüscher, 1959) has been introduced to designate substances secreted by animals, the biological function of which is the transfer of information between individuals of the same species.

Pheromones are often secreted in mixtures of two or more compounds. In this case, one compound might possibly be involved in the orientation of the insect, another compound in courtship behavior, synchronizing the partners physiologically. Sometimes, as in the case of *Bombyx mori,* one single compound: 10-*trans*,12-*cis*-hexadeca-dienol, secreted by the females, apparently triggers both orientation and mating behavior in the male (Butenandt *et al.*, 1959). Long-distance orientation triggered by the pheromone does not follow a gradient, but probably is directed against the wind (Schwinck, 1954).

Pheromones or pheromone complexes are extremely selective and at the same time highly active. The biological amplification mechanism involved has been compared with a radiotube. In *Bombyx,* one molecule of

TABLE III

Amino Acid Composition of Honey Bee Drone Semen[a]

	mg/100 gm fresh weight		
	Seminal plasm		
Amino acid	Free	Bound	Sperm
Tyrosine	37	46	820
Methionine	28	32	470
Leucine	46	57	1250
Cystine	38	44	780
Isoleucine	42	51	590
Tryptophan	31	48	410
Lysine	73	92	1260
Phenylalanine	44	60	930
Arginine	20	137	3920
Glutamic acid	87	103	1040
Glycine	19	38	640
Alanine	20	41	710
Aspartic acid	23	37	670
Serine	32	41	580
Threonine	11	26	379

[a] Data from Novak et al. (1960).

Bombykol, received by the antenna, both induces an electrophysiological and a behavioral response in the male (Schneider et al., 1967).

In Lepidoptera, sex pheromones are often organic acids and their esters, saturated or unsaturated alcohols, with 12–16 C atoms. Most frequent are acetates and C_{12-14} unsaturated alcohols (Jacobson et al., 1970).

"Complex pheromones" are now known to occur in Tortricidae, Pyralidae, and Noctuidae. In Tortricidae, the combination between 9-cis- and 11-trans-tetradecenyl acetate is known to occur (Roelofs and Comeau, 1971). In Adoxophyes orana, these two moieties are highly synergistic (Ritter, 1971).

In Pyralidae, 11-cis-tetradecenyl acetate is probably accompanied by dodecyl acetate (Klun and Brindley, 1970).

In Noctuids, combinations between 9-cis-tetradecenyl acetate and 9-cis,12-trans-tetradecenyl acetate are found (Jacobson et al., 1970).

Both sex and aggregation pheromones occur in Coleoptera, and distinction between these categories is often difficult. In Attagenus megatoma, the female sex pheremone is 3-trans,5-cis-tetracadienoic acid (Silverstein et al., 1967). In bark beetles (Ipidae) sex and aggregation pher-

TABLE IV

QUANTITY AND COMPOSITION OF SUGARS IN DIFFERENT PARTS OF THE MALE ORGANS
IN *Apis mellifera*[a]

| | | Carbohydrate (μg/100 mg tissue) | | | | | |
| | Fresh weight | Leaving | | | Returning | | |
Organ	(mg)	Fructose	Glucose	Trehalose	Fructose	Glucose	Trehalose
Testes	0.67	669	748	288	28	21	42
Seminal vesicle	1.63	122	67	26	9	6	13
Mucous gland	7.22	72	109	34	6	5	7
Penis bulb	1.56	321	302	51	2	9	18

[a] Data from Blum *et al.* (1962)

emones are often complex mixtures. When boring initially in conifers, they produce a mixture of wood fragments and excrements, which may attract both males and females. The active components have been described as aggregation pheromone, assembling scent, sex attractant, ovipositional attractant, etc. They apparently release a chain of behavioral responses.

In *Dendroctonus frontalis* the active substance is a mixture of the terpenalcohol *transverbenol* and a dioxabicyclo derivate, frontalin (Kinzer *et al.,* 1969). In the aggregation pheromone of *D. brevicomus,* frontalin is substituted by brevicomin (Silverstein *et al.,* 1968). In the cotton boll weevil, a mixture of two terpenalcohols and two terpenaldehydes is secreted (Tumlinson *et al.,* 1970).

Male pheromones which have a role in the interplay of stimuli and responses involved in courtship are probably found in many orders, but are especially known to occur in the Rhopalocera. In *Eumenis semele,* the male acquiesces the female by bringing two brushlike structures on the forewing in contact with her antennae. In *Lycorea,* "hair pencils," situated on the male abdomen, are brushed against the female antennae. A similar use of hair pencils is reported from *Danais plexippus* by Brower *et al.* (1965). In *Lycorea ceres,* the substance secreted is a mixture of 1-hexadecanol- (cetyl) -acetate, 11-*cis*-octodecan-l-ol acetate and 2,3-dihydro-7-methyl-*l-H*-pyrrolizidin-l-one (Meinwald and Meinwald, 1966).

A mechanism assuring the concidence between reproduction and the presence of the specific host plant is reported by Riddiford and Williams (1967; Riddiford, 1967). In *Antherea polyphemus,* mating only takes place in the presence of oak leaves *(Quercus rubra).* The substance emanated from the leaves has been identified as 2-*trans*-hexenal (Riddiford, 1967). Behavioral aspects of courtship are discussed in Volume III. The field of pheromones is covered to a larger extent by M. Jacobson, Volume II.

VIII. Insemination: The Copulatory Act

A. IMPREGNATION

It has been thought that the highly specific shape of structures and appendages of male and female copulatory apparatus constitutes a decisive mechanical factor in species isolation, acting as a system of key and lock (Fig. 32). But it would rather seem that intraspecific matings are assured by precopulatory behavior, and probably by the mutual stimulation of specific sensory sites during the copulatory act. For, as shown in the case of mantids (Roeder, 1935; Roeder *et al.,* 1960) and of some Lepidoptera (Lorkovic, 1953), removal of the inhibitory effect of the brain by decapitation greatly facilitates copulation, even between species of different genera. In Pieridae, this has proved to be a method in artificial production of interspecies hybrids (Lorkovic, 1953). In mature honey bee drones, decapitation and application of narcotics such as chloroform produces a prompt release of the complicated penis eversion–ejaculation reflex (Bishop, 1920; Mackensen and Roberts, 1948).

No doubt, accessory structures promote the attachment of the partners during copulation and the deposition of sperm at the critical sites in the female gonoducts.

During insemination, the sperm is deposited in the bursa copulatrix, and sometimes in the common oviduct and even the lateral oviducts (Apis). In extreme cases, as in several Hemiptera–Heteroptera (Ludwig, 1926; Bonhag and Wick, 1953), the sperm is placed directly in the female spermatheca.

Only in few cases have the mechanisms involved been studied in greater detail.

Erection of the phallus may be brought about by special hydraulic mechanisms. In the milkweed bug *Oncopeltus fasciatus,* the ejaculatory duct is a blind tube folded back in itself to form a crosier-shaped organ. The anterior end of the duct is modified into an erection fluid reservoir and its posterior end into an erection fluid pump provided with dilator muscles.

Erection of the phallus is accomplished by the displacement of the fluid into the phallus by internal compression of the abdomen and by pulsations of the erection fluid pump. As erection proceeds during copulation, the aedeagus gradually penetrates into the spermathecal duct and spermatheca. The same mechanism probably holds for *Lygaeus* (Bonhag and Wick, 1953; Ludwig, 1926).

In the honey bee drone, the phallus takes an inverted position in the male bursa genitalis. The innermost part is enlarged into a bulbus. The basic part forms a thin-walled chamber from which two large membranous pneumophyses project. Contraction of the abdominal wall results in eversion of the endophallus together with its lobes. As this takes place while the phallus is being introduced, the pneumophyses attach themselves to the wall of the female vaginal pouch. The semen is released from the top of the bulb after it fills the vaginal pouch, and is immediately followed by the mucus, which in its turn is pushed forward by an epithelial plug torn off the mucous glands. The abdominal wall contracts with such vigor that the mucous glands, the seminal vesicles, and even a large part of the intestine slide into the endophallus (Woyke, 1955). The pressure thus exerted causes the sperm to fill the median and lateral oviducts, and, as multiple matings take place, the latter may be distended considerably. The endophallus is separated from the male along preformed lines (Bishop, 1920; Ruttner, 1956a,b).

The mechanism by which the sperm subsequently pass the narrow spermathecal duct and reach the spermathecal cavity are still subject to controversial explanations. Mention was made earlier (p. 66) of the independent motility of sperm. Although in some cases this explains the transfer to the spermatheca, mechanical explanations have been offered in other cases.

Thus, in the Lepidoptera (Norris, 1932) contractions of the bursa copulatrix, peristaltic movements of the seminal ducts, and compression of the abdomen have been thought to aid in the filling of the spermatheca. In *Rhodnius,* the seminal fluid associated with the spermatophore, deposited in the bursa causes peristaltic contraction in the oviduct (Davey, 1958).

In the honey bee queen, the "sperm pump" of the spermathecal duct (Bresslau, 1906) may either act as a sphincter muscle, or may aid in sperm transport and, thereby, in the mechanical filling of the spermatheca. It is known that the vaginal pouch of the honey bee queen is provided with a "valve fold" (Laidlaw, 1944). When the proximal part of the vaginal pounch and the oviducts are filled with semen, compression of the abdominal wall causes the valve to close and to occlude and compress the genital chamber. As, by their own motility, the sperm become oriented parallel to the spermathecal duct, it is supposed that they are easily

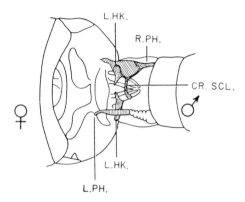

Fig. 32. Position of external appendages during copulation in *Blatella*. L. HK., lateral hook; L. PH., left phallomere; R. PH., right phallomere; CR. SCL., crescent selerite (after Khalifa, 1950).

pressed into this duct and in the spermatheca, aided by the sperm pump (Ruttner, 1956a,b, 1957) . As in parasitic Hymenoptera, only those species have a sperm pump which can alternatively deposit fertilized (female) and unfertilized (male) eggs, and it has been concluded that the sperm pump controls the flow of semen to the ovulated egg. It has also been supposed that this control is effected by the periodic activity of the spermathecal gland and the subsequent activation of the spermatozoa (Flanders, 1939) .

In the cases mentioned above, any physiological explanation depends upon the internal pressure relations between the different genital cavities. If these are filled with a continuous fluid medium, hydrostatic pressure will be equal throughout the system. In this case, only distention of the spermathecal wall could provide the explanation. But in the honey bee, this is a rigid structure.

B. SPERMATOPHORES

The optimal transfer of sperm is often accomplished through the transfer of spermatophores (Fig 33) . Generally, these are proteinous secretions of the male accessory glands in which semen is embedded. The spermatophores often have a characteristic shape, fitting into the female vaginal chamber. They are generally present in the lower orders, and are notably scarce in higher orders such as the Hymenoptera, or even absent as in Diptera. On the other hand, in Apterygota, e.g., Thysanura, sper-

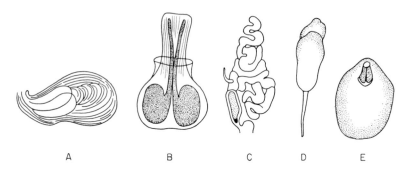

A   B   C   D   E

Fig. 33. Spermatophores. **A,** *Blatella germanica;* **B,** *Sialis lutaria* (Neuroptera); **C,** *Anabolia nervosa* (Trichoptera); **D,** *Galleria mellonella* (Lepidoptera); **E,** *Pimpla instigator* (Hymenoptera) (after Khalifa, 1949, 1950).

matophores generally occur. They are deposited on the substratum and actively taken up by the female. It has been argued (Khalifa, 1949) that in insect evolution spermatophores represent a primitive condition. However this may be, their formation, also in the higher orders, is far from being a rudimentary process and highly contributes to a proper filling of the female spermatheca.

In Dictyoptera, the spermatophores consist of three layers secreted by the large peripheral accessory glands (utricule majores), the epithelium of the ejaculatory duct, and the phallic gland. The seminal fluid is produced by the median accessory glands (Gupta, 1947). The seminal vesicles deposit two separate sperm sacs in the middle layer. The three substances constituting the external layers are immiscible proteins (Khalifa, 1950) which harden before the spermatophore is deposited. A lamellar proteinaceous mass also forms the bulk of the spermatophore in *Anabolia nervosa* (Trichoptera) but here the lamellae are wound irregularly. The spermatophores are often provided with tubes through which the semen is transferred to the female spermathecal duct. This transfer may take place in different ways. In Orthoptera and Dictyoptera, the spermatophore is placed at the vaginal orifice. It is supposed that the sperm is squeezed out by swelling of parts of the gelatinous capsule *(Liogryllus,* Regen, 1924; *Oecanthus,* Hohorst, 1936). In *Rhodnius* (Hemiptera), *Anabolia* (Trichoptera), *Ephestia, Plodia,* and *Galleria* (Lepidoptera), and *Pimpla* (Hymenoptera), the spermatophore is deposited in the bursa copulatrix. In these instances, mechanical pressure by the bursal wall may contribute to its emptying.

The protein material of the spermatophores is often absorbed by the female. In the cricket *Oecanthus,* the female simply devours the empty spermatheca. In *Galleria,* and probably other Lepidoptera, and in *Ana-*

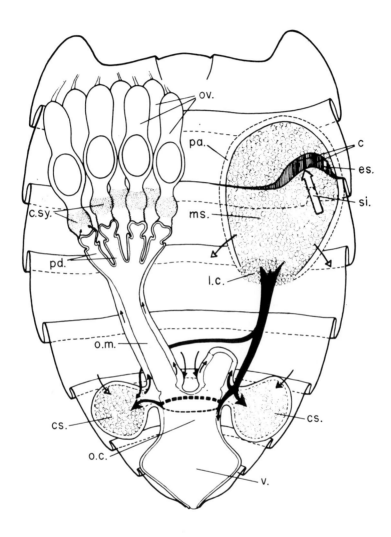

Fig. 34. Schematic drawing of the pathways of spermatozoa upon traumatic insemination in *Cimex*. Deposited through the ectospermalege into the Ribaga organ (mesospermalege), the spermatozoa take their course through the hemolymph to the
seminal conceptacles which they penetrate through their wall (from Carayon, 1970). c,
copulation scars; c.sy, syncytial body, l.c., conducting lobe; o.c., common oviduct; ov.,
ovarioles; si., incision showing normal course of male paramere; v, vagina; cs., seminal
concepticle; es., ectospermalege; ms., mesospermalege; o.m., mesodermal oviduct; pd,
pedicels.

bolia (Trichoptera), the protein spermathecal mass and sperm sacs are digested and probably absorbed by the bursal wall. The presence of proteinase within the bursa of *Galleria* has been demonstrated (Khalifa, 1950).

C. TRAUMATIC INSEMINATION

In four families of Cimicoidea, i.e., Cimicidae, Polyctenidae, Anthocoridae, and Nabidae, peculiar conditions of mating and insemination are found. Courtship behavior is very rudimentary; larvae, males and females, even of other species, may be subject to copulation attempts. Traumatic insemination is observed, sperm being injected outside the female genital apparatus, and often in the haemocoel. In the resulting condition of spermathemia, the spermatozoids find their way to the ovarioles which are penetrated from the outside.

In *Alloeorhynchus, Prostemma,* and *Pagasa* (Nabidae), injection takes place through the female genital wall, which may be provided with a diverticulum in which sperm is received (Spermalege) (Carayon, 1952a,b).

In the primitive *Primicimex cavernius,* and in some Anthocoridae, the abdominal integument is perforated in predestined regions. In some Anthocoridae, the underlying region is provided with a mesodermal "mesospermalege" (Carayon, 1964) composed of prohemocytes.

In Cimicidae, an ectodermal spermalege is formed at the adult molt, and situated at the dorsal or ventral side of the abdomen, according to the species. This ectospermalege is developed in both males and females and homosexual inseminations apparently occur, e.g., in *Afrocimex* (Carayon, 1959).

Only in females a mesospermalege is formed underlying the ectospermalege. The resulting complex spermalege varies greatly between species. In *Cimex lectularius,* its function has been described by Cragg (1915). Sperm is injected through the ectospermalege into the mesospermalege, the cells of which phagocyte the seminal fluid and part of the spermatozoids. The common oviduct is provided with two seminal conceptacles, in which the remaining sperm is collected within a few hours. It subsequently ascends into the ovarioles (Fig. 34). In many Cimicidae, a strand of tissue develops between the mesospermalege and the ovary and the spermatozoids, into which the spermatozoa take their course to the ovary (Carayon, 1970).

In Polyctenidae, females may be fertilized when still in the last larval instar (Carayon, 1964).

IX. Determination of Sex and Sexual Characters: Parthenogenesis

A. BISEXUAL REPRODUCTION

Determination of sex is a function of genetic constitution and environment. With regard to genetic sex determination, opinions differ with regard to plasticity and localization of sex-determining genes rather than to matters of principle. The classical theory founded by Bridges (1925) and Goldschmidt (1931, 1955) states that in most insects, sex depends upon the balance of male-tendency genes located in the autosomes, and female-tendency genes in the heterochromosome or X chromosome. In the male, the X chromosome may be unpaired in the diploid state (XO) or paired with a different chromosome (XY). Females have the constitution XX. In Lepidoptera, the heterochromosome would carry male-tendency genes. Here, the females would have the XY constitution, and XX represents males. This theory gradually shifts to a more broad conception stating that ". . . sex depends upon a balance between male-tendency functioning genes and female-tendency functioning genes plus the action of the environment. . . . It is not necessary that all male-tendency genes be scattered in the autosomes and female-tendency genes in the heterochromosomes or vice versa" (Kerr, 1962). Autosomes, too, may have heterochromatic regions, and these may even vary between chromosomes from different tissues as in *Rhynchosciara angelae* and *Rhynchosciara milleri* (Ficq and Pavan, 1957; Pavan and Breuer, 1955). It furthermore is not necessary to assume that all sex-determining genes have the same degree of penetrance; in other words, they may have a varying intensity of physiological expression (Breuer and Pavan, 1952, 1953, 1955; and Pavan and Breuer, 1955; Ficq and Pavan, 1957). "So it is possible to conceive the idea that an animal has a gene or genes with inhibiting or exciting effects on the female- or male-determining genes. The same is true for the influence of the environment; it can be so strong as to reverse the genetic balance" (Kerr, 1962). The physiological expression of sex-determining genes during development involves a hierarchical system. In *Lampyris noctiluca*, implantation of larval male gonads into young female larval changes these females into males, with respect to both internal and external sex characters (Naisse, 1963, 1965). The endocrine basis of this effect will be discussed in Chapter 3 of this volume.

B. PARTHENOGENESIS

Sex determination in haploid parthenogenetic forms cannot be explained adequately by the principle of genetic balance alone. In many arrhenotokous Hymenoptera, males develop from nonfertilized eggs and are haploid, while fertilized eggs give rise to diploid females. Thus, females are biparental and males uniparental (impaternate). To maintain the idea of genetic balance, Manning (1949, 1950) has claimed that in this case, the X chromosome is lost during spermatogenesis, leaving the spermatozoids without heterochromatin. Accordingly, both male and female have only one sex chromosome, but the female has thirty autosomes and the male fifteen. This concept is not in accord with cytological data (Sanderson and Hall, 1951; Ruttner and Mackensen, 1952).

Da Cunha and Kerr (1957) have proposed the hypothesis that there are genes for maleness (m) which do not have accummulative effect (mm = M) and genes for femaleness which do accumulate (ff = 2 F). If we suppose $M > F$ and $2F > M$, the phenomena are accounted for. The best founded theory, however, has been proposed by P. W. Whiting (1940, 1943a,b) on the basis of his work with the parasitic wasp *Habrobracon juglandis,* a species in which males may be uniparental as well as biparental. According to this theory, sex determination in this arrhenotokous insect depends upon a series of multiple alleles, nine of which have been identified. They are designated as Xa, Xb, Xc, . . ., Xk. Haploid (Xa, Xb, Xc) or homozygous diploid forms (Xa/Xa, Xb/Xb, etc.) are male; heterozygous diploids (Xa/Xb, Xc/Xd, etc.) are females.

Mackensen (1951), assuming that sex determination in the honeybee follows the same pattern, explains the absence of diploid males in *Apis* by the hypothesis that homozygoty for a sex allele is lethal in this species. This is supported by viability data of fertilized eggs upon artificial inbreeding. However, it has been found recently that diploid drone larvae exist, but that these larvae are normally eliminated by the worker bees (Woyke, 1963, 1965; Woyke and Knytel, 1966; Kerr and Nielsen, 1967). Evidence in favor of Mackensen's hypothesis has been found by Rothenbuhler (1957, 1958). The number of sex alleles in *Apis* has been estimated to average 13 in a panmictic population (Laidlaw *et al.,* 1956).

Telytokous parthenogenesis takes place when nonfertilized eggs produce females. This is the most common type of parthenogenesis, found in many insect orders. In several species, males may even be extremely rare or unknown, generations being exclusively impaternate. This type of parthenogenesis usually falls into the XX-XO or XX-XY case of sex determination. As a rule the cytological basis is some form of apomixis or ameiosis. Usually only one maturation division takes place in the egg, and the division is an equational one. The resulting nucleus is diploid.

When such a female produces genotypical males, this involves the loss of an X chromosome. In some aphids, this may be brought about in a large percentage of individuals by a combination of short photoperiod and intermediate temperature (Lees, 1959). It may, however, also be that the early stages of meiosis in the egg are quite normal, and the chromosome number becomes haploid. The fusion of the nuclei of male and female gametes in normal fertilization is, however, replaced by fusion nucleus and the second polar body, two polar nuclei or two cleavage nuclei. In this automictic parthenogenesis, diploidization may even gradually proceed during embryonic development. Thus, in the phasmid, *Clitumnus extradentatus*, the slowly developing embryo arising from the virgin egg consists at first solely of haploid cells, then of a mixture of haploid and diploid, and finally solely of diploid cells (Bergerard, 1958). As the haploid ovum has the X chromosome, the resulting embryo is female. In parthenogenetic races of the psychid, *Solenobia triguetella*, Seiler and Schäffer (1960) have established that the embryo arises from the fusion of the two central polar nuclei. As only the first polar body contains the X chromosome, the resulting embryos have the constitution XO or XY and are female. In most cases of automictic parthenogenesis, however, heterozygoty is replaced by homozygoty (Suomalainen, 1962).

Deuterotokous parthenogenesis occurs where telytoky is prevailing but regularly some males are produced, as in some parasitic Hymenoptera *(Habrolepis, Tropidophryne)*. Apparently, automixis is not a constant feature in these species, but is alternated with occasional ameiosis.

C. PARTHENOGENESIS AND POLYPLOIDY

The association of polyploidy and parthenogenesis is especially apparent in those species in which bisexual and parthenogenetic geographic races occur.

Somatic parthenogenetic polyploidy has been observed in Orthoptera (triploid and tetraploid races and species), Lepidoptera (triploid and tetraploid races and species), Diptera (triploid species), Colcoptera (triploid, tetraploid, and pentaploid races and species), and Hymenoptera (female tetraploidy in one species) (Suomalainen, 1962). Within the genus *Otiorrhynchus*, species from Northern Europe more frequently show parthenogenetic polyploidy than more southern forms. It has been argued that polyploid forms are ecologically superior (Lindroth, 1954). Polyploidy in the germ line has been observed in *Miastor* (Cecidomyiidae), where the germ cells are octoploid in both sexes, but the gametes are reduced to haploid conditions (White, 1946, 1947). In the parasitic wasp *Bracon hebetor* Say, occasional uniparental females arise from patches of tetraploid tissue in an ovary where otherwise the germ cells are diploid (Speicher and Speicher, 1938).

D. GYNANDROMORPHS

Loss of X chromatin and activity of polar bodies or supernumerary spermatozoids during and after fertilization may be causes by which gynandromorphs arise. In such forms tissues with male and female genotypes intermingle to provide a mosaic of male and female characteristics. Gynandromorphs may arise from binucleate ova of which only one nucleus is fertilized as in *Habrobracon,* (Grebb, 1933) and many Lepidoptera (von Lengerken, 1928; Cockayne, 1935). In *Drosophila,* Morgan and Bridges (1919) have shown that loss of an X chromosome during early cleavage in the female leads to gynandromorphism. In honey bees, where polyspermy prevails, one or more of the supernumerary sperm entering the egg may undergo cleavage to produce haploid male tissue in an otherwise female individual. Rothenbuhler *et al.* (1951), by inseminating queens with sperm from drones of different strains, have shown that the male tissue of the gynandromorph was strictly paternal in origin.

E. INTERSEXES

Intersexes are not mosaics of male and female genotypes but are forms with intermediate grades of maleness and femaleness. Anatomical and morphological characters may be mosaics of male, female, and intermediate phenotypes, but the cells have the same genotype. In these forms, genetic balance of sex-determining genes is shifted in somatic tissues in such a way as to prevent primary and secondary sexual characters from attaining their full phenotypic expression. This genetic imbalance may result from the gene constitution within the chromosomes but may also be a function of the environment.

1. "Strength" of Sex-Determining Genes in Racial Intercrossings

Goldschmidt (1932) has observed the fact that in *Porthetria dispar* (L.) intersexes occur more frequently in crossings between geographic races inhabiting Europe, North Africa, and Asia. Female-tendency genes (F) are admittedly in the Y chromosome, male-tendency genes (M) in the X chromosome. These genes are supposed to vary in "strength" between races and to be balanced in the XY females of each race. Intersexes develop where strong F's are combined with weak M's and vice versa.

2. Intersexes in Interspecific Hybrids

Intersexes have been observed in interspecific crossings in several insect orders. Most probably, this may be explained in the same way as above, assuming differences in "strength" between sex-determining genes. Examples are found in Anoplura *(Pediculus capitis* × *P. corporis)* where intersexes are mostly masculinized females (Keilin and Nuttall, 1919), Lepidoptera *(Lycia hirtaria* × *Poecilopsis rachelae;* Cockayne, 1938), and Diptera *(Glossina swynnertoni* × *G. morsitans;* Vanderplank, 1945).

3. Gene Balance in Polyploid Forms of Drosophila

The occurrence of intersexes in some polyploid forms of *Drosophila melanogaster* (Meig) may be explained by the degree of genetic imbalance between X chromosomes and autosomes as proposed by Bridges (Frost, 1960; Goldschmidt, 1955; Table IV).

4. Intersex Mutants in Drosophila

Several *Drosophila* species have mutant loci that can convert females into intersexes (see Table V). Examples are *D. simulans* (Sturtevant, 1921; Gowen and Fung, 1957) and *D. virilis* (Lebedeff, 1934, 1939).

5. Effect of Temperature on Gene Function Balance

High temperatures may promote the penetrance of male- as well as female-functioning genes in normal as well as in genetically intersexual strains of insects.

Kosminsky (1911) found that, in normally balanced races of *Lymantria dispar,* intersexes were produced by rearing at high temperatures. In *Drosophila,* Dobzhansky (1930) showed that in intersexed specimens, the degree of femaleness was increased by rearing at higher temperatures. In both cases, however, the forms produced were sterile, and the range of variation was narrow. In *Carausius morosus,* where facultative parthenogenesis prevails, sex differentiation so completely depends upon temperature that it is possible to obtain a continuous series of sexual forms, ranging from nearly 100% females to 100% males. In this species, males are known to be extremely rare, (1 in 1000–10,000 individuals). Male and female, though both apterous, differ externally in a number of characteristics. Uniparental eggs incubated at 23°C practically all develop into females. Eggs incubated at 30°C during the first 30 days of embryonic development give as much as 100% males. Treatments of 7 and 14 days at 30°C result in intersexes, the degree of masculinity in-

TABLE V

CHROMOSOME CONSTITUTION IN RELATION TO SEX
IN *Drosophila melanogaster* (Meigen) [a]

Chromosome constitution[b]	Sex[c]	X/A ratio
2A XXX	Metafemale (sterile)	1.50
3A XXXX	Metafemale (fertile)	1.30
2A XX 2A XXY 3A XXX 4A XXXX	Female	1.00
4A XXX	Intersex	0.75
3A XX 3A XXY	Intersex	0.67
2A X 2A XY 2A XYY 4A XX	Male	0.50
3A X	Metamale	0.33

[a] After Kerr (1962).

[b] A = set of autosomes.

[c] Metafemale and Metamale (Stern, 1959) denote abnormally high expression of secondary sex characteristics.

creasing with the length of the stay at 30°C. This is clearly not a case of genetic intersexuality, as the males produced contain the female number of chromosomes (64). Genetic males have 63 chromosomes. As regards the females, weakly intersexed specimens are capable of oviposition and have normal progeny. Highly intersexed specimens may form normal eggs but may not be able to oviposit, due to defects in the differentiation of the genital ducts. (Bergerard, 1958, 1961, 1962; Bergerard and Seugé, 1959).

In Culicidae, elevation of temperature during larval development may cause males to become intersexes. This has been found in *Aedes stimulans* (Horsfall and Anderson, 1961, Anderson and Horsfall, 1963), *Aedes aegypti* (Craig, 1965), *Aedes communis* (Brust and Horsfall, 1965), *Aedes sierrensis* (Horsfall et al., 1964). Different degrees of feminization are obtained in adults reared from male larvae at temperatures between 25° and 28°C.

In intersexual strains of *Lymantria dispar* reared at 16°, 22°, and 27°C, Mosbacker (1966) found that the degree of femaleness correlates with the temperature.

In intersexes of the Psychid *Solenobia triquetuella,* adults are masculinized by exposing the egg to 34°C for 12 hours or to 4°–6°C for ½–3 days (Seiler, 1935).

In intersexual triploids of *Drosophila melanogaster,* raising the temperature from 20°–27°C merely causes a weak response, the morphology of the external genitalia being more feminine. But a thermal shock of 27°–30°C during 24 hours, applied during the second larval instar, causes a complete feminization of all organs developed from the genital disc. Very short treatments (6 hours) at 30°C applied to the egg during or immediately after oviposition cause the gonads to feminize (Laugé, 1969a,b,c).

It follows from these interesting observations that the expression of sex characters is determined by a chain of processes, some of which have started even before cleavage of the egg has taken place.

References

Adiyodi, K. G. (1967). *J. Insect Physiol.* **13**, 1189–1195.
Allen, E. R., and Cave, M. D. (1969). *Z. Zellforsch. Mikrosk. Anat.* **101**, 63–71.
Anderson, D. S. (1960) . *J. Insect Physiol* **5**, 120–128.
Anderson, E. (1964). *J. Cell Biol.* **20**, 131–155.
Anderson, J. F., and Horsfall, W. R. (1963). *J. Exp. Zool.* **154**, 67–107.
Anderson, L. M. (1971). *J. Cell Sci.* **8**, 735–750.
Anderson, L. M., and Telfer, W. H. (1969). *Tissue Cell* **1**, 633–644.
Anderson, L. M., and Telfer, W. H. (1970). *J. Cell. Physiol.* **76**, 37–54.
Anderson, W. A., and Spielman, A. (1971). *J. Cell Biol.* **50**, 201–222.
Anonymus. (1970) . *Sterile-Male Technique Contr. Fruit Flies, Panel, JAEA,* pp. 1–175.
Basile, R. (1969). *Genetics* **61**, Suppl., 261–273.
Bayreuther, K. (1956). *Chromosoma* **7**, 508–557.
Beament, J. W. L. (1946). *Quart. J. Microsc. Sci.* **87**, 393–439.
Beament, J. W. L. (1947). *J. Exp. Biol.* **23**, 213–233.
Beams, H. W., and Kessel, R. G. (1969). *J. Cell Sci.* **4**, 241–264.
Beklemishev, V. (1934). *Med. Parasitol.* **3**, 460–479.
Bell, W. J. (1970). *J. Insect Physiol.* **16**, 291–299.
Bell, W. J. (1971). *J. Insect Physiol.* **17**, 1099–1112.
Bentz, F. (1969). *C. R. Acad. Sci.* **269**, 494–496.
Bergerard, J. (1958). *Bull. Biol. Fr. Belg.* **92**, 87.
Bergerard J. (1961). *Bull. Biol. Fr. Belg.* **95**, 273.
Bergerard J. (1962). *Endeavour* **21**, 137–143.
Bergerard, J., and Seugé, J. (1959). *Bull. Biol. Fr. Belg.* **93**, 16.
Berlese, A. (1909). *Insetti* **1**, 1004.
Beyerinck, M. W. (1876–1877). *Tijdschr. Entomol.* **20**, 186–198.
Bhandari, K. G., and Nath, V. (1930). *Z. Zellforsch. Mikrosk. Anat.* **10**, 604–624.
Bier, K. (1952). *Verh. Deut. Zool. Ges.* **46**, 369–374.
Bier, K. (1963a). *J. Cell Biol.* **16**, 436–440.
Bier, K. (1963b). *Wilhelm Roux' Arch. Entwicklungs mech. Organismen* **154**, 552–575.

Bier, K. (1965). *Zool. Jahrb., Abt. Allg. Zool. Physiol. Tiere* **71**, 371–384.
Bier, K. (1970). *Zool. Anz., Suppl.* **33**, 7–29.
Bishop, G. H. (1920). *J. Exp. Zool.* **31**, 225–266.
Blum, M. S., Glowska, Z., and Taber, S. (1962). *Ann. Entomol. Soc. Amer.* **55**, 135–139.
Blumenfeld, M., and Schneiderman, H. A. (1969) . *Biol. Bull.* **135**, 466–475.
Bodnaryk, R. P., and Morrison, P. E. (1966). *J. Insect Physiol.* **12**, 963–976.
Bonhag, P. F. (1955a). *J. Morphol.* **96**, 381–440.
Bonhag, P. F. (1955b). *J. Morphol.* **97**, 283–312.
Bonhag, P. F. (1956). *J. Morphol.* **99**, 433–464.
Bonhag, P. F. (1958). *Annu. Rev. Entomol.* **3**, 137–160.
Bonhag, P. F. (1959). *Univ. Calif., Berkeley, Publ. Entomol.* **16**, 81–124.
Bonhag, P. F. (1961). *J. Morphol.* **108**, 107–129.
Bonhag, P. F., and Wick, J. R. (1953). *J. Morphol.* **93**, 177–284.
Brandenburg, J. (1956). *Z. Morphol. Oekol. Tiere* **45**, 343–364.
Brandt, A. (1874). *Mem. Acad. Sci., St. Petersbourg* **21**, No. 7.
Breland, O. P., Gassner, G., Riess, R. W., and Biesele, J. J. (1966). *Can. J. Genet. Cytol.* **8**, 759–773.
Breland, O. P., Barker, K. R., and Eddleman, D. (1967). *J. Cell Biol.* **35**, 162A.
Breland, O. P., Barker, K. R., Eddleman, C D., and Biesele, J. J. (1968). *Ann. Entomol. Soc. Amer.* **61**, 1037–1039.
Bresslau, E. (1906). *Zool. Anz,* **29**, 299–323.
Breuer, M. E., and Pavan, C. (1952). *Cienc. Cult. (Sao Paulo)* **4**, 115.
Breuer, M. E., and Pavan, C. (1953). *Proc. Int. Congr. Genet., 9th, 1953* p. 778.
Breuer, M. E., and Pavan, C. (1955) *Chromosoma* **7**, 371–386.
Bridges, C. B. (1925). *Amer. Natura.* **69**, 127–137.
Brower, L. P., Brower, J., and Cranston, F. P., (1965). *Zoologica* **50**, 1–39.
Brown, E. H., and King, R. C. (1964). *Growth* **28**, 41–81.
Browne, L. B. (1960). *J. Insect Physiol.* **5**, 16–22.
Brunet, P. C. J. (1951). *Quart. J. Microsc. Sci.* **92**, 113–127.
Brunet, P. C. J. (1952). *Quart. J. Microsc. Sci.* **93**, 47–69.
Brust, R. A., and Horsfall, W. R. (1965). *Can. J. Zool.* **43**, 17–53.
Bryan, J. H. D. (1954). *Biol. Bull.* **107**, 64–79.
Buchner, P. (1923). *Arch. Protistenk.* **39**, 34–61.
Buchner, P. (1925). *Z. Morphol. Oekol. Tiere* **4**, 88–245.
Buchner, P. (1928). *Ergeb. Biol.* **4**, 1–129.
Buchner, P. (1953). "Endosymbiose der Tiere mit pflanzlichen Microorganismen," pp. 1–771. Birkhäuser, Basel.
Bushland, R. C. (1960). *Advan. Pest Control Res.* **3**, 1–25.
Bushland, R. C. (1971). In "Sterility Principle for Insect Control or Eradication," pp. 3–14. IAEA, Vienna.
Bushland, R. C., and Hopkins, D. E. (1951). *J. Econ. Entomol.* **44**, 725–731.
Bushland, R. C., and Hopkins, D. E. (1953). *J. Econ. Entomol.* **46**, 648–656.
Butenandt, A., Beckmann, R., Stamm, D., and Hecker, E. (1959). *Z. Naturforsch. B* **14**, 283–284.
Callahan, P. S., and Cascio, T. (1963). *Ann. Entomol. Soc. Amer.* **56**, 535–556.
Camenzind, R. (1962). *Rev. Suisse Zool.* **69**, 377.
Cantacuzène, A. (1968). *Z. Zellforsch. Mikrosk. Anat.* **90**, 113–126.
Cappe de Baillon, P. (1920). *Cellule* **31**, 1–245.
Cappe de Baillon, P. (1933) . *C. R. Acad. Sci.* **196**, 809–811.

Carayon, J. 1952a). *Tijdschr. Entomol.* **95**, 111–142.
Carayon, J. (1952b). *C. R. Acad. Sci.* **234**, 751–753.
Carayon, J. (1952c). *C. R. Acad. Sci.* **234**, 1317–1319.
Carayon, J. (1959). *Rev. Zool. Bot. Afr.* **60**, 81–104.
Carayon, J. (1964). *In* "Psychiatrie animale" (A. Brion and H. Ey, eds.), p. 283–294. Paris.
Carayon, J. (1970). *Colloques Int. du Centre Nat. de la Rech. Sc., Tours,* **189**, 215–247.
Cassaunel, C. (1971). *C. R. Acad. Sci.* **272**, 83–86.
Cave, M. D., and Allen, E. R. (1969). *J. Cell Sci.* **4**, 593–609.
Cave, M. D., and Allen, E. R. (1970). *Exp. Cell Res.* **58**, 201–212.
Chang, T. H., and Riemann, J. G. (1967). *Ann. Entomol. Soc. Amer.* **60**, 975–979.
Cobben, R. H. (1968). *Agric. Res. Reports* **707**, 1–475.
Cockayne, E. A. (1935). *Trans. Roy. Entomol. Soc. London* **83**, 509–521.
Cockayne, E. A. (1938). *Biol. Rev.* **13**, 107–132.
Coles, G. C. (1965). *J. Exp. Biol.* **43**, 425–431.
Cragg, F. W. (1915). *Indian J. Med. Res.* **2**, 32–79.
Craig, G. B. (1965). *Proc. Int. Congr. Entomol., 12th, 1964* p. 263.
Cruikshank, W. J. (1971). *J. Insect Physiol.* **17**, 217–232.
Cummings, M. R., and King, R. C. (1970). *J. Morphol.* **130**, 467–478.
Cummings, M. R., Brown, N. M., and King, R. C. (1971). *Z. Zellforsch. Mikrosk. Anat.* **118**, 482–492.
Curtis, C. F. (1968). *Bull. Entomol. Res.* **57**, 509–523.
Da Cunha, A. B., and Kerr, W. E. (1957). *Forma Funct.* **1**, 33–36.
Dapples, C. C., and King, R. C. (1970). *Z. Zellforsch. Mikrosk. Anat.* **103**, 34–47.
Davey, K. G. (1958). *J. Exp. Biol.* **35**, 694–701.
Davey, K. G. (1965). "Reproduction in the Insects." Oliver & Boyd, London.
David, W. A., and Gardiner, B. O. C. (1962). *Bull. Entomol. Res.* **53**, 91–109.
Dejmal, R. K., and Brookes, V. J. (1968). *J. Insect Physiol.* **14**, 371–381.
de Loof, A. (1971). *Z. Zellforsch. Mikrosk. Anat.* **115**, 351–360.
de Loof, A. (1972). Ph.D. Thesis, Ghent.
de Loof, A., and de Wilde, J. (1970). *J. Insect Physiol.* **16**, 157–169.
de Loof, A., and Lagasse, A. (1970). *Proc., Kon. Ned. Akad. Wetensch., Ser. C* **73**, 284–297.
de Loof, A., and Lagasse, A. (1972) . *Z. Zellforsch. Mikrosk. Anat.* **130**, 545–552.
de Loof, A., Lagasse, A., and Bohijn, W. (1972). *Proc., Kon. Ned. Akad. Wetensch., Ser. C* **75**, 125–143.
Dethier, V. G. (1947). *J. Exp. Zool.* **105**, 199–207.
de Wilde, J., and de Boer, J. A. (1961). *J. Insect Physiol.* **16**, 152–161.
de Wilde, J., Duintjer, C. S., and Mook, L. (1959). *J. Insect Physiol.* **3**, 75–85.
Dobzhansky, T. (1930). *Wilhelm Roux, Arch. Entwicklungsmech. Organ.* **123**, 719–746.
Doncaster, L., and Cannon, H. G. (1920). *Quart. J. Microsc. Sci.* **64**, 303–328.
Dufour, D., Taskar, S. P., and Perron, J. M. (1970). *J. Insect Physiol.* **16**, 1369–1377.
Egarov, T. A., and Smolin, A. N. (1962). *Biokhimiya* **27**, 476–480.
Eidmann, H. (1931). *Z. Angew. Entomol.* **18**, 57–112.
Engelmann, F. (1968). *Annu. Rev. Entomol.* **13**, 1–26.
Engelmann, F. (1969). *Science* **165**, 407–409.
Engelmann, F. (1970). "The Physiology of Insect Reproduction." Pergamon, Oxford.
Engelmann, F., and Penney, D. (1966). *Gen. Comp. Endocrinol.* **7**, 314–325.
Engels, W. (1966). *Zool. Anz., Suppl.* **29**, 243–251.
Engels, W. (1970). *Zool. Anz., Suppl.* **33**, 30–39.

Engels, W., and Bier, K. (1967). *Wilhelm Roux' Arch. Entwicklungsmech. Organismen* 158, 64–88.
Engels, W., and Drescher, W. (1964). *Experientia* 20, 445–447.
Favard-Séréno, C. (1969). *J. Microsc. (Paris)* 8, 401–414.
Favard-Séréno, C. (1971). *J. Microsc. (Paris)* 11, 401–424.
Favard-Séréno, C., and Durand, M. (1963). *Develop. Biol.* 6, 206–218.
Ficq, A. (1969). *Exp. Cell Res.* 55, 243–247.
Ficq, A., and Pavan, C. (1957). *Nature (London)* 180, 983–984.
Flanders, S. E. (1939). *Ann. Entomol. Soc. Amer.* 32, 11–26.
Flanders, S. E. (1942). *Ann. Entomol. Soc. Amer.* 35, 251–266.
Flanders, S. E. (1950). *Can. Entomol.* 32, 134–140.
Frost, J. N. (1960). *Proc. Nat. Acad. Sci. U.S.* 46, 47–51.
Frühauf, E. (1924). *Z. Zool.* 121, 656.
Gassner, G. (1967). *J. Cell Biol.* 35, 166A.
Geigy, R., and Aboim, A. N. (1944). *Rev. Suisse Zool.* 51, 410–417.
Gerrity, R. G., Rempel, J. G., Sweeny, P. R., and Church, N. S. (1967). *Can. J. Zool.* 45, 497–503.
Gier, H. T. (1936). *Biol. Bull.* 71, 433–452.
Goldschmidt, R. (1931). *Quart. Rev. Biol.* 6, 125–142.
Goldschmidt, R. (1932). *Biol. Bull.* 63, 337–356.
Goldschmidt, R. (1955). "Theoretical Genetics," pp. 1–63. Univ. of California Press, Berkeley.
Goss, R. J. (1954). *Ann. Entomol. Soc. Amer.* 47, 190–207.
Gowen, J. W., and Fung, S. F. C. (1957). *Heredity* 11, 397–402.
Grebb, R. J. (1933). *Biol. Bull.* 65, 179–186.
Gresson, R. A. R. (1930). *Quart. J. Microsc. Sci.* 73, 617–632.
Gresson, R. A. R. (1931). *Quart. J. Microsc. Sci.* 74, 257–274.
Gresson, R. A. R., and Threadgold, L. T. (1962). *Quart. J. Microsc. Sci.* 103, 141–145.
Grison, P. (1957). *Ann. Epiphyt.* 8, 305–381.
Grosch, D. S. (1962). *Annu. Rev. Entomol.* 7, 81–106.
Grosz, J. (1903). *Zool. Jahrb., Abt. Anat. Ontog. Tiere* 18, 71–173.
Groulade, J., Lamy, R., and Bounhiol, J. J. (1961). *C. R. Acad. Sci.* 252, 3112–3114.
Günthart, T. (1910). *Zool. Jahrb., Abt. Anat. Ontog. Tiere* 30, 301–372.
Gupta, P. D. (1947). *Proc. Nat. Inst. Sci. India* 13, 65–71.
Hadorn, E., and Zeller, H. (1943). *Wilhelm Roux' Arch. Entwicklungsmech. Organismen* 142, 276–300.
Hagan, H. R. (1931). *J. Morphol.* 51, 1–117.
Halkka, L., and Halkka, O. (1968). *Science* 162, 803–805.
Hallez, J. (1909). *C. R. Acad. Sci.* 148, 317.
Hallez, P. (1885). *C. R. Acad. Sci.* 101, 444–446.
Hallez, P. (1886). *C. R. Acad. Sci.* 103, 606–608.
Hamon, C. (1969). *Bull. Soc. Sci. Bretagne* 44, 49–63.
Hansen-Delkeskamp, E. (1969). *Z. Naturforsch. B* 24, 1331–1335.
Hausman, S. J., Anderson, L. M., and Telfer, W. H. (1971). *J. Cell Biol.* 48, 303–313.
Hesselhaus, F. (1922). *Zool. Jahrb., Abt. Anat. Ontog. Tiere* 43, 369–464.
Highnam, K. C. (1964). *Symp. Roy. Entomol. Soc. London* 2, 26–42.
Highnam, K. C., and Haskell, P. T. (1964). *J. Insect Physiol.* 10, 843–864.
Highnam, K. C., and Lusis, O. (1962). *Quart. J. Microsc. Sci.* 103, 73–83.
Hill, L. (1962). *J. Insect Physiol.* 8, 609–619.

Hinton, H. E. (1960). *J. Insect Physiol.* **4**, 176–183.
Hinton, H. E. (1961). *J. Insect Physiol.* **7**, 224–257.
Hinton, H. E. (1962). *Sci. Progr. (London)* **50**, 96–113.
Hinton, H. E. (1969). *Annu. Rev. Entomol.* **14**, 343–368.
Hinton, H. E. (1970). *Sci. Amer.* **223**, 84–91.
Hogben, L. (1920). *Proc. Roy. Entomol. Soc. London, Ser. B* **91**, 268–292 and 305–330.
Hohorst, W. (1936). *Z. Morphol. Oekol. Tiere* **32**, 227–275.
Hollweg, G. (1970). *Naturwissenschaften* **57**, 140.
Horsfall, W. R., and Anderson, J. F. (1961). *Science* **133**, 1830.
Horsfall, W. R., Anderson, J. F., and Brust, R. A. (1964). *Can. Entomol.* **96**, 1369–1372.
Hudson, B. N. A. (1956). *J. Exp. Biol.* **33**, 478–492.
Hughes, M., and Berry, S. J. (1970). *Develop. Biol.* **23**, 651–664.
Hughes, M., and Davey, K. G. (1969). *J. Insect Physiol.* **15**, 1607–1616.
Hughes-Schräder, S. (1924). *J. Morphol.* **39**, 157–205.
Humphrey, G. F., and Robertson, M. (1949). *Austr. J. Sci.* **12**, 29–30.
Hyde, R. R. (1914). *J. Exp. Zool.* **17**, 141–172, 173–212.
Imms, A. D. (1957). "A General Textbook of Entomology," 9th ed. Methuen, London.
Jacob, J., and Sirlin, J. L. (1959). *Chromosoma* **10**, 210–228.
Jacobson, M., Green, N. Warthen, D., Harding, C., and Toba, H. H. (1970). *In* "Chemicals Controlling Insect Behavior" (M. Beroza, ed.), p. 3–20. Academic Press, New York.
Johansson, A. S. (1955). *Biol. Bull.* **108**, 40–44.
Johansson, A. S. (1958). *Nytt Mag. Zool.* **7**, 1–131.
Kahle, W. (1908). *Zoologie* **21**, 1–80.
Karlson, P., and Lüscher, M. (1959). *Nature (London)* **183**, 55–56.
Kaufmann, B. P., McDonald, M. P., Bernstein, M. H., von Borstel, R. C., and Das, N. K. (1953). *Carnegie Inst. Wash., Yearb.* **52**, 238–248.
Keilin, D., and Nuttall, G. H. F. (1919). *Parasitology* **11**, 279–328.
Kerr, W. E. (1962). *Annu. Rev. Entomol.* **7**, 157–176.
Kerr, W. E., and Nielsen, R. A. (1967). *J. Apicult. Res.* **6**, 3–9.
Kessel, R. G., and Beams, H. W. (1969). *J. Cell Biol.* **42**, 185–201.
Khalifa, A. (1949). *Trans. Roy. Entomol. Soc. London* **100**, 449–471.
Khalifa, A. (1950). *Parasitology* **40**, 283–289.
King, P. E., and Fordy, M. R. (1970). *Z. Zellforsch. Mitkrosk. Anat.* **109**, 158–170.
King, P. E., and Richards, J. G. (1969). *Proc. Roy. Entomol. Soc. London, Ser A* **44**, 143–157.
King, P. E., Ratcliffe, N. A., and Fordy, M. R. (1971). *Z. Zellforsch. Mikrosk. Anat.* **119**, 43–57.
King, R. C. (1960). *Growth* **24**, 265–323.
King, R. C. (1964). *Quart. J. Microsc. Sci.* **105**, 209–211.
King, R. C., and Aggarwal, S. K. (1965). *Growth* **29**, 17–83.
King, R. C., Robinson, A. C., and Smith, R. F. (1956). *Growth* **20**, 121.
King, R. C., Aggarwal, S. K., and Aggarwal, U. (1968). *J. Morphol.* **124**, 143–166.
Kinzer, G. W., Fentiman, A. F., Page, T. F., Foltz, R. L., Vité, J. P., and Pitman, G. B. (1969). *Nature (London)* **221**, 477.
Klun, J. A. and Brindley, T. A. (1970). *J. Econ. Entomol.* **63**, 779.
Koch, A. (1936). *Z. Morphol. Oekol. Tiere* **32**, 92–134.
Koch, A. (1938). *Z. Morphol. Oekol. Tiere* **34**, 584–609.
Koch, A. (1949). *Mikrokosmos* **38**, 6.

Koch, E. A., and King, R. C. (1966). *J. Morphol.* **119**, 283–304.

Koch, E. A., and King, R. C. (1968). *J. Cell Biol.* **39**, 74A.

Koch, E. A., and King, R. C. (1969). *Z. Zellforsch. Mikrosk. Anat.* **102**, 129–152.

Koch, E. A., Smith, P. A., and King, R. C. (1967) . *J. Morphol.* **121**, 55–70.

Korschelt, E. (1887). *Nova Acta Leopold. Carol.* **51**, 181–252.

Kosminsky, P. (1911). *Zool. Jahrb., Abt. Allg. Zool. Physiol. Tiere* **30**, 321–328.

Krzystofowicz, A. (1971). *Acta Biol. Cracov., Ser. Zool.* **14**, 299–305.

Kunz, W. (1967). *Chromosoma* **21**, 446–462.

Kunz, W., and Petzelt, C. (1970). *J. Insect Physiol.* **16**, 941–947.

Laabs, A. (1939). *Z. Morphol. Oekol. Tiere* **36**, 123–179.

La Brecque, G. C. (1961). *J. Econ. Entomol.* **54**, 684–689.

La Brecque, G. C., Meifert, D. W., and Smith, C. N. (1962). *Science* **136**, 388–389.

La Brecque, G. C., and Smith, C. N. (1968) . "Principles of Insect Chemosterilization." Appleton, New York.

LaChance, L. E. (1967). *In* "Genetics of Insect Vectors of Disease" (J. W. Wright and R. Pal, eds.) , pp. 617–650.

LaChance, L. E., and Crystal, M. M. (1965). *Genetics* **51**, 699–708.

LaChance, L. E., and Leopold, R. A. (1969). *Can. J. Genet. Cytol.* **11**, 648–659.

LaChance, L. E., and Leverich, A. P. (1968). *Ann. Entomol. Soc. Amer.* **61**, 164–**173**.

LaChance, L. E., and Leverich, A. P. (1969). *Ann. Entomol. Soc. Amer.* **62**, 790–796.

LaChance, L. E., and Riemann, J. G. (1964) . *Mutat. Res.* **1**, 318–333.

LaChance, L. E., Schmidt, C. H., and Bushland, R. C. (1967). *In* "Pest Control: Biological, Physical and Selected Chemical Methods" (W. W. Kilgore and R. L. Doutt, eds.), pp. 147–196.

Laidlaw, H. H. (1944). *J. Morphol.* **74**, 429–465.

Laidlaw, H. H., Gomes, F. P., and Kerr, W. E. (1956). *Genetics* **41**, 179–188.

Lamy, M. (1967a). *C. R. Acad. Sci.* **264**, 767–770.

Lamy, M. (1967b). *C. R. Acad. Sci.* **265**, 990–993.

Laufer, H. (1960). *Ann. N. Y. Acad. Sci.* **89**, 490–515.

Laugé, G. (1969a). *Bull. Soc. Zool. Fr.* **94**, 341–362.

Laugé, G. (1969b). *Ann. Embryol. Morphog.* **2**, 245–269.

Laugé, G. (1969c). *Ann. Embryol. Morphog.* **2**, 273–299.

Lauverjat, S. (1964). *C. R. Acad. Sci.* **258**, 4348–4351.

Laven, H. (1967). *In* "Genetics of Insect Vectors of Disease" (J. W. Wright and R. Pal, eds.), pp. 17–65. Elsevier, Amsterdam.

Laven, H. (1968) . *Anz. Schädlingsk.* **60**, 1–7.

Laven, H., Jost, E., Meyer, H., and Selinger, R. (1971). *In* "Sterility Principle for Insect Control or Eradication," pp. 415–424. IAEA, Vienna.

Laverdure, A. M. (1969). *Bull. Soc. Zool. Fr.* **94**, 299.

Lebedeff, G. A. (1934). *Amer. Natur.* **68**, 68–69.

Lebedeff, G. A. (1939). *Genetics* **24**, 553–586.

Lees, A. D. (1959). *J. Insect Physiol.* **3**, 92–117.

Lensky, Y., and Alumot, E. (1969). *Comp. Biochem. Physiol.* **30**, 569–575.

Lilienstern, M. (1932). *Z. Morphol. Oekol. Tiere* **26**, 110–134.

Lindroth, C. H. (1954). *Entomol. Tidskr.* **75**, 111–116.

Lorkovic, Z. (1953). *Physiol. Comp. Oecol.* **3**, 312–320.

Louis, C., Jarraya, A., and Pesson, P. (1969). *C. R. Acad. Sci.* **269**, 2557–2559.

Ludwig, W. (1926). *Z. Wiss. Biol., Abt. A.* **5**, 291–380.

Lusis, O. (1963). *Quart. J. Microsc. Sci.* **104**, 57–68.

McFarlane, J. E. (1970). *Comp. Biochem. Physiol.* 37, 133–141.
McGregor, H. G., and Stebblings, H. (1970) . *J. Cell Sci.* 6, 431–449.
Mackensen, O. (1951). *Genetics* 36, 500–509.
Mackensen, O., and Roberts, W. C. (1948). *U.S. Dep. Agr., Bur. Entomol. Plant Quarantine,* ET250, 2–33.
Maeta, I. J., and Kurihara, M. (1971). *Konchu* 39, 138–158.
Makings, P. (1958). *Proc. Roy. Entomol. Soc. London* 33, 136–148.
Mandl, A. M. (1964). *Biol. Rev.* 39, 288–371.
Manning, F. J. (1949). *Microscope* 7, 175, 209, 237, 259, 303, and 329.
Manning, F. J. (1950). *Microscope* 8, 6, 63, and 129.
Martoja, R. (1964). *Bull. Soc. Zool. Fr.* 89, 614–641.
Masner, P. (1965). *Acta Entomol. Bohemoslov.* 62, 254–276.
Masner, P., Slǎma, K., and Landa, V. (1968). *Nature* 219, 395–396.
Medler, J. T. (1962). *Can. Entomol.* 94, 825–833.
Meinwald, J., and Meinwald, Y. C. (1966) . *J. Amer. Chem. Soc.* 88, 1305.
Melius, E., and Telfer, W. H. (1969). *J. Morphol.* 129, 1–16.
Meng, C. (1970). *Wilhelm Roux'Arch. Entwicklungsmech. Organismen* 165, 35–52.
Menon, M. (1966). *J. Anim. Morphol. Physiol.* 12, 76–80.
Menon, M. (1969). *J. Morphol.* 127, 409–430.
Metchnikoff, E. (1866) . *Z. Wiss. Zool.* 16, 128–132.
Mitlin, H., Lusk, G. J., and Wiygull, G. (1967). *Ann. Entomol. Soc. Amer.* 60, 1155–1158.
Miya, K., Kurichare, M., and Tanimura, I. (1969). *J. Fac. Agr., Iwate Univ.* 9, 221–237.
Morgan, T. H., and Bridges, C. B. (1919). *Carnegie Inst. Wash. Publ.* 278, 1–122.
Morgenthaler, H. M. (1952). *Arch. Julius Klaus-Stift. Vererbungsforsch. Sozialanthropol. Rassenhyg.* 27, 206–211.
Mosbacker, G. C. (1966). *Verh. Deut. Zool. Ges.* 30, 509–521.
Muckenthaler, F. A., and Mahowald, A. P. (1966). *J. Cell Biol.* 28, 199–208.
Mukerji, R. N. (1930). *Proc. Roy. Soc., Ser. B.* 106, 131–139.
Müller, H. J. (1927). *Science* 66, 84–87.
Müller, H. J. (1938). *Amer. J. Cancer* 32, 565–581.
Müller, H. J. (1940). *Zoologica (New York)* 98, 1–220.
Mulnard, J. (1950). *Bull. Acad. Roy. Med. Belg.* [S] 36, 767.
Mulnard, J. (1954). *Arch. Biol.* 65, 261–314.
Musgrave, A. J. (1937). *Proc. Zool. Soc. Lond* 107B, 337–364.
Naisse, J. (1963). *C. R. Acad. Sci.* 256, 799–860.
Naisse, J. (1965). *Arch. Anat. Microsc. Morphol. Exp.* 54, 417–428.
Nath, V. (1929). *Z. Zellforsch. Mikrosk. Anat.* 8, 655.
Nath, V. (1966). *Int. Rev. Cytol.* 9, 305–320.
Nath, V., and Mehta, D. R. (1930). *Quart. J. Microsc. Sci.* 73, 7–24.
Nath, V., and Mohan, P. (1929). *J. Morphol.* 48, 253–279.
Nath, V., Gupta, B. L., and Lal, B. (1958). *Quart. J. Microsc. Sci.* 99, 315–322.
Nelsen, O. E. (1931) . *J. Morphol.* 51, 467–525.
Nicholson, A. J. (1921). *Quart. J. Microsc. Sci.* 65, 396–448.
Nigon, V., and Gillot, S. (1964). *Exp. Cell Res.* 33, 29–33.
Nigon, V., and Nonnenmacher, J. (1961) . *Develop. Biol.* 3, 210–224.
Nolte, H. W. (1937). *Z. Morphol. Oekol. Tiere* 33, 165–200.
Nonidez, J. F. (1920). *Biol. Bull.* 39, 207–230.
Norris, M. J. (1932). *Proc. Zool. Soc. London* 102, 595–611.

Norris, M. J. (1933). *Proc. Zool. Soc. London* **91**, 903–933.
Novak, A. F., Blum, M. S., Taber, S., and Luizzo, J. A. (1960). *Ann. Entomol. Soc. Amer.* **53**, 841–843.
Nussbaum, N. B. (1948). *Opusc. Entomol., Suppl.* **7**, 1–101.
Nussbaum-Hilarowicz, J. (1917). *Z. Wiss. Zool.* **117**, 554.
Ochsé, W. (1946). *Rev. Suisse Zool.* **53**, 534–537.
Odhiambo, T. R. (1969a). *Tissue Cell* **1**, 155–182.
Odhiambo, T. R. (1969b). *Tissue Cell* **1**, 325–340.
Odhiambo, T. R. (1969c). *Phil. Trans. Roy. Soc. London, Ser. B* **256**, 85–114.
Odhiambo, T. R. (1970). *Tissue Cell* **2**, 233–248.
Odhiambo, T. R. (1971). *Tissue Cell* **3**, 309–324.
Orr, C. W. M. (1964). *J. Insect Physiol.* **10**, 103–119.
Palévody, C. (1971). *C. R. Acad. Sci., Ser. D* **272**, 3165–3168.
Palm, N. B. (1948). *Opusc. Entomol., Suppl.* **7**, 1–101.
Pan, M. L., Bell, W. J., and Telfer, W. H. (1969). *Science* **165**, 393–394.
Panelius, S. (1968). *Chromosoma* **23**, 333–345.
Pardi, L. (1946). *Bull. 1st. Entomol. Univ. Bologna* **15**, 25–84.
Patchin, S., and Davey, K. G. (1968). *J. Insect Physiol.* **15**, 1815–1820.
Pavan, C., and Breuer, M. E. (1955). *Rev. Brasil. Biol.* **15**, 329–339.
Payne, F. (1932). *J. Morphol.* **53**, 523.
Payne, M. A. (1933). *J. Morphol.* **54**, 321–346.
Pringle, J. A. (1938). *Trans. Roy. Entomol. Soc. London* **87**, 271–290.
Proverbs, M. D. (1969). *Ann. Rev. Entomol.* **14**, 81–102.
Pryor, M. G. M. (1940). *Proc. Roy. Soc., Ser. B* **128**, 378–393.
Przelecka, A., and Dutkowski, A. (1965). *Bull. Acad. Pol. Sci., Cl. 2* **13**, 573–575.
Quatropiani, A. L., and Anderson, E. (1969). *Z. Zellforsch. Mikrosk. Anat.* **95**, 495–510.
Quickenden, K. L. (1969). *J. Insect Physiol.* **16**, 171–183.
Ramamurthy, P. S (1968). *Indian J. Exp. Biol.* **6**, 185–187.
Rau, A. (1942). *Z. Morphol. Oekol. Tiere* **39**, 369–522.
Raven, C. P. (1961). "Oogenesis: The Storage of Developmental Information," pp. 1–270. Pergamon, Oxford.
Regen, J. (1924). *Sitzungsber. Akad. Wiss. Wien, Math.-Naturwiss. Kl., Abt. 1* **133**, 347–359.
Reinecke, L. H., Klassen, W., and Norland, J. E. (1969). *Ann. Entomol. Soc. Amer.* **62**, 511–525.
Rembold, H. (1967). *Int. Apicult. Congr.* **21**, 467.
Rempel, J. G., and Church, N. S. (1965). *Can. J. Zool.* **43**, 915–925.
Riddiford, L. M. (1967). *Science* **158**, 139–141.
Riddiford, L. M., and Williams, C. M. (1967). *Science* **156**, 541.
Ries, E. (1931). *Z. Morphol. Oekol. Tiere* **20**, 232–367.
Ries, E. (1932). *Z. Zellforsch. Mikrosk. Anat.* **16**, 314–388.
Ries, E., and Weel, P. B. (1934). *Z. Zellforsch. Mikrosk. Anat.* **20**, 565.
Ritter, F. J. (1971). *Meded. Fak. Landb. Wet. Gent* **36**, 874–882.
Robertson, J. G. (1961). *Can J. Zool.* **39**, 245–263.
Roeder, K. D. (1935). *Biol. Bull.* **69**, 203–220.
Roeder, K. D., Tozian, L., and Weiant, E. A. (1960). *J. Insect Physiol.* **4**, 45–62.
Roelofs, W. L., and Comeau, A. (1971). *J. Insect Physiol.* **17**, 435.
Roonwal, M. L. (1936). *Bull. Entomol. Res.* **27**, 1–14.
Roth, L. M. (1964). *J. Insect Physiol.* **10**, 915–945.

Roth, L. M., and Stay, B. (1962). *Psyche* **69**, 165–208.

Roth, T. F., Frelinger, J. A., and De Borde, D. (1968). *J. Cell Biol.* **39**, 115a–116a.

Rothenbuhler, W. C. (1957). *J. Heredi.* **48**, 160–168.

Rothenbuhler, W. C. (1958). *Proc. Int. Congr. Entomol., 10th, 1958* pp. 867–873.

Rothenbuhler, W. C., Gowen, J. W., and Park, O. W. (1951). *Genetics* **36**, 573.

Royer, M. (1970). *C. R. Acad. Sci.* **270**, 3246–3250.

Ruttner, F. (1956a). *Insectes Soc.* **3**, 351–359.

Ruttner, F. (1956b). *Bee World* **37**, 2–15 and 23–24.

Ruttner, F. (1957). *Z. Vergle. Physiol.* **39**, 577–600.

Ruttner, F., and Mackensen, O. (1952). *Bee World* **33**, 53–62 and 71–79.

Sanderson, A. R., and Hall, D. W. (1951). *Endeavour.* **10**, 33.

Scheinert, W. (1933). *Z. Morphol. Oekol. Tiere* **27**, 76–128.

Schlottmann, L. L., and Bonhag, P. F. (1956). *Univ. Cal. Berkeley Publ. Entomol.* **11**, 351–394.

Schneider, D., Block, B. C., and Priesner, E. (1967). *Z. Vergl. Physiol.* **54**, 192–209.

Schneider, G. (1940). *Z. Morphol. Oekol. Tiere* **36**, 595–644.

Schröder, C. (1928) . "Handbuch der Entom." Jena, Fischer Verlag.

Schwinck, I. (1954). *Z. Vergl. Physiol.* **35**, 167–174.

Scott, A. C. (1936). *J. Morphol.* **59**, 485–515.

Scott, A. C. (1938). *Z. Morphol. Oekol. Tiere* **33**, 633–653.

Seiler, J. (1935). *Rev. Suisse Zool.* **42**, 437–445.

Seiler, J., and Schäffer, K. (1960). *Chromosoma* **11**, 29–102.

Shanun, V. P., Hollingworth, R. M., and Passhke, J. D. (1970). *J. Insect Physiol* **16**, 429–436.

Silverstein, R. M., Rodin, J. O., Burkholder, W. E., and Gorman, J. E. (1967). *Science* **157**, 85.

Silverstein, R. M., Brownlee, R. G., Bellas, T. E., Wood, D. L., and Browne, L. E. (1968). *Science* **159**, 1373.

Slăma, K., and Williams, C. M. (1966). *Biol. Bull.* **130**, 235–246.

Slifer, E. H. (1937). *Quart. J. Microsc. Sci.* **79**, 493–506.

Smith, P. A., and King, R. C. (1968). *Genetics* **60**, 335–351.

Snodgrass, R. E. (1925). "Anatomy and Physiology of the Honey Bee." New York.

Snodgrass, R. E. (1933). *Smithson. Misc. Collect.* **89**, 1–148.

Snodgrass, R. E. (1936). *Smithson. Misc. Collect.* **95**, 1–96.

Snodgrass, R. E. (1937). *Smithson. Misc. Collect.* **96**, 1–107.

Snodgrass, R. E. (1941). *Smithson. Misc. Collect.* **99**, 1–86.

Snodgrass, R. E. (1957). *Smithson. Misc. Collect.* **135**, 1–60.

Sobels, F. H. (1963). "Repair from Genetic Radiation Damage and Differential Radiosensitivity in Germ Cells." Pergamon, Oxford.

Speicher, K. G., and Speicher, B. R. (1938). *Biol. Bull.* **74**, 247.

Stay, B. (1965). *J. Cell Biol.* **26**, 49–62.

Steiner, L. F., and Christenson, L. D. (1956). *Proc. Hawaii. Acad. Sci.* **31**, 17–18.

Stern, C. (1959). *Triangle* **4**, 131–135.

Strübing, H. (1956). *Zool. Beitr.* **2**, 331–357.

Stüben, M. (1969). *Mitt. Biol. Bundesanst. Land- Forstwirt., Berlin-Dahlem* **133**, 1–84.

Sturtevant, A. H. (1921). *Genetics* **6**, 179–207.

Suomalainen, E. (1962). *Annu. Rev. Entomol.* **7**, 349–363.

Swift, H., and Kleinfeld, R. (1953) . *Physiol. Zool.* **26**, 301–311.

Tates, A. D. (1971). Dissertation, Leiden University.

Telfer, W. H. (1954). *J. Gen. Physiol.* **37**, 539–558.

Telfer, W. H. (1960). *Biol. Bull.* **118**, 338–351.

Telfer, W. H. (1965). *Annu. Rev. Entomol.* **10**, 161–184.

Terando, M. L., and Feir, D. (1967a). *Comp. Biochem. Physiol.* **20**, 431–436.

Terando, M. L., and Feir, D. (1967b). *Comp. Biochem. Physiol.* **21**, 31–38.

Theunissen, J. (1971). In "Sterility Principle for Insect Control or Eradication," pp. 329–340. IAEA, Vienna.

Thomas, K., and Nation, J. L. (1966). *Biol. Bull.* **130**, 254–264.

Thompson, W. R., and Parker, H. L. (1928). *Ann. Soc. Entomol. Fra.* **97**, 425–465.

Thomsen, E. (1952). *J. Exp. Biol.* **29**, 137–172.

Tokuyasu, K. T., Peacock, W. J., and Hardy, R. W. (1972a). *Z. Zellforsch. Mikrosk. Anat.* **124**, 479–506.

Tokuyasu, K. T., Peacock, W. J., and Hardy, R. W. (1972b). *Z. Zellforsch. Mikrosk. Anat.* **127**, 492–525.

Truckenbrodt, W. (1970). *Z. Zellforsch, Mikrosk. Anat.* **108**, 339–356.

Tumlinson, J. H., Gueldner, R. C., Hardee, D. D., Thompson, A. C., Hedin, P. A., and Minyard, J. P. (1970). *In* "Chemicals Controlling Insect Behaviour" (M. Beroza, ed.), pp. 41–59. Academic Press, New York.

Uichanco, L. B. (1924). *Philipp. J. Sci.* **24**, 143–247.

Ulrich, H. (1936). *Z. Indukt. Abstamm.-Vererbungsl.* **71**, 1.

Ulrich, H. (1962). *Verh. Deut. Zool. Ges.* **26**, 139.

Vanderberg, J. P. (1963). *Biol. Bull.* **125**, 556–575.

Vanderplank, F. L. (1945). *Proc. Roy. Entomol. Soc. London, Ser. A* **20**, 105–106.

Vlasblom, A. G., and Wolvekamp, H. P. (1954). *Physiol. Comp. Oecol.* **4**, 240–246.

Voinov, D. N. (1925). *Arch. Zool. Exp. Gen.* **63**, 437.

von Kraft, A. (1960). *Zool. Jahrb., Abt. Anat. Ontog. Tiere* **78**, 457–556.

von Lengerken, H. (1928). *Biol. Zentralbl.* **48**, 475–509.

Wallis, D. I. (1962). *J. Insect Physiol.* **8**, 453–469.

Weber, H. (1938). "Lehrbuch der Entomologie." Fischer, Jena.

Weber, H. (1954). "Grundriss der Entomologie," pp. 1–428. Fischer, Stuttgart.

Weidner, H. (1934). *Z. Angew. Entomol.* **21**, 239–290.

Went, D. F. (1971). *J. Exp. Zool.* **177**, 301.

Wesenberg-Lund, C. (1913) . *Fortschr. Naturwiss. Forsch.* **8**, 161–286.

Weyer, F. (1928). *Z. Wiss. Zool.* **131**, 345–501.

Wheeler, W. M. (1910). *J. Exp. Zool.* **8**, 377–438.

White, M. J. D. (1946). *J. Morphol.* **79**, 323–369.

White, M. J. D. (1947). *J. Morphol.* **80**, 1–24.

Whiting, A. R. (1940). *J. Exp. Zool.* **83**, 249–269.

Whiting, P. W. (1940). *J. Morphol.* **66**, 323–355.

Whiting, P. W. (1943a). *Biol. Bull.* **85**, 238–243.

Whiting, P. W. (1943b). *Genetics* **28**, 365–382.

Whitten, M. J. (1971). "Sterility Principle for Insect Control or Eradication," pp. 399–413. IAEA, Vienna.

Wick, J. R., and Bonhag, P. F. (1955). *J. Morphol.* **96**, 31–59.

Wigglesworth, V. B. (1936). *Quart. J. Microsc. Sci.* **79**, 91–121.

Wigglesworth, V. B. (1948). *J. Exp. Biol.* **25**, 1–14.

Wigglesworth, V. B. (1972). "The Principles of Insect Physiology," 7th ed. Methuen, London.

Wigglesworth, V. B., and Salpeter, M. M. (1962). *J. Insect Physiol.* **8**, 635–641.

Wilkens, J. L. (1969). *J. Insect Physiol.* **15**, 1015–1024.

Williams, C. M., and Buxton, P. A. (1916). *Trans. Roy. Entomol. Soc. London* pp. 86–100.

Woyke, J. (1955). *Bull. Acad. Pol. Sci.* **3**, 175–180.

Woyke, J. (1963). *J. Apicult. Res.* **2**, 77–84.

Woyke, J. (1965). *J. Apicult. Res.* **4**, 143–148.

Woyke, J., and Knytel, A. (1966). *J. Apicult. Res.* **5**, 149–154.

Wülker, W., and Winter, G. (1970). *Z. Zellforsch. Mikrosk. Anat.* **106**, 348–370.

Young, W. C., and Plough, H. H. (1926). *Biol. Bull.* **51**, 189–198.

Zinsmeister, P. P., and Davenport, R. (1971). *Exp. Cell Res.* **67**, 273–278.

Chapter 3

REPRODUCTION—ENDOCRINE CONTROL

Jan de Wilde and Arnold de Loof

I. Control of Oogenesis 97
   A. Endocrine and Nervous Effects 97
   B. Rebound Effects 120
   C. Gonotropic Dissociation 128
   D. Adult Diapause 129
   E. Environmental Control of Oogenesis 131
II. Control of Semen Production 136
   A. Humoral Control of Spermatogenesis 136
   B. Humoral Control of Accessory Gland Activity 137
   C. Humoral Control of Sex Differentiation 139
III. Control of Sexual Behavior and Oviposition 141
   A. Independence of Sexual Behavior from Gonadal Function 141
   B. Effect of Corpora Allata on Sexual Behavior 141
   C. Endocrine Effects on Oviposition 142
   D. Environmental Control of Oviposition 143
IV. Social Relations in Control of Reproduction 144
   A. Interrelation of Sexes 144
   B. Pheromones and Inhibition of Reproduction in Worker Castes in
      Social Insects 148
   References 150

I. Control of Oogenesis

A. ENDOCRINE AND NERVOUS EFFECTS

1. Role of the Corpora Allata in the Control of Ovarian Activity

Ito (1918) suggested the endocrine nature of the corpora allata in *Bombyx mori* and observed their secretory activity during oogenesis. It was, however, only after several decades that Weed-Pfeiffer (1936, 1939) succeeded in removing these glands in sixth-instar larvae and young adults of the grasshopper, *Melanoplus differentialis*. Females thus treated show defects in oogenesis, oocyte growth being arrested at the beginning of yolk deposition. Weed-Pfeiffer concluded that a hormone from the corpus allatum is required for the normal functioning of the follicle cells. Moreover, she observed a reduced secretory activity of the oviduct wall after allatectomy. Wigglesworth (1936), in a series of classic experiments, established the control of ovarian activity by the corpora allata in *Rhodnius prolixus* and revealed the following basic facts pertaining to extrinsic control as well as mode of action:

1. In the adult *Rhodnius*, the corpus allatum is activated shortly after the insect has taken a blood meal. This is followed by follicle activity and yolk deposition in the ovary.

2. If the insect is decapitated after the meal, ovarian activity only takes place up to the point where yolk should be deposited. Subsequently, the oocyte is absorbed, presumably by the cells of the disintegrating follicle.

3. The same phenomenon is observed when the insect is fasting. In this case, the corpus allatum does not show signs of renewed activity.

4. Joining the decapitated female in parabiosis with a well-fed male or female with an intact corpus allatum, or implanting an active gland, results in normal yolk deposition.

Thomsen (1942) performed quantitative measurements of corpora allata in adult females of *Calliphora erythrocephala*. During sexual maturation, the glands increase significantly in size. During this growth, their endocrine activity markedly increases. Extirpation of the corpora allata in newly emerged females prevented yolk formation in the ovarioles in more than 75% of the cases. In 24-hour-old flies, the effect was obtained in only 60% and, if the operation was performed after 48 hours, no more than 30% responded. Reimplantation of active glands in most cases completely restored ovarian activity.

Day (1943b), working with two other cyclorrhaphous flies, *Lucilia sericata* and *Sarcophaga securifera,* removed the whole complex of corpus allatum and corpus cardiacum. After early extirpation, oogenesis only proceeded up to the stage of yolk deposition. In case oogenesis had already advanced beyond this stage, oosorption took place. As the operated flies were fed only sugar and water, these experiments are not wholly conclusive (see Section I, E, 3).

In the fleshfly *Sarcophaga bullata* (Wilkens, 1969), adult females allatectomized at pupation matured eggs fully if fed liver, but only partially

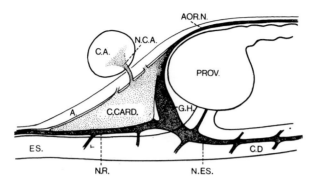

Fig. 1. The corpus cardiacum (C. CARD.) and some adjacent organs of *Calliphora erythrocephala,* seen from the left. The C. CARD. and the hypocerebral ganglion (G. H.) are located in the triangular space between the esophagus (ES.), the aorta (A), and the proventriculus (PROV.). The corpus allatum (C.A.) is innervated by 2 nervi corporis allati (N.C.A.), one on either side of the aorta. The C. CARD. and the hypocerebral ganglion are connected with the brain by the "cardiac-recurrent nerve," consisting of the nervi corporis cardiaci (not shown), which have joined the recurrent nerve (N. R.). Behind the hypocerebral ganglion 2 pairs of nerves are found; viz., the nervi esophagei (N.ES) , which innervate the crop duct, and the aortic nerves (AOR.N.), which run backwards on either side of the aorta. The length of the C. CARD. proper is 100 μm [Redrawn after Normann and Duve (1969)].

when fed an amino acid diet. Seventy percent of females allatectomized at emergence deposited yolk when fed on either of the diets. Yolk was not deposited after the neurosecretory cells were removed. Reimplantation of neurosecretory cells into brain-cauterized females stimulated vitellogenesis, whereas implanting corpora allata or brain tissue was without effect. According to Wilkens, in *Sarcophaga* the neurosecretory cells produce the gonadotropic hormone, while the juvenile hormone is involved in the regulation of vitellogenic protein synthesis (Wilkens, 1969) .

In cyclorrhaphous Diptera, the endocrine situation is complicated, as a separate corpus allatum is only present in the adult stages (Fig. 1) , while larvae have a complex postcerebral "ring gland" or "Weismann's ring" (Fig. 2) . Studies of Burtt (1937) on *Calliphora* and of Hadorn (1937) and Scharrer and Hadorn (1938) on *Drosophila* have shown that the dorsal part of this organ is homologous with the corpora allata, while the ventral part corresponds with the corpora cardiaca.

Vogt (1943) implanted ring glands of first-stage *Drosophila* larvae into adults, from which both corpora allata and corpora cardiaca had been removed. Ovarian growth was stimulated by these larval glands.

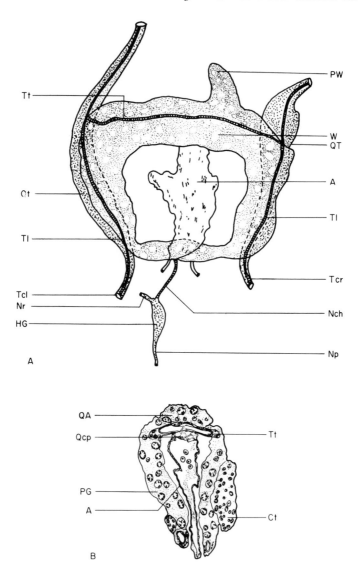

Fig. 2. Weismann's (ring gland) of *Calliphora*. (A) frontal view; (B) slightly oblique section. Aorta (A), corpus allatum (CA), imarginal tracheal cells (Ct), hypocerebral ganglion (HG), nervus cardiohypocerebralis (Nch), **nervus proventricularis** (Np), nervus recurrens (Nr), posterior part of Weismann's ring (PW), right and left cerebral trachea (Tcr) and (Tcl), Longitudinal trachea (Tl), transversal trachea (Tt), Weismann's ring (W), prothoracic gland (PG) (from Joly, 1968).

This stimulating effect proved to be located in the dorsal part, containing the corpus allatum.

From cross transplantations of adult ovaries into larvae of different *Drosophila* species, Vogt (1940) concluded the existence of a specificity of gonadotropic action. These observations, however, are biased by the difference in hormone level normally present in different *Drosophila* species (Vogt, 1942).

Detinova (1945) and Mednikova (1952) brought indirect evidence of the gonadotropic activity of the corpora allata in female adults of *Anopheles maculipennis* and *Anopheles atroparvus*. Histological signs of activity are conspicuous 6 hours after a blood meal. This coincides with the fact that ligating the head prevents ovarian development only when applied within 6 hours after the meal.

In *Aedes aegypti*, according to Gillett (1956), this critical period for ovarian activation occurs only after 8–14 hours at 28°C. Transfusion of hemolymph obtained from donors after this period induced yolk formation in the ovaries of mosquitoes decapitated immediately after the meal (Gillett, 1958).

Larsen and Bodenstein (1959), in an extensive study with *Culex pipiens, Culex molestus,* and *Aedes aegypti,* applied ovarian transplantations, ligation, and hemolymph transfusion. In such experiments, the secretions of the brain and postcerebral glands are all necessarily involved and the function of the corpus allatum cannot be studied separately. Of special importance, therefore, are their experiments involving injection of corpus allatum extracts of the cockroaches, *Blaberus* and *Periplaneta*. Such extracts induced yolk formation in early decapitated mosquitoes in a significant number of cases. Their general conclusion is that the corpus allatum provides the hormone activating the ovaries. The mode of activation of the corpus allatum they suggested will be discussed in Section I, E, 3.

Contrary to this report of Larsen and Bodenstein, Lea (1969) found that implantation of extra corpora allata from either autogenous or anautogenous donors (see p. 134, this chapter) did not stimulate egg maturation in anautogenous *Aedes aegypti* or *Culex pipiens* fed only on sugar. Implanting a cockroach corpus allatum (CA) did not induce egg maturation in anautogenous mosquitoes fed on sugar although the CA of larval or adult cockroaches were shown to function in *Aedes aegypti*. Therefore, the effect of Larsen and Bodenstein's whole cockroach extract on mosquitoes may not have been due to CA hormone. Anautogenous *Culex* and *Aedes,* allectomized 3–5 days after emergence, matured eggs following a blood meal. Apparently, the CA had already secreted a sufficient quantity of hormone for maturation of the anautogenous ovary before the first blood meal. The moment of allatectomy is important also in the Colorado beetle. Only when the CA are extirpated together with the corpora cardiaca (CC) at pupal–adult ecdysis is ovarian development completely inhibited (de Loof and de Wilde, 1970b).

Joly (1945) performed careful differential extirpations of corpora allata and corpora cardiaca in the dytiscid beetles *Macrodytes* and *Cybister*. As in other cases mentioned above, allatectomy interferes with the yolk-forming phase of oogenesis. Implantation of active corpora allata of either sex into diapausing females induces ovarian activity. Implantation of these glands into an inactive ovary most markedly affects the adjacent ovarioles. Also in *Carabus catenulatus*, the CA was found to be indispensable to oogenesis (Joly, 1950).

With the Colorado beetle, de Wilde and de Boer (1961) and de Loof and Lagasse (1970a) also found that allatectomy causes a standstill in ovarian activity followed by resorption of terminal ocytes (Fig. 3). This

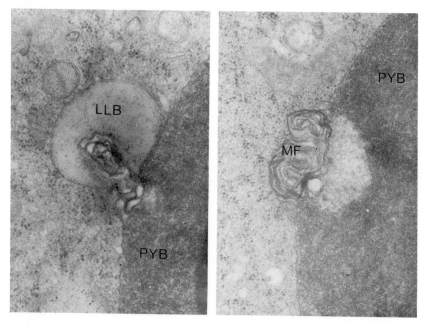

Fig. 3. A lysosomelike body (LLB), injects its contents into a proteid yolk body (PYB) during oosorption following allatectomy in the Colorado beetle. As a result the PYB is gradually dissolved, probably by the action of enzymes, MF = myelin figure (de Loof and Lagasse, 1970a).

is reversed by implantation of active corpora allata of either sex or by application of Röller's *dl*-juvenile hormone (de Wilde, 1969).

Extirpation of the CA in *Tenebrio* causes an arrest of oogenesis (El-Ibrashi, 1965; Lender and Laverdure, 1965; Mordue, 1965b).

In the roaches *Leucophaea* (Scharrer, 1946; Engelmann, 1957), *Periplaneta* (Girardie, 1962), *Diploptera* (Engelmann, 1959), and *Nauphoeta* (Lüscher, 1968a) and in *Locusta migratoria* (Joly, 1960), *Schistocerca gregaria* (Highnam et al., 1963; Pener, 1965), *Schistocerca paranensis* (Strong, 1965a), and *Anacridium aegypticum* (Geldiay, 1967), allatectomy has exactly the same results. The corpora allata are indispensable for yolk deposition.

Subsequent additions to this list include Thysanura *(Thermobia;* Rohdendorf, 1965), Hemiptera *(Adelphocoris,* Ewen, 1966; *Cimex,* Davis, 1964; *Pyrrhocoris,* Sláma, 1964c), and Lepidoptera *(Pieris,* Karlinsky, 1963, 1967a,c).

It should be noted that in many of the preceding cases the effect of the corpora allata lacks sex specificity. In *Rhodnius* (Wigglesworth, 1948) and *Drosophila* (Vogt, 1943; Bodenstein, 1947) larval corpora allata induce ovarian activity in decapitated or allatectomized adults. Since, conversely, adult corpora allata produce juvenile effects in larval stages (Novák, 1951; Wigglesworth, 1948; Fukuda, 1962), it has long been presumed that the "C.A. gonadotropic factor" is identical with the juvenile hormone. This has recently been supported by the fact that synthetic *Cecropia* juvenile hormone (Röller) has both juvenile and gonadotropic effects (Röller and Dahm, 1968).

Allatectomy has failed to interfere with ovarian development in several reported cases. In *Carausius morosus,* Plugfelder (1937) removed the corpora allata from adults, and even from the third and fourth instar larva, without interfering with ovarian maturation. Implantation of extra corpora allata even resulted in retardation of oogenesis and regressive development of the genital ducts. Similar results were obtained in *Sipyloidea sipylus* by Possompès (1956). We may agree with Joly (1947) that these results are accounted for by the peculiar nature of the adult stage in these phasmids. In fact, the adult is neotenic, and we may therefore assume that some quantity of juvenile hormone remains present throughout "adult" development. Probably the ovaries require only a low hormone level to be activated. High levels of corpus allatum hormone apparently are required to induce juvenile characters. The persistence of juvenile hormone in this species already follows from the fact that the morphogenetic effects of allatectomy in larvae only become apparent after a delay of two or three molts.

In *Bombyx mori,* Bounhiol (1938) found that removal of the corpora allata in the last two larval stages does not interfere with ovarian activity, but results in precocious adults with normal fecundity. Fukuda (1944) reported similar results. Ovarian activity in these cases is linked with the general progress of postembryonic growth in a much different way than in *Carausius.* In adult saturniid moths no gradual sexual maturation is found. In fact, oogenesis has already started in the pupa. At the time somatic development of the adults is realized, oogenesis is practically completed. Moreover, the adults are unable to feed.

This may perhaps explain why, in these species, the juvenile hormone does not appear to be necessary in the adult. In addition to above-mentioned cases, allatectomy performed in the pupal or adult stage does not affect *Phryganidia* (Bodenstein, 1938), *Hyalophora* (Williams, 1952), *Philosamia* (Ichikawa and Nitshiitsutsuji-Uwo, 1959), *Leucania* (Tsiu-

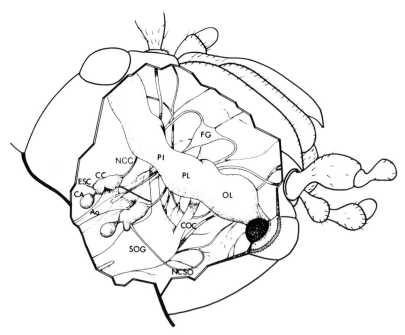

Fig. 4. The nervous system and associated retrocerebral glands in the head of the Colorado beetle, *Leptinotarsa decemlineata.* The esophagus has been omitted. Aorta (Ao), corpus allatum (CA), corpus cardiacum (CC), circumesophageal connective (COC), extrinsic secretory cells of the CC (ESC), frontal ganglion (FG), nervus corporis cardiaci (NCC), nervus cardiaco-subesophagealis (NCSO), optic lobe (OL), pars intercerebralis (PI), protocerebral lobe (PL), subesophageal ganglion (SOG). [Drawing by M. P. Van der Schelde, Wageningen. From Schooneveld (1970).]

Ngun and Quo, 1963), and *Galleria* (Röller, 1962). However, total egg output is reduced partially or completely in *Bombyx* (Yamashita *et al.,* 1961), *Galleria* (Röller, 1962), *Leucania separata* (Tsiu-Ngun and Quo, 1963), and *Polygonia c-aureum* (Endo, 1970), when allatectomy is performed in the larva. However, when either the brain or the corpora allata are extirpated from female pupae of the moth *Manduca sexta,* the resulting adults are unable to complete adult postemergence egg maturation (Sroka and Gilbert, 1971). In *Calliphora,* Possompès (1949) extirpated the corpus allatum homologue of the ring gland of the last instar larva. The emerged adults, although devoid of their corpora allata, still produced viable eggs. Mortality, however, was high after the operation. These results seem to contradict those of Thomsen (1942), but it should be remembered that in her experiments some 25% of early extirpated flies still showed oogenesis. It may be, therefore, that this group corresponds to the surviving flies of Possompès' experiments and that in these cases oogenesis had already been induced in the pupa. Allatectomy in *Sarcophaga bullata,* performed within 12 hours after pupation, did not prevent oogenesis (Wilkens, 1968).

Wigglesworth (1948) has pointed out that the active removal of juvenile hormone is a general phenomenon in the metamorphosis of insects. We may conclude, then, that the renewed activity of the corpus allatum in the adult is a requirement of vitellogenesis only in those cases where ovarian activity is started after the completion of metamorphosis. When oogenesis is started in an immature stage a certain amount of corpus allatum hormone will usually be present in the blood.

2. Activation of the Corpora Allata

In adult insects we may distinguish between the factors inducing renewed growth of the corpus allatum (trophic effect) and those responsible for the regulation of its secretory activity. These factors may be both humoral and nervous. The nervous connections of the corpus allatum are manifold (Figs. 4 and 5).

First, there is the innervation from the brain by way of the nervi corporis cardiaci and the nervi corporis allati. This innervation is partly reflectory and partly neurosecretory (Thomsen, 1952; Lüscher and Engelmann, 1955; Engelmann, 1957; Nayar, 1958b). Second, the stomatogastric nervous system is connected with the gland via the hypocerebral ganglion, providing autonomous innervation via the corpora cardiaca. Third, innervation takes place from the subesophageal ganglion, sometimes directly (*Thysanura,* Gabe, 1953; *Gryllus,* Huber, 1955; Leucophaea, Engelmann, 1957; *Periplaneta,* Harker, 1960) and sometimes via the corpora cardiaca *(Leptinotarsa,* de Wilde, 1969; Schooneveld, 1970) (Fig. 4). Humoral control of the corpora allata is effected by the protocerebral neurosecretory cells and their neurohemal organs, the corpora cardiaca.

a. Role of Neurosecretion in Corpus Allatum Activity. There is abundant evidence that in many species the activity of the medial neurosecretory cells (MNSC) in the brain is a primary requirement for the activity of the corpora allata. Thomsen (1952) and Highnam (1962a) have convincingly confirmed this by direct extirpation of these cells. There is also evidence that the MNSC may even activate the gland when the nervous connections with the brain are severed or when the gland is reimplanted elsewhere in the body (Thomsen, 1952; Engelmann, 1957; de Wilde and de Boer, 1961; Strangways-Dixon, 1962). The neurosecretory substance is stored in the corpora cardiaca or, as in *Oncopeltus,* in the aorta wall (Johansson, 1958b), and it is not a matter of surprise that, in the absence of MNSC, these stores may keep the corpus allatum active for some time. In fact, Thomsen (1952) has shown that, in *Calliphora,* implantation of active corpora cardiaca at least partly compensates for the removal of the MNSC. In *Oncopeltus,* the store of neurosecretory substance in the aorta wall may lead to the same effect (Johansson, 1958b).

This, however, does not necessarily mean that the corpora allata are normally activated by the humoral pathway. Engelmann (1957) with *Leucophaea* and Nayar (1958b) with *Iphita* have shown that neurosecretory tracts from the protocerebrum pass through the corpora cardiaca and reach the corpora allata. Enlargement of the glands has been seen to follow the appearance of Gomori-positive material along these tracts. Whether this material originates from other types of neurons than those ending in the corpora cardiaca is not known with certainty. The importance of direct neurosecretory transport to the corpus allatum may be judged from the fact that, in dytiscids, extirpation of the corpus cardiacum results in degeneration of the corpus allatum (Joly, 1945). And in *Sarcophaga* (Day, 1943b) and *Schistocerca* (Highnam, 1962a,b) denervation of the gland prevents its activation by the brain. Surgical operations involving nerve sections and brain cauterization would seem to demonstrate that the activation of the corpora allata in *Schistocerca paranensis* is mediated through the lateral neurosecretory complexes, each corpus allatum being under the independent control of the ipsilateral neurosecretory cells (LNSC). According to these findings, the medial neurosecretory system is not clearly involved in the control mechanism and no function can be attributed to the nervous connections between the CA and the subesophageal ganglion (SEG) (Strong, 1965b). But it is possible that the operations may have had side effects on the MNSC (Highnam, 1969). Girardie (1963, 1965) submits that in *Locusta,* the corpora allata are directly stimulated and inhibited by the products of different neurosecretary cells. Thomsen (1952) reported that the lateral cells had only a limited influence on oocyte maturation in *Calliphora.*

b. *The Nervus Allato-subesophagealis (NAS) and the Nervus Cardi-aco-subesophagealis (NCS).* Engelmann (1957) reports that in *Leucophaea* inactive corpora allata, after the nervous connections with the brain are interrupted, can still be activated by the latter, provided the NAS is intact. According to Engelmann's experiments, once activated, implanted glands will remain functioning also without any nervous connection; the NAS does not seem to be a regulating nerve, but exerts a trophic action.

In *Leptinotarsa,* the innervation from the SEG appears to terminate in a special region of the corpus cardiacum, characterized by large "extrinsic" glandular cells. Hence, the nerve has been adequately named N. Cardi-aco-subesophagealis (Schooneveld, 1970).

3. Inhibition of the Corpora Allata

In *Leptinotarsa,* it has been found that corpora allata from immature females, when implanted in the thorax of allatectomized females, will be activated and induce ovarian activity when long-day conditions are applied. Upon return to short-day conditions oogenesis is arrested and diapause induced. When transsection of the NCS is effected in immature females, subsequently placed under short photoperiods, diapause is induced after a latent period twice as long as in control operations (de Wilde and de Boer, 1969). It would seem, therefore, that in *Lepinotarsa* the nerve exerts an inhibitory function on the corpora allata in diapause induction. The region of the corpora cardiaca innervated by the NCS is characterized by large secretory cells, which show histologically an active picture during diapause (Schooneveld, 1970).

Severance of the nervi corporis cardiaci (NCC) often results in histological changes in the corpus allatum. Day (1943b) removed the hypocerebral ganglion in *Sarcophaga securifera* and *Lucilia sericata* and thereby disrupted the nervous connection between the brain and the corpora allata. He observed an increase in the cytoplasmic content of their cells and an enlargement of their nuclei; physiological activity appeared unaltered. Scharrer (1952), who severed the nervi corporis cardiaci in *Leucophaea,* observed similar histological effects and concluded that there was an increase in secretory activity of the corpus allatum. In more recent studies on other cockroach species, non-neurosecretory fibers have been found in the NCC, fibers which apparently originate in the brain lobes (Brousse-Gaury, 1968).

Johansson (1958a) with *Oncopeltus* and Strangways-Dixon (1962) with *Calliphora* did not observe any effect of denervation on corpus allatum function nor any change in volume. Engelmann and Lüscher (1956) and Engelmann (1959) with *Diploptera,* in experiments involving cutting the nervi corporis cardiaci and destroying parts of the protocerebrum (leaving the neurosecretory cells intact), found very clear stimulation of the corpora allata, both tropic and functional. In *Tenebrio,* section of the NCC I shows that a direct relationship exists between the brain and the CA which is responsible for ensuring the synergistic action of the neurosecretory cells and the CA in controlling oocyte development (Mordue, 1965b). The discrepancy among these results may well be explained by assuming that the neurosecretory cells exert a constant tropic effect on the corpora allata, but that in most insect orders the function of these glands is regulated by inhibitory fibers from the brain. As mentioned, the nervi corporis cardiaci are mixed in nature, i.e., they contain both conductive and neurosecretory axons. Interrupting the neurosecretory pathways, as has been seen, may be compensated by direct release of their substance in the blood. The effect of severing the inhibitory fibers, however, depends on the degree of inhibition they exert. Their centers apparently go through waves of activity, controlled by the activity of the ovaries, or in viviparous roaches, by the eggs in the brood sac (see Section I, B). If the degree of inhibition is only slight, cutting the cardiac nerve is without effect.

This conclusion is not in agreement with the idea that the medial neurosecretory cells are the overall controlling center of the corpora allata, although this may hold true for *Calliphora* (Thomsen, 1942). However, it seems inevitable, in view of the experiment reported by Lüscher and Engelmann (1955), as follows: In *Leucophaea* each of the mixed nervi corporis cardiaci splits in the caudal part of the corpus cardiacum to form three branches. One of these innervates the ipsilateral, another, more lateral branch the contralateral corpus allatum (Fig. 5).

Cutting one of the medial cardiacum nerves results in activation of the corpus allatum at the same side. The same effect, however, is obtained when the lateral, noncrossing branch of this nerve is cut, although neurosecretory transport could still take place from the other side. It remains to be explained why, in *Calliphora,* where the ovaries go through cycles of activity, correlated variations in volume of the corpora allata are independent of their innervation (Strangways-Dixon. 1962). This will be discussed in Section I, B.

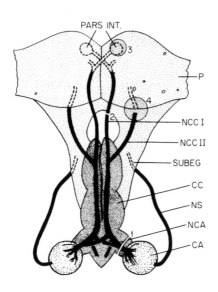

Fig. 5. Nervous connections of corpora allata and corpora cardiaca with protocerebrum (P) and subesophageal ganglion (SUBEG), in *Leucophaea*. Nervus corporis cardiaci interior (NCC I), nervus corporis cardiaci exterior (NCC II), corpus cardiacum (CC), nervus allatosuboesophagealis (NS), nervus corporis allati (NCA), corpus allatum (CA). Transsections of nerves supplying the corpora cardiaca and corpora allata in pregnant females at locations 1 and 2 resulted in inactivation of the ipsolateral corpus allatum. Operations at 3 and 4 had no effect on corpus allatum activity [after Engelmann (1957) and Engelmann and Lüscher (1957).]

Injection of extract containing oostatic hormone into ovariectomized *Musca domestica* increased the area of the corpus allatum indicating an inactivation of the glands (Adams, 1970).

4. Physiological Action of the Corpora Allata

There is no doubt that the cells of the corpora allata exhibit cyclic secretory activity and that these cycles are correlated with their "juvenile" or gonadotropic effects (Kaiser, 1949; Engelmann, 1962; Scharrer and von Harnack, 1958; Strangways-Dixon, 1961b). However, it is still uncertain whether their product is fully synthesized within their cells, or whether they transform or transmit the hormone they receive from the neurosecretory cells. It is generally agreed that their activating effect on the ovaries is not a specific property of corpus allatum hormone. Although its direct effect on the follicle cells (except in flies where a neurosecretory factor seems to act as the gonadotropin) can hardly be doubted (Joly, 1945), it has a more general effect on the composition of the *milieu intérieur*. This is partly due to its influence on distinct biochemical processes, partly to its effect on feeding behavior.

a. The Corpus Allatum Hormone in Relation to Metabolism. The chemical processes occurring within an organism will be referred to here as metabolism. Because all these chemical reactions are catalysed by enzymes, regulation of metabolism can only be obtained by a change in the enzymatic activities. Essentially the methods for selectively altering the metabolic rate are (1) by changing the activity of enzymes, either by a direct action on enzyme conformation or by a change in the permeability barriers resulting in an increased accessibility of substrates and (2) by changing the quantity of enzymes, e.g., as a result of the *de novo* synthesis of enzyme proteins (de Kort, 1971).

At the present time, the question of whether the CA secretes a hormone which influences general metabolism is no longer considered relevant. Neither the fact that oxygen consumption is stimulated by the corpus allatum in normal and castrated females of *Calliphora* (Thomsen, 1949; Thomsen and Hamburger, 1955), in the Colorado beetle (de Wilde and Stegwee, 1958), and in *Leucophaea* (e.g., Sägesser, 1960) nor the observation that allatectomy generally results in hypertrophy of fat-body cells (Thomsen, 1942; Day, 1943b; Weed-Pfeiffer, 1945; Vogt, 1947; Bodenstein, 1953; de Loof and Lagasse, 1970b) allows us to draw the conclusion that JH would influence a great variety of enzymes in a direct way.

In *Carausius* it has been found that after allatectomy, the blood sugar level is markedly lowered, and tissue carbohydrates are increased. Tissue lipids increase after the operation (L'Hélias, 1955). After allatectomy in *Melanoplus,* a marked accumulation of fats has been observed in the fat body. That this effect was not indirectly caused by lack of ovarian activity was shown by the fact that castration alone did not produce this change (Weed-Pfeiffer, 1945).

Day (1943b), in *Lucilia* and *Sarcophaga,* found the oenocytes to be small and their nuclei pycnotic after allatectomy. Vogt (1947) found similar effects in *Drosophila.* Thomsen (1956), in *Calliphora,* however, did not observe any change.

Stegwee *et al.* (1963) have shown that in *Leptinotarsa* one of the most marked effects of allatectomy is the disintegration of flight-muscle sarcosomes, and that these giant mitochondria are regenerated very shortly after reimplantation of active corpora allata. As respiratory chain enzymes are organized within these mitochondria, the effect on energy metabolism is considerable (de Kort, 1969).

While high corpus allatum activity stimulates both reproduction and flight-muscle development in the Colorado potato beetle, degeneration of these muscles is observed during reproduction in several other insects. In still other insects the flight muscles are unaffected (see de Kort, 1969).

In several insects both ovariectomy and allatectomy result in a rise of blood protein concentration and hypertrophy of the fat body. A gradual

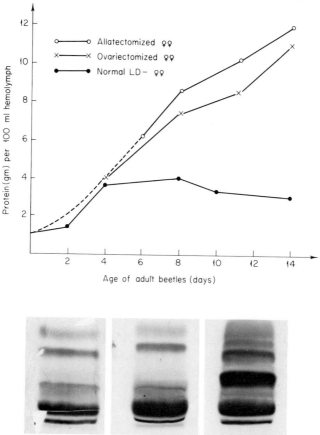

Normal ♀   Ovariectomized ♀   Allatectomized ♀

Fig. 6. Protein concentration (top) and protein pattern (bottom) of the hemolymph of normal, ovariectomized, and allatectomized Colorado beetle females, bred under long-day conditions (from de Loof, 1969).

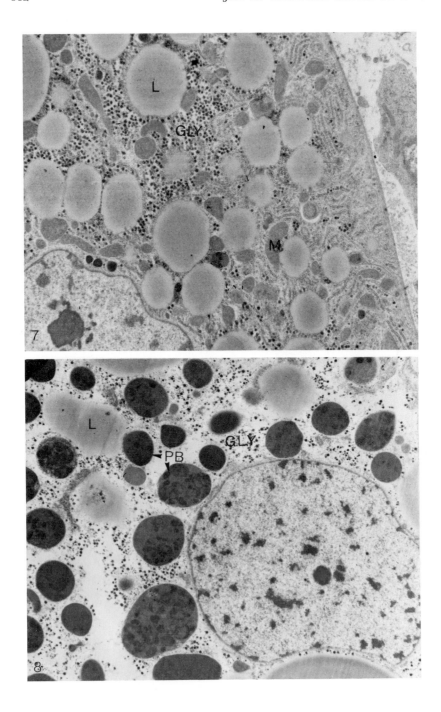

rise of total protein content of the hemolymph after allatectomy in female *Schistocerca* (Highnam *et al.,* 1963) and *Locusta* (Minks, 1967) has been established. As Minks has shown, this rise is mainly due to the accumulation of a protein synthesized in the fat body, and which is not especially vitellogenic. After ovariectomy the total protein content of the blood rises to a similar degree (12% as compared with 6% in the controls), but this is due to a protein other than that which accumulates after allatectomy.

Even more pronounced differences were found in the Colorado potato beetle. Although both allatectomy and ovariectomy result in a rise in blood protein concentration to 11% and the fat body hypertrophies after both operations, the basic causes are very different. After ovariectomy especially the vitellogenic female protein accumulates, while after allatectomy the rise of blood protein concentration is due to "diapause proteins" or "short-day proteins," the synthesis of which is apparently repressed by juvenile hormone (JH) (de Loof and de Wilde, 1970a,b) (Fig. 6). The ultrastructure of the fat body is substantially different in both cases. Ovariectomy results in accumulation of lipid droplets and glycogen but not of proteins. Allatectomy also causes lipid and glycogen deposition, but proteid bodies are deposited in large quantities and mitochondria are nearly absent (Figs. 7 and 8). Absence of JH seems to inhibit the development of mitochondria in the Colorado beetle (Stegwee *et al.,* 1963; de Kort, 1969; de Loof and Lagasse, 1970b).

Results of Lüscher *et al.* (1971) are in accordance with the above. They were able to show that in *Leucophaea* the JH is also responsible for the synthesis of a vitellogenic female protein but that it represses the synthesis of another protein. In these functions, JH could be replaced by farnesyl methylester.

It follows from the above data that the CA in several species modifies specific protein syntheses, both by inductive and repressive capacities. An attempt to integrate these activities with other endocrine effects is offered in Fig. 9.

The JH is involved in the synthesis of vitellogenins in *Rhodnius* (Coles, 1964, 1965a,b), *Leucophaea* (Engelmann and Penney,

---

Fig. 7. Ultrastructure of the fat body of an ovariectomized Colorado beetle female, bred under long-day conditions. Many lipid droplets (L) and glycogen particles (GLY) are stored. Mitochondria (M) are numerous [from de Loof and Lagasse (1970b).]

Fig. 8. Ultrastructure of the fat body of an allatectomized Colorado beetle female, bred under long-day conditions. Aside from lipids (L) and glycogen (GLY), also many proteid bodies (PB) are deposited. Mitochondria are nearly absent [from de Loof and Lagasse (1970b).]

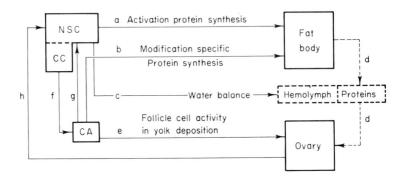

Fig. 9. Schematic representation of endocrine relations in adult locusts (from Minks, 1967).

1966; Engelmann, 1965b, 1969, 1971; Scheurer, 1969), *Sarcophaga* (Wilkens, 1967a) *Periplaneta* (Adiyodi and Nayar 1967, and *Nauphoeta* (Lüscher, 1968a).

b. Effects on Feeding Behavior. That the corpus allatum may influence oogenesis indirectly by its effect on feeding behavior has been shown in a most remarkable way by Strangways-Dixon (1961b) with *Calliphora.* The corpora allata of this fly go through cycles of activity, associated with the periodical synchronous formation of a batch of eggs in the ovarioles (Fig. 10). In the initial phase of oogenesis, these flies, when given the choice between carbohydrate and protein food, have a preference for sugar solutions. At the same time, the corpora allata show a maximum of secretory activity. Later in the cycle, this activity is lowered, and the flies obtain a preference for proteinaceous diets. This is correlated with the last phase of oogenesis, during which protein yolk is deposited by the follicles. Preference for sugar appears to be related quantitatively to the level of corpus allatum hormone. Allatectomy results in a sustained preference for protein food.

In *Leptinotarsa,* allatectomy results in the typical behavior pattern associated with diapause. Feeding activity ceases after some days, and after entering the soil the beetle becomes immobile. It need hardly be emphasized that the metabolic level is profoundly affected by this change in behavior.

5. Significance of the Neurosecretory Cells (NSC) and the Corpora Cardiaca

a. The Median Neurosecretory Cells. In most insects so far studied, the protocerebral neurosecretory cells are indispensable for oogenesis. They perform their function either by activating the corpora allata, by stimulating protein synthesis, which is a prerequisite to proteid yolk formation, or by producing a true gonadotropic hormone, as has been stated for *Sarcophaga* (Wilkens, 1968).

Destruction or extirpation of the NSC in the pars intercerebralis results in failure to mature oocytes in *Calliphora* (Thomson, 1948, 1952; Possompès, 1956), *Schistocerca gregaria* (Highnam, 1962a,b,c; Hill, 1962), *Aedes taeniorrhynchus* (Lea, 1964, 1967), *Tenebrio* (Mordue, 1965b), *Schistocerca paranensis* (Strong, 1965a,b), *Gomphocerus rufus* (Loher, 1965, 1966a,b), *Anacridium* (Geldiay, 1965, 1967), *Locusta migratoria* (Girardie, 1966), *Aedes aegypti* (Lea, 1967), *Sarcophaga* (Wilkens, 1967a, 1968), *Leptinotarsa* (de Wilde and de Boer, 1969), *Carausius* (Mouton, 1971).

This does not necessarily mean, however, that the NSC control egg maturation in a direct way. In most of the insects cited above cauterization of the NSC results in a lowered food intake which will result in a low protein concentration in the hemolymph and cessation of oocyte maturation. It also may interfere with diuresis, with similar results.

Therefore, the relation between NSC and oogenesis can only be studied properly if NSC cauterization has been carried out in such a way that it neither lowers food intake, nor disturbs diuresis. In experiments with *Schistocerca* (Hill, 1965) and *Leptinotarsa* (de Wilde and de Boer,

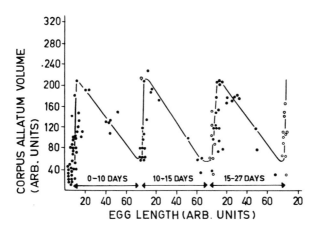

Fig. 10. Cyclic changes in corpus allatum volume, in relation to the reproductive cycle in *Calliphora* (after Strangways-Dixon. 1961b). ● normal measurements; ○ oocytes adjacent to mature eggs.

1969) these conditions were fulfilled, and an effect of the medial neurosecretory cells (MNSC) on oogenesis established. In the case of *Schistocerca,* this is explained by a direct effect on the synthesis of vitellogenic proteins (Highnam, 1962a,b), in *Leptinotarsa* by an effect, partly on the fat body, in conjunction with the corpus allatum (vitellogenic protein synthesis), partly via the corpus allatum on the terminal oocyte (de Loof and de Wilde, 1970b; de Loof and Lagasse, 1970a). In *Schistocerca,* the juvenile hormone is merely considered as being the gonadotropic hormone.

In the experiments of Thomsen and Möller (1963), concerning the relationship between NSC and intestinal protease activity in *Calliphora,* the effect on food intake may have been a factor of importance.

There are only a few insects in which the NSC do not appear to be necessary for oogenesis. Oogenesis can be induced in isolated abdomens of *Rhodnius* (Wigglesworth, 1936, 1948) and *Leucophaea* (Chambers and Brookes, 1967) merely by implantation of active CA or by injection of synthetic Röller juvenile hormone (Bell and Barth, 1970). Adult females of *Pieris brassicae,* in which a ligature has been placed behind the head or the thorax early in adult life, started oogenesis after implantation of an active CA or application of farnesol analogues (Karlinsky, 1967a). Removal of the neurosecretory A cells in *Oncopeltus* merely results in reduced fecundity. In *Leucophaea* and *Rhodnius,* the NSC do not activate the CA. In these insects the CA hormone seems to regulate protein metabolism associated with vitellogenesis (Engelmann, 1970).

Comparable experiments with isolated abdomens of other insects have yielded different results. Untreated isolated pupal abdomens of the moth *Malacosoma pluviale,* showed very little ovariole development; topical application of farnesyl methyl ether to these abdomens blocked ovarian and adult development completely. Both activities were stimulated by injection of ecdysone (Sahota, 1969). In isolated abdomens of 2-day-old pupae of *Galleria mellonella* normal ovarial development takes place only when both a prothoracic gland and a brain had been implanted (Dutkowski and Przelecka, 1969). The need for ecdysone seems unusual, but we may not forget that in the above-mentioned moths ovarian development occurs in the pupal stage.

Experiments with Diptera, especially those performed by Thomsen and associates (Thomsen and Hamburger, 1955; Thomsen and Möller, 1963; Thomsen and Thomsen, 1970) with *Calliphora erythrocephala,* by Orr (1964a,b) with *Phormia regina,* and by Wilkens (1967a,b, 1968, 1969) with *Sarcophaga bullata* showed that the NSC are of considerable importance for oogenesis.

From her experiments with *Calliphora,* Thomsen concludes an influence of the NSC on protein metabolism, but according to Wilkens (1969), in *Sarcophaga,* the CA regulates vitellogenic protein synthesis, whereas neurosecretion by the pars intercerebralis provides a gonadotropic hormone.

The neurosecretory cells can be subdivided into Gomori-positive and Gomori-negative cells based on their reactivity towards specific histological stains as paraldehyde fuchsine and chrome hematoxylin. A further subdivision can be made on the basis of their affinity for counterstains. Moreover, with the electron microscope several types of secretory granules are found, some of which are sometimes present within the same NSC. Classifications have been proposed based on these parameters. It is not possible to correlate the histological signs of neurosecretory cell activity with egg development in *Leucophaea* (Engelmann, 1957), *Oncopeltus* (Johansson, 1958c), and *Schistocerca paranensis* (Strong, 1965a). In other insects, such as *Carausius* and *Clitumnus* (Dupont-Raabe, 1952), *Tenebrio* (Arvy and Gabe, 1953), *Apis mellifera* (Formigoni, 1956), *Carausius* (Herlant-Meeuwis and Paquet, 1956), *Kalotermes* (Noiret, 1957), *Iphita* (Nayar, 1958b), *Schistocerca gregaria* (Highnam and Haskell, 1964), *Tenebrio* (Mordue, 1965a), *Calliphora* (Bloch *et al.,* 1966), and *Polistes* (Strambi, 1967), a distinct correlation between oocyte maturation and the amount of stainable material in the NSC is found. However, one must be careful in using the amount of stainable material in NSC as a parameter of secretory activity. The amount of secretory granules in a NSC is a steady state governed by the rates of production and transport. A cell completely filled with granules may be inactive, because release is low (Highnam, 1962a,b; Highnam and Lusis, 1962; Schooneveld, 1970), or may, in other cases, reflect a high degree of activity (Dupont-Raabe, 1952; Herlant-Meeuwis and Paquet, 1956; Noirot, 1957). A very active cell which releases the granules immediately after their synthesis in the Golgi complexes will appear empty. A cell full of stainable neurosecretory material may result from a lack of release of material or from synthesis occurring in excess of release.

In recent years a few detailed studies appeared which clearly showed that both the juvenile hormone and an unknown hormone from the NSC are necessary for vitellogenesis in *Schistocerca* (Highnam, 1962a,b), in *Aedes taeniorrhynchus* (Lea, 1964, 1967), *Locusta* (Girardie, 1966), *Locusta* (Minks, 1967, *Sarcophaga* (Wilkens, 1967a, 1968, 1969), and *Leptinotarsa* (de Loof and de Wilde, 1970b). In the Colorado beetle both hormones are necessary for the synthesis of the vitellogenic female protein, the most important proteid yolk precursor in the hemolymph. In none of these studies have separate effects of both hormones been completely classified.

It follows from the above data that it is not yet possible to draw a unitarian picture of the role of neurosecretory hormones in insect oogenesis. It would seem that variations occur according to developmental and physiological differences between the species. It would, however, seem that the scheme given in Fig. 9, which is taken from Minks (1967), is valid for many more insect species than *Locusta migratoria*, for which it was originally drawn.

b. The Corpora Cardiaca. The release of neurosecretory hormone from the corpora cardiaca is the final phase of hemocoelic neurosecretion. The activity of the neurosecretory cells and the liberation of their product by the neurohemal end organ should not be confused. In fact, continuous secretory activity may be observed in the perikarya, while at the same time the releasing function of the corpora cardiaca is intermittent and is influenced by sensory and electric stimulation.

In *Schistocerca*, blood protein concentration rises in females brought into contact with males and in females subjected to enforced activity. This correlates with a rapid release of neurosecretory material from the Corpora cardiaca. The system may also be induced to release its contents by electric stimulation of the central nervous system. This suggests that the release is under nervous control. Increase in the level of blood protein is followed by proteid yolk formation in the ovaries. Removal of the medial neurosecretory cell causes blood protein to be lowered, but it rises rapidly after implantation of corpora cardiaca (Highnam, 1962a,b). However, these experiments still do not preclude an indirect control of ovarian activity via the corpora allata, nor do the experiments of Thomsen (1952) who, after extirpation of medial neurosecretory cells in *Calliphora*, found that implantation of corpora cardiaca may replace the function of these cells. Lüscher (1968b) reported that the corpora cardiaca have a protective influence on oogenesis in *Nauphoeta cinerea*. De Loof (1969) also found that, following allato-cardiacectomy, resorption of the oocytes started about 3 days earlier than after extirpation of the CA alone. In *Hyalophora cecropia*, the increase in oviposition rate following mating is due to a hormone which is produced by the intrinsic cells of the corpora cardiaca (Truman and Riddiford, 1971).

6. The Role of Molting Hormone in Initiating Ovary Development

As already mentioned on p. 116, ecdysone seems to be necessary for oogenesis in several Lepidoptera, such as *Malacosoma pluviale* (Sahota, 1969) and *Galleria mellonella* (Dutkowski and Przelecka, 1969). The initial differentiation of the ovary of *Iphita limbata* will not occur unless it remains in an environment deprived of the juvenile hormone for a short period, a phenomenon that could be qualified as a "sensitizing process." This is needed for the ovary to respond to the vitellogenic action of the hormone from the corpus allatum. Ecdysone acting in the absence of juvenile hormone is known to initiate full realization of adult characters. This apparently included those of the female gonads (Nayar, 1969). Recently Spielman *et al.* (1971) reported that in *Aedes aegypti*, *Culex pipiens*, and *Anopheles quadrimaculatus*, ovarian development may be stimulated by exogenous ecdysonelike compounds which are found in various plants. Ecdysone analogues increase fecundity of blood-starved mosquitoes but these compounds have a negative effect when blood meals are abundant. The effect of ecdysone in oogenesis cannot occur until 2 days after the adult molt. The generally accepted source of growth hormone in insects are the prothoracic glands which disappear during metamorphosis, but it is also presumed (Romer, 1971) that an additional source may be found in the oenocytes.

Experiments by Plugfelder (1969), in which supernumerary amounts of corpora allata were implanted in the last larval instar of *Carausius*, showed that in those individuals which matured after a few extra larval molts, oogenesis is disturbed on the level of both vitellogenesis and chorion formation. The malfunction of the follicle cells may be explained in the same was as above for *Iphita*. Laverdure (1970a,b) found that in *Tenebrio*, both *in vivo* and *in vitro*, the differentiation of the transistory zone and vitellarium formation, but also the growth of the oocyte, is ensured by ecdysone. A higher titer of ecdysone is needed for the continuation of differentiation than for starting oocyte growth. Ecdysone has to act on the ovary throughout maturation. The cephalic complex is not directly involved in vitellogenesis but stimulates the prothoracic glands. When farnesyl methyl ester is simultaneously added with ecdysone to the culture medium, the ovary no longer responds to the stimulating action of the prothoracic gland hormone. A dose of 5 μg of methylester of farnesol per ml culture medium has no action at all on ovary development. In *Calliphora*, growth of the oocyte is not regulated by hormones but for the differentiation the cerebral complex together with the ring gland is necessary (Leloup, 1970).

7. Sterilizing Effects of Juvenile Hormone and Its Mimetics

In their experiments leading to the discovery of the "paper factor" juvabione, Slăma and Williams (1966) observed that this substance, when applied to larvae of Pyrrhocoridae, induces either permanent larvae or sterile adults. Applied to adult females, it induces sterility. Subsequently, Masner *et al.* (1968) found that, upon application of this substance or of the "Law and Williams mixture" to males, a sufficient amount is transmitted in a veneric way to induce sterility in females during subsequent matings. Slăma and Williams (1966) with the egg of *Pyrrhocoris,* and Riddiford (1970) with the egg of *Hyalophora,* found that early application of JH or mimetics has an ovicidal effect.

Most of the above results have recently been confirmed in a variety of insects and with a large number of JH mimetics (Sorm, 1971; Riddiford, 1971; Bowers, 1971). It is now possible to classify these effects into the following categories:

a. Application to Larva or Pupa. Disturbance of metamorphosis, resulting in either an extra larval or pupal instar or a metatethelic pupa or adult. In the last-mentioned case, the development of the gonads has been partly or completely suppressed. As a result, no eggs are produced or merely fragments are deposited (see Chapter 6 of this volume).

b. Application to Adult Females. Repression of developmental information in the eggs beyond the stage of blastoderm formation, resulting in a standstill of embryogenesis at this phase (Riddiford, 1970, 1971).

c. Application to Adult Male. Transmission of the substance to female(s) during mating, with the above effect.

d. Application to the Newly Deposited Egg. Disturbance of developmental programming beyond the stage of blastokinesis, resulting in lethal organizational defects.

8. Control of Accessory Gland Activity

As we have seen before (Chapter 2), the secretions of accessory glands are largely of mucoproteid nature. It is therefore of considerable interest that in female *Melanoplus* (Weed-Pfeiffer, 1936), *Leucophaea* (Scharrer, 1946; Engelmann, 1957), *Rhodnius* (Wigglesworth, 1936), *Calliphora* (Thomsen, 1942) and *Gomphocerus* (Hartmann, 1971), [but not in *Lucilia* and *Sarcophaga* (Day, 1943b)], the development and secretory activity of the accessory glands are stimulated by the corpora allata (Fig. 11). Shaaya and Bodenstein (1969) found that juvenile hormone influences protein and protocatechuic acid synthesis in the accessory sex glands in *Periplaneta americana.*

B. REBOUND EFFECTS

Feedback mechanisms are a general feature in endocrine regulations. It is, therefore, not a matter of surprise that in the control of insect repro-

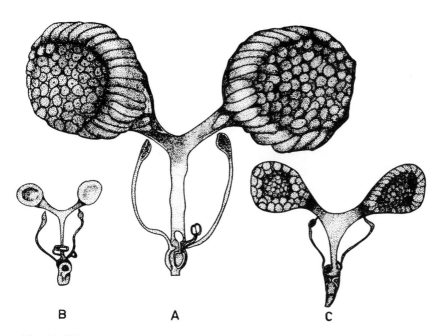

Fig. 11. Effect of maturation and allatectomy on ovaries and accessory glands in *Calliphora* (after Thomsen, 1942.) A, sexually mature female; B, newly emerged female; C, female after allatectomy.

duction the activity of subordinated organs such as the ovaries influences the function of the superordinated endocrine system.

The results of Nayar (1958b) with the bug *Iphita limbata* point to a direct participation of the ovaries in the controlling mechanism. After injection of aqueous extract from active ovaries containing mature eggs into females with a beginning of oogenesis, egg development was stopped in the latter, and signs of degeneration were observed. Such extracts, curiously enough, seem to promote the release of neurosecretory material by the corpora cardiaca and at the same time inhibit the corpus allatum. Ovarian activity is cyclical in this case.

Adams *et al.* (1968) reported that in *Musca domestica* the penultimate oocyte does not develop to maturity until the terminal oocyte had been transformed into an ovarian egg and deposited. This inhibition appears to be controlled by a hormone, released by the ovary, which was referred to as "oostatic hormone." The oostatic hormone inhibits the release of JH from the CA and thus indirectly affects yolk deposition in young oocytes (Adams, 1970) .

In *Lucilia cuprina,* a feedback mechanism regulates the total number and stage of development of the ovarian follicles in each ovariole (Fig. 12).

1. The mature ovum produces an oostatic hormone which prevents growth of the penultimate follicle either directly or via the corpus allatum.

2. Two yolkless follicles produce a substance which inhibits germarial activity.

3. A protein meal breaks (1) so that the penultimate oocyte resumes growth and yolk deposition may occur.

4. The corpus cardiacum is stimulated by a protein meal to release neurosecretory material.

5. The neurosecretory material stimulates the follicle cells to participate in vitellogenesis (Clift, 1971).

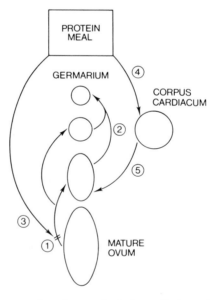

Fig. 12. Schematic representation of control of the cyclical ovarian development in *Lucilia cuprina.* Mature ovum produces oostatic hormone which prevents growth of penultimate follicle. (2) Two yolkless follicles produce a substance which inhibits germarial activity. (3) A protein meal breaks (1) so that the penultimate oocyte resumes growth and yolk deposition may occur. (4) The corpus cardiacum is stimulated by a protein meal to release neurosecretory material which (5) stimulates the follicle cells to adopt the configuration required for vitellogenesis. Once some yolk deposition has occurred, the one yolkless follicle may not be able to produce enough inhibitor to prevent germarial activity (from Clift, 1971).

Several authors have suggested that the size of the corpora allata correlates positively with their activity. Parameters such as glandular volume, nuclear volume, or the ratio cytoplasm/nucleus of the CA cells has been correlated with the intensity of several presumedly subordinated processes. Only few authors (Odhiambo, 1966a,b; Thomsen and Thomsen, 1970; Scharrer, 1971; Panov and Bassurmanova, 1970) paid attention to the ultrastructure of the glands; the subcellular organization very well reflects gland activity.

There is no doubt that in several insects the corpora allata also go through periodic fluctuations as judged by the above parameters. Fluctuations have been observed in the Dictyoptera, *Leucophaea maderae* (Engelmann, 1957, 1959, 1960; Engelmann and Lüscher, 1956; Scharrer, 1961; Scharrer and von Harnack, 1958; Lüscher and Engelmann, 1955), *Diploptera punctata* (Engelmann, 1959), and *Periplaneta americana* (Mills *et al.*, 1966). In the phasmid *Carausius morosus* (Plugfelder 1937); in the Orthoptera, *Trichopterus* (Cazal and Guerrier, 1946), *Locusta migratoria migratorioides* (Joly, 1958; Highnam and Haskell, 1964; Cassier, 1965a,b,c; Fain-Maurel and Cassier, 1969; Johnson, 1971, Fig. 16), *Locusta migratoria manilensis* (Quo, 1965), *Schistocerca gregaria* (Highnam, 1962a,c; Highnam and Haskell, 1964), *Gryllus* (Huignard, 1964), *Gomphocerus rufus* (Loher, 1965), *Schistocerca* sp. (Strong, 1965a,b), and *Euthystira brachyptera* (Müller, 1965); in the Coleoptera, *Dytiscus marginalis* (Joly, 1948, 1950), *Hydrophilus* (Kaiser, 1954), *Nebria brevicollis* (Ganagarajah, 1965) and *Galeruca tanaceti* (Siew, 1965b); in the Lepidoptera, *Galleria mellonella* (Röller, 1962) and *Leucania separata* (Tsiu-Ngun and Quo, 1963); in the Diptera, *Calliphora erythrocephala* (Thomsen, 1942; Strangways-Dixon, 1961b, 1962; Lea and Thomsen, 1969), *Drosophila* (Vogt, 1943), *Sarcophaga serucifera* (Day, 1943b), *Sarcophaga bullata* (Wilkens, 1967a), *Melophagus ovinus* (Day, 1943a), *Culex molestus* (Larsen and Bodenstein, 1959), *Culex pipiens* (Larsen and Bodenstein, 1959), and *Phormia regina* (Orr, 1964b); in the Hemiptera, *Rhodnius prolixus* (Wigglesworth, 1936, 1948), *Oncopeltus fasciatus* (Johansson, 1954, 1958a), *Iphita limbata* (Nayar, 1958b), *Drepanosiphum platanoides* (Dixon, 1963), *Chrysocoris purpureus* (Nair, 1963), and *Pyrrhocoris apterus* (Slăma, 1946b,c); in the Hymenoptera, *Apis mellifera* (Plugfelder, 1948; Lukoschus, 1956) and *Bombus* (Palm, 1949).

The corpora allata most often seem to need their connections with the central nervous system to perform this cyclic activity, which has been reported to disappear when these connections are severed [Plugfelder (1937, 1939) with *Carausius*; Engelmann and Lüscher (1956) and En-

gelmann (1957) with *Leucophaea;* Engelmann (1959) with *Diploptera*]
or to become asynchronized (Engelmann, 1962, with *Leucophaea*).

The interpretation of these data in terms of feedback mechanism is a
matter of great caution; Johansson (1958), with *Oncopeltus,* concludes
that "growth of the corpus allatum and its production of hormone seem
to be controlled in two different ways." Staal (1961), with *Locusta,* submits that "the growth of the corpora allata in normal individuals and the
gradual increase in secretory activity during development are two different processes." Mordue (1965a,b,c) comparing the secretory activity of
the CA and egg production in mated and unmated *Tenebrio,* comes to
similar conclusions. As in vertebrates, the essential processes in the
trophic activity of the nervous system in insects are greatly ignored.

At first sight, castration experiments seem to be most suitable to elucidate rebound effects in reproduction. Thomsen (1942) observed a
significant increase in corpus allatum volume after castration in female *Calliphora.* This was confirmed by Strangways-Dixon (1961a) who found
that this increase is already obvious 3 days after castration. Day (1943b)
in *Lucilia,* Weed-Pfeiffer (1945) in *Melanoplus,* Bodenstein (1947) in
Drosophila, Wigglesworth (1948) in *Rhodnius,* and von Harnack and
Scharrer (1956) in *Leucophaea* obtained similar effects. These results
indicate that active ovaries have a restraining function on the corpora allata. Strangways-Dixon (1961b) suggests that the hypertrophied corpora

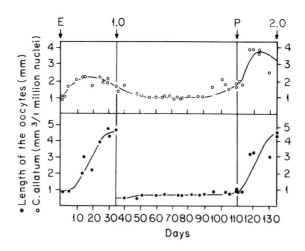

Fig. 13. Morphometric changes of corpora allata correlated with growth of terminal
oocytes in *Leucophaea* during two successive egg maturation periods (after Engelmann,
1960). E, emergence; P, parturition; 1.0, first ovulation; 2.0 second ovulation.

allata are a consequence of hyperactivation by unusually high concentrations of yolk precursors which are mobilized and, in the absence of ovaries, remain in the blood. This would mean that the castration effect is indirect.

A decrease in corpus allatum area following ovariectomy was observed in *Musca domestica* (Adams, 1970). According to this author a small CA releases hormone whereas a large gland stores hormone. No hypertrophy of the CA was found in ovariectomized grasshoppers *Schistocerca* (Highnam, 1962b), *Locusta* (Joly, 1964), and *Gomphocerus* (Loher, 1965, 1966b). Evidently, our knowledge of circulation and of neuroendocrine interactions is insufficient to explain these contradictory results.

Lea and Thomsen (1969), observing the response of the median neurosecretory cell nuclei of the host to an implanted CA, came to the conclusion that in *Calliphora* the activity of the glands was not correlated with either the size of the glands or egg maturation.

Special conditions exist in viviparous roaches, where it is a matter of necessity that ovarian function is arrested during the development of embryos in the brood sac (Fig. 13). In *Leucophaea* and *Diploptera* during this period, which may last several months, the brain restrains the activity of the corpora allata by way of the nervi corporis allati (see also Section I, A, 3). In addition, there are indications that humoral factors are involved. In *Leucophaea,* the inhibition may be released at any time by removal of the egg cases from the brood sac. The stimuli they exert are mechanical, and are transmitted to the brain via the ventral nerve cord. They probably enter the cord in the last abdominal synganglion. Severance of the ventral nerve cord also released inhibition, but with a significantly longer delay than that observed after egg case removal.

The now unrestrained corpora allata then show cycles of activity correlated with waves of oogenesis. The same is true for implanted, isolated corpora allata. This suggests a hormonal feedback effect by the activated ovaries in the manner described. In *Diploptera,* the presence of eggs in the brood sac is apparently not the factor inhibiting the corpora allata; moreover, no suggestion is available as to the nature of this factor.

On the other hand, it is suggested that the stimuli provided by the hatching young normally provide the sign for renewed activity of the corpora allata (Engelmann, 1957, 1959, 1960, 1962; Fig. 14).

Another physiological criterion is the concentration of hemolymph proteins. Corpora allata seem to be more active in insects with a high blood protein titer.

In the Colorado potato beetle the blood protein level in ovariectomized females amounts to 11% as against 3.5% in normal long-day treated females (de Loof and de Wilde, 1970a). In short-day treated females, in which the CA are very small, the blood protein concentration also rises to 11%.

In these investigations, the titer of juvenile hormone in the hemolymph was measured, which would seem to provide the most direct information of CA activity. But again, this method is not without its objections, as a hormone titer is a steady-state governed by both the rates of production

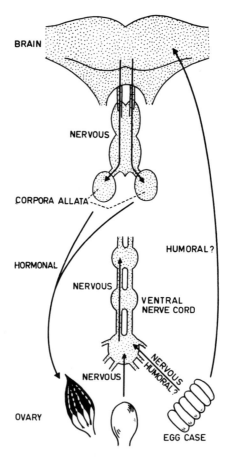

Fig. 14. Diagram illustrating the reproductive cycle and its control in *Leucophaea* (after Engelmann, 1962). Mating impulses are transmitted via the ventral nerve cord to the protocerebrum, resulting in a release of corpus allatum activity and subsequent induction of follicular activity. During pregnancy, the corpora allata are inhibited, presumably by a nervous and humoral mechanism emerging from egg cases present in the blood sac.

and breakdown (de Wilde *et al.*, 1971). Be that as it may, the JH titer in ovariectomized females was 7200 *Galleria* units/ml (G. U./ml); in the control (long-day) females, 2000 G. U./ml, which appears to confirm the correlation (Fig. 15). How to explain the high blood protein concen-

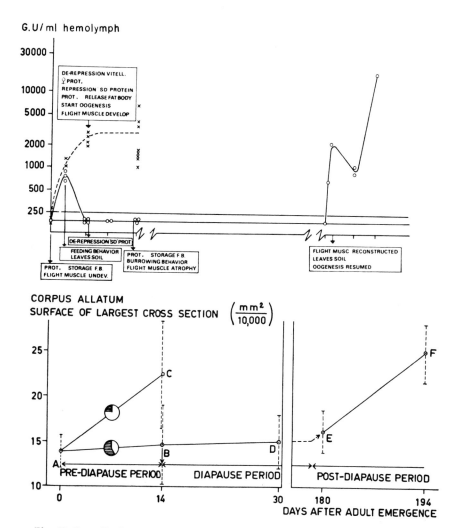

Fig. 15. Juvenile hormone (JH) titer (above) and corpus allatum size (below) in the adult female *Leptinotarsa* (after de Wilde *et al.*, 1968). Some physiological phenomena are indicated near the respective hormone titers. Dashed line represents the titer in long-day treated females. Solid line represents the titer in short-day treated adults (from de Wilde *et al.*, 1971).

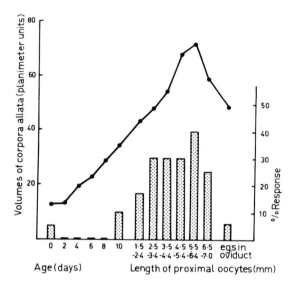

Fig. 16. The changes in the volumes of the corpora allata and the presence of juvenile hormone in the hemolymph of adult female *Locusta* during somatic growth and the first ovarian cycle. The small black bars indicate 100% negative results (courtesy of Johnson, 1971).

tration in short-day (SD) females, in which the JH titer is near to zero? In SD females the vitellogenic female protein is absent and the high protein content is due to specific "short-day proteins," which are only synthesized when JH is absent (de Loof and de Wilde, 1970b) (Fig. 6). When there is a correlation between CA activity and protein concentration, only specific yolk precursor proteins may be involved.

Recent work on *Leptinotarsa* has made it possible to compare the different physiological parameters involved in reproduction and diapause with CA dimensions, as shown in Fig. 15. In Fig. 16 the correlation between CA volume and JH titer in adult *Locusta* females is represented (Johnson, 1971).

C. Gonotropic Dissociation

As Swellengrebel (1929) was the first to point out, during hibernation nutritive activity continues but ovarian activity is arrested in *Anopheles maculipennis*. This phenomenon was given the name *gonotrophic dissociation*. It is distinguished from diapause, as exhibited, for example, in other *Anopheles* and *Culex* species, by the fact that in these last instances feeding activity is arrested and metabolism as a whole remains at a low level. In gonotrophic dissociation, as in diapause, mosquitoes show an enlarged fat body.

It is known that in anautogenous mosquitoes such as *Anopheles maculipennis,* ovarian activity depends on food intake. Apparently, during hibernation this mechanism is put out of action, presumably by an inhibitory effect on the corpus allatum. This inhibition is induced by short photoperiods and intermediate temperatures (Vinogradova, 1958).

D. ADULT DIAPAUSE

Gonotrophic dissociation also prevails during prediapause feeding of adult insects with normal diapause, but here it is a transient phase resulting in complete arrest of activity. Only a few studies deal in more detail with the state of the ovaries during adult diapause and their endocrine control.

In *Macrodytes* (Joly, 1945) the polytrophic ovarioles constantly pass down oocytes enveloped in their follicles during diapause, accompanied by trophocytes. A series of about eleven oocytes is formed, which gradually increases in size. The most caudal oocyte, measuring 1–2 mm, is resorbed by its follicle which then forms a corpus luteum ("zone of autolyzing residues").

This apparently occurs at the stage where the oocyte is disconnected from its accompanying trophocytes and alimentary egg formation becomes exclusively a function of the follicle and of the oocyte itself.

Implantation of ten pairs of active corpora allata in diapausing females induces normal egg development and subsequent oviposition.

Allatectomy in active, ovipositing females after a delay of 2 weeks results in an irregular degeneration of oocytes in different stages of vitellogenesis, and after several months, in a regressive development of the ovarioles. In fact, only the germarium retains its normal size.

It thus would seem that, during diapause in *Macrodytes,* the corpora allata are not completely inactive. This is supported by the fact that during the reproductive season the corpora allata have a cyclic activity associated with periodic oosorption of the terminal oocyte in a similar way as during diapause. Apparently, during this period, the activity of the corpus allatum is at its minimum.

In *Leptinotarsa,* in the telotrophic ovary the vitellarium is inactive during diapause. The complete syndrome of diapause, including a change from feeding behavior to burrowing and subterranean rest, the degeneration of the flight muscles, the cessation of oogenesis, the synthesis of a specific diapause protein in the hemolymph, and the much reduced rate of oxygen consumption is produced by allatectomy. Subsequent implantation of one or two pairs of active corpora allata completely restores the active condition. It follows that during diapause in this insect, the corpora allata are nonfunctioning (de Wilde and Stegwee, 1958; de Wilde *et al.*, 1959; de Wilde and de Boer, 1961, 1969; de Loof and de Wilde, 1970b). The state of diapause in this insect is accompanied by an extremely low activity of many types of neurosecretory cells (A, A_1, C, L, and SOG-A NSC). Also histologically the involuted state of the corpora allata is remarkable (Schooneveld, 1970). Similar conditions have been observed in other beetles with a photoperiodically controlled imaginal diapause, e.g., *Galeruca tanaceti* (Siew, 1965a,b,c) and *Hypera postica* (Tombes, 1966; Tombes and Bodenstein, 1967; Tombes and Smith, 1966). Also in *Anacridium* (Geldiay, 1967), when diapause is induced by short photoperiods, the neurosecretory A cells do not seem to release their hormone. In *Nomadacris,* where diapause is also under photoperiodic control (Norris, 1962), the corpora allata cease to be active (Strong, 1967), as judged by their involuted state. The evidence seems to favor the idea that the primary failure is that of the neurosecretory cells, and that this failure is responsible for the inactive state of the corpora allata. Indeed, diapause in *Leptinotarsa* could be induced by cauterization of the pars intercerebralis, and this condition was at least temporarily reversed by implantation of active CA–CC complexes (de Wilde and de Boer, 1969). According to the histological pattern, in *Leptinotarsa,* grown under short-day conditions, the rate of inactivation of the neurosecretory cells and corpus allatum is strongest in the second half of the prediapause period, characterized by a decrease in the rate of O_2 consumption and marked changes in the enzyme pattern of the flight muscles (El-Ibrashi, 1965; de Kort, 1969). Further decrease in activity of these centers occurs gradually, and only after several months of diapause has the release of NS-A material come to a nearly complete standstill (Schooneveld, 1970). It follows that the complex physiological syndrome is gradually induced when neurosecretory and JH titers sink below critical levels. This also follows from the JH titer in the hemolymph, which shows an initial rise after emergence, even in short-day beetles, but subsequently sinks to an immeasurable level (Fig. 15).

The central role of the juvenile hormone in adult diapause of *Hypera* and *Leptinotarsa* has also been confirmed by applications of JH and its mimetics. In *Hypera postica,* Bowers and Blickenstaff (1966) have been able to break aestivation diapause and induce egg maturation by external application of *trans, trans*-10,11-expoxyfarnesenic acid methylester. The same result with this substance and with the synthetic *dl*-juvenile hormone have been obtained by de Wilde (1969) in *Leptinotarsa.*

At the level of ovarian activity, gonotrophic dissociation, phasic castration (see Section IV, B, 1), and adult diapause probably are all cases of "pseudo-allatectomy" (see Section I, E, 3), but the syndrome may depend on specific neuroendocrine deficiencies. Also, it is now increasingly clear that in different species, the effector systems may respond in a very different way to the presence or absence of one and the same hormone.

E. ENVIRONMENTAL CONTROL OF OOGENESIS

1. Photoperiod

Adult diapause has been shown to be under photoperiodic control in many cases, e.g., *Leptinotarsa* (de Wilde, 1954, 1962a), *Psylla pyri* (Bonnemaison and Missonnier, 1955); *Stenocranus minutus* (Müller, 1957), *Ceutorrynchus pleurostigma* (autumnal race) (Ankersmit, 1961), *Nomadacris septemfasciata* (Norris, 1959), *Psyllioides* (Ankersmit, 1961), *Coccinella septempunctata* (Hodek and Cerkasov, 1961), *Anthonomus*

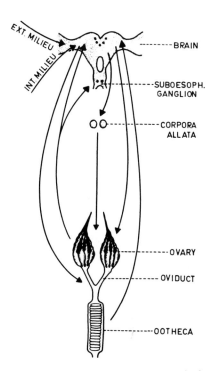

Fig. 17. Neuroendocrine integration by the brain in control of reproductive processes in adult female insects (according to Scharrer, 1958).

grandis (Newsom, 1963), *Listroderes obliquus* (Newsom, 1963), *Galeruca tanaceti* (Siew, 1965a, *Hypera postica* (Tombes, 1966), and *Anacridium aegyptium* (Geldiay, 1967). It therefore seems highly probable that in these insects the photoperiod controls the function of the neurosecretory cells and the corpus allatum, as described in Section I, D. Since the corpora allata are controlled by the brain and subesophageal ganglion, the conclusion seems justified that this photoperiodic induction takes place in the central nervous system, presumably in the brain (de Wilde, 1962a, 1969, 1970), which may be considered to be the center of neuroendocrine integration (Scharrer, 1959; Fig. 17). In this respect, it is important to note that photoperiodic induction takes place in the absence of the compound eyes (de Wilde *et al.,* 1959) and that its site of action is in the brain (Lees, 1964; Williams and Adkisson, 1964).

Judging from experiments on pupal diapause in *Antheraea* the photoperiodic receptor is probably located in the side lobes of the brain (Williams, 1969).

2. Temperature

Temperature may have two types of effect on reproduction: a general and immediate effect through its influence on body temperature and sensory responses, and a signalized or "token" effect either by itself or by its interaction with photoperiod. These two aspects are present in many ecological factors.

Eurythermic insects with respect to reproduction are *Bruchus obtectus* (range 8°–40°C, optimum 21°–30°C) (Menusan, 1935) and *Panolis flammea* (range 8°–27°C, optimum 14°–18°C) (Zwölfer, 1931). Stenothermic insects with a very low optimum for reproduction are *Boreus hiemalis, Operophtera brumata,* and *Biorrhiza pallida (forma aptera),* all of which reproduce in the winter season with optima around 5°C. A high optimum is a characteristic for reproduction in *Schistocerca gregaria* and *Locusta migratoria* (32°–38°C), in *Thermobia domestica,* and in *Galleria mellonella* (± 37°C), which shares the optimum with the honey bee colony in which it parasitizes.

The general rule that high temperatures tend to avert short-day photoperiod induction holds for adult diapause in a long-day insect such as *Leptinotarsa,* which can display short-day responses within a range of 18°–30°C (Goryshin, 1958) and in a short-day insect such as the autummal race of *Ceuthorrhynchus pleurostigma* (Ankersmit, 1961).

Break of adult diapause in *Leptinotarsa* is promoted by temperatures but by temperatures above 30°C. This is not a typical "token" effect, since the same temperature allows for reactivation and reproduction (de **Wilde, 1957**).

3. Feeding and Nutrition

As oogenesis is a metabolic and synthetic activity with a high energy demand, it is evident that nutrition is a most important factor. A source of glucose and essential amino acids is generally needed. Multiple unsaturated fatty acids are necessary for reproduction in *Anthonomus grandis* (Vanderzant and Richardson, 1965) and in *Blattella germanica* (Gordon, 1959). The physiological effects of nutrition are discussed in Vol. V, Chapter 1. Next to these basic processes, the "token" stimuli provided by the food are a very important element in assuring the coincidence of oogenesis and oviposition with the necessary feeding substratum. These token effects often are mediated by the neuroendocrine system.

We have dealt earlier with the complicated relations between nutrition, endocrines, and reproductive organs in *Calliphora* (Strangways-Dixon, 1961a,b, 1962). This insect has a preference for sugar solutions in the initial phase of an oogenetic cycle, whereas later in the cycle, when proteid yolk is formed, it has a preference for proteinaceous diets.

These observations point to the eminent importance of neuroendocrine control of feeding behavior. In *Locusta* and *Schistocerca*, the frontal ganglion is the autonomous center controlling swallowing activity of the foregut. Removal of the frontal ganglion in adult *Locusta* results in a failure to undergo sexual maturation (Clarke and Langley, 1961, 1963a,b,c; Gillott, 1964; Clarke and Gillott, 1965), probably as a consequence of starvation. Feeding patterns exist in adult locusts (Hill *et al.*, 1966; Strong, 1967; Hill and Goldsworthy, 1968), but a direct relation between the activity of the frontal ganglion and oogenesis has not been proven.

In starved *Rhodnius* females (Wigglesworth, 1936) the function of the telotrophic ovary remains normal for some time only during nutrimentary egg formation by way of the nutritive strands. At the phase where these strands are normally interrupted and the follicle takes over, oosorption occurs.

Very much the same condition prevails in *Oncopeltus* (Johansson, 1958a). Here it has been proven that nutrition is primarily needed to activate the corpus allatum. If a starved female, or one that is only receiving glucose, is implanted with a corpus allatum from a fed female, egg production is resumed for some time. The endocrine condition in the newly starved female has been termed by Johansson "pseudoallatectomy," and such corpora allata are inhibited by the brain, presumably along the nervous pathway.

Extirpation of the median neurosecretory cells did not produce pseudoallatectomy, but as mentioned (see Section I, A, 2, a), in *Oncopeltus* neurosecretory material can be stored in the aorta wall, and this source probably was not depleted.

In *Leptinotarsa,* starvation or interrupted feeding has very much the same effect as allatectomy (de Wilde *et al.,* 1959; de Wilde and de Boer, 1961) or removal of the medial neurosecretory cells (de Wilde and de Boer, 1969), but here not only oosorption but the complete *diapause* syndrome is induced (Fig. 18).

Many adult insects, especially Coleoptera, must go through a period of *Reifungsfrass* before oogenesis will take place. Other species do not require this "maturation feeding" to initiate oogenesis, but the number of eggs produced is much influenced by proper nutrition.

Both conditions prevail in mosquitoes, in which several species or races develop eggs without nutrition being required (autogenous forms), and others only start oogenesis after blood meal (anautogenous forms). In both forms, adult nutrition influences fecundity both qualitatively and quantitatively (Roubaud and Mezger, 1934; Woke, 1937; Yeoli and Mer, 1938). It appears that, in anautogenous mosquitoes, feeding induces ovarian activity by the endocrine pathway, the activating center being lo-

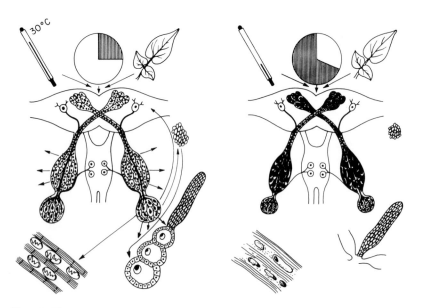

Fig. 18. Elements of the diapause syndrome (right) and the reproductive state (left) induced by photoperiod, temperature, and food condition in the Colorado beetle, *Leptinotarsa decemlineata* (from de Wilde, 1970).

cated in the head (Detinova, 1945; Mednikova, 1952; Clements, 1956; Gillett, 1956, 1958; Larsen and Bodenstein, 1959).

Gillett (1957) has suggested that abdominal distension by food intake may be the stimulating mechanism for oogenesis in mosquitoes. But this is certainly not the explanation in *Leptinotarsa* (Grison, 1957) and in *Oncopeltus* (Johansson, 1958a), where the chemical composition of the food, independent of the quantity taken in, is of predominant importance. The effect of host–plant quality on fecundity of several tropical insects has been studied by de Jong (1938).

In *Leptinotarsa*, feeding with physiologically aged potato leaves causes an arrest of oogenesis, followed by the development of the diapause syndrome. This is primarily a neuroendocrine effect, comparable with "pseudo-allatectomy" (de Wilde and Ferket, 1967; de Wilde *et al.*, 1969).

Chemical information derived from the host or host plant is often essential for stimulation of oogenesis. Many hymenopterous parasites have to feed on the hemolymph of their hosts before they start egg production. This has been termed "host feeding" (Flanders, 1935). Initiation of reproduction by a specific host plant factor may also occur. The sugar-beet moth, *Scrobipalpa ocellatella*, although it does not imbibe any liquids from sugar-beet leaves, nevertheless needs the stimulation by olfaction or contact chemoreception provided by the leaves of its host plant, to perform a normal rate of egg production (Robert, 1970).

4. Host–Parasite Interrelations

a. Phasic Castration and Related Phenomena. Many species of endoparasitic Hymenoptera have small, alecithal eggs which, when deposited in the host, obtain nourishment from its fluids by way of a trophic membrane. Such "hydropic" eggs may be stored before oviposition in the paired oviducts and the basal part of the ovary. Some species are adapted for storing their full number of eggs, e.g., *Apanteles glomeratus* L. Storage may last during the life of the female and until a suitable host is found.

In species with polylecithal, "anhydropic" eggs, ovulation occurs only when environmental conditions are favorable for immediate oviposition, i.e., when suitable hosts are available. In the absence of such hosts, the terminal oocytes are resorbed by the follicle, while oogenesis proceeds until this stage. In the prolonged absence of hosts in several Encyrtids, ovulation even ceases completely. Such species are then in a of "phasic castration" (Flanders, 1935, 1942). In the case of Pteromalids, oosorption is followed by a long period of castration dependent not on the host but apparently on abiotic conditions. This condition is probably identical with gonotrophic dissociation (Section I, C).

b. *Parasitic Castration.* Parasites living in the hemocoel and competing for nutriment with growing ovaries of adult hosts often appear to use the endocrine pathway for parasitic castration.

The nematode, *Sphaerularia bombi,* living in bumblebee queens, inhibits ovarian development and reproductive behavior, the queens remaining flower-visiting and searching for nesting sites. This is at least partly the result of the parasite's ability to inhibit growth and secretory activity of the corpora allata, either directly or by way of the brain (Palm, 1948). Parasitic castration of the solitary bee *Andrena vaga* by female parasites of the strepsipteran genus *Stylops* is probably partly caused by a marked suppression of growth and secretion of the host's corpora allata (Brandenburg, 1956). According to Panov *et al.* (1972) the parasitic Dipteran *Clytiomyia hellus* causes the corpora allata of its host, *Eurygaster integriceps,* to degenerate, thereby causing parasitic castration.

II. Control of Semen Production

A. HUMORAL CONTROL OF SPERMATOGENESIS

As we have seen before, humoral control of oogenesis by the neurosecretory cells and corpora allata takes place at the level of vitellogenesis and does not affect oogonial differentiation. It is therefore not surprising that the corpora allata do not regulate spermatogenesis, since, in this process, alimentary effects play a secondary role as compared with differentiation phenomena.

Schmidt and Williams (1953) have obtained differentiation of spermatocytes of dormant pupae of *Hyalophora cecropia* and *Samia walkeri* into spermatids when cultured in hanging drops of blood obtained from pupating larvae or developing adults of these species. This development did not occur when the medium consisted of blood from early last instar larvae or diapausing pupae. Blood from larvae entering the prepupal stage gradually became active by the time cocoon spinning was completed. The active principle, according to the foregoing authors, is destroyed at 80°C and is nondialyzable. The role of this "macromolecular factor" (MF) was further defined by Kambysellis and Williams (1971a), in experiments with *Philosamia cynthia.* It was found that the factor is not complexed with ecdysone, but has a separate action. Even in the absence of ecdysone, the MF stimulates meiosis and spermatogenesis in hemolymph-free cultures of isolated germinal cysts.

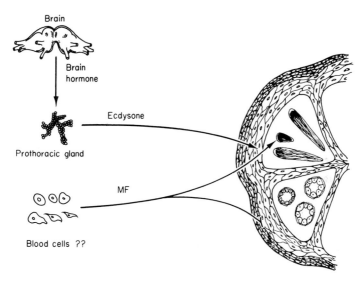

Fig. 19. Diagrammatic representation of the control of spermatogenesis in *Samia cynthia*. Ecdysone plays a permissive role in spermatogenesis. Its sole function is to alter the penetrability of the testis walls and thereby facilitate the entry of the macromolecular factor (MF) and perhaps other blood-borne molecules into contact with the germinal cysts (redrawn after Kambysellis and Williams, 1971b).

The MF shows a fluctuating titer in diapausing pupae, but the titer rises drastically upon injury. It is assumed that the factor originates from the hemocytes. It is nonspecific; MF-like activities are demonstrated in assays of calf serum.

In cultures of intact testes, the MF is only active in the presence of α- or β-ecdysone, even in concentrations of $2 \times 10^{-7} M$. It was concluded that the sole function of ecdysone is to alter the penetrability of the testis walls and thereby facilitate the entry of MF (Kambysellis and Williams, 1971b). This interpretation is represented in Fig. 19. Similar results were obtained by Takeda (1972) with the diapausing pharate pupa of *Monema flavescens*.

B. Humoral Control of Accessory Gland Activity

Seminal fluid is a product of the male accessory glands. Growth and function of these glands are controlled by the corpora allata to a varying degree in different species. Excluding or extirpating the corpora allata in young males of *Rhodnius* (Wigglesworth, 1936), *Melanoplus* (Weed-Pfeiffer, 1936), *Leucophaea* (Scharrer, 1946) and *Schistocerca* (Loher,

1960; Highnam, 1965; Cantacuzène, 1967) results in deficient growth and function of the mesadenia. In *Calliphora* (Thomsen, 1942) the effect is only slight, whereas in *Oncopeltus* (Johansson, 1958b) neither growth nor function of the accessory glands is affected.

Conversely, castration of male insects does not seem to influence the corpora allata (Day, 1943b; Bodenstein, 1947; Kaiser, 1949) .

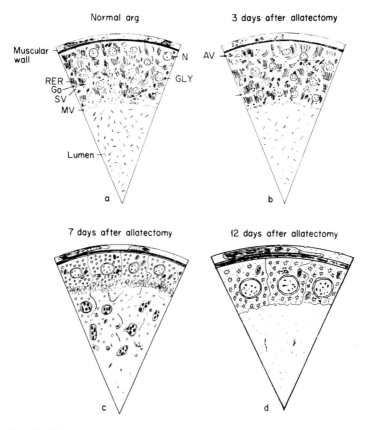

Fig. 20. Schematic representation of degeneration of accessory reproductive glands of the Colorado beetle after allatectomy. a, normal gland of adult male; b, 3 days after allatectomy; rough endoplasmic reticulum begins to swell (thin arrow). Autophagic vacuoles (AV, thick arrows) appear in all cells; c, 7 days after allatectomy; outer and inner gland cells separated by zone containing microvillous structures. In outer cells nuclei do not degenerate. RER breaks down into swollen vesicles packed with ribosomes. Inner gland cells degenerate completely. d, 12 days after allatectomy; only outer cells remain (from de Loof and Lagasse, 1972).

Mention was made in Chapter 2 of this volume of the detailed ultrastructural studies on the mesadenia and adjacent elements of *Schistocerca gregaria*. It is appropriate to relate here the endocrine effects on these structures.

In *Schistocerca gregaria,* ultrastructural signs of accessory gland activity (with the exception of the functional seminal vesicle) parallel changes in the secretory activity of the corpus allatum (Odhiambo 1971a). Allatectomy greatly reduces the nuclear and cytoplasmic secretory phenomena in all glandular elements, with the exception of the functional geminal vesicle (Odhiambo 1966c, 1971b).

It is supposed that the corpus allatum controls the maturation of the accessory glands by regulating the production of their mRNA (Odhiambo 1966c).

The accessory glands of *Gomphocerus rufus,* which are, just as in *Schistocerca,* built up of 16 tubules (Hartmann, 1970), are inactivated by allatectomy. Cauterization of the pars intercerebralis causes an alteration of the structure of the grandular secretions which leads to cessation of spermatophore production 10–15 days after the operation. Both operations also inhibit the flow of spermatozoa from the testes to the accessory glands (Hartmann, 1971).

In *Leptinotarsa,* the accessory reproductive glands also degenerate shortly after allatectomy. The granular endoplasmic reticulum becomes swollen, and autolytic vacuoles appear in the gland cells. Subsequently, a zone of microvillar structures is formed between the outer and inner layer of gland cells. The inner cells degenerate completely; the outer cells only partially. These latter cells apparently are the matrix from which the inner layer can be regenerated (de Loof and Lagasse, 1972). This sequence of affairs is represented in Fig. 20.

C. Humoral Control of Sex Differentiation

Mention was made in Chapter 2, Section IX, of the remarkable experiments which Naisse (1966a,b,c, 1969) has been able to carry out with *Lampyris noctiluca*. In this beetle the differentiation of both primary and secondary sex characters is still reversible in the larval stage.

Implantation of larval testes into female larvae of instar 4–6 causes a masculinization of the recipients. The androgenic factor provided by the testes is no longer produced when the apical complex is absent; consequently this factor probably originates from the apical cells. Implantation of larval ovaries into male larvae does not influence the metamorphosis of the recipients into adult males.

Allatocardiacectomy performed in male larvae approaching the fourth instar causes these larvae to feminize; in later instars this operation is without effect. Substitution of the brain and corpora cardiaca–corpora allata system of a male in place of the neuroendocrine complex of a female L_5 results in testiculization of the ovary and the formation of an apical complex characteristic for testicular follicles.

Since during the third molt, several "small grain" neurosecretory cells of the pars intercerebralis are particularly active in the male, it is very probable that the activity releases the induction of apical complex formation by a combination of brain hormone and juvenile hormone.

Parabiosis between castrated L_4 males (which have not yet developed the apical cells) and decerebrated and allatocardiacectomized L_4 females results in testiculization of female ovaries (Fig. 21).

It thus appears that sex differentiation in the male *Lampyris* is due to a sequence of endocrine events, in which the first mover is a male-specific "small granule" type of cerebral neurosecretion.

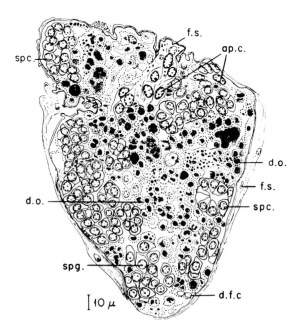

Fig. 21. Scheme of a masculinized ovarian follicle obtained by parabiosis between a castrated male larve and a decerebrated female larve, both of the fourth instar. Apical cells (ap.c.), degenerating follicle cells (d.f.c.), follicular sheat (f.s.), degenerating oogonia (d.o.), spermatocytes (spc.) spermatogonia (spg.) (from Naisse, 1969).

III. Control of Sexual Behavior and Oviposition

A. INDEPENDENCE OF SEXUAL BEHAVIOR FROM GONADAL FUNCTION

Sexual behavior in insects appears to be independent of the gonads. After castration, in both males and females, normal copulation takes place. This has been found in Orthoptera (*Gryllus*, Regen, 1910; *Leucophaea*, Engelmann, 1960; *Brysotria*, Barth, 1962), in Lepidoptera (*Lymantria*, Oudemans, 1899; *Galleria*, Röller *et al.*, 1962), and in Hymenoptera (*Polistes*, Deleurance, 1948).

B. EFFECT OF CORPORA ALLATA ON SEXUAL BEHAVIOR

Data differ as to the dependence of sexual behavior on corpus allatum activity. In *Melanoplus* (Weed-Pfeiffer, 1936), *Diploptera* (Engelmann, 1960), and *Galleria* (Röller *et al.*, 1962), allatectomy leaves mating behavior unaltered.

In *Leucophaea*, mildly active corpora allata cause the female to accept the male (Engelmann and Barth, 1968). This may be an endocrine effect on olfactory threshold for male odor (Engelmann, 1960) or an effect on female pheromone secretion, releasing courtship in the male (Barth, 1962). In another roach, *Byrsotria fumigata* (Barth, 1962), allatectomy in females, when carried out in the early adult stage, interferes with mating behavior. Such females fail to produce sex pheromone. Implantation of active corpora allata initiates pheromone production. This effect is direct and remains after castration. The corpora allata in the male do not influence sexual behavior.

In *Schistocerca*, the corpora allata are essential for maturation in the adult male. In the gregarious adult males this includes yellow pigmentation, sexual behavior, and the production of a sex pheromone which accelerates maturation in surrounding young adults (Loher, 1960). These factors do not appear when the corpora allata are removed, but they are restored by implantation of either a male or a female corpus allatum (Pener, 1967).

In *Locusta migratoria*, male sexual behavior as well as the yellow pigmentation are dependent on the corpus allatum (Staal, 1961), and sexual behavior is also impaired after cauterization of the pars intercerebralis. It is restored by reimplantation of midbrain (Girardie and Vogel, 1966). In *Nomadacris septemfasciata*, sexual maturation of the male is prevented by allatectomy and restored by reimplantation of the CA (Pener, 1968).

C. ENDOCRINE EFFECTS ON OVIPOSITION

Although available data are extremely scarce, it may be mentioned
that in *Dixippus,* rhythmic contractions of the oviduct muscularis are
stimulated by extract from the brain and corpora cardiaca (Enders,
1955). In the bug *Iphita limbata,* oviposition behavior in immature females is released by transfusion of blood from donors in the early oviposition stages. Implantation of clusters of active neurosecretory cells into
females still in their oviposition period results in immediate release of
oviposition behavior (Nayar, 1958b; Fig. 22).

In female *Aedes aegypti,* juvenile hormone initiates sexual receptivity
by acting directly on the terminal ganglion, on some site closely associated with the terminal ganglion, or on a site which in turn secretes a second
humoral factor. Matrone, the male accessory-gland pheromone, induces postinsemination refractory behavior by acting on the same site
(Gwadz, 1972).

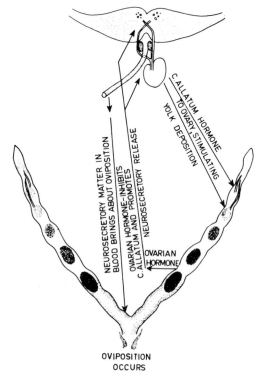

Fig. 22. Presumed interdependence of reproductive organs and neurosecretory system
in the adult *Iphita* female (according to Navar, 1958b).

D. ENVIRONMENTAL CONTROL OF OVIPOSITION

Whereas high light intensities inhibit oviposition in *Actias selene*, they are a necessary condition for oviposition in *Pieris brassicae* (Benz, 1970). This very probably depends on the natural circadian rhythm of oviposition activity which in some insects is nocturnal, in other species diurnal. The presence of specific host plant, prey, or host factors is a condition in many phytophagous, predatory, or parasitic species. Specific stimuli emerging from host plants and releasing ovipositional responses are very numerous and are important factors determining oligophagous or monophagous host specificity. Readers are referred to de Wilde and Schoonhoven (1969) for a recent symposium on this subject.

In *Pieris brassicae*, fresh leaves containing mustard oil glucosides such as Cruciferae, Tropaeolum, and Capparis are necessary for oviposition (Benz, 1970). In behavioral experiments, Ma and Schoonhoven (1973) have indeed proved that the chemical ovipositional stimulus for *Pieris* consists of mustard oil glucosides. The tarsal B hairs on the foreleg are used by the female to perceive this stimulus. These hairs are slightly curved and fit in a membranous socket. In the Colorado potato beetle, a volatile factor produced by several solanaceous plants is necessary to maintain oviposition (Bongers, 1970). In *Acanthoscelides* a factor from *Phaseolus* beans is necessary for oviposition to occur (Labeyrie, 1960).

Very various mechanical and chemical stimuli initiate and stimulate oviposition in parasitic Diptera and Hymenoptera. The specific stimuli regulating feeding and oviposition responses are the main factors deter-

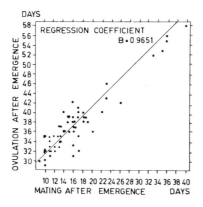

Fig. 23. Correlation between times of mating and ovulation after emergence in *Leucophaea*, providing indirect evidence for the effect of mating on egg maturation (according to Engelmann, 1960).

mining host or host plant specificity. The literature on this vast field of ecophysiology is very dispersed. Readers are referred to Bombosch and Volk (1965), Chandler (1965), Engelmann (1970), Herrebout (1969), and Iperti (1965) for further reading.

IV. Social Relations In Control of Reproduction

A. INTERRELATION OF SEXES

1. Effect of Copulation on Oogenesis

No eggs develop until after impregnation in *Glossina* (Mellanby, 1937), *Cimex* (Mellanby, 1939), several *Anopheles* species (Roy, 1940), and the roaches *Leucophaea* and *Diploptera* (Fig. 23).

In the two last-named species, according to Engelmann (1960), mating impulses in the female originate from receptors in the genital apparatus and are conducted via the ventral nerve cord to the brain. The allatum function is subsequently released and induction of oogenesis and accessory gland activity takes place. According to Roth and Stay (1959), in *Diploptera* mating impulses are only generated by the insertion of a spermatophore in the female genital chamber. In *Drosophila* (Laurinat, 1930), mating causes a considerable increase in egg production. In *Schistocerca* (Norris, 1954) and *Periplaneta* (Wharton and Wharton, 1957), mating depresses sex pheromone production in the female and thus decreases the chance of renewed impregnation before the time the ootheca is deposited.

As has been mentioned before, in *Schistocerca,* copulation results in the discharge of material from the corpora cardiaca (Highnam, 1962a). This suggests that the integrating function of the brain is involved in this type of sexual synchronization (see also Section IV, A, 3).

Next to various stimuli received during courtship, tactile stimulation during the copulatory act or either the presence of a spermatophore or the filling of the spermatheca by spermatozoa (Davey, 1965) may be of importance. To this may be added the stimulation of ovarian activity by male secretions transferred in the seminal fluid. The activity of these substances has been demonstrated in *Drosophila* by Chen and Diem (1961), Leahy and Lowe (1967), Garcia Bellido (1964), and Merle (1968). It has been found in *Aedes* (Leahy and Craig, 1965) and in *Acanthoscelides* (Huignard, 1969). It would seem, therefore, that the neuroendocrine control mechanism of oogenesis can be activated by the nervous and humoral pathway in several manners, represented in Fig. 24A–C.

In *Rhodnius,* transport of semen from the spermatophore into spermatheca depends upon a secretion from the male (Davey, 1958). Any operation preventing this transport blocks the increase in oogenesis which normally follows mating. Virgin spermatheca, when implanted in large numbers, mimic the effect of mating. The spermathecal factor in its turn causes the release of a factor from the protocerebral neurosecretory cells. This factor stimulates oogenesis (Davey, 1970). In *Acanthoscelides,* oosorption occurs unless a spermatophore is present in the female tractus

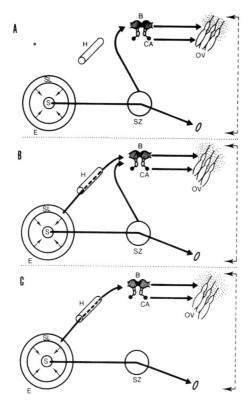

Fig. 24. Schematic representation of the different possibilities of ovarian stimulation by the presence of substances originating from males (B, brain; CA, corpus allatum; E, ejaculatum; H, hemocoel; S, spermatozoa; SL, seminal liquid). (A) The spermatozoids in the spermatheca (or in an organ with similar function) activate neurosecretory cells, which stimulate the ovaries either in a direct way either by influencing other glands, e.g., the corpora allata; (B) the same mode of action as under (A) but sensitive cells, which activate the neurosecretory cells, are also activated by the secretions of the male; (C) same as (B), but no activation by the spermatheca (redrawn after Labeyrie, 1970).

(Huignard, 1969). It appears useful to differentiate between initiation and stimulation of oogenesis. In the case of insects such as *Diploptera* (Engelmann, 1960), *Glossina* (Mellanby, 1939), and several *Anopheles* species (Roy, 1940), where oogenesis is started only after adult ecdysis, mating is often a condition to oogenesis, while in insects such as *Laspeyresia* and *Zeiraphera,* where oogenesis already begins in the pupal stage, oogenesis is merely stimulated and egg production increased by mating (Benz, 1970).

But the distinction between the two types of effects is certainly not only based upon these morphogenetic differences. In *Rhodnius* (Davey, 1970), *Acanthoscelides* (Huignard, 1969), and *Leptinotarsa* (J. de Wilde, unpublished observations), oogenesis is started in the adult stage and is merely stimulated by mating. In *Dysdercus fasciatus,* mating has no influence at all on egg production or oviposition (Odhiambo, 1968).

2. *Effect of Copulation on Oviposition*

Not only may impregnation provide the initial stimulus for oogenesis, but also the deposition of eggs is in some cases directly dependent on impregnation.

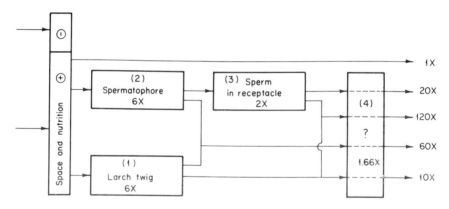

Fig. 25. Scheme of the effects of different factors on oviposition of *Zeiraphera diana.* (1) larch twig in rearing box, (2) spermatophore in bursa copulatrix, (3) viable spermatozoa in receptaculum seminis, (4) multiplier unit of unknown nature. Space and nutrition are regarded as a deblocking unit which, if positive, forwards a weak oviposition stimulus leading to the deposition of the basic number of X eggs. This unit includes also the presence of suitable oviposition sites. The different stimuli multiply the primary input X by the factors indicated in each unit. Any combination is possible (redrawn after Benz, 1970).

In *Rhodnius,* a myotropic factor is released during mating which causes the females to oviposit more readily. As in the stimulation of oogenesis, this factor is probably released by the protocerebral neurosecretory cells (Davey, 1967).

Stimulation of oviposition by mating in *Pieris* and *Zeiraphera* does not depend directly on the presence of spermatozoa in the spermatheca. It is supposed that the stimulation is transferred by the neural pathway (Benz, 1970). The effect of different factors on oviposition of *Zeiraphera diana* is represented in Fig. 25. In *Actias selene,* mated females oviposit earlier than virgin females.

As in oogenesis, it is useful to distinguish between the initiation and the stimulation of oviposition by mating. In *Oryzaephilus,* no oviposition occurs without copulation. As a consequence, the ovulated eggs accumulate, and this appears to inhibit further oogenesis (Leroi, 1970). In *Diploptera* (Engelmann, 1959; Roth and Stay, 1961), similar conditions are observed.

In *Brysothria* (Barth, 1962), many individuals of *Leucophaea* (Engelmann, 1970), and *Nauphoeta* (Roth, 1964), only part of the eggs are ovulated in the absence of copulation.

In *Periplaneta,* the number of oothecae is reduced (Roth and Willis, 1956). In *Thermobia* (Sweetman, 1938), *Acanthoscelides* (Bushnell and Boughton, 1940), *Bupalus,* and *Ephestia* (Brandt, 1947), oviposition is retarded and reduced when copulation does not occur.

In *Drosophila,* the accelerating effect of mating on egg production can be mimicked by implantation of male mesadenia (Merle, 1970). In the tsetse fly *Glossina pallidipes,* which matures a single oocyte at a time, mating is necessary to initiate ovulation (Odhiambo, 1970b).

3. *Effect of Male Pheromone on Egg Production*

In Schistocerca, a fraction of the females mature eggs only when exposed to the effect of male pheromone; in other females, the rate of oogenesis is merely increased. Highnam and Lusis (1962) have demonstrated that, in females reared without mature males, the neurosecretory system retains its material. The presence of mature males brings about the release of neurosecretory substance, and consequently stimulates egg formation. How the male pheromone affects neurosecretion is as yet unknown.

In *Actias selene,* virgin females kept in the same room as males secrete an aphrodisiac substance which is perceived by the females through their antennae (Benz and Schmidt, 1968).

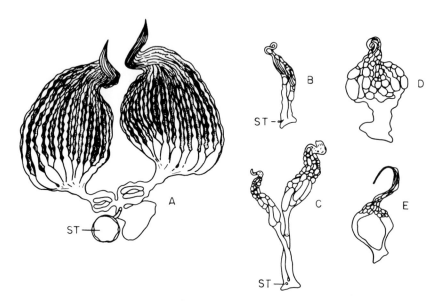

Fig. 26. Ovaries of some social Hymenoptera in relation to caste development and presence of the queen (ST, spermatheca). (A) honey bee queen, mature, (B) honey bee worker, queenright colony, (C) honey bee worker, egg laying, in absence of queen, (D) *Vespa germanica,* queen; (E) *Dolichovespula* sp., worker (modified after Hess, 1942).

B. PHEROMONES AND INHIBITION OF REPRODUCTION IN WORKER CASTES IN SOCIAL INSECTS

In social Hymenoptera, the development of the ovaries in the female worker caste is greatly reduced at the adult molt, but these ovaries still retain their capacity to produce complete eggs. Their activity is known to be suppressed by the presence of the queen. Queenless colonies usually acquire egg-laying workers. The fragmentary development of the ovaries in the honey bee worker is presumed to be the result of deficient larval nutrition, the queen larvae receiving an abundant quantity of royal jelly, which is especially rich in 10-hydroxydecenoic acid. In the absence of a queen, however, in a large percentage of the workers the underdeveloped ovarioles are activated and a number of them produce eggs of a variable degree of completeness (Fig. 26).

Hess (1942) has found that the queen suppresses ovarian growth only in those members of the colony which maintain direct contact with the "queenright" group, probably via the mouthparts. Butler (1954), de Groot and Voogd (1954), Voogd (1955), Verheyen-Voogd (1959), and Pain (1956) have subsequently shown that this effect is due to a substance emerging from the queen that is licked from her body and distributed from one worker to another. It was subsequently shown (Butler and Simpson, 1958) that the substance is a pheromone produced by the mandibular glands of the queen, and presently (Butler et al., 1961) the main component of this pheromone has been identified as 9-oxodec-trans-2-enoic acid. According to Velthuis (1970) another component emerges from the subepidermal glands of the abdomen. Opinions still differ as to the mechanism of action of these substances, some authors claiming a direct effect of "queen substance" on metabolism (Butler and Gibbons, 1958), and others considering the substance as a chemical releaser, acting through the intermediate of the sense organs and central nervous system (Voogd, 1955; Verheyen-Voogd, 1959). Similar effects are present in ant colonies (Bier, 1954; Stumper, 1956; Carr, 1962), but the substance concerned is unknown. In the ant *Dolichoderus quadripunctatus* (Torossian, 1965), 9-oxodecenoic acid has a slight activity. In *Plagiolepis pygmaea*, the queen prevents the workers from laying reproductive eggs, but allows them to lay a smaller type of sterile eggs which are fed to the larvae. This is done by an effect on the trophocytes (Passera, 1966, 1969).

In termites, where the colony has a permanent bisexual structure, loss of the functional queen and king is compensated by the development of substitute reproductives. The situation is complicated, since the formation of these substitute reproductives involves a metamorphic molt. Moreover, both male and female should be present to exert the full suppressing effect on their formation. In the female *Zoothermopsis*, the head appears to be the source of the pheromone (Light, 1944), and in *Kalotermes*, the substance is apparently released caudally with the excrements and distributed after being taken up by the grooming workers (Lüscher, 1956). In *Kalotermes*, in addition to the inhibitory pheromone, there is at least one stimulatory factor which is given off by the male reproductive organs and stimulates the production of female supplementary organs. There is evidence that the corpora allata and prothoracic glands are involved in the mechanism of action of these pheromones (Lüscher, 1957), but we ignore in which way they affect the regulating center of hormone balance. It seems certain that in honey bee workers, in the absence of "queen substance," the activity of the corpora allata is increased (Müssbichler, 1952). This is interesting because, in the worker, the size of the corpora allata is already larger than in the queen. It would seem, therefore, that this is another case where the size of the corpus allatum does not correlate with its activity. However, in egg-laying workers there is a correlation between the volume of the terminal oocytes and the corpus allatum (von Gast, 1967). Workers of "queenright" colonies are thus in a state comparable with "phasic castration" or "gonotropic dissociation."

The problem of the defective condition of worker ovaries at the adult molt is one of postembryonic development. Treatment of worker larvae with juvenile hormone results in the development of queen-like adults in which the ovaries are fully developed (Wirtz and Beetsma, 1972).

References

Adams, T. S. (1970). *J. Insect Physiol.* **16**, 349–360.
Adams, T. S., Hinz, A. M., and Pomonis, J. G. (1968). *J. Insect Physiol.* **14**, 983–994.
Adiyodi, K. G., and Nayar, K. K. (1967). *Biol. Bull.* **133**, 271–286.
Ankersmit, G. W. (1961). *Proc. Int. Symp. Ontog. Insects, Prague, 1959,* pp. 277–282.
Arvy, L., and Gabe, M. (1953). *C. R. Acad. Sci.* **237**, 844–846.
Barth, R. H. (1962). *Gen. Comp. Endocrinol.* **2**, 53–69.
Bell, W. J., and Barth, R. H. (1970). *J. Insect Physiol.* **16**, 2303–2313.
Benz, G. (1970). *Colloq. Int. Cent. Nat. Rech. Sci.* **189**, 175–206.
Benz, G., and Schmidt, K. (1968). *Experientia* **24**, 1279–1281.
Bier, K. (1954). *Insectes Soc.* **1**, 7–19.
Bloch, B., Thomsen, E., and Thomsen, M. (1966). *Z. Zellforsch. Mikrosk. Anat.* **70**, 185–208.
Bodenstein, D. (1938). *Biol. Zentral bl.* **58**, 328–332.
Bodenstein, D. (1947). *J. Exp. Zool.* **104**, 101–152.
Bodenstein, D. (1953). *Biol. Bull.* **124**, 105–115.
Bombosch, S., and Volk, S. (1965). *In* "Ecology of Aphidophagous Insects," pp. 117–120. CSR, Prague.
Bongers, W. (1970). *Meded. Landbouw Hogesch, Wageningen* **70**, 1–77.
Bonnemaison, L., and Missonnier, J. (1955). *C. R. Acad. Sci.* **240**, 1277–1279.
Bounhiol, J. (1938). *Bull. Biol. Fr. Belg., Suppl.* **24**, 1–199.
Bowers, W. S. (1971). *Mitt. Schweiz. Entomol. Ges.* **44**, 115–130.
Bowers, W. S., and Blickenstaff, C. C. (1966). *Science* **154**, 1673–1674.
Brandenburg, J. (1956). *Z. Morphol. Oekol. Tiere* **45**, 343–364.
Brandt, H. (1947). *Z. Naturforsch. B* **2**, 301–308.
Brousse-Gaury, P. (1968). *C. R. Acad. Sci.* **266**, 1972–1975.
Burtt, E. T. (1937). *Proc. Roy. Soc., Ser. B* **124**, 13–23.
Bushnell, R. J., and Boughton, D. C. (1940). *Ann. Entomol. Soc. Amer.* **33**, 361–370.
Butler, C. G. (1954). *Trans. Roy. Entomol. Soc. London* **105**, 11–29.
Butler, C. G., and Gibbons, D. A. (1958). *J. Insect Physiol.* **2**, 61–64.
Butler, C. G., and Simpson, J. (1958). *Proc. Roy. Entomol. Soc. London, Ser. A* **33**, 120–122.
Butler, C. G., Callow, R. K., and Johnston, N. C. (1961). *Proc. Roy. Soc., Ser. B* **155**, 417–432.
Cantacuzène, A.-M. (1967). *C. R. Acad. Sci.* **264**, 93–96.
Cantacuzène, A.-M. (1967). *C. R. Acad. Sci.* **265**, 224–227.
Carr, C. A. H. (1962). *Insectes Soc.* **9**, 197–211.
Cassier, P. (1965a). *Ann. Sci. Nat. Zool. Biol. Anim.* [12] **7**, 213–358.

Cassier, P. (1965b). *Bull. Soc. Zool.* **90**, 39–51.
Cassier, P. (1965c). *C. R. Acad. Sci.* **260**, 3480–3482.
Cazal, P., and Guerrier, Y. (1946). *Arch. Zool. Exp. Gen.* **84**, 303–334.
Chambers, D. L., and Brookes, V. J. (1967). *J. Insect Physiol.* **13**, 99–111.
Chandler, A. E. F. (1965). *In* "Ecology of Aphidophagous Insects," pp. 113–116. CSR, Prague.
Chen, P. S., and Diem, C. (1961). *J. Insect Physiol.* **7**, 289–298.
Clarke, K. U., and Gillott, C. (1965) . *Nature (London)* **208**, 808–809.
Clarke, K. U., and Langley, P. (1961). *Nature (London)* **190**, 811.
Clarke, K. U., and Langley, P. (1963a). *J. Insect Physiol.* **9**, 363–373.
Clarke, K. U., and Langley, P. (1963b). *J. Insect Physiol.* **9**, 411–421.
Clarke, K. U., and Langley, P. (1963c). *J. Insect Physiol.* **9**, 423–430.
Clements, A. N. (1956). *J. Exp. Biol.* **33**, 211–223.
Clift, A. D. (1971). *J. Insect Physiol.* **17**, 601–606.
Coles, G. C. (1964). *Nature (London)* **203**, 323.
Coles, G. C. (1965a). *J. Exp. Biol.* **43**, 425–431.
Coles, G. C. (1965b). *J. Insect Physiol.* **11**, 1325–1330.
Davey, K. G. (1958). *J. Exp. Biol.* **35**, 694–701.
Davey, K. G. (1965). *J. Exp. Biol.* **42**, 373–378.
Davey, K. G. (1967). *J. Insect Physiol.* **13**, 1629–1636.
Davey, K. G. (1970). *Colloq. Int. Cent. Nat. Rech. Sci.* **189**, 249–256.
Davis, N. T. (1964). *J. Insect Physiol.* **10**, 947–963.
Day, M. F. (1943a). *Psyche* **50**, 1–8.
Day, M. F. (1943b). *Biol. Bull.* **84**, 127–140.
de Groot, A. P., and Voogd, S. (1954). *Experientia* **10**, 384–385.
de Jong, J. K. (1938). *Treubia* **16**, 445–468.
de Kort, C. A. D. (1969). *Meded. Landbouw hogesch., Wageningen* , 1–63.
de Kort, C. A. D. (1971). *Meded. Rijksfac. Landbouwwetensch.,* **36**, 848–857.
Deleurance, E. P. (1948). *C. R. Acad. Sci.* **226**, 514–516 and 601–603.
de Loof, A., (1969). Ph.D. Thesis, University of Ghent, Belgium.
de Loof, A., and de Wilde, J. (1970a). *J. Insect Physiol.* **16**, 157–169.
de Loof, A., and de Wilde, J. (1970b). *J. Insect Physiol.* **16**, 1455–1466.
de Loof, A., and Lagasse, A. (1970a). *Proc., Kon. Ned. Akad. Wetensch., Ser. C* **73**, 284–297.
de Loof, A., and Lagasse, A. (1970b) *Z. Zellforsch. Mikrosk. Anat.* **106**, 439–450.
de Loof, A., and Lagasse, A. (1972). *Z. Zellforsch. Mikrosk. Anat.* **130**, 545–552.
Detinova, T. S. (1945). *Zool. Zh.* **34**, 291–298.
de Wilde, J. (1954). *Proc. Int. Photobiol. Congr., 1st,* 96–101.
de Wilde, J. (1957). *Z. Pflanzenkr. (pflanzepathol.) pflanzenschutz* **64**, 589–593.
de Wilde, J. (1962a). *Annu. Rev. Entomol.* **7**, 1–26.
de Wilde, J. (1962b). *Acta Physiol. Pharmacol. Neer.* **11**, 111.
de Wilde, J. (1969). *Proc. Int. Congr. Endocrinol., 3rd, 1968* pp. 356–365.
de Wilde, J. (1970). *Memo. Soc. Endocrinol.* **18**, 487–514.
de Wilde, J., and de Boer, J. A. (1961). *J. Insect Physiol.* **6**, 152–161.
de Wilde, J., and de Boer, J. A. (1969). *J. Insect Physiol.* **15**, 661–676.
de Wilde, J., and Ferket, P. (1967). *Meded. Rijksfac. Landbouwwetensch., Gent* **32**, 387–392.
de Wilde, J., and Stegwee, D. (1958). *Arch. Neer. Zool.* **13**, Suppl., 227–289.
de Wilde, J., and Schoonhoven. L. M. (1969) . *Proc. 2nd Int. Symp. Insect and Host Plant* **12**, 471–810.

de Wilde, J., Duintjer, C. S., and Mook, L. (1959). *J. Insect Physiol.* 3, 75–85.
de Wilde, J., Staal, G. B., de Kort, C. A. D., de Loof, A., and Baard, G. (1968). *Proc., Kon. Ned. Akad. Wetensch.* 71, 321–326.
de Wilde, J., Bongers, W., and Schooneveld, H. (1969). *Entomol. Exp. Appl.* 12, 714–720.
de Wilde, J., de Kort, C. A. D., and de Loof, A. (1971). *Mitt. Schweiz. Entomol. Ges.* 44, 79–86.
Dixon, A. F. G. (1963). *J. Anim. Ecol.* 32, 33–48.
Dupont-Raabe, M. (1952). *Arch. Zool. Exp. Gen.* 89, 128–138.
Dutkowski, A., and Przelecka, A. (1969). *Z. Pol.* 19, 151–166.
El-Ibrashi, M. T. (1965). *Comm. Agr. Univ. Wageningen No.* 65–11, pp. 1–63.
Enders, E. (1955). *Verh. Deut. Zoo. Ges., Erlangen* pp. 113–116.
Endo, K. (1970). *Develop. Growth Differentiation* 11, 297–304.
Engelmann, F. (1957). *J. Insect Physiol.* 1, 257–278.
Engelmann, F. (1959). *Biol. Bull.* 116, 406–419.
Engelmann, F. (1960). *Ann. N. Y. Acad. Sci.* 89, 416–436.
Engelmann, F. (1962). *Gen. Comp. Endocrinol.* 2, 183–192.
Engelmann, F. (1965a). *Arch. Anat. Microsc. Morphol. Exp.* 54, 387–404.
Engelmann, F. (1965b). *Amer. Zool.* 5, 673.
Engelmann, F. (1966). *Symp. Insect Endocrines, Brno.*
Engelmann, F. (1969). *Science* 165, 407–408.
Engelmann, F. (1970). "The Physiology of Insect Reproduction." Pergamon, Oxford.
Engelmann, F. (1971). *Arch. Biochem. Biophys.* 145, 439–447.
Engelmann, F., and Barth, R. H. (1968). *Ann. Entomol. Soc. Amer.* 61, 503–505.
Engelmann, F., and Lüscher, M. (1956). *Verh. Deut. Zool. Ges., Hamburg* pp. 215–220.
Engelmann, F., and Penney, D. (1966). *Gen. Comp. Endocrinol.* 7, 314–325.
Ewen, A. B. (1966). *Can. J. Zool.* 44, 719–727.
Fain-Maurel, M. A., and Cassier, P. (1969). *C. R. Acad. Sci.* 268, 2721–2723.
Flanders, S. E. (1935). *Ann. Entomol. Soc. Amer.* 28, 438–444.
Flanders, S. E. (1942). *Ann. Entomol. Soc. Amer.* 35, 251–266.
Formigoni, A. (1956). *Ann. Sci. Nat. Zool. Biol. Anim.* [11] 18, 283–291.
Fukuda, S. (1944). *J. Fac. Sci., Univ. Tokyo, Sect. 4* 6, 477–532.
Fukuda, S. (1962). *Annot. Zool. Jap.* 35, 199–212.
Gabe, M. (1953). *Bull. Soc. Zool. Fra.* 78, 178.
Ganagarajah, M. (1965). *J. Insect Physiol.* 11, 1377–1387.
Garcia Bellido, A. (1964). *Z. Naturforsch. B* 19, 491–495.
Geldiay, S. (1965). *Gen. Comp. Endocrinol.* 5, 680–681.
Geldiay, S. (1967). *J. Endocrinol.* 37, 63–71.
Gillett, J. D. (1956). *Ann. Trop. Med. Parasitol.* 50, 375–380.
Gillett, J. D. (1957). *Nature (London)* 180, 656–657.
Gillett, J. D. (1958). *J. Exp. Biol.* 35, 685–693.
Gillott, C. (1964). *Helgoläender Wiss. Meeresunters.* 9, 141–149.
Girardie, A. (1962). *J. Insect Physiol.* 8, 199–205.
Girardie, A. (1963). *J. Insect Physiol.* 10, 599–609.
Girardie, A. (1965). *C. R. Acad. Sci.* 261, 4876–4878.
Girardie, A. (1966). *Bull. Soc. Zool. Fr.* 91, 423–439.
Girardie, A., and Vogel, A. (1966). *C. R. Acad. Sci.* 263, 543–546.
Gordon, H. T. (1959). *Ann. N. Y. Acad. Sci.* 77, 290–351.
Goryshin, N. I. (1958). "Col. Beetle and Its Control," Vol. 2, pp. 136–149. Acad. Sci. USSR, Moscow.

Grison, P. (1957). *Ann. Epiphyt.* [2] **3**, 305–381.
Gwadz, R. W. (1972). *J. Insect Physiol.* **18**, 259–266.
Hadorn, E. (1937). *Proc. Nat. Acad. Sci. U. S.* **23**, 478–484.
Harker, J. (1960). *Cold Spring Harbor Symp. Quant. Biol.* **25**, 279–287.
Hartmann, R. (1970). *Z. Morphol. Tiere* **68**, 140–176.
Hartmann, R. (1971). *Z. Vergl. Physiol.* **74**, 190–216.
Herlant-Meeuwis, H., and Paquet, L. (1956). *Ann. Sci. Nat. Zool. Biol. Anim.* [12] **18**, 163–169.
Herrebout, W. M. (1969). *Neth. J. Zool.* **19**, 1–104.
Hess, G. (1942). *Schweiz. Bienen-Ztg.* **1**, 33–109.
Highnam, K. C. (1962a). *Quart. J. Microsc. Sci.* **103**, 57–72.
Highnam, K. C. (1962b). *J. Endocrinol.* **24**, 1–2 and 4–5.
Highnam, K. C. (1962c). *Mem. Soc. Endocrinol.* **12**, 379–390.
Highnam, K. C. (1962d). *New Sci.* **14**, 86–88.
Highnam, K. C. (1965). *Zool. Jahub., Abt. Allg. Zool. Physiol. Tiere* **71**, 558–582.
Highnam, K. C. (1969). *Proc. Int. Congr. Endocrinol., 3rd, 1968.*
Highnam, K. C., and Haskell, P. T. (1964). *J. Insect Physiol.* **10**, 849–864.
Highnam, K. C., and Lusis, O. (1962). *Quart. J. Microsc. Sci.* **103**, 73–83.
Highnam, K. C., Lusis, O., and Hill, L. (1963). *J. Insect Physiol.* **9**, 587–596.
Hill, L. (1962). *J. Insect Physiol.* **8**, 609–619.
Hill, L. (1965). *J. Insect Physiol.* **11**, 1605–1615.
Hill, L., and Goldsworthy, G. J. (1968). *J. Insect Physiol.* **14**, 1085–1098.
Hill, L., Mordue, W., and Highnam, K. C. (1966). *J. Insect Physiol.* **12**, 1197–1208.
Hodek, I., and Cerkasov, J. (1961). *Entomol. Exp. Appl.* **4**, 179–190.
Huber, F. (1955). *Z. Tierpsychol.* **12**, 12–48.
Huignard, J. (1964). *C. R. Acad. Sci.* **259**, 1557–1560.
Huignard, J. (1969). *C. R. Acad. Sci.* **268**, 2938–2940.
Ichikawa, M., and Nitschiitsutsuji-Uwo, J. (1959). *Biol. Bull.* **116**, 88–94.
Iperti, G. (1965). *In* "Ecology of Aphidophagous Insects," pp. 105–106. CSR, Prague.
Ito, H. (1918). *Bull. Emp. Tokyo Sericult. Coll.* **1**, 63–103.
Johansson, A. S. (1954). *Nature (London)* **174**, 89.
Johansson, A. S. (1958a). *Nytt. Mag. Zool.* **7**, 1–132.
Johansson, A. S. (1958b). *Nytt. Mag. Zool.* **7**, 1–132; and references cited in Chapter 3.
Johansson, A. S. (1958c). *Int. Symp. Neurosecretion, 2nd, 1958.*
Johnson, R. A. (1971). Ph. D. Thesis, University of Sheffield.
Joly, L. (1960). Ph. D. Thesis, University of Strassbourg, France.
Joly, P. (1945). *Arch. Zool. Exp. Gen.* **84**, 49–164.
Joly, P. (1947). "Lecture." Conf. Sci. Int. Endocrinol. Arthropodes, Paris.
Joly, P. (1948). *Bull. Biol. Fr. Belg., Suppl.* **33**, 81–86.
Joly, P. (1950). *C. R. Soc. Biol.* **144**, 1217–1220.
Joly, P. (1958). *Annee Biol.* **34**, 97–118.
Joly, P. (1964). *J. Insect Physiol.* **10**, 437–442.
Joly, P. (1968). "Endocrinologie des Insectes." Masson, Paris.
Kaiser, P. (1949). *Wilhelm Roux' Arch. Entwicklungsmech. Organismen* **144**, 99–131.
Kaiser, P. (1954). *An. Acad. Brasil. Cienc.* **26**, 283–288.
Kambysellis, M. P., and Williams, C. M. (1971a). *Biol. Bull.* **141**, 527–540.
Kambysellis, M. P., and Williams, C. M. (1971b). *Biol. Bull.* **141**, 541–552.
Karlinsky, A. (1963). *C. R. Acad. Sci.* **256**, 4101–4103.
Karlinsky, A. (1967a). *C. R. Acad. Sci.* **264**, 1735–1738.
Karlinsky, A. (1967b). *C. R. Acad. Sci.* **265**, 2040–2042.

Karlinsky, A. (1967c). *Gen. Comp. Endocrinol.* **9**, 511–512.
Labeyrie, V. (1960). *C. R. Acad. Sci.* **250**, 2626–2628.
Labeyrie, V. (1970). *Colloq. Int. Cent. Nat. Rech. Sci.* **189**, 21–44.
Larsen, J. R., and Bodenstein, D. (1959). *J. Exp. Zool.* **140**, 343–381.
Laurinat, K. (1930). *Z. Indukt. Abstamm.- Vererbungsl* **57**, 139–205.
Laverdure, A. M. (1970a). Ph. D. Thesis, Faculty of Sciences of Orsay University of Paris.
Laverdure, A. M. (1970b). *Ann. Endocrinol.* **31**, 516–521.
Lea, A. O. (1964). *J. Med. Entomol.* **1**, 40–44.
Lea, A. O. (1967). *J. Insect Physiol.* **13**, 419–429.
Lea, A. O. (1969). *J. Insect Physiol.* **15**, 537–541.
Lea, A. O., and Thomsen, E. (1969). *J. Insect Physiol.* **15**, 477–482.
Leahy, S. M. G., and Craig, G. B. (1965). *Mosquito News*, **25**, 440–452.
Leahy, S. M. G., and Lowe, M. L. (1967). *Life Sci.* **6**, 151–156.
Lees, A. D. (1964). *J. Exp. Biol.* **41**, 119–133.
Leloup, A. M. (1970). *Année Biol.* **9**, 447–453.
Lender, T., and Laverdure, A. M. (1965). *C. R. Acad Sci.* **261**, 557–559.
Leroi, B. (1970). *Colloq. Int. Cent. Nat. Rech. Sci.* **109**, 331–348.
L'Hélias, C. (1955). *Physiol. Comp. Oekol.* **4**, 74–88.
Light, S. F. (1944). *Univ. Calif., Berkeley, Publ. Zool.* **43**, 413–454.
Loher, W. (1960). *Proc. Roy. Soc., Ser. B* **153**, 380–397.
Loher, W. (1965). *Zool. Jahrb., Abt. Allg. Zool. Physiol. Tiere* **71**, 677–684.
Loher, W. (1966a). *Verh. Deut. Zool. Ges., Jena* **1965**, 386–391.
Loher, W. (1966b). *Z. Vergl. Physiol.* **53**, 277–316.
Lukoschus, F. (1956). *Z. Morphol. Oekol. Tiere* **45**, 157–197.
Lüscher, M. (1956). *Rev. Suisse Zool.* **63**, 261–267.
Lüscher, M. (1957). *Verh. Deut. Ges. Angew. Entomol.* **14**, 144–150.
Lüscher, M. (1968a). *J. Insect Physiol.* **14**, 499–512.
Lüscher, M. (1968b). *J. Insect Physiol.* **14**, 685–688.
Lüscher, M., and Engelmann, F. (1955). *Rev. Suisse Zool.* **62**, 649–657.
Lüscher, M., Bühlmann, G., and Wyss-Huber, M. (1971). *Mitt. Schweiz. Entomol. Ges.* **44**, 197–206.
Ma, W. C., and Schoonhoven, L. (1973). In press.
Masner, P., Slăma, K., and Landa, V. (1968). *Nature* **219**, 395–396.
Mednikova, M. V. (1952). *Zool. Zh.* **31**, 676–685.
Mellanby, K. (1937). *Parasitology* **29**, 131–141.
Mellanby, K. (1939). *Parasitology* **31**, 193–199.
Menusan, H. (1935). *J. Econ. Entomol.* **20**, 448–453.
Merle, J. (1968). *J. Insect Physiol.* **14**, 1159–1168.
Merle, J. (1970). *Colloq. Int. Cent. Nat. Rech. Sci.* **109**, 311–330.
Mills, R. R., Greenslade, F. C., and Couch, E. F. (1966). *J. Insect Physiol.* **12**, 767–779.
Minks, A. K. (1967). *Arch. Neer. Zool.* **17**, 175–257.
Mordue, W. (1965a). *J. Insect Physiol.* **11**, 493–503.
Mordue, W. (1965b). *J. Insect Physiol.* **11**, 505–511.
Mordue, W. (1965c). *J. Insect Physiol.* **11**, 617–629.
Mouton, J. (1971). *Gen. Comp. Endocrinol.* **18**, 610.
Müller, H. J. (1957). *Beitr. Entomol.* **7**, 203–225.
Müller, H. P. (1965). *Z. Vergl. Physiol.* **50**, 447–497.
Müssbichler, A. (1952). *Z. Vergl. Physiol.* **34**, 207–221.
Nair, M. K. (1963). *J. Histochem. Cytochem.* **2**, 495–499.

Naisse, J. (1966a). *Arch. Biol.* **77**, 139–201.
Naisse, J. (1966b). *Gen. Comp. Endocrinol.* **7**, 85–104.
Naisse, J. (1966c). *Gen. Comp. Endocrinol.* **7**, 105–110.
Naisse, J. (1969). *J. Insect Physiol.* **15**, 877–892.
Nayar, K. K. (1958a). *Proc. Indian. Acad. Sci.* **67**, 233–251.
Nayar, K. K. (1958b). *Int. Symp. Neurosecretion, 2nd, 1958* pp. 102–104.
Nayar, K. K. (1969). *Gen. Comp. Endocrinol., Suppl.* **2**, 565–571.
Newsom, L. D. (1963). Personal communication.
Noirot, C. (1957). *C. R. Acad. Sci., Ser. D* **245**, 743–745.
Normann, T. C., and Duve, H. (1969). *Gen. Comp. Endocrinol.* **12**, 449–459.
Norris, M. J. (1954). *Anti-Locust Bull.* **18**, 1–44.
Norris, M. J. (1959). *Entomol. Exp. Appl.* **2**, 154–168.
Norris, M. J. (1962). *Ann. Appl. Biol.* **50**, 600–603.
Novák, V. J. A. (1951). *Nature (London)* **167**, 132–133.
Odhiambo, T. R. (1966a). *J. Insect Physiol.* **12**, 819–828.
Odhiambo, T. R. (1966b). *J. Insect Physiol.* **12**, 995–1002.
Odhiambo, T. R. (1966c). *Acta Trop.* **23**, 264–271.
Odhiambo, T. R. (1968). *Entomol. Exp. Appl.* **11**, 379–388.
Odhiambo, T. R. (1971a). *Tissue Cell* **3**, 309–324.
Odhiambo, T. R. (1971b). *J. Exp. Zool.* **177**, 447–454.
Orr, C. W. M. (1964a). *J. Insect Physiol.* **10**, 53–64.
Orr, C. W. (1964b). *J. Insect Physiol.* **10**, 103–119.
Oudemans, J. T. (1899). *Zool. Jahrb., Syst.* **12**, 71–88.
Pain, J. (1956). *Insectes Soc.* **3**, 199–202.
Palm, N. B. (1948). *Opusc. Entomol., Suppl.* **7**, 1–101.
Palm, N. B. (1949). *Kgl. Sv. Vetenskapakad., Handl.* [4] **1**, 1–24.
Panov, A. A., and Bassurmanova, O. K. (1970). *J. Insect Physiol.* **16**, 1265–1282.
Panov, A. A., Bassurmanova, O. K., and Belyaeva, T. G. (1972). *J. Insect Physiol.* **18**, 1787–1792.
Passera, L. (1966). *C. R. Acad. Sci.* **263**, 1095–1098.
Passera, L. (1969). Ph. D. Thesis, Arch. Orig. Centre Dic., CNRS, Toulouse.
Passera, L. (1970). *Colloq. Int. Cent. Nat. Rech. Sci.* **109**, 129–146.
Pener, M. P. (1965). *J. Zool.* **147**, 119–136.
Pener, M. P. (1967). *J. Insect Physiol.* **13**, 665–684.
Pener, M. P. (1968). *Entomol. Exp. Appl.* **11**, 94–100.
Pflugfelder, O. (1937). *Z. Wiss. Zool.* **149**, 477–512.
Pflugfelder, O. (1939). *Z. Wiss. Zool.* **152**, 304–408.
Plugfelder, O. (1948). *Biol. Zantralbl.* **69**, 233–241.
Plugfelder, O. (1969). *Wilhelm Roux' Arch. Entwicklungsmech. Organismen* **64**, 182–198.
Possompès, B. (1949). *C. R. Acad. Sci.* **228**, 1527–1529.
Possompès, B. (1956). *Trans. Int. Congr. Entomol. 10th, 1956* Vol. 2, pp. 267–268.
Quo, P. (1965). *Acta Entomol. Sinica* **14**, 211–224.
Regen, J. (1910). *Zool. Anz.* **35**, 427–432.
Riddiford, L. M. (1970). *Develop. Biol.* **22**, 249–263.
Riddiford, L. M. (1971). *Mitt. Schweiz. Entomol. Ges.* **44**, 177–186.
Robert, P. (1970). *Colloq. Int. Cent. Nat. Rech. Sci.* **189**, 147–162.
Rohdendorf, E. (1965). *Zool. Jahrb., Abt. Allg. Zool. Physiol. Tiere* **71**, 685–693.
Röller, H. (1962). *Naturwissenschaften* **49**, 524.

Röller, H., and Dahm, K. H. (1968). *Recent Progr. Horm. Res.* **24**, 651–680.
Röller, H., Piepho, H., and Holz, I. (1962). *J. Insect Physiol.* **9**, 187–194.
Romer, F. (1971). *Naturwissenschaften* **58**, 324–325.
Roth, L. M. (1964). *J. Insect Physiol.* **10**, 915–945.
Roth, L. M., and Stay, B. (1959). *Science* **130**, 271.
Roth, L. M., and Stay, B. (1961). *J. Insect Physiol.* **7**, 186–202.
Roth, L. M., and Willis, E. R. (1956). *Ann. Entomol. Soc. Amer.* **49**, 195–204.
Roubaud, E., and Mezger, J. (1934). *Bull. Soc. Pathol. Exot.* **27**, 666–668
Roy, D. N. (1940). *Nature (London)* **145**, 747–748.
Sägesser, H. (1960). *J. Insect Physiol.* **5**, 264–285.
Sahota, T. S. (1969). *Can. J. Zool.* **47**, 917–920.
Scharrer, B. (1946). *Endocrinology* **38**, 46–55.
Scharrer, B. (1952). *Biol. Bull.* **102**, 261–272.
Scharrer, B. (1958). *Int. Symp. Neurosecretion, 2nd, 1957,* pp. 79–84.
Scharrer, B. (1959). *Symp. Comp. Endocrinol.* pp. 134–148.
Scharrer, B. (1961). *Biol. Bull.* **121**, 370.
Scharrer, B. (1971). *Z. Zellforsch. Mikrosk. Anat.* **120**, 1–16.
Scharrer, B., and Hadorn, E. (1938). *Proc. Nat. Acad. Sci. U.S.* **24**, 236–242.
Scharrer, B., and von Harnack, M. (1958). *Biol. Bull.* **115**, 508–520.
Scheurer, R. (1969). *J. Insect Physiol.* **15**, 1411–1419.
Schmidt, E. L., and Williams, C. M. (1953). *Biol. Bull.* **105**, 174–187.
Schooneveld, H. (1970). *Neth. J. Zool.* **20**, 151–237.
Shaaya, E., and Bodenstein, D. (1969). *J. Exp. Biol.* **170**, 281–292.
Siew, Y. C. (1965a). *J. Insect Physiol.* **11**, 1–10.
Siew, Y. C. (1965b). *J. Insect Physiol.* **11**, 463–479.
Siew, Y. C. (1965c) . *J. Insect Physiol.* **11**, 937–981.
Slăma, K. (1964a). *Biol. Bull.* **3**, 499–510.
Slăma, K. (1964b). *J. Insect Physiol.* **10**, 283–303.
Slăma, K. (1964c) . *J. Insect Physiol.* **10**, 773–782.
Slăma, K., and Williams, C. M. (1966). *Nature (London)* **210**, 329.
Sorm, F. (1971). *Mitt. Schweiz. Entomol. Ges.* **44**, 7–16.
Spielman, A., Gwadz, R. W., and Anderson, W. A. (1971) . *J. Insect Physiol.* **17**, 1807–1814.
Sroka, P., and Gilbert L. I. (1971). *J. Insect Physiol.* **17**, 2409–2420.
Staal, G. B. (1961). Ph. D. Thesis, Wageningen.
Stegwee, D., Kimmel, E. C., de Boer, J. A., and Henstra, S. (1963). *J. Cell Biol.* **19**, 519–527.
Strambi, A. (1967). *C. R. Acad. Sci.* **264**, 2031–2034.
Strangways-Dixon, J. (1961a). *J. Exp. Biol.* **38**, 225–235.
Strangways-Dixon, J. (1961b). *J. Exp. Biol.* **38**, 637–646.
Strangways-Dixon, J. (1962). *J. Exp. Biol.* **39**, 293–306.
Strong, L. (1965a). *J. Insect Physiol.* **11**, 135–146.
Strong, L. (1965b). *J. Insect Physiol.* **11**, 271–280.
Strong, L. (1967). *J. Insect Physiol.* **13**, 495–507.
Stumper, R. (1956). *Mitt. Schweiz. Entomol. Ges.* **19**, 373.
Sweetman, H. L. (1938). *Ecol. Monogr.* **8**, 285–311.
Swellengrebel, N. H. (1929). *Ann. Inst. Pasteur, Paris* **43**, 1370–1380.
Takeda, M. (1972). *J. Insect Physiol.* **18**, 571–580.
Thomsen, E. (1942). *Vidensk. Medd. Dan. Naturh. Foren.* **106**, 319–405.
Thomsen, E. (1948). *Nature (London)* **161**, 439–440.

Thomsen, E. (1949). *J. Exp. Biol.* **26**, 137–172.

Thomsen, E. (1952). *J. Exp. Biol.* **29**, 137–172.

Thomsen, E. (1956). *Bertil Hanstrom Zool. Pap.* pp. 298–306.

Thomsen, E., and Hamburger, K. (1955). *J. Exp. Biol.* **32**, 692–699.

Thomsen, E., and Möller, H. (1963). *J. Exp. Biol.* **40**, 301–321.

Thomsen, E., and Thomsen, M. (1970). *Z. Zellforsch. Mikrosk. Anat.* **110**, 40–60.

Tombes, A. S. (1966). *Ann. Entomol. Soc. Amer.* **59**, 376–380.

Tombes, A. S. ,and Bodenstein, D. (1967). *Amer. Zool.* **7**, 722.

Tombes, A. S., and Smith, D. S. (1966). *Amer. Zool.* **6**, 575–576.

Torossian, C. (1965). *C. R. Soc. Biol.* **159**, 2518.

Truman, J. W., and Riddiford, L. M. (1971). *Biol. Bull.* **140**, 8–14.

Tsiu-Ngun, W., and Quo, F. (1963). *Acta Entomol. Sinica* **12**, 411–421.

Vanderzant, E. S., and Richardson, C. D. (1965). *J. Insect Physiol.* **10**, 267–272.

Velthuis, H. J. (1970). *Z. Vergl. Physiol.* **70**, 210–222.

Verheyen-Voogd, C. (1959). *Z. Vergl. Physiol.* **41**, 527–582.

Vinogradova, E. B. (1958). *Uch. Zap. Leningrad, Gos. Univ., Ser. Biol. Nauk* **46**, 52–60.

Vogt, M. (1940). *Biol. Zentralbl.* **61**, 242–252.

Vogt, M. (1942). *Wilhelm Roux' Arch. Entwicklungsmech. Organismen* **141**, 424–454.

Vogt, M. (1943). *Biol. Zentralbl.* **63**, 467–470.

Vogt, M. (1947). *Z. Zellforsch. Mikrosk. Anat.* **34**, 160–164.

von Gast, R. (1967). *Insectes Soc.* **14**, 1–12.

von Harnack, M., and Scharrer, B. (1956). *Anat. Rec.* **125**, 558.

Voogd, C. (1955). *Experientia* **11**, 181–182.

Weed-Pfeiffer, I. G. (1936). *Proc. Soc. Exp. Biol. Med.* **34**, 883–885.

Weed-Pfeiffer, I. G. (1939). *J. Exp. Zool.* **82**, 439–461.

Weed-Pfeiffer, I. G. (1945). *J. Exp. Zool.* **99**, 183–233.

Wharton, M. L., and Wharton, D. R. A. (1957). *J. Insect Physiol.* **2**, 229–239.

Wigglesworth, V. B. (1936). *Quart. J. Microsc. Sci.* **79**, 91–121.

Wigglesworth, V. B. (1948). *J. Exptl. Biol.* **25**, 1–14.

Wilkens, J. L. (1967a). Ph.D. Thesis, University of California, Los Angeles.

Wilkens, J. L. (1967b). *Amer. Zool.* **7**, 723–724.

Wilkens, J. L. (1968). *J. Insect Physiol.* **14**, 927–944.

Wilkens, J. L. (1969). *J. Insect Physiol.* **15**, 1015–1024.

Williams, C. M. (1952). *Biol. Bull.* **103**, 120–138.

Williams, C. M. (1969). *Symp. Soc. Exp. Biol.* **23**, 285–300.

Williams, C. M., and Adkisson, P. (1964). *Biol. Bull.* **127**, 511—525.

Wirtz, P., and Beetsma, Y. (1972). *Entomol Exp. Appl.* **15**, 517–520.

Woke, P. A. (1937). *Amer. J. Hyg.* **25**, 372–380.

Yamashita, Y., Tani, K., and Kobayashi, M. (1961). *Acta Sericol.* **39**, 12–15.

Yeoli, M., and Mer, G. G. (1938). *Trans. Roy. Soc. Trop. Med. Hyg.* **31**, 437–444.

Zwölfer, W. (1931). *Z. Angew. Entomol.* **17**, 475–562.

Chapter 4

PHYSIOLOGICAL AND BIOCHEMICAL CHANGES DURING INSECT DEVELOPMENT

Ivar P. S. Agrell and Anders M. Lundquist

I.   Introduction 159
II. Embryonic Development 160
     A. Structural Changes during Embryogenesis 160
     B. Metabolic Pattern of Embryogenesis 173
     C. Dynamics of Embryonic Organization 188
III. Postembryonic Development 208
     A. Growth 209
     B. Metamorphosis 215
IV. Prospects for Future Work in the Physiology and Biochemistry of
     Insect Development 231
     References 233

I. Introduction

Insect development has attracted great interest from early times not only among scientists but also among laymen. The seemingly sudden and unexpected changes which appear during the life cycle of insects have caused much speculation. During this century an ever-accumulating bulk of definitive information has been collected about the driving forces that occur during insect development, making it somewhat less mysterious. Progressively refined biochemical and physiological techniques have also been applied to the developmental physiology of insects, thereby greatly accelerating the accumulation of knowledge within this field. Therefore, the literature concerning insect development is difficult to survey; to facilitate the penetration of this domain, particularly for the nonspecialist, comprehensive reviews, appearing at suitable intervals, are necessary. During the years which have passed since 1964, when the first edition of this chapter was printed, the references have increased almost exponentially. However, although much valuable information has been added thereby, no aspects on insect development have been fundamentally changed. Thus, the general layout applied for the first edition of this chapter can still be used.

II. Embryonic Development

The cleidoic insect egg represents a closed system and embryonic development is completed with greater independence from environmental factors than the embryogenesis of different types of marine or freshwater eggs of various other invertebrates or vertebrates, from which so much fundamental knowledge for the understanding of the forces operating during embryogenesis has been obtained. For this reason, the insect egg is decidedly less suitable for experimental work and has not contributed as much to the general physiology of development. Furthermore, since the insect egg is a very special case of a yolk-rich egg, the course of events during insect embryogenesis is far from easy to interpret. Nevertheless, even though insect embryogenesis has so many unique characteristics, it also exhibits some features of general interest.

A. Structural Changes during Embryogenesis

A prerequisite for the understanding of the mechanisms during embryonic development is some knowledge of the structural changes. Therefore, it is essential to include a short review of these complicated series of events in the insect egg. Experimentalists have emphasized the earlier development of the insect, where some fundamental ideas can be discerned and are available for discussion. For information concerning morphology, especially of the later embryonic stages, we recommend the extensive review by Johannsen and Butt (1941).

1. Organization of the Insect Egg

With few exceptions, the insect egg is rich in yolk, which has a nonpolar distribution. The eggs are centrolecithal. Yolk-poor eggs can be regarded as secondary adaptations to an external nutritional supply during embryogenesis, e.g., during parasitism and viviparity. The cytoplasm enmeshes the yolk particles as a reticulum, which reaches the egg surface and may surround the egg as a sheet of cytoplasm, the periplasm. The thickness of the periplasm and also the amount of cytoplasm in the egg vary considerably among insect groups. A close correlation seems to exist between the quantity of cytoplasm and the phylogenetic level. The pterygotes form a graded series in this respect, with the more primitive groups having only a very small quantity of egg cytoplasm, and the eggs of the more advanced orders exhibiting an increasing thickness of periplasm culminating in the eggs of Lepidoptera and Diptera (Krause, 1939). (See Fig. 1, where these differences between an egg of the primitive type and an egg of the advanced type can be seen.) As will be emphasized later, there is also a close correspondence between embryonic determination and quantity of periplasm. During oogenesis, the insect egg has grown considerably through the deposition of yolk. Thus, the egg nucleus occupies only a very small fraction of the egg volume, often located in the anterior half of the egg and surrounded by a small island of cytoplasm.

Outside the oolemma the egg is surrounded by two membranes, an inner vitelline membrane and an outer chorion. The intact egg is usually extremely impermeable, but the permeability increases if the chorion is removed. The insect egg is, however, permeable to gases, and respiratory exchange between the interior of the egg and the environment occurs. The eggshell of both aquatic and terrestrial insects may exhibit special morphological adaptations to facilitate respiration (see review by Hinton, 1969). The function of these structures in terrestrial eggs is, in most cases, to provide an adequate oxygen supply and at the same time to keep the water loss as low as possible. Since the water molecule is smaller than the oxygen molecule, the shell cannot be both permeable to oxygen and impermeable to water.

In its external morphology the usually elongated insect egg in most cases clearly demonstrates a bilateral symmetry. According to the so-called Hallez' law, the bilateral axial system of the oocyte in the insect ovary has the same orientation as that of the maternal organism, which produces the egg. This seems to be true for the anterioposterior axis, but not for the dorsoventral axis, at least not in all insect species. In the orthopteran *Acheta* (Netzel, 1965, 1968), in the coleopteran *Acanthoscelides* (Mulnard, 1954), and in *Drosophila* (Gill, 1964), the dorsoventral axis of the oocyte does not coincide with that of the mother. In *Drosophila* this axis is radially oriented in the ovary. The inner structure of the egg may reflect its bilateral symmetry, for instance, in the shaping of the periplasm. Furthermore, the oocyte nucleus may occupy an eccentric posi-

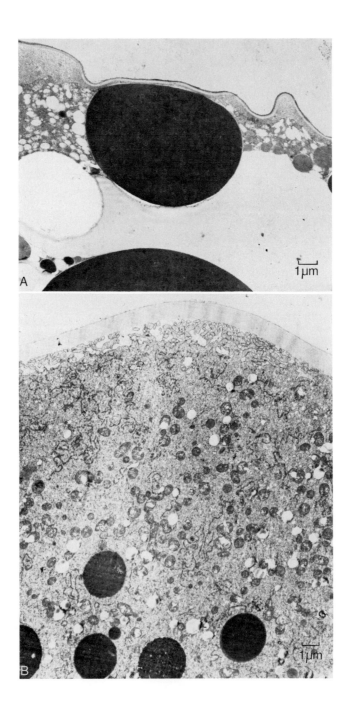

tion, e.g., anteriodorsally in *Drosophila* (Gill, 1964) and posteriodorsally in *Acheta* (Netzel, 1968). The movement of the nucleus from the center of the oocyte is the first sign of polarity in these eggs. The different kinds of yolk granules may also be unevenly distributed in the egg (Rempel and Church, 1965). The factors which determine the anterioposterior and dorsoventral polarity of the egg are not known. At least in *Acheta,* centrifugation does not affect the polarity of the oocyte (Netzel, 1968). The oocyte nucleus may play a role in the establishment of polarity (Netzel, 1968). Factors determining polarity may reside in the follicle or the ovary (Schlottmann and Bonhag, 1956; Gill, 1963, 1964; Netzel, 1968). The axial system of the embryo always coincides with that of the egg.

The inner structure of the insect egg may show a certain stratification. In the lepidopterous egg (Sehl, 1931; Müller, 1938), the layer below the periplasm is poor in cytoplasm, while the inner column of the egg center is much richer in cytoplasm. The same is found for the egg of the honey bee (Schnetter, 1934a). There are indications of a similar structure in the locust egg (Roonwal, 1936) and in the *Tenebrio* egg (Ewest, 1937). In the living *Tenebrio* egg the area of the future embryo is also outlined.

The ultrastructure of the insect egg was first investigated in *Drosophila* (Okada and Waddington, 1959; King, 1960; summarized by King et al., 1966). The usually occurring organelles were demonstrated and different kinds of yolk granules were described. Stacks of annulate lamellae were

---

Fig. 1. The structure of insect eggs. (A) *Acheta domestica.* Electron micrograph of the structure at the surface of the posterior part of the egg during early cleavage. Beneath the hyaline vitelline membrane a homogenous surface layer without yolk granules is seen. Possibly, this represents some kind of periplasm. Below this zone there is a restricted cytoplasmic layer containing smaller yolk granules and some mitochondria. The rounded lacunae possibly represent lipid droplets which have been eluted during fixation. The inner part of the egg contains very large yolk granules. Some of these penetrate into the outer layers. The space between these granules is filled with a hyaline, structureless material. (B) *Calliphora erythrocephala.* Electron micrograph of the structure at the surface of the posterior part of the egg during early cleavage. Beneath the hyaline vitelline membrane the surface of the egg is extensively folded. An outer, very thick periplasmic layer gradually merges into an inner cytoplasmic layer filled with yolk granules. The periplasm is rich in mitochondria and has an abundant endoplasmic reticulum. The ground plasm contains free ribosomes. The rounded lacunae possibly represent lipid droplets, which have been eluted during fixation. Below, the space between the yolk granules is filled with the same kind of cytoplasmic material which is found in the periplasm. Both types of eggs were dechorionized in hypochlorite solution, prefixed in glutaraldehyde, and fixed in osmium tetroxide. During their stay in glutaraldehyde the eggs were punctured with a fine needle and, after a while, cut in halves in order to facilitate the penetration of the fixatives. The preparations were contrasted with uranylacetate. Methods according to Mahowald (1963a, 1968b).

found in the periplasm. Wolf (1969a) described the ultrastructure of the egg in the gall midge *Wachtiella*. See also Fig. 1.

A marked polarity characterizes the periplasm in respect to the pole plasm. In many endopterygote insect eggs the periplasm of the posterior pole contains preformed structures, the oosome material (Huettner, 1923; Mukerji, 1930; Wilson, 1953; Counce, 1959). This material consists either of a basophilic body, the oosome, or of basophilic granules of varying size and shape, the polar granules. The term "germ cell determinants" is often used for these structures. Since their function is not fully understood and since they may have other functions besides germ-cell determination, the more neutral terms are advisable.

2. Mitosis and Nuclear Migration

The early cleavage in the insect egg concerns the nucleus and its plasma island only. A subdivision of the big yolk-rich egg as a whole cannot be achieved. In the small, spherical eggs of collemboles the nuclear division is temporarily accompanied by total cleavage (Philiptschenko, 1912; Jura, 1965).

As in all embryonic material, the early mitotic activity in the insect egg is high, and in some groups it is very high. There seems to exist a certain tendency for the eggs of the more primitive groups, which are also less rich in cytoplasm, to show a slower mitotic activity than those of the more advanced groups, which are richer in cytoplasm. In Orthoptera and Odonata, the duration of each cleavage cycle at ordinary temperature is a matter of hours (Seidel, 1929; Roonwal, 1936; Mahr, 1960b). In less primitive groups such as the Hymenoptera and Coleoptera, the single cleavage cycle takes about 1 hour (Schnetter, 1934a; Ewest, 1937), in Lepidoptera, less than 1 hour (Maschlanka, 1938). In the most advanced group, Diptera, the cleavage cycle takes only few minutes; in the *Culex* egg, 15 minutes (Idris, 1960); and in the *Drosophila* egg, 10 minutes (Rabinowitz, 1941). The latter is probably the most rapid mitotic cycle reported from animal material. However, it has never been ascertained whether there is a real causal connection between cytoplasmic content and cleavage rate.

As stated, the cleavage concerns both the nuclei and their cytoplasmic islands. A cleavage nucleus together with its cytoplasmic island is called a cleavage energid. Of interest is the rapid increase not only in nuclear but also in cytoplasmic material. The increase in cytoplasmic material is probably an illusion in many cases and represents an accumulation of cytoplasm around the nuclei in the shape of cytoplasmic islands through a drainage from the more or less continuous cytoplasmic reticulum. The interphase time may be too short to allow a sufficiently extensive protein synthesis.

The early nuclear divisions are synchronous. As a general rule this synchronized mitotic activity will continue until the nuclei have moved out to the egg periphery. In all groups of Pterygota which do not have an aberrant embryonic development, this seems to take place after 9–10 mitotic cycles. There are a few reports of an early asynchrony (Roonwal, 1936; Tiegs and Murray, 1937), but these statements should be verified. The main cause of the synchrony seems to be a free syncytial contact between the dividing nuclei. Syncytial junctions make a free transport between the nuclei possible, which enables them to retain a sufficient unity for a synchronous cleavage. The cleavage center (see below) is a possible source of controlling factors. A pumping mechanism may be provided by the cytoplasmic movements during the mitosis itself, by which the cytoplasmic reticulum is successively incorporated into the nuclear islands.

In most cases the nuclear cleavage starts at a cleavage center (CC), more or less in the middle of the egg (Fig. 4) (see Krause and Sander, 1962). Around this center the dividing nuclei form a cluster. The nuclear divisions may proceed in waves from the CC (Geyer-Duszyńska, 1959; Mahr, 1960a; Wolf, 1969a; Bantock, 1970), in which case the synchrony is not strictly complete. The energids move from the CC toward the periphery of the egg and, by degrees, form a hollow sphere. At last they reach the egg surface and form the blastoderm. Also in the case of total cleavage in Collembola, the same movement of the nuclei in plasma islands toward the egg surface may occur; only this migration now takes place within blastomeres (Philiptschenko, 1912). Later the boundaries between these disappear.

Even if it may seem so, early cleavage in insect eggs cannot be regarded as a uniform sequence of nuclear multiplication. Often, specific morphological or physiological changes occur during a specific cleavage stage (Counce, 1961). The radiation sensitivity may, for instance, exhibit a maximum during a certain cleavage division (von Borstel, 1957).

The driving forces for the nuclear movements in the insect egg have been much discussed, e.g., by Campbell (1959), and all kinds of mechanisms for pulling, pushing, and contraction have been proposed. One perhaps too simple, but possible explanation depends on the fact that during the divisions the egg cytoplasm between the dividing nuclei within the nuclear sphere is successively incorporated into the nuclear islands (Eastham, 1928; Strasburger, 1934; Schnetter, 1934a). Thus, when the nuclei are moved around through the unidirected bubbling of the cytoplasm created by the mitotic activity, they will be gradually shifted from a region of decreasing cytoplasmic content into a cytoplasm-rich region around the egg periphery. Streaming movements or oscillations occur in the egg syncytium of many insects (e.g., Rempel and Church, 1965; Wolf, 1969a; Wolf and Krause, 1971). These movements may be correlated to the cleavage divisions in time, but their relation, if any, to the directed nuclear movements is not clear in most cases. However, in the dragonfly egg the migration of the energids may be promoted by oscillations in the yolk (Schanz, 1966). Another possibility is that the energids move actively. The spindle apparatus may be involved. For instance, Strasburger (1934) stated that the centrioles are peripherally placed and the astral rays are inwardly directed in the dividing *Calliphora* egg. If so, the nuclei should have the possibility of migrating in a similar manner as the sperm nucleus moves in some eggs. According to an interesting observation by Wolf (1969a), the cleavage nuclei of the midge *Wachtiella* are surrounded by complex, multilayered nuclear envelopes during their moving phase. It was suggested that this is an ultrastructural differentiation related to the migration of the nuclear islands. However, during the corresponding stage in *Drosophila,* normal nuclear envelopes were described by Okada and Waddington (1959). In the egg of the beetle *Leptinotarsa,* development is retarded when nuclei are removed during early cleavage (Schnetter, 1965), while transplantation of nuclei into newly laid eggs accelerates development in some cases (Schnetter, 1967). It was concluded that the mitotic rhythm is fixed and that the nuclear migration toward the periphery depends on the number of energids. More ultrastructural and experimental evidence is needed, however, to elucidate the mechanisms of nuclear migration. Also, the ooplasmic factors, which govern this morphogenetic process, remain unknown, whether they originate in the CC or in other parts of the egg.

3. Blastoderm Formation and Mitotic Gradients

The cleavage units may reach the egg surface with the nuclei foremost. Thus, if a periplasm is present, the nuclei may move in there first, while the cytoplasmic islands are later incorporated (Schnetter, 1934a). The periplasm may secondarily increase in thickness by accumulation of cytoplasm from the interior of the egg. Usually the nuclei do not reach the egg periphery simultaneously; however, this seems to be the case in the higher Diptera. In some groups nuclei may reach the egg surface at a girdle-shaped area, and those parts of the egg periphery which later form the germ area are invaded first. When the nuclei have reached the egg surface, the next cleavage may represent a real cytoplasmic segmentation and cell membranes are formed. The superficial cleavage is then initiated.

Often, however, some superficial cleavage divisions occur before cytokinesis. In those cases, a syncytial blastoderm stage (preblastoderm stage) precedes the formation of the true, cellular blastoderm. In the dipterans *Drosophila* and *Wachtiella,* the formation of the cellular blastoderm has been studied on the ultrastructural level (Mahowald, 1963a; Wolf, 1969a). The cell membranes develop by invagination of the oolemma. The membrane folds fuse laterally when they reach the yolk. This leaves the blastoderm cells completely surrounded by membranes. Below these another membrane forms and encloses the yolk. Fibrous material is seen in the cytoplasm adjacent to the folds. In unfertilized eggs, or in eggs where the nuclei are prevented from reaching the periplasm, a subdivided "blastoderm" (pseudoblastoderm) without nuclei may be formed (e.g., Haget, 1963; Schnetter, 1965; Wolf, 1969b). Thus the formation of the blastoderm seems to be a rather autonomous process, independent of the nuclei.

The superficial cleavage divisions are generally reported as being nonsynchronous. Whereas the synchronous mitotic cycles as a rule seem to be all of the same length, the mitotic rate decreases when the nuclei have reached the periphery. This apparently depends on a prolongation of the interphase. Nucleoli are seen for the first time during this period (e.g., Mahowald, 1963a; Sauer, 1966; Schwalm, 1969). The decrease in mitotic rate and the appearance of nucleoli indicate the onset of synthetic activities. As will be seen later, these changes coincide with the start of RNA synthesis in the egg. During the superficial cleavage the mitotic activity is more differentiated than during the intravitelline, synchronous cleavage. In more primitive groups it will be higher in the germ anlage (Seidel, 1929; Sauer, 1964, 1966; Schwalm, 1965), and, in the absence of a thick periplasmic layer, the nuclei with their plasma islands have free mobility and move into the germ area. In higher groups which have an egg periplasm, the mitotic activity within the blastoderm may be graded. Thus, waves of mitoses have been reported in Coleoptera (Tiegs and Murray, 1937; Schnetter, 1965; Rempel and Church, 1965), in Hymenoptera (Schnetter, 1934a; von Borstel, 1957; Wolf and Krause, 1971), and in Diptera (Agrell, 1962; Riemann, 1965; Wolf, 1969a). In the beetle *Acanthoscelides,* mitotic waves were observed by Mulnard (1947), but his results were not confirmed by Jung (1966a). In most cases, a wave starting from the anterior pole, or double waves starting from both the anterior and the posterior pole, was demonstrated.

A more thorough investigation has been made of the *Calliphora* egg (Fig. 2) (Agrell, 1962). In this embryo the synchrony of the nuclear divisions continues for eight mitotic cycles, and by this time all the nuclei

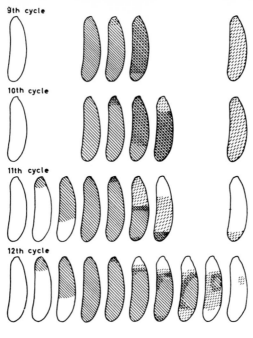

9th cycle

10th cycle

11th cycle

12th cycle

☐ inter- ▨ meta- ▧ ana- ▨ telo-phases

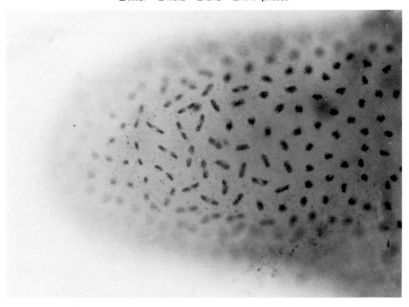

Fig. 2. Mitotic gradients in the cleaving egg of *Calliphora erythrocephala*. Above: scheme of the mitotic waves during the 4 superficial cleavage divisions following the period of intracitelline, synchronous cleavage. No distinction was made between pro- phase and metaphase. From Agrell (1962). Below: the anterior part of the egg during the 11th cleavage cycle.

have reached the periplasm. During the ninth cycle the mitotic activity is graded. The cleavage starts at the anterior pole and moves backward as a wave. This is repeated during the tenth cycle. Behind the cleavage wave the nuclei enter telo–interphase. During the eleventh and twelfth cycles another mitotic center appears at the posterior end and a double mitotic gradient is established. The length of the single mitotic cycle increases during these stages. After the twelfth cycle the nuclei of the blastoderm remain for a long time in interphase before the processes of invagination start. The same cleavage pattern was found in another calliphorid, *Cochliomyia,* by Riemann (1965). According to a short statement by Schnetter (1934a), the mitotic wave should start in the zone of the honey bee egg, where the cleavage nuclei first reach the periplasm and from there spread out in both directions. This should imply that the mitotic activity would be accelerated by the periplasm, while a delay seems more likely. Perhaps the direction of this double mitotic wave in the honey bee egg may be regarded as undecided until further notice.

During the nuclear migration towards the egg surface some nuclei are left behind as the yolk nuclei. Especially in primitive groups, these may also be descendants of nuclei returned from the blastoderm into the interior of the egg. The yolk nuclei represent a case of very early nuclear differentiation. A yolk nucleus together with its cytoplasmic island is called a vitellophage. The vitellophages show a reduced cleavage rate, but grow considerably and may undergo endomitosis. In the fly embryo their number varies appreciably in different individuals at each definite stage (Agrell, 1964b). In some insect eggs the yolk is partitioned in a secondary cleavage process, after the ordinary cleavage has occurred.

As previously mentioned, the periplasm of the posterior pole in many endopterygote insect eggs has an aberrant structure containing the stainable oosome material. All or some of the nuclei which reach the posterior pole plasm will form the germ line. Chance seems to be the only factor determining which nuclei enter this region (Huettner, 1923). The pole plasm exerts a pronounced inhibitory influence on the mitotic rate of these nuclei and they acquire a mitotic rhythm of their own. The polar plasm is reached by the nuclei at very different times. To take two extremes, in *Miastor* this occurs already at the second cleavage (Kahle, 1908; White, 1950), while in *Drosophila* the nuclei enter the polar plasm only after the eighth to ninth division (Huettner, 1923). In *Miastor* only one of the cleavage nuclei enters the polar plasm, in *Drosophila* an indefinite, greater number (5–11).

When the nuclei have entered the polar plasm, cellularization occurs in the posterior pole region. The so-called pole cells bud off and form a polar cap. The germ cells are descendants of the pole cells. It seems efficient that the cells of the germ line at the earliest possible occasion separate themselves from the rest of the embryo to escape differentiating influences. Thus, the early determination of the germ cells need not be regarded as an early differentiation. The implications of this type of germ-cell formation are discussed by Painter (1959).

In more primitive insect groups, such as Orthophera and Odonata, a periplasm can be missing and no polar plasm has been observed. However, in these groups an early appearance of germ cells in the posterior part of the embryo has been demonstrated (Heymons, 1895). Even in the primitive collembole egg the primordial germ cells can be distinguished cytologically as early as in the blastoderm stage (Jura, 1967). How the germ line is determined in lower insects is not known, but a ready assumption is that this determination cannot be very divergent from that which characterizes the higher insect groups. Perhaps some kind of polar plasm, possibly containing a more dispersed oosome material, has been overlooked. In the *Acheta* egg the periplasm is definitely thicker at the posterior pole (Agrell, 1964b).

4. Formation of Embryo Area and Germ Layers

After some time the blastoderm becomes differentiated into a ventral embryonic area (the germ anlage) and an extraembryonic region in the remainder of the egg. In more advanced egg types the germ anlage is differentiated without rearrangement of the egg constituents, while in primitive eggs blastoderm nuclei migrate into the embryonic region. Sometimes two embryonic areas are formed which later come together to form the definite germ anlage. In the primitive eggs of Odonata and Orthoptera the formation of the germ anlage is a very complicated process, involving dynamic processes such as contractions and streaming movements in the egg syncytium and decomposition of yolk under the embryonic area through the activity of vitellophages (Sauer, 1964, 1966; Schwalm, 1965; Schanz, 1966; Seidel, 1966; Sander and Vollmar, 1967). There is a very close correlation between the abundance of cytoplasm in the egg and the amount of blastoderm that will form the germ anlage. In those insect groups regarded as primitive, where the eggs contain only small amounts of cytoplasm, consistently only a very small primary embryonic area develops. With increasing amount of plasma, the germ anlage will occupy an ever-increasing area of the blastoderm until finally, in the higher Diptera almost the whole of the blastoderm develops into the embryo. The thin extraembryonic area of the blastoderm gives rise to the embryonic membranes, primarily to the outer serosa, secondarily, through processes of invagination or immersion of the germ area, to the inner amnion. The egg is divided into compartments by the extraembryonic membranes. Differences in pH and concentration of some ions between these compartments have been detected and may have functional significance (Roemhild, 1968). The mitotic activity seems to be more or less restricted to the embryonic area where a rapid cell proliferation can be observed. However, the nuclei of the embryonic membranes have apparently undergone some kind of endoreduplication. Thus, in the *Acheta* egg, some preliminary microspectrophotometric measurements on Feulgen-stained nuclei indicated about four times higher deoxyribonucleic acid content in the serosa nuclei, and also in the yolk nuclei, than in the nuclei of the early germ area (Agrell, 1964b). The polyploidy of these nuclei has later been confirmed by Grellet (1971b) in eggs of three orthopteran species by cytophotometric measurements of DNA. While the nuclear volume in these eggs on the average decreases during development, the nuclear volume of the serosa and yolk nuclei increases (Sauer, 1966; Grellet, 1971b).

By the formation of the primary germ layers the germ anlage is transformed into the germ band. The formation of the germ layers within the embryonic area of eggs which are rich in yolk is always an indistinct process and the insect egg is definitely no expection. On the contrary, the nature of the gastrulation in the insect egg is very obscure and is still the object of discussion. Certainly an invagination generally occurs in the shape of a ventral groove, but the inner layer thus generated, the hypoblast, does not produce endoderm primarily, as should be expected, but mesoderm. In a strict sense, one should perhaps use the term endomesoderm, as the hypoblast secondarily produces some endoderm. The endoderm should, in fact, have three origins: one primary provisional endoderm formed during the intravitelline separation by a modified epiboly and consisting of yolk cells, and two secondary endoderms, one separated from the hypoblast, and one arising from the ectodermal pockets stomodaeum and proctodaeum. Even some pole cells may be incorporated into the gut epithelium (Poulson, 1947). Thus the endoderm, especially the midgut epithelium, has a mixed origin. Furthermore, as endoderm in the form of yolk cells is separated before the formation of the cortical cell layer conventionally termed blastoderm, no true blastula stage should occur. The so-called blastula is therefore really a postgastrula stage. This may be enough to stress the very unique character of the formation of the germ layers through multiphased gastrulation in the insect egg. Surveys of the implications are given by Roonwal (1936) and Weygoldt (1960).

Generally, the different foldings of the embryo which occur during embryogenesis tend to be accompanied by local mitotic activity (Agrell,

1964a). This also concerns the invaginations at gastrulation in the fly embryo (Agrell, 1962). Thus, these invaginations are apparently not only achieved by cell migration. The mechanics of dipteran gastrulation are discussed by Anderson (1966) and Davis *et al.* (1968).

As mentioned, the germ band may move into the yolk interior of the egg in connection with the formation of the embryonic membranes. At this time segmentation is initiated. Following the protocephalon the anterior segments are often the earliest demarcated. Then the segmentation proceeds from the anterior toward the posterior end. In eggs of primitive groups the posterior segments are produced by the proliferative growth of a segment formation zone. In the less regulative eggs of the higher insect groups, in which the embryonic area is much larger, the segments are formed directly by subdivision of the embryonic part of the blastoderm, and growth processes are of less significance. During the processes of segmentation a high degree of mobility is demonstrated through a shift in position which is termed blastokinesis. In the typical case, blastokinesis represents a subsequent revolution of the embryo around the egg. During this movement, first the germ band rotates 180° in relation to the egg axis so that the posterior embryonic end points to the anterior pole of the egg (anatrepsis); then the embryo performs a reversed movement (catatrepsis) and the final result is a restored correspondence between the axes of the embryo and the egg. The blastokinetic movements are most pronounced in those insect eggs which have only a short germ band and thus much free space for motions, i.e., in the Orthoptera, Odonata, and Hemiptera. Blastokinesis can still be traced in Neuroptera, Coleoptera, Hymenoptera, and Lepidoptera, but for obvious reasons it does not occur in the higher Diptera. However, even in the latter group the posterior end of the growing germ band is extended around the posterior pole and along the dorsal surface of the egg and later retracted, a process which may be regarded as the last rudiment of blastokinesis. From time-lapse studies and constriction experiments Sander (1968) concluded that anatrepsis in the hemipteran *Euscelis* must be due to contractile structures in the yolk system exerting a pull upon the posterior end of the germ anlage. This may well be the case in other insect eggs too. Possibly insect eggs contain a special embryonic actomyosin system (Moser *et al.,* 1970). The embryo may also be carried away by streaming movements in the egg (Mahr, 1961). Although isolated embryos may show autonomous movements (Slifer, 1932a), the germ band apparently does not take any active part in anatrepsis. The mechanisms of anatrepsis in different insects are discussed by Krause and Sander (1962) and Sander (1968).

The continued insect embryogenesis representing the subsequent formation of the different organs does not offer common denominators suitable enough for a short review. For these the reader is referred to suitable textbooks.

B. METABOLIC PATTERN OF EMBRYOGENESIS

The morphological stages of development should have some demonstrable correspondence to metabolic changes, by which the embryogenetic mechanisms could be causally interpreted. However, the insect egg is a small object and not easy to obtain in sufficiently large and homogeneous quantities for most biochemical analysis. This difficulty is likewise reflected in the biochemical work done up to now; the investigations made on the metabolism during insect embryogenesis can at the moment give only some glimpses of the causal connections. Furthermore, it is often difficult to make a comparison between results obtained with different species, not only because different methods of separation and analysis have been used, but also because the results are not expressed on comparable bases. Results expressed per unit of wet weight may be misleading, because drastic changes in water content may occur during development. Measurements made separately in the embryo and the yolk and expressed per unit of dry weight seem to be desirable.

1. Changes in Energy Metabolism

The integral energy metabolism is reflected in the respiratory metabolism. Measurements of the gaseous exchange of the egg have been made in different insect groups, e.g., Fink (1925), Melvin (1928), Bodine (1929), and Verma (1965). The general course of these respiratory curves shows a successive and uncomplicated increase in energy consumption during proceeding embryogenesis.

It has been suggested that the so-called formative period of embryogenesis, when the germ area develops, should be characterized by a lower and steadier respiratory level than the later part of embryogenesis (Melvin, 1928; Edwards, 1953; Ludwig and Wugmeister, 1955). However, this supposed lag period in energy metabolism seems to a great extent to depend upon an optical illusion when looking at the respiratory curves. When a curve is reproduced on an arithmetical scale, the slope of the curve appears less obvious at lower values than at higher. If one redraws the curves of Melvin (1928), for example, on a semilogarithmic scale, their course will be that of a fairly straight line, indicating no lag period but rather a continuous increase in respiration. Thus the postulation of a particularly low metabolism during the formative period is quite an over-estimation. There may be something to it, but only for the reason that the respiration of the whole egg includes the respiration of the embryo as well as the still unchanged yolk. The respiration of the true embryo will be superimposed upon the general level of yolk respiration. As a result, there is a tendency for the combined respiratory curve to flatten out during the time when the embryo area is small. Thus, the isolated grasshopper embryo has been observed to have a definitely lower absolute respiration than the yolk, but the difference is rapidly leveled out (Bodine and Boell, 1936). If these respiratory values are recalculated on the basis of the nitrogen content, the embryo demonstrates a much higher metabolism than the yolk. At an early germ-band stage the respiratory rate already is about four times higher in the embryo than in the yolk (Trowbridge and Bodine, 1940). The yolk respiration shows no increase during this period. The fact that possible gradations in development cannot be observed in the respiratory curve during embryogenesis is not unique for the insect egg but seems to be the rule for all animal groups (Boell, 1955).

In our laboratory we have tried to detect the kind of respiratory rhythm which occurs during the single mitotic cycle of eggs with total cleavage (Zeuthen, 1951). As material we have used eggs of the fly *Calliphora* in a sensitive Cartesian diver system. Also in eggs where hundreds of nuclei were dividing synchronously, no such respiratory cycles could be detected (Agrell, 1964b). Perhaps the absence of rhythmical changes in metabolism is distinctive for a dividing syncytium.

Nevertheless, the respiratory curve of the developing insect egg may show a more diversified behavior. Thus, there is the same marked increase in respiratory rate at fertilization known from eggs of other animal groups, indicating similar structural changes at fertilization. In the eggs of the fruitfly and of the silkworm the respiration may increase more than 50% soon after fertilization (Boell and Poulson, 1939; Wolsky, 1949). Whether this metabolic activation of the egg is also reflected in the respiratory increase sometimes reported from the first day of embryonic development cannot be decided (see Ludwig and Wugmeister, 1955). An indication of an increase in respiratory activity during the blastokinetic movements is given by Tuft (1949) for the *Rhodnius* egg. On the other hand, earlier measurements on grasshopper eggs seem to indicate that this effect is small compared to the increase by a change in basal metabolism (Burkholder, 1934).

Some insect eggs pass through a more or less obligatory stage of developmental delay, a so-called diapause. Such a period is characterized by a lowered metabolism (Fig. 3A). Also in the cases where such an egg may

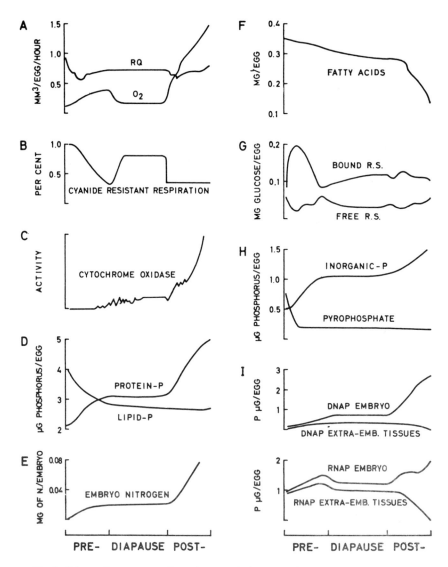

Fig. 3. Schematic representation of some biochemical changes during embryonic development in the egg of one and the same insect species, the grasshopper *Melanoplus differentialis*. (A) from Boell (1935); (B) from Robbie *et al.* (1938); (C) from Allen (1940); (D) and (H) from Thompson and Bodine (1938); (E) from Trowbridge and Bodine (1940); (F) from Slifer (1930); (G) from Hill (1945)—R. S., reducing substances; (I) from Lu and Bodine (1953).

carry through its development in unbroken succession, the respiratory curve will show a temporarily reduced increase of its slope during the corresponding embryonic period (Bodine, 1929). These changes in respiratory rate can be correlated to the cell-proliferating activity in the embryo (Slifer, 1931). Also, the amounts of DNA and RNA apparently do not increase during diapause (Fig. 3I) (Lu and Bodine, 1953). The low metabolic activity is reflected by changes on the ultrastructural level. The chromatin, for instance, becomes condensed and the nucleoli small and compact (Okada, 1970). The mechanisms responsible for the onset and termination of diapause have been much discussed (e.g., Roemhild, 1965, 1968; Smallman and Mansingh, 1969; Krause and Krause, 1971), but the subject will not be treated here.

The respiratory quotient (RQ) has been observed during the development of some insect eggs (Fig. 3A). The general tendency seems to be a high RQ, near 1, at the beginning of the embryonic development and then a more or less rapid fall (Boell, 1935; Ludwig and Wugmeister, 1955; Rutschky and Joseph, 1957). This should indicate an early utilization of carbohydrate and then a fat metabolism. In the grasshopper egg an observed temporary strong decrease in RQ has been interpreted as a conversion of fat into carbohydrate (Boell, 1935).

The direct observation of the energy storage in the egg of carbohydrate and fat (and protein) seems to confirm the conclusions drawn from the results of the respiratory measurements (Fig. 3F and G) (Slifer, 1930; Needham, 1931; Hill, 1945; Rothstein, 1952; Chino, 1957; Urbani and Bellini, 1959; Allais et al., 1964; Kinsella and Smyth, 1966; Svoboda et al., 1966; Quickenden, 1970; Lipsitz and McFarlane, 1971). Carbohydrate catabolism predominates during early development. During the rest of the developmental period mainly lipids are utilized and lipids constitute the major source of energy during embryogenesis. The loss of lipids occurs in the neutral lipid fraction and is due to triglyceride catabolism. Needham (1931) postulated that carbohydrates and especially lipids are the preponderant sources of energy in the cleidoic egg. He also postulated that the different energy-yielding substrates are catabolized during embryogenesis in the sequence carbohydrates, proteins, and lipids. The typical insect egg is of the cleidoic type and exhibits a pattern of energy metabolism which is in agreement with Needham's hypothesis. Protein catabolism is very slight or does not occur at all (see below). The only exception to the general rule thus far reported is the egg of the mealworm, Tenebrio molitor, in which glycogen appears to be the main source of energy (Ludwig and Ramazzotto, 1965). The advantages of lipid catabolism are obvious. They contain more energy and release more metabolic water than carbohydrates and proteins per unit of weight. Lipids (and carbohydrates) are completely metabolized. Thus, excretion is no problem and no end products containing unutilized energy are formed. The early utilization of carbohydrates may depend on the need for an energy source which is easily available and easily transported. The energy metabolism of the insect egg, especially with regard to lipids, has been comprehensively reviewed by Kinsella (1966a).

The percentage distribution of fatty acids does not change during embryonic development in the cockroach *Periplaneta* (Kinsella, 1966b). No significant changes in the saturation of fatty acids were observed during development in grasshopper eggs by Slifer (1932b). Phospholipids increase during embryogenesis in insect eggs (Allais *et al.*, 1964; Kinsella, 1966a,b,c; Kinsella and Smyth, 1966; Lipsitz and McFarlane, 1970, 1971). Raw material for phospholipid biosynthesis may be derived from the neutral lipid fraction. In the locust embryo, transfer of phospholipids from the yolk to the embryo seems to occur before blastokinesis; after blastokinesis phospholipids are synthesized (Allais *et al.*, 1964). No changes in the total sterol content of the developing egg have been detected (Allais *et al.*, 1964; Kinsella, 1966d; Svoboda *et al.*, 1966), but qualitative changes may occur. Phospholipids and sterols are important components of the membranes in the cell. The increase in phospholipids may be related to the differentiation of membranes, especially in the nervous system. On the other hand, the insect embryo, like the adult, is probably unable to synthesize sterols (Kinsella, 1966a,d). Thus, the sterols necessary for embryonic development must be present in the egg from the beginning as a storage depot built up during oogenesis, and the sterol content does not increase during embryogenesis.

Carbohydrate metabolism was studied in the grasshopper egg by Hill (1945). The largest variation occurs in the extraembryonic part of the egg. The level of free reducing sugars in the egg is lower and more stable than that of bound reducing sugars (Fig. 3G). In the egg of the silkworm an interesting reversible conversion of glycogen into sorbitol and glycerol has been demonstrated during diapause (Chino, 1958). Thus, during this period, glycogen is not utilized for energy consumption. A corresponding increase in glycogen content after diapause is reported by Moulinier (1957). Okada (1970) observed that glycogen granules disappear before diapause and reappear after diapause. A high content of glycerol may increase the frost resistance (Salt, 1961). In the grasshopper *Aulocara* an increase in trehalose and mannitol and a decrease in mannose occur at the onset of diapause (Quickenden, 1970).

The nonreducing disaccharide trehalose is the principal free neutral sugar in the eggs of the grasshoppers *Melanoplus* and *Aulocara* (Randall and Derr, 1965; Quickenden, 1970). Dutrieu (1961) found trehalose in the silkworm egg, but, in the egg of the blowfly *Calliphora,* no trehalose was detected. Trehalose plays an important part in the metabolism and transport of carbohydrates in insects during the postembryonic and adult stages.

The changes in distribution of glycogen, lipids, and mitochondria have been cytochemically analyzed in the chrysomelid egg (Jura *et al.,* 1957). All three cellular components increased in the cytoplasmic islands during the cleavage period. The conversion of yolk into embryonic material has been followed through measurements of the iron and copper distribution (Bodine and Wolkin, 1934; Bodine and Fitzgerald, 1948b).

Appreciable changes in water content may occur during the development of insect eggs. Water is often lost (e.g., Ludwig and Ramazzotto, 1965; Kinsella and Smyth, 1966). More surprisingly, the moisture content in some cases increases enormously, for instance, in orthopteran eggs (e.g., Rothstein, 1952; Furneaux and McFarlane, 1965a,b; McFarlane, 1966; Grellett, 1971a; Moloo, 1971). The reason must be a real water uptake from the environment, as the metabolically formed water amounts to only a smaller fraction. The absorption seems to be an active process requiring energy, although passive osmosis may also contribute. Changes in the amount of lipoid material in the shell and differential cuticular tanning of the egg membranes may be involved in the regulation of water uptake.

It seems generally accepted that the total nitrogen remains constant throughout embryogenesis. No ammonia production occurs. In the grasshopper egg, the embryo nitrogen follows closely the growth curve and a corresponding decrease in yolk protein is established (Fig. 3E) (Trowbridge and Bodine, 1940). For the egg of the Japanese beetle a possible continuous conversion of soluble into nonsoluble protein was demonstrated by Ludwig and Rothstein (1952). Also, in the developing egg of the silkworm, structural proteins and soluble proteins vary inversely (Leonardi, 1956), and it was likewise found that albumins decrease when globulins increase (Pigorini, cited in Needham, 1931). Proteins are a very minor or negligible source of energy during embryogenesis. The suggestion that protein catabolism may be of importance in *Oncopeltus* (Babcock and Rutschky, 1961) has not been substantiated by later findings (Kinsella, 1966a). The final product of the slight protein catabolism, which occurs in the insect egg, should be uric acid as in other cleidoic eggs, but the observations seem controversial.

A high content of free amino acids in the body fluids is a peculiarity of insects. During embryogenesis it seems reasonable that most of the free amino acids in the egg are formed through degradation of yolk proteins, and that they are incorporated into the proteins of the growing embryo. Synthesis of amino acids has, however, been detected in insect eggs (Bunde and Pepper, 1968; Wegener et al., 1971). Thus, the level of free amino acids reflects the balance between yolk proteolysis, protein synthesis, amino acid synthesis, and possibly amino acid degradation. In the developing Drosophila egg the total amount of ninhydrin-positive substances changes little (von der Crone-Gloor, 1959). In the Culex egg, the total concentration of free amino acids and peptides increases rapidly during the formation, elongation, and contraction of the germ band (Chen and Briegel, 1965). In the egg of the grasshopper Chortophaga, older stages contain higher concentrations of free amino acids (Shaw, 1955). A higher concentration of free amino acids during diapause has been found in orthopteran eggs (McFarlane and Hogan, 1966; Bunde and Pepper, 1968; Roberts and Smith, 1971). Glutamine and glutamic acid vary inversely in some eggs, which indicates interconversion of these compounds (von der Crone-Gloor, 1959; Colombo et al., 1962; Chen and Briegel, 1965). The changes in tyrosine are correlated to cuticle formation (Colombo et al., 1962; Chen and Briegel, 1965). Changes in other individual amino acids may be correlated to special developmental events such as the initiation or termination of diapause and blastokinesis (e.g., McFarlane and Hogan, 1966; Roberts and Smith, 1971; Pant and Agrarval, 1965), but the causal connections are not understood. Some amino acids may be related to yolk metabolism, others to the metabolism of the embryo (Colombo et al., 1962). Qualitative differences in the spectrum of amino acids have also been recorded for different species. A study of the distribution of glutathione in a beetle egg showed an accumulation of this SH substance in the anterior part of the embryo (Brauer and Newman, 1959).

The amino acid and protein metabolism in the insect egg is reviewed by Chen (1966).

Changes in the riboflavin content were determined during the development of grasshopper eggs (Bodine and Fitzgerald, 1948a) and a conversion of riboflavin into pteridines was described. Pteridine metabolism has been thoroughly studied in the eggs of the bugs Oncopeltus and Pyrrhocoris (Hudson et al., 1959; Forrest et al., 1966; Smith and Forrest, 1969).

The polyamines are nitrogenous, basic compounds which are involved in growth and differentiation interacting with nucleoproteins in the chromatin. In the Drosophila egg, the concentration of the polyamine spermidine was high during the period immediately following fertilization and then dropped rapidly to a level maintained during the remainder of embryogenesis. Another polyamine, putrescine, showed a low concentration throughout the developmental period. A rapid synthesis of spermidine apparently triggered by the early events following fertilization was postulated (Herbst and Dion, 1970).

Phosphorus metabolism has been the object of very thorough investigations in the developing grasshopper egg (Lu and Bodine, 1953) where a differential analysis was also made of the embryo and the extraembryonic tissues. Total phosphorus is constant in the whole egg during development, but increases in the embryo proportionally with its growth as do almost all the separate phosphorus fractions. A separation was made of nuclear and cytoplasmic phosphorus compounds. The lipid phosphorus was more predominant in the nuclei as was acid-soluble phosphorus in the cytoplasm. Lipid phosphorus and protein phosphorus change inversely (Fig. 3D) (Thompson and Bodine, 1938). The amount of labile phosphates is high in the grasshopper egg when development is initiated, but diminishes rapidly (Fig. 3H) (Thompson and Bodine, 1938). This may point to the existence of an easily available energy reserve in the unfertilized egg. In the silkworm egg the energy-rich phosphates change along a U-shaped curve, while the amount of inorganic phosphate shows the inverse course, i.e., first ascending and then descending (Chino, 1956).

2. Nucleic Acids and Protein Synthesis

As in many other animal eggs, cytoplasmic DNA has been detected in some insect eggs (Lu and Bodine, 1953; Levenbook et al., 1953; Durand, 1955, 1961; Nigon and Daille, 1958). Autoradiographic studies of oogenesis in the cricket Acheta (Durand, 1958, 1961; Favard-Séréno and Durand, 1963), in the bug Rhodnius (Vanderberg, 1963), and in Drosophila (Jacob and Sirlin, 1959) indicate that the follicle cells or the nurse cells may be the source of this cytoplasmic DNA. It is also possible that DNA is synthesized in the ooplasm during oogenesis (Nigon and Gillot, 1964; Muckenthaler and Mahowald, 1966). Muckenthaler and Mahowald (1966) concluded that ooplasmic DNA synthesis occurs in the oocyte of Drosophila and that the synthesis is both mitochondrial and extramitochondrial. However, they did not exclude the possibility that templates for this synthesis are provided by the nurse cells.

Ooplasmic DNA is sometimes regarded as a "storage DNA," a DNA reserve necessary for the high mitotic activity during cleavage. Thus, the egg of the cricket should contain a DNA reserve sufficient for at least ten division cycles (Durand, 1955, 1961). In the fruitfly the DNA content of the egg has increased only five times after 13 hours of development, while during this period the nuclear multiplication must have been more than a thousandfold (Nigon and Daille, 1958). The amount of DNA is apparently constant during early cleavage in the cricket egg (Durand, 1961) and in the house fly egg (Painter and Kilgore, 1967). Such a lag period may indicate an early utilization of stored DNA. The DNA of the ooplasm may, however, have other functions. Thus, a large part of it must be mitochondrial DNA (Muckenthaler and Mahowald, 1966). Furthermore, according to Nigon and Gillot (1964) the cytoplasmic material, which is labeled by thymidine during oogenesis in the *Drosophila* egg, does not detectably yield its label to the synthesis of DNA in the cleavage nuclei. In a survey, Telfer (1965) concluded that the nature and origin of the extranuclear DNA in insect eggs remain obscure.

Autoradiographic experiments on beetle eggs indicated that DNA is synthesized from the onset of development (Lockshin, 1966). In labeling experiments, Harris and Forrest (1967a) did not investigate the stages before the formation of the blastoderm in the egg of the bug *Oncopeltus,* but found a relatively high rate of synthesis during the latter stage.

DNA-phosphorus increases during development in the grasshopper egg (Lu and Bodine, 1953) (Fig. 3I) and in the silkworm egg (Chino, 1956). Devi *et al.* (1963) observed an almost linear increase in DNA content during embryogenesis in the egg of the beetle *Tribolium.* In the *Oncopeltus* egg there is a large increase in DNA following a pattern indicating a lower rate of cell division during later stages (Harris and Forrest, 1967a). In the house fly egg the DNA content increases rapidly after an initial lag period and then remains almost constant during the later part of embryonic development (Painter and Kilgore, 1967). In the cricket egg an increase in DNA content is not found until the end of synchronous cleavage (Durand, 1961).

Early studies on RNA in insect eggs include those of Lu and Bodine (1953) (Fig. 3I) and Chino (1956), who found an increase in RNA-phosphorus content during the development of the grasshopper egg and the silkworm egg. During the last decade, RNA and protein synthesis in insect eggs have been studied using radioactive precursors. However, a special methodical problem exists. It is difficult to get a sufficient penetration of labeled compounds because of the impermeability of the egg. Thus, labeled precursors have been injected into the egg. Labeling with radioactive carbon dioxide has also been used, which may obscure the results because of unspecific labeling. Finally, it has been possible to get adequate labeling into dechorionized eggs in aqeous solutions. Two further complications may make interpretation difficult. First, the permeability of the egg may vary during development. Secondly, variations in the size of the pool of precursors are not known in most cases. In spite of these difficulties, some tentative generalizations may be ventured.

In most animal eggs, intense RNA synthesis starts in connection with gastrulation. During cleavage mainly maternal RNA stored during oogenesis is used. Although RNA synthesis may start somewhat earlier than during the so-called "gastrulation" stage, this general pattern of synthesis seems to be valid also for insect eggs. Thus, RNA synthesized by the oocyte nucleus or the nurse cells is stored during oogenesis (Bier, 1967, 1970; de Wilde, Chapter 2). In the egg of the cricket *Acheta* (Hansen-Delkeskamp *et al.,* 1967), synthesis of rRNA and possibly also mRNA should start during the heterochronous cleavage divisions. Synthesis of tRNA possibly starts earlier. In the bug *Oncopeltus* (Harris and Forrest, 1967a; Smith and Forrest, 1971) synthesis of rRNA, of 5 S RNA, and of tRNA should commence at gastrulation. Lockshin (1966) concluded from autoradiographic evidences that RNA synthesis in coleopteran eggs begins when the nuclei reach the periplasm. According to Schnetter (1970), synthesis of rRNA starts during the blastoderm stage in the beetle *Leptinotarsa*. On the other hand, Eudy and Dobrogosz (1970) did not detect synthesis of rRNA, 5 S RNA, and tRNA in the fly *Phormia* until very late after gastrulation, when approximately 50% of the developmental period had elapsed.

The fact that RNA is not synthesized during early development implies that the maternal RNA in the egg must be relatively stable. Thus the rRNA formed during oogenesis in the cricket egg should be stable at least up to the stage of yolk cleavage (Hansen-Delkeskamp, 1969). In this egg a small RNA fraction, which was regarded as mRNA, was labeled during oogenesis. This fraction persists in the developing egg. Protein synthesis occurs during early development, before any measurable RNA synthesis is detected. In beetle eggs, Lockshin (1966) similarly found that protein synthesis starts before RNA synthesis. In these eggs actinomycin D does not inhibit development before the blastoderm stage. These findings may indicate the existence of preformed mRNA (masked mRNA) in insect eggs. However, synthesis of mRNA during the early development of the insect egg cannot be excluded (Duspiva, 1969).

The intense RNA synthesis during the formative period does not appear to continue undiminished till hatching. The results of Hansen-Delkeskamp (1968) for *Acheta* and Harris and Forrest (1967a) for *Oncopeltus* both indicate a decrease in rRNA synthesis after the first differentiation of the germ band and then a comparatively low level of synthesis during the remainder of embryogenesis. The synthesis of 5 S RNA parallels that of rRNA in the *Oncopeltus* egg. The synthesis of tRNA in this egg follows the same general pattern as that of rRNA but shows some differences, which may signify that tRNA synthesis is independent of rRNA synthesis (Smith and Forrest, 1971).

It was mentioned earlier that there is a correlation between the amount of cytoplasm in the egg and the phylogenetic level of the different insect groups. Also, the development of the egg takes less time in the more advanced groups. During the development the yolk is transformed into the cytoplasm of the growing embryo. From the beginning, the eggs of the advanced type are equipped with a larger supply of cytoplasm built up during oogenesis. Thus, the initial embryonic area can be larger and development is completed within a shorter time. The content of RNA in the egg seems to be a biochemical measurement reflecting these differences in the content of cytoplasm (Hansen-Delkeskamp, 1968). Thus, the initial concentration of rRNA is registered lower in the primitive egg of the orthopteran *Acheta* than in the more advanced eggs of the hemipteran *Oncopeltus* and the coleopteran *Leptinotarsa* (Hansen-Delkeskamp, 1968; Harris and Forrest, 1967a; Schnetter, 1970). In the egg of the dipteran *Musca*, which is of the most advanced type, the concentration of rRNA seems to be appreciably higher than in the eggs mentioned above (Painter and Kilgore, 1967; Gadallah *et al.*, 1971b). However, different methods of assay have been used and the results may not be directly comparable. In the eggs of *Acheta, Oncopeltus,* and *Leptinotarsa,* the level of rRNA increases during the period of intense RNA synthesis. The relative increase in amount is, however, considerably higher in the *Acheta* egg. In the dipterans *Musca* and *Phormia,* the levels of total RNA and rRNA change comparatively little and may possibly even be constant (Painter and Kilgore, 1967; Gadallah *et al.,* 1970b, 1971b; Eudy and Dobrogosz, 1970).

The amounts of 5 S RNA and tRNA seem to vary in the same way as the amount of rRNA. Thus the levels of 5 S RNA and tRNA do not vary significantly in the *Phormia* egg (Eudy and Dobrogosz, 1970), while the amounts of 5 S RNA and tRNA in *Oncopeltus* increase during the period of increase in rRNA (Smith and Forrest, 1971).

During the development of the grasshopper egg, acid-soluble phosphorus shows a reversed course to that of nucleic acid phosphorus (Lu and Bodine, 1953). The level of acid-soluble DNA precursors is low and changes little in the eggs of both the beetle *Tribolium* (Devi *et al.*, 1963) and the housefly (Painter and Kilgore, 1967). The amount of acid-soluble RNA precursors during the development of these eggs, on the other hand, is higher and shows an increase in *Tribolium* and a small decrease in the housefly. In both cases the changes are the same as the changes in

RNA content, which may indicate some kind of dynamic equilibrium. Ribosides, deoxyribosides and, in smaller amounts, free purine and pyrimidine bases were identified in the acid-soluble fraction of the unfertilized *Drosophila* egg; however, no nucleotides were detected (Travaglini *et al.,* 1958). In the *Oncopeltus* egg there is a rough correlation between the disappearance of certain purine nucleosides and the synthesis of DNA and RNA. It was postulated that the purine nucleosides act as stored precursors for nucleic acid synthesis (Forrest *et al.,* 1967). The same correlation was, however, not established in another bug, *Pyrrhocoris* (Smith and Forrest, 1969). Moreover, the pyrimidine nucleosides do not behave in the same way.

Some attempts have been made to elucidate the macromolecular interactions at the transcriptional level in the insect egg. Das *et al.* (1964) showed that the nuclei in *Drosophila* contain an atypical, "juvenile" histone during cleavage. When the nuclei reach the periplasm the normal, "adult" histones appear. After two further cleavage divisions the definite blastoderm is formed and nucleoli appear. It was assumed that the change in histone content is correlated to the onset of transcriptional activity before gastrulation. Harris and Forrest (1970) investigated the templating activity for RNA synthesis of isolated chromatin from *Oncopeltus* eggs. They found a decrease in the templating activity *in vitro* during the period of diminishing RNA synthesis *in vivo* (see above). During the same period the histone/DNA ratio increases and the RNA to DNA ratio decreases in the chromatin. They concluded that the reduction in template efficiency must in part be due to a decrease in the number of sites available for transcription and that their results are consistent with the model of gene activation, in which RNA has a regulative function on the chromatin level. Changes in the amounts and types of RNA polymerase may also influence RNA synthesis. A correspondence has been shown between the RNA polymerase activity in isolated nuclei of *Oncopeltus* eggs and the rate of RNA synthesis *in vivo* (Harris and Forrest, 1970, 1971). Certain pteridine compounds have an inhibitory effect on the synthesis of DNA, rRNA, 5 S RNA, and tRNA in developing *Oncopeltus* eggs (Harris and Forrest, 1967b; Smith and Forrest, 1971). A direct interaction *in vitro* between the pteridine isoxanthopterin and nucleic acids has also been shown (Lagowski and Forrest, 1967). A regulative function of pteridines *in vivo* has not, however, been demonstrated. Hybridization experiments with DNA and RNA from housefly eggs indicated that some of the RNA synthesized during later stages has a nucleotide sequence, which is different from that of the RNA in the newly laid egg (Gadallah *et al.,* 1971a).

Protein synthesis begins early in insect development. In the cricket *Acheta* protein synthesis was found during very early cleavage stages and in beetle eggs protein synthesis from the onset of development was detected autoradiographically (Hansen-Delkeskamp, 1969; Lockshin, 1966). The rate of protein synthesis increases in beetle eggs when the nuclei reach the periplasm, and in the *Acheta* egg when the germ anlage is formed. Stage-dependent changes in the protein pattern have been demonstrated in the *Acheta* egg (Koch, 1966; Wegener *et al.*, 1971). Ribosomes in monomeric, dimeric, and polymeric forms have been isolated from unfertilized and fertilized housefly eggs (Gadallah *et al.*, 1970a) and their ability to initiate protein synthesis in a cell-free system has been investigated (Gadallah *et al.*, 1971c).

3. Enzyme Development

The changes in activity of a number of enzymes during the course of embryonic development in the insect egg have been the object of some series of observations. These investigations often seem to have been made more out of consideration for available methods than for the possible biological importance of the enzymes. Nevertheless, even if the physiological significance of some of the enzymes is obscure, these records of enzymic changes may be of interest for the elucidation of the sequence of protein synthesis. However, one must always keep in mind that it is extremely difficult to tell whether a measured change concerns the true amount, or, rather, the activity of the enzyme. Furthermore, an activity measured biochemically *in vitro* of course reflects neither the true activity *in vivo* nor any spatial differentiation of enzyme activity that may occur.

The best investigated object is the grasshopper egg. One may distinguish between enzymes which seem to appear exclusively in the embryo, in the yolk, or in both. To the first category belongs cytochrome oxidase. The level of this enzyme is measurable in the egg before embryogenesis starts; a yolk depot exists, but an increase in activity occurs only very late in development and is therefore related only to the embryonic growth (Fig. 3C) (Allen, 1940). In spite of the initially rather constant level of the enzyme, a distinct variation in cyanide sensitivity exists, indicating changes in the functional state of the enzyme generated by limiting factors somewhere else in the respiratory chain (Fig. 3B) (Robbie *et al.*, 1938; Robbie, 1941). Corresponding experiments with carbon monoxide inhibition and methylene blue activation are not so conclusive (Bodine and Boell, 1937). A cytochemical determination of the sites of cytochrome oxidase activity in the beetle egg revealed that the highest concentrations were found in the areas of the head and the caudal plate

(Coleman, 1959). In the egg of *Bombyx mori,* the enzymes of the respiratory chain in early embryonic stages exhibit a pattern different from later stages (Chino, 1963). Later embryonic stages have the normal set of respiratory enzymes found in other insect and mammalian tissues.

Changes in the activities of different enzymes in the pentose phosphate pathway, the glycolytic pathway, and the citric acid cycle have been measured during the development of the cricket egg (Achazi, 1969; Achazi and Duspiva, 1971), and the results agree essentially with the picture of energy metabolism obtained by other measurements (see Section II, B, 1). Most activities increase during development. It was concluded that glucose catabolism via the glycolytic pathway and the citric acid cycle predominates in early stages and that lipids later on substitute partly for glucose. Anaerobic energy production seems to be limited to the stage of dorsal closure. This is in contrast to the findings in embryos of many other animals, where anaerobic glycolysis plays a greater role. A correlation between a rise in activity of glucose-6-phosphate dehydrogenase and the increase in RNA synthesis (see above) was found and a possible relation to the synthesis of nucleotide precursors was suggested. In the housefly egg, the activity of this enzyme remains unchanged during the entire incubation period (Kilgore and Painter, 1964). It was suggested that maternal glucose-6-phosphate dehydrogenase is stored in the egg. An increase in lactate dehydrogenase activity during embryonic development was found in the housefly (Kilgore and Painter, 1964), as well as in the cricket (Achazi, 1969; Achazi and Duspiva, 1971).

A respiratory enzyme of less clear physiological importance, catalase, has been studied during the development of the grasshopper egg (Williams, 1936; Bodine *et al.,* 1954). At the start of embryonic development there is an increase both in the embryo and the yolk, but when the activity in the yolk levels out, a very rapid increase occurs in the embryo, approximately corresponding to its growth rate. In the grasshopper egg the change in catalase activity does not follow the respiratory curve, while this is the case in some butterfly eggs (Kozhanchikov, 1940).

In the grasshopper egg lipases seem to occur predominantly in the yolk because of their decreasing activity throughout embryogenesis, especially the rapid fall during the period of most intense growth of the embryo (Carlson, 1941). In addition, an increased activity during the late embryogenesis in the silkworm egg of lipases should be mentioned (Gaeta and Zappanico, 1959), as well as of a dipeptidase (Urbani and Rossi, 1959). The activity of proteases increases toward the end of development in the egg of the locust (Shulov *et al.,* 1957). Acid and alkaline phosphatases increase during development in silkworm (Ito *et al.,* 1954;

Chino, 1961) and grasshopper eggs (Fitzgerald, 1949). Qualitative and quantitative changes in the activity of soluble esterases have been found during the embryonic development of *Oncopeltus* (Salkeld, 1965). Eudy and Dobrogosz (1970) demonstrated a rapid increase in activity of β-galactosidase and of esterases during the last 30% of development in the egg of the fly *Phormia*. In another fly, *Crysomyia*, an increase in total activity of β-glucuronidases during embryogenesis was reported by Varute and Sawant (1971a). A microsomal, heat-labile fraction decreased in percentage of total activity during development, while a lysosomal, heat-stable fraction increased. Tyrosinase in the grasshopper egg is supposed to be exclusively an extraembryonic enzyme and is suggested to be synthesized in the serosa cells (Bodine and Allen, 1941). The maximum activity is reached fairly early during embryogenesis and then a steady decrease follows (Bodine and Boell, 1935). The natural protyrosinase activator shows the reversed course in operation (Bodine *et al.*, 1939). Another type of enzyme seems to be exclusively restricted to the embryo, probably to the nervous structures, namely, the choline esterases. All investigations about these enzymes from different insect eggs agree in this respect, e.g., in the grasshopper egg (Tahmisian, 1943), in butterfly and beetle eggs (Staudenmayer, 1955; Chino and Yushima, 1954; Yushima, 1957), and in the egg of the milkweed bug (Salkeld and Hudson, 1964; Salkeld, 1964). Mehrotra (1960) found that the components of the cholinergic system in eggs of *Musca* and *Oncopeltus* appear in sequence. Choline acetylase is detected first, and simultaneously neuroblasts are first seen. Acetylcholine esterase appears later, and at the same time *(Oncopeltus)* or still later *(Musca)* acetylcholine is first demonstrated. In a survey of the literature, Smallman and Mansingh (1969) concluded that the sequence of appearance of the components in the cholinergic system during insect embryogenesis is still unclear. However, in most cases all the components appear comparatively late and increase in level up to hatching. These changes are correlated to neurogenesis.

Esterases have been studied cytochemically in the bug *Oncopeltus* (Salkeld and Hudson, 1964; Salkeld, 1964). A relation between the functional differentiation of certain tissues or organs and the appearance of certain types of esterases was postulated. Phosphatases have been observed by cytochemical means in the fruitfly embryo (Yao, 1950). While acid phosphatase demonstrates no changes during embryogenesis, alkaline phosphatase appears suddenly near the future thorax at the contraction of the germ band. From there, the activity spreads to other parts of the embryo so that an activity gradient is formed, but this disappears from most tissues before hatching. Similar changes in alkaline phosphatase activity occur in the egg of the termite *Odontotermes* (Banerjee, 1964), although they deviate from those in *Drosophila* in some points.

Finally, it should be mentioned that lytic enzymes, which dissolve the egg membranes during hatching, so-called "hatching enzymes," have been demonstrated in insect eggs (Slifer, 1937; Du Praw, 1963).

C. DYNAMICS OF EMBRYONIC ORGANIZATION

There exist several comprehensive reviews dealing with the analysis of the driving forces during insect embryogenesis, e.g., those by Richards and Miller (1937), Seidel *et al.* (1940), Bodenstein (1950, 1953, 1955), Pflugfelder (1952), Krause (1958a), Counce (1961), Seidel (1961, 1966), Krause and Sander (1962), and Anderson (on Diptera; 1962, 1966). Those readers who want to acquire a more extensive knowledge on this subject than can be given within the scope of the present account are advised to consult these reviews, especially the most recent of them.

1. Regulation and Determination

Insect eggs demonstrate regulative as well as determinative embryonic development. A wide variety exists in this respect within the group as a whole and the degree of determination seems intimately connected with the phylogenetic level. Thus, in those insects which are regarded as primitive, the embryogenesis is highly regulative, while the embryonic development of the more advanced groups shows an increased degree of determination. The upper limit is reached in the higher Diptera (Cyclorapha).

The establishment of the order of regulative capacity must have an experimental basis. The principle of such experiments with the insect egg is a destruction or separation of selected parts of the egg, representing different anlagen at various developmental stages, and then an observation of to what extent these missing regions can be regenerated during the subsequent embryogenesis. Thus, for a certain embryonic region, the normal development is put into relation to the fate of an experimentally induced defect produced at a certain embryonic stage. What is called prospective significance is compared to prospective potency. In the mosaic egg the two are congruent, while in regulative eggs the prospective potency is greater than the prospective significance. The operation technique for producing adequate defects is, in principle, simple, viz., cauterization, puncturing, UV and X-ray irradiation, ligating, and transplantations. Even ultrasonic treatment has been employed (Counce and Selman, 1955). One thing must be emphasized. The degree of regulation observed in these experiments is dependent to a very high degree on the techniques used. Different species can be compared only if the same methods have been employed. With more refined techniques a certain regulation has been shown also in eggs earlier regarded as strictly determinative. Epigenetic events probably take place against the background of a preformed pattern in both regulative and determinative eggs.

By elimination of a desired number of cleavage nuclei in the dragonfly egg through ultraviolet spot irradiation, it was shown that the remaining nuclei were able to populate the whole egg periphery and to direct a completely normal development. This regulative capacity persisted at least up to the eighth cleavage step (Seidel, 1934). This demonstrates clearly that the cleavage nuclei are originally undifferentiated and totipotent. The totipotency of the cleavage nuclei has been repeatedly confirmed in different species in experiments involving elimination or dislocation of cleavage nuclei (e.g., Hegner, 1909; Reith, 1925; Pauli, 1927; Ewest, 1937; Maschlanka, 1938; von Borstel, 1957; Schnetter, 1965). Even in the higher Diptera the cleavage nuclei are totipotent. Also, the already mentioned accidental incorporation of the cleavage nuclei into the pole plasm points to the indeterminate character of these nuclei. The demonstration of a totipotency of the cleavage nuclei necessarily leads to the conclusion that if determination is early it must be inherent in the egg cytoplasm.

Cytoplasmic influence upon the course of embryonic development can be observed at an early cleavage stage from the so-called activation center (AC) discovered in the dragonfly egg by Seidel (1929). This center is placed near the posterior pole. If this center, localized in the interior of the egg, is destroyed by cauterization or cut off from the rest of the egg by ligation, no development of an embryonic area will occur. The same result will be obtained when the nuclei with their plasma islands are prevented from reaching this region, or when this egg portion is completely separated from the rest of the egg, some nuclei just having reached there.

The operation of the activation center is transient. Within a comparatively short period of time, a greater and greater part of the posterior end of the egg can be inactivated without affecting the embryogenesis. In later blastoderm stages, before the nuclei accumulate to form the germ plate, its action has ceased. The conclusion was drawn that through the interaction of the cleavage nuclei (and/or their cytoplasmic islands) and a factor in the activation center, an active principle is formed which successively diffuses in an anterior direction, thereby evoking an embryonic development. The migration of the active principle may be directly seen as a forward brightening in the egg. By time-lapse photography the AC was characterized as an initial region of yolk movements, yolk disintegration, and vitellophage activity (Schanz, 1966; Seidel, 1966). An activation center has been accepted to exist also in cricket eggs by Mahr (1960b), in hemipteran eggs by Krause (1958a), in beetle eggs by Reith (1936) and Ewest (1937), in ant eggs by Reith (1931), and in mosquito eggs by Idris (1960). In the beetle eggs, the contribution of the cleavage nuclei may not be necessary. The action of the AC is not necessary for the initiation of rRNA synthesis in the cricket egg (Hansen-Delkeskamp, 1968). However, in many cases no AC has been detected in eggs of higher insects. The whole concept of an activation center was questioned by Haget (1953).

The activation center does not act directly upon the morphogenetic processes within the embryo area. The immediate action should be upon another center, the so-called differentiation center (DC). In most insects this center has its focus in the presumptive prothorax. A distinction is often made between the "morphological" DC and the "physiological" DC (e.g., Seidel, 1964). These may not always correspond in their range. Morphologically the DC is defined as an initial region of germ anlage formation, often also of mesoderm formation and other processes of differentiation. Physiologically it is defined by experimental means, e.g., determination of the area necessary for normal development by elimination of specific parts in the egg. Through ligation experiments on dragonfly eggs with a varied width of the constriction, Seidel (1934) showed that no diffusible substance was responsible for the action of the DC, but that a wave of contraction starts from there by which the yolk retracts from the shell. A space is thereby made available into which the blastoderm cells can move from the embryonic area. The yolk system acts as a mold for the formation of the germ anlage. If the ligation is made only just so tight that it prevents this motility, the formation of the embryo area is also prevented. Thus, the DC constitutes a center for morphogenetic movements. It has further been shown (e.g., Seidel, 1934) by adequate destruction of surface layers that the impulse for this contraction does not emanate from the blastoderm but from the yolk system in the interior of the egg. Developmental factors are probably transferred from the interior of the egg to the germ anlage. In several eggs, it has been shown that determinative processes occur in the germ anlage, leading to a progressively narrower prospective potency of its different parts, which thus become destined to form certain regions of the body. The potential areas giving rise to the specific body regions may change in extent and position during development. Often they are initially concentrated around the DC. The differentiation center has been studied in more detail, as well as in the already mentioned dragonfly egg, in eggs of Orthoptera (e.g., Mahr,

1957, 1960b; Seidel, 1964; Heinig, 1967), Coleoptera (Ewest, 1937; Küthe, 1966), and Hymenoptera (Schnetter, 1934a). No DC could be demonstrated clearly in cicada eggs by Sander (1959). Some evidence for the existence of a DC in the lower dipteran *Culex* was given by Idris (1960). However, Davis (1970) found no conclusive evidence for the existence of a DC in the egg of another *Culex* species. In the egg of the fly *Dacus*, a DC was demonstrated by Anderson (1962). A scheme of control centers in the insect egg described above is given in Fig. 4.

Another type of developmental model was first put forward by Sander (1959). This model concerns the development of the metameric pattern. It was postulated that the segments are determined by the interaction of an anterior and a posterior center in the egg. Ooplasmic factors diffuse or are transported from the poles toward the equator and form a double gradient. Reactions take place between these factors or between these factors and other ooplasmic constituents. Ultimately this leads to a fixation of the segmental pattern. Probably these anterior and posterior cen-

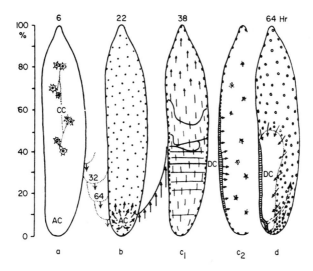

Fig. 4. A scheme of the interaction between the different centers in the egg of the dragonfly *Platycnemis*. (a) Stage of 8 nuclei with cleavage center (CC) and activation center (AC); (b) the posterior nuclei at the 128-nuclear stage move into the activation center and an activation is released. Arrows indicate reaction products or structural changes in the cytoplasm; (c_1) blastoderm stage with presumptive segmental areas of anlagen; (c_2) yolk contraction and accumulation of blastoderm cells in the prothoracic differentiation center (DC); (d) separation of the serosa from the embryo area and the first beginning of blastokinesis. According to Seidel from Krause (1958b).

ters do not directly correspond to the control centers described above (CC, AC, and DC). Some of the experiments leading to the adoption of this hypothesis will be briefly summarized. If the egg is transversely constricted during early development, incomplete embryos lacking segments proximally may be formed in the anterior and posterior isolates. The segment pattern of the partial embryos becomes gradually more complete, if the operation is performed at a progressively later stage of development. Results of this type have been obtained in the hemipteran *Euscelis* (Sander, 1959), in the coleopteran *Bruchidius* (Jung, 1966b), and in the dipteran *Protophormia* (Sander *et al.,* 1970). The results of Idris (1960) and Nitschmann (1959) in the dipterans *Culex* and *Calliphora* may be interpreted in the same way. Davis (1970) interpreted corresponding results in the fly *Lucilia* as possibly dependent on a greater sensitivity of the egg to ligation during earlier stages. Ligation experiments in the orthopteran *Acheta* had an entirely different outcome. In this species, the metameric pattern is probably produced by other mechanisms (Sander *et al.,* 1970). As pointed out by Sander (1971), the loss of segments after constriction indicates nonmosaic development, but not regulation in the sense that parts of the egg deviate from their prospective fate in the direction towards the normal pattern. The results can be described as an example of negative or reductive regulation. If posterior pole material is translocated anteriorly in the egg before ligation, it may be incorporated in the posterior part of the anterior egg fragment. In that case more segments are formed in the anterior isolate than after ligation only. Results of this type have been obtained in *Euscelis* (Sander, 1959, 1962) and in *Bruchidius* (Jung and Krause, 1967) and may further support the existence of anterior and posterior centers. The results of similar experiments by Achtelig and Krause (1971) in the hymenopteran *Pimpla* are not so conclusive.

A determination of the metameric pattern by the action of anterior and posterior centers has also been put forward to explain the formation of an interesting type of malformation found in some insect eggs (Yajima, 1960). The malformed embryo sometimes consists of two abdomens pointing in opposite directions with their proximal parts fused together in the midline and without head and thorax ("double abdomen"). Two heads may also form an embryo in a similar manner ("double cephalon"). The anatomy of such monsters is described by Kalthoff and Sander (1968) and Yajima (1970). Double abdomen has been shown to occur spontaneously in a culicid midge (Price, 1958) and in *Drosophila* (Bull, 1966). Duplications of this type were obtained in *Euscelis* by Sander (1959, 1962) in the posterior egg fragment after translocation of posterior pole material anteriorly and ligation of the egg in front of the translocated material. Centrifugation of *Culex* eggs during cleavage resulted in a frequent duplication of head structures (Davis, 1970). Most of the experimental results of this type have, however, been obtained in chironomid midges. After centrifugation in the nuclear cleavage stage, Yajima (1960) (Fig. 5) obtained the double abdomen malformation when the anterior end of the egg was centrifugally oriented, and the double cephalon malformation when the posterior end of the egg was centrifugally oriented. By tilting the egg in the gravitational field, all gradations between overdimensioned head and abdomen could be obtained, until eggs placed with their long axes at right angles to the centrifugal force exhibited a normal development. The experiments were further complicated by a repeated centrifugation at later stages by which the doubleness was lost. Centrifugation only at the blastoderm stage produced a random mixture of fragments of the normal embryo. Double abdomen was produced by UV irradiation of the anterior part of the egg, and double cephalon by UV irradiation of the posterior part of the egg (Yajiima, 1964). A coop-

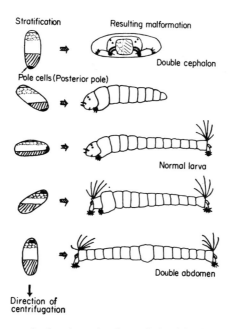

Fig. 5. Semidiagrammatic drawings showing relationships between the direction of centrifugation of the *Chironomus* egg and the type of the resulting malformation. The white, unmarked zone denotes the position of the cytoplasm in the centrifuged egg. From Yajima (1960).

eration between cytoplasmic constituents moved by centrifugation and immovable anterior and posterior centers determining the developmental fate of the cytoplasm surrounding them was postulated. An interaction between the two centers should result in formation of a thorax. However, no correlation between the direction of the centrifugal force and the resulting malformation was obtained after centrifugation of the eggs in another chironomid (Gauss and Sander, 1966; Overton and Raab, 1967). Ultrastructural studies indicated that all cytoplasmic components except the oolemma were translocated by centrifugation (Overton and Raab, 1967). Thus, it was suggested that the anterior and posterior centers were not immovable but shifted by centrifugation and mixed. In that case, duplications should result if the action of one center is suppressed by the other. In *Smittia,* another chironomid, double abdomen malformations are produced in a very high frequency after UV irradiation of the anterior end of the egg during cleavage. This system has been thoroughly investigated by Kalthoff (1970a,b, 1971a,b,c). Double abdomen may be obtained also after irradiation of eggs constricted in the middle (Sander, cited by Kalthoff, 1970a). Thus, changes in the anterior end and not influences emanating from the posterior end should cause the malformation. From further experiments, the following conclusions were drawn. The targets of irradiation are probably stored during oogenesis. They are found in the ooplasm, probably peripherally. They are localized in the anterior part of the egg, the concentration decreasing posteriorly. The irradiated targets affect the body segment pattern far beyond the irradiated area. The picture thus formed agrees well with the hypothesis of anterior and posterior centers as formulated by Sander.

Centrifugation of higher dipteran eggs results in normal development to a great extent (Pauli, 1927; Davis, 1970). No duplications are formed. Similar results were obtained with eggs of beetles and ants (Hegner, 1909; Reith, 1933). However, double abdomen, as mentioned, occurs as an inherited malformation in *Drosophila.* The maternal genotype is the controlling factor in the production of the abnormality (Bull, 1966). This indicates preformation of the centers controlling the metameric pattern.

The mechanisms involved in establishing the transverse pattern, i.e., the bilateral symmetry, must be different from those responsible for the establishment of the longitudinal pattern (see discussion by Sander, 1971; Krause and Krause, 1965). After longitudinal fragmentation of the *Euscelis* egg during cleavage, positive regulation may occur, even to the extent that complete embryos are formed in both separated parts. This is in contrast to the loss of segments, that is, negative regulation, occurring after transverse constriction during the same stage.

Embryo culture *in vitro* might be an important tool in the study of insect embryogenesis. The embryo is, for instance, more easily subjected to chemical influences *in vitro,* since the membranes of the intact egg are highly impermeable. However, although improved, the methods are still not satisfactory. Culture during more or less limited periods is possible, but no embryo has yet been cultured throughout the entire period of embryogenesis (see review by Counce, 1966). The dependence of the embryo on the yolk system has, for instance, been studied in different species by culturing embryos together with and separated from the yolk (Krause, 1963; Koch, 1964; Krause and Krause, 1964, 1965, 1971). The cells of dissociated *Drosophila* embryos in a fairly advanced stage (6–16 hours) have been cultured *in vitro* (Horikawa and Fox, 1964; Lesseps, 1965; Shieldo and Sang, 1970). Several cell types, e.g., neuron-like cells and muscle cells, were identified. Reaggregation following a characteristic pattern was observed, different cell types taking up specific positions in relation to the surface of the aggregate (Lesseps, 1965). Thus, selective affinities between different cell types may be an important

TABLE I

SOME CHARACTERISTICS OF THE PRIMITIVE AND THE ADVANCED TYPE OF INSECT EGG

	Primitive characteristics	Advanced characteristics
Taxonomic group	Exopterygota	Endopterygota
Type of ovariole	Panoistic	Meroistic
Type of development	Regulative	Determinative
Developmental rate	Slow	Rapid
Content of cytoplasm	Low	High
Periplasm	Thin (or absent)	Thick
Pole plasm, oosome material, and pole cells	Not demonstrated	Present
Germ anlage formation	By morphogenetic activities in the blastoderm	Without rearrangements in the blastoderm
Size of germ anlage	Small	Large
Posterior segments	Added by growth	Formed within a preexisting structure
Blastokinesis	In typical form (anatrepsis and catatrepsis)	In rudimentary form (extension and contraction of the germ band)
RNA content	Low	High
Increase in RNA during development	Large	Small

factor in insect embryogenesis as in the embryogenesis of other animal groups.

As has already been mentioned, the regulative capacity of the insect egg has a very wide variance. This capacity has a certain inverse parallelism to what is regarded as the increasing phylogenetic level of the insect group. (Some of the characteristics of the regulative and the determinative types of insect eggs are summarized in Table I.) Thus, the eggs of what are regarded as lower insect groups have a considerable capacity of regulation. Even at a blastodermal stage with a fully developed germ anlage, induced defects may be repaired. Eggs of Odonata and Orthoptera have been especially studied in this respect (Seidel, 1929, 1964; Krause, 1934; Ray, 1937; Krause and Krause, 1956; Sauer, 1962; Schwalm, 1965; Heinig, 1967; Sander et al., 1970). Only at the stage of segmentation has this regulative capacity decreased and been restricted to single organ areas. Especially in these groups the dynamic influence of the yolk system is an extremely important factor in the morphogenesis and differentiation of the germ anlage and the embryo (see above). Between the one extreme, the regulative eggs of Odonata and Orthoptera, and the other, the only slightly regulative eggs of the higher Diptera, the eggs of all other insect groups can be arranged in a series of varying regulative ability.

In the cicada egg, the regulative capacity is still comparatively high (Sander, 1959, 1962), but the pattern of regulation is, as mentioned above, different from that of Orthoptera (Sander et al., 1970). In Neuroptera ligation experiments lead to development of harmonious whole embryos (Du Bois, 1936). For hymenopteran eggs it has also been shown by ligation experiments that the dimension of the prospective potency in the honey bee egg is substantially greater than the areas of normal organ formation (Schnetter, 1934b; Sauer-Löcher, 1954); the same was found for ant eggs (Reith, 1931). Among Coleoptera, the regulative capacity of the egg shows some variation. Thus, the eggs of *Tenebrio, Sitona, Bruchus, Bruchidius,* and *Dermestes* have an obvious ability for regulation (Ewest, 1937; Reith, 1936; Brauer and Taylor, 1936; Jung, 1966b, 1971; Jung and Krause, 1967; Küthe, 1966), while this capacity is slight in other coleopteran eggs, as is the case in the eggs of chrysomelids (Hegner, 1911; Haget, 1953; Jura, 1957; Schnetter, 1965). In *Dermestes* large defects in the periplasm and also deeper are regulated before the preblastoderm stage (Küthe, 1966). The activity of the yolk system seems to be important. If the periplasm is totally destroyed, development can still proceed as far as the beginning of gastrulation. In the chrysomelid *Leptinotarsa,* on the other hand, early periplasmic defects are mostly not regulated, although the yolk system possesses a considerable regulative capacity (Schnetter, 1965). Still within the Lepidoptera, a certain regulative capacity has been found (Maschlanka, 1938; Takami, 1943; Lüscher, 1944; Krause and Krause, 1965). In the *Tineola* egg, the larval determination should be completed only at the stage of amnion formation (Lüscher, 1944). Concerning the eggs of the lower Diptera (Nematocera), evidences indicating regulation have accumulated in recent years. Regulation in nematoceran eggs is discussed above in the section covering anterior and posterior control centers (also see the review by Anderson, 1966).

The eggs of higher dipterans have long been considered as typical mosaic eggs (see reviews by Anderson, 1962, 1966). For instance, a localized burning, irrespective of the developmental stage and region of the egg, will give only persisting lesions (Reith, 1925). From cauterization, centrifugation, and ligation experiments in the fly *Lucilia*, Davis (1970) concluded that larval determination is early in this fly. Thus, the general embryonic pattern in these eggs is apparently established already in the unfertilized egg, probably by a cooperation between the oocyte, the nurse cells, and the follicle cells during oogenesis. The fact that periplasmic damage is not regulated (e.g., Reith, 1925) and that centrifugation affects development only slightly (Pauli, 1927), indicates that a mosaic of determinative factors is localized in an immovable cortical layer. However, regulative capacities still exist. After ultrasonic treatment of the *Drosophila* egg at preblastodermal stages, some readjustment occurred and a normal but delayed development took place (Counce and Selman, 1955). Also, as mentioned above, stage-dependent losses of segments occur after ligation in fly eggs (Nitschmann, 1959; Sander *et al.,* 1970). Thus, the same type of epigenetic interactions as in more regulative insect eggs seem to take place. According to Anderson (1966), these examples of regulation may be compatible with a mosaic development, since the regulation occurs only within relatively small areas of the periplasm, the fate of the principal areas still being irrevocably fixed.

Not only the larval characters, but also the imaginal qualities, are successively determined in the egg, although this determination commences somewhat later and independently of the larval determination. Irradiation experiments with ultraviolet light made on *Tineola* eggs as early as the cleavage stage produced only larval defects. Imaginal defects were not obtained until the blastoderm stage. Pure imaginal defects were also produced in the *Drosophila* egg by UV irradiation (Geigy, 1932), by puncturing (Howland and Child, 1935), by ether treatment (Gloor, 1947), and by X-ray irradiation (Bryant and Schneiderman, 1969). As in the lepidopterous egg the imaginal structures should be determined by the blastoderm stage. Because the nuclei have shown themselves to be more sensitive to ultraviolet light than the cytoplasm (Goldman and Setlow, 1956), one may risk the assumption that the imaginal determination represents a nuclear differentiation, while the early larval determination was laid down in the egg cytoplasm. Each presumptive area in the blastoderm of higher dipterans, with the exception of the mesodermal and neural areas and the pole cells, consists of two types of cells, those determined to form larval structures and those determined to form adult structures (Anderson, 1963, 1964, 1966). This separation may be a basic characteristic of endopterygote development.

As earlier emphasized, there exists among the insect group a negative correlation between the regulative capacity and the amount of cytoplasm in the egg and thus, accordingly, to the size of the initial embryonic area. In the most regulative eggs only a small embryonic area is primarily formed, while in the least regulative eggs almost the complete surface of the egg is occupied by the embryo from the early beginning. This implies a much higher faculty of motion for the different constituents of the egg in the regulative egg, which is also demonstrated during germ-anlage formation and blastokinesis. There must exist a definite connection between such a faculty of rearrangement and the regulative capacity of the embryo. In the cricket egg there seems to be a correlation between the potential of rearrangement within the blastoderm and the regulative capacity of the different regions of the germ anlage (Sauer, 1962; Schwalm, 1965). Certainly some kind of preformed pattern is imposed upon all insect eggs during the oocyte stage. Nevertheless, this induced pattern may not be so different among the eggs of the various insect groups as is indicated by the much varied determination demonstrated by the reported experiments. Perhaps a decreased regulative capacity and an expanding congruence between prospective significance and prospective potency is, to a greater extent than expected, a mere expression of an increasing immobility of the regulative system. If so, determination in the centrolecithal egg may imply something else than determination in the holoblastically cleaving egg.

2. Embryonic Induction

Processes of induction, which have been so intensely studied in the amphibian egg, are not very well known in the insect egg. Certainly the interaction between the cleavage energids and the AC and other events occurring during the syncytial stage may be regarded as examples of induction. As defined by Krause (1958a), these interactions take place within an ooplasmic reaction system. The inductive interaction between two cell complexes, e.g., between germ layers, occurs within an interblastemic reaction system. There are only a few direct experimental approaches to this type of process. Fundamental to the understanding of the course of induction are the experiments performed on the *Chrysopa* egg by Seidel *et al.* (1940) and Bock (1942) (Fig. 6). The experiments were performed at the stage of germ-layer formation, whereby parts of the hypoblast (endomesoderm) and of adjoining sections of the ectoderm were removed and the subsequent development was followed. If the whole of the presumptive hypoblast was removed, all ectodermal organs in such a mesoderm-free embryo continued and completed their embryological differentiation in an almost normal manner. Malformations occurred, but they must be regarded as being of minor importance. A per-

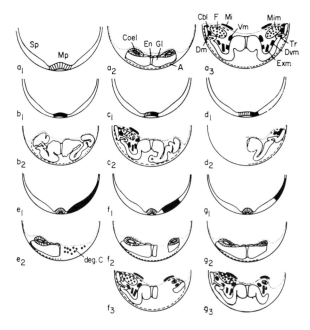

Fig. 6. Induction of the ectodermal side plates (Sp) upon the endomesodermal mid-plate (Mp) at the stage of germ-layer formation of *Chrysopa perla*. Schematic cross sections through the ventral half of a thoracic segment. (a_1)–(a_3) normal development; (b_1)–(g_1) different regions killed by cauterization (black areas); (b_2)–(g_2), (f_3)) (g_3) the result of the operations upon organ segregation; A, amnion; Coel, coelom; En, endoderm; Gl, ganglion; Cbl, cardioblasts; F, fat body; Mi, midgut; Mim, muscles of midgut; Dm, dorsal muscles; Vm, ventral muscles; Tr, Tracheae; Dvm, dorsoventral muscles; Exm, muscles of extremities. From Krause (1958b).

missible conclusion is that the ectoderm has an almost complete capacity for autodifferentiation independent of the mesoderm. When only a part of the hypoblast was destroyed, the remaining mesodermal elements spread beneath the differentiating ectoderm and formed as many organs of mesodermal origin as their quantity allowed. The bilateral character of the mesodermal anlage was demonstrated by the fact that the part of the hypoblast on one side could not replace the part on the other side; if, on the other hand, parts of the ectodermal side plates were removed, a mesodermal differentiation occurred only in contact with the remaining ectoderm. Mesodermal elements that migrate out into an ectoderm-free space simply degenerate. Thus it seems clear that an inductive system exists in the *Chrysopa* egg and that the inductor is represented by the ectoderm, and the reactor by the mesoderm. This condition is quite the opposite to that occurring in the amphibian embryo. The very rigid nature of the inductor system is also evident. Closely corresponding results have been obtained on the egg of *Leptinotarsa* by Haget (1953), where, additionally, there was probably an inductional activity of the mesoderm, in its turn upon the endoderm, on the formation of the intestine. The regulation of grasshopper embryos after cutting (Krause and Krause, 1956) was also evaluated as a process of induction (Krause, 1958a). The remaining fragment of the germ plate provokes, in competent amnion material, a formation of the missing part. In some groups, the formation of the gonad sheath may be dependent on an inductive action of the primordial germ cells, although the experimental results are conflicting (e.g., Jura, 1964; Davis, 1970; Yajima, 1970; see Anderson, 1966). A recent comprehensive survey of the induction in the insect egg is that by Krause (1958b).

3. Interrelation between Nucleus and Cytoplasm

In the foregoing sections, evidence has been presented for the concept of the insect egg as a system of ooplasmic polarity, where the nuclei are originally totipotent. Questions immediately arise concerning the nature of the cytoplasmic agents of determination and the role and action of the nuclei during the advancing embryogenesis.

Sometimes the periplasm within the egg has a spatially differentiated structure (Section II, A, 1). Thus, the developmental centers may in some eggs coincide with accumulations of cytoplasm, which are preformed or appear during clevage (Schnetter, 1934a; Maul, 1967, 1970a,b). However, in many insect eggs, this is apparently not the case (e.g., von Kraft, 1960; Jung, 1966a). Also, the relation between the determinative events and these structural features, if any, is obscure. No ultrastructural differences between different egg regions have been established, at least not before the blastoderm stage when gastrulation is imminent (Mahowald, 1963b; Netzel, 1968; Wolf, 1969a). The only exception is the oosome material. The evidences for biochemical differences between egg regions, either preformed or appearing during early development, are sparse. In the honey bee egg the stainability for thionine increases in the early embryo in those areas where obvious developmental processes proceed (Schnetter, 1934a). This indicates a varied localization of RNA. However, it may be difficult to decide whether this localized accumulation of RNA denotes a delimited synthesis of RNA or possibly only a concentration of cytoplasm. Anterioposterior gradients of basophilia, possibly indicating a varied distribution of ribosomal RNA, have been reported in coleopteran eggs (Haget, 1953; Mulnard, 1947; Jura et al., 1958) and in the hymenopteran Pimpla (Meng, 1968). Whether the gradient of RNA emanating from the nurse cells during oogenesis involves the fixation of a preformed, anterioposterior pattern of determining factors has not been ascertained. In the unfertilized and in the developing cricket egg, qualitative and quantitative differences between the proteins of the anterior and posterior halves of the egg have been demonstrated (Koch and Heinig, 1968; Nünemann and Moser, 1970). However, at the germ-anlage stage no differences could be detected in the pattern of RNA synthesis between the posterior part of the egg, which contains the germ anlage, and the anterior part of the egg (Sauer, 1970).

Some direct experiments have been made to elucidate the different functions of the cytoplasm and the nuclei during insect embryogenesis. These experiments constitute a differential inactivation of nuclei and cytoplasm by a varied irradiation with ultraviolet light on Drosophila eggs (Goldman and Setlow, 1956) and on parasitic wasp eggs (von Borstel, 1957). Analysis reveals that the action spectrum for nuclear damage looks like nucleoprotein absorption, whereas the action spectrum for cytoplasmic damage should resemble more the absorption by nucleic acids. The nuclei are more sensitive to irradiation than the cytoplasm. The conclusion can be drawn that RNA itself is the cytoplasmic agent of determination or is intimately related to this factor. Damage to cytoplasmic RNA is morphologically reflected only at a late stage (Goldman and Setlow, 1956). However, if eggs were irradiated around 2300 Å, at a wavelength at which proteins absorb more of the energy than nucleic acids, damaging effects were also produced, but at an earlier stage, and these effects were more profound. This may show that cytoplasmic proteins are also used in the determination of the egg and during an earlier stage than cytoplasmic

RNA (von Borstel, 1957). Since induction of the malformation double abdomen in the chironomid *Smittia* by ultraviolet light is photoreversible, Kalthoff (1971a) concluded that the ooplasmic factors determining the metameric pattern in this organism include or have some connection to nucleic acids.

Sooner or later the totipotent nuclei must become differentiated. When the nuclei reach the periplasm such a differentiation may occur by an interaction between the nuclei and their new cytoplasmic surroundings. Chromosome elimination in lower dipteran eggs is a case of visible nuclear differentiation, where the nature of the surrounding cytoplasm decides the fate of the nuclei (Section II, C, 4). Also the polyploidy observed in the serosa and yolk nuclei (Section II, A, 4) is an example of early nuclear differentiation on the cytological level. During development, the nuclei may decrease in volume (Sauer, 1966; Grellet, 1971b); they may show ultrastructural changes (Schwalm, 1969) or changes in histone content (Das *et al.,* 1964). All these changes may be signs of nuclear differentiation. However, most changes are not visible. Nuclear transplantation experiments, similar to the classical experiments on amphibian eggs by Briggs and King (1957), may possibly demonstrate the disappearing totipotency of the nuclei and the appearance of differences between the nuclei of different regions in the egg. Unfortunately such experiments performed in Coleoptera, Hymenoptera, and Diptera have not been very successful so far on insect eggs owing to methodical difficulties (Du Praw, 1963, and quoted by Gurdon, 1964; Graham, cited by Gurdon, 1964; Geyer-Duszyńska, 1967; Schnetter, 1967; Illmensee, 1968, 1970; Schubiger and Schneiderman, 1971; Zalokar, 1971). By using genetically marked donor nuclei, it has been shown that nuclei from as late a period as the preblastoderm stage injected into newly laid unfertilized or fertilized eggs may, at least in some cases, take part in embryonic development and even support development into adult structures. As yet, nothing can be concluded about the state of differentiation achieved by the nuclei during different stages and in different regions of the egg.

The irradiation experiments mentioned above intimated an expected action not only of the cytoplasm but also of the nuclei upon the embryonic development (cf. Taege, 1963; Truckenbrodt, 1965). However, there is additional direct evidence for the governing role of the nucleus upon embryogenesis from genetic investigations mostly on *Drosophila.* Some examples will be mentioned here (for further references, see Counce, 1961; Anderson, 1966). By hybridization of different *Chironomus* species, a progeny was obtained in which no nucleolus was formed in the nuclei during embryogenesis (Beerman, 1960). The development of these hybrids ceased shortly after the blastoderm stage. The nucleolus is absent during early development, but its presence later on should be necessary for the synthesis of ribosomal RNA (Section II, B, 2). Individuals lacking nucleolar organizers have also been produced in *Drosophila* (Scriba, 1964). Lack of certain chromosomes or parts of chromosomes in the egg is often a lethal condition resulting in an abnormal development specific for each type of deficiency (Poulson, 1940; Scriba, 1963, 1964, 1967). The primary cause of the abnormal development should be the loss of a specific locus or specific loci, which apparently normally become active during the time when abnormal development is first seen (Scriba, 1967). Many lethal mutations of single genes causing specific embryonic abnormalities have been described. An example is "deep orange" (Counce, 1956). Female embryos of this type cease development at an early cleavage stage; male embryos degenerate during gastrulation. Many lethal factors are first expressed during the preblastoderm or the blastoderm stage. This may indicate that important interactions between the nuclei and the periplasm are initiated during this period.

It is also conceivable that the nuclei may direct embryonic processes simply through a varied mitotic activity. Synthesis of specific proteins, and thereby cellular differentiation, is directed during interphase rather than during mitosis, and there exists a clear tendency for an antagonism between mitotic activity and cellular differentiation (Agrell, 1964a). Thus, a graded mitotic activity within an embryo may tentatively be regarded as an actual cause of differentiation because the polarity in the embryo may be increased by a mitotic gradient. As mentioned earlier, mitotic gradients have been demonstrated in some more determinate insect eggs, especially in the fly egg (Agrell, 1962). It is obvious that when a mitotic gradient replaces a stage of complete synchrony, those parts of the egg which are later struck by the mitotic wave may have the interphase time of their nuclei extended, as compared to the parts where the mitotic activity started. With continued asynchronous division the interphase may occupy an increasingly greater part of the whole cell cycle. Therefore, the differences in interphase time within the egg may not be restricted only to that cell cycle which corresponds to the first mitotic wave, but may persist during following cell cycles. Thus, a polarity in the embryo may be gradually strengthened by the repeated mitotic gradients. There is a feedback reaction, since the immediate result of the differentiation process itself causes initial small differences arising within a tissue to become rapidly amplified. Thus, an area of low mitotic activity may be a center of early differentiation. One must not be confused by the fact that in more regulative eggs the differentiation center, placed in the future germ band, is characterized by a higher mitotic activity than the rest of the blastoderm, which develops into the serosa. It seems very likely that in a strict sense the serosa cells differentiate earlier than the cells of the true embryo.

A mitotic gradient has been observed up to now only in more determinate eggs, where a continuous sheet of blastoderm cells develops within a periplasm. Thus, it seems likely that increasing polarity produced by the graded mitotic activity may affect not the larval but the imaginal differentiation. A certain degree of support for this opinion is given by the experiments made on the action of ether gas upon the developing *Drosophila* egg (Gloor, 1947; cf. the discussion of the bithorax phenomenon by Lewis, 1963). By this treatment, only pure imaginal transformations were obtained, such as, for instance, the so-called bithorax phenomenon, a change of the metathorax into a segment similar to mesothorax. The mechanism of the ether effect upon embryogenesis is not known. However, as for other narcotics, the most obvious effect of ether is upon the mitotic activity. Mitoses are delayed and also so-called C-mitotic disturbances are produced. An ether effect leading to imaginal malformations was produced during a period when mitotic gradients should be at play. Thus, ether may affect the system of mitotic gradients in the blastoderm, thereby producing imaginal malformations. In fact, in some preliminary experiments a very pronounced effect of ether upon the mitotic state in the *Calliphora* egg was found (Agrell, 1964b).

4. Fate and Function of Pole Cells

As was mentioned earlier, the posterior pole plasm of the egg in higher insects may contain a preformed structure, the oosome material, which is probably related to germ-cell determination. In this possibly unique system, the factors responsible for the determination and differentiation of certain cells appear to be assembled in specific organelles which can be studied ultrastructurally and cytochemically. In recent years the literature on the subject has increased. Thus it may be justified to treat this topic in a special section. The literature has been surveyed by Meng (1968) and that pertaining to Diptera has been surveyed by Anderson (1966). The polar granules are discussed, especially from the ultrastructural point of view, in a review by Mahowald (1971c).

When the posterior pole plasm or the pole cells are destroyed or eliminated, normal embryos may be formed, but they always lack primordial germ cells. If they give rise to adults, these are sterile. This was first shown by Hegner (1911) and has since then been repeatedly confirmed in many species. Since the nuclei which invade the posterior pole plasm are totipotent, the posterior pole plasm must contain the factors necessary for germ-cell formation.

More experiments are necessary, however, to elucidate the nature and mode of action of the germ-cell determining factors. These factors may, for instance, reside in the oosome material, in the posterior pole plasm itself, or in both these locations. The mechanism of germ-cell determination is probably not exactly the same in different insect groups. Therefore each group studied will be discussed separately.

In some insects certain chromosomes are eliminated in all somatic nuclei, while the full chromosome set is retained in the germ line. Chromosome elimination has been clearly demonstrated in lower Diptera. The moment and course of this elimination are strictly determined (Geyer-Duszynska, 1959). The chromosome loss occurs during early cleavage. The classic example is the gall midges, where, for example, in *Miastor* all 48 chromosomes are retained in the germ cells, while the chromosome number of the soma is reduced during the third cleavage division to twelve in the females and six in the males (Kahle, 1908; White, 1950). The somatic elimination of the chromosomes probably depends on a failure to produce normal midanaphase tension (Nicklas, 1959). Possibly the centromeres do not function normally (Geyer-Duszyńska, 1961). Somatic loss of chromatin may be a more widespread phenomenon than has been observed up to now. Thus, in the higher dipterans *Calliphora* and *Drosophila,* it has been found that a specific terminal fragment is lost from one of the chromosomes during a late cleavage division, when the chromatids stick to each other and form a so-called pseudochiasma (Melander, 1963). Probably this chromosome diminution takes place in all somatic nuclei.

Chromosome elimination and pole-cell formation has been studied experimentally in gall midges with the aid of cauterization, constriction, centrifugation, and UV microbeam techniques (Geyer-Duszyńska, 1959, 1966; Bantock, 1961, 1970). By separating the different components of the posterior pole region it has been possible to elucidate their function in the process of germ-cell determination and differentiation. The nuclei are protected from chromosome elimination only in the presence of the oosome material. The cytoplasm of the posterior pole is indispensable for pole-cell formation; the oosome material and the specific germ-line chromosomes are not necessary for pole-cell formation. Later the gametes differentiate normally only if the full set of chromosomes is retained in the germ line. During oogenesis the specific germ-line chromosomes are probably active in synthesis of RNA, possibly mRNA (Kunz, 1970; Kunz *et al.,* 1970). According to Wolf (1969b), it is not possible to separate the oosome material from the posterior pole plasm by experimental means in gall midge eggs, in which case the role of the oosome material and the posterior pole plasm remains obscure.

In the lower Diptera all the pole cells develop as germ cells. In the higher Diptera, some pole cells become vitellophages or are incorporated in the wall of the gut (Anderson, 1966). The germ cells are nevertheless in both groups solely derived from pole cells. By centrifugation of *Drosophila* eggs the polar granules are displaced from the posterior pole (Imaizumi, 1958; Jazdowska-Zagrodzinska, 1966). No pole cells are then formed at the posterior pole or elsewhere in the centrifuged egg. The pole plasm apparently remains at the posterior pole when the polar granules are displaced (Jazdowska-Zagrodzińska, 1966). It was concluded that both the polar granules and the pole plasm in association are necessary for pole-cell formation. However, it cannot be excluded that the polar granules alone are responsible for the formation of pole cells. Mahowald (1968b) has pointed out that the polar granules are dispersed by the centrifugation. In that case they may not be present in sufficient concentrations in their new locations to initiate pole-cell formation there.

Some experiments by Schnetter (1965) indicate that the oosome material is necessary for germ-cell formation in the beetle *Leptinotarsa*. In the egg of the hymenopteran *Pimpla,* pole cells are formed only in the presence of the oosome (Achtelig and Krause, 1971); the presence of the posterior pole plasm alone is not sufficient. However, if the pole cells or the posterior pole plasm with the oosome are removed, embryos with normal gonads are obtained. These embryos give rise to fertile adults (Günther, 1971). Thus, in this insect, the germ cells are not invariably derived from the pole cells in the egg. The oosome, although necessary for pole-cell formation, may not be germ-cell determining. Possibly the oosome is active during another phase of the life cycle taking part in the protein synthesis and growth of the posterior part of the oocyte (Meng, 1970). In another hymenopteran, *Formica,* the oosome may have a function in caste determination (Bier, 1954).

It may, however, in most cases be regarded as very likely that the oosome material is a preformed, ooplasmic structure determining the developmental fate of a certain region in the egg. Its chemical composition and its ultrastructure give some clues to its mode of action. The oosome material is basophilic and contains proteins and RNA (Jura *et al.*, 1958; Counce, 1963; Nicklas, 1959; Bhuiyan and Shafiq, 1959; Bantock, 1970; Mahowald, 1962; Meng, 1968). A strong alkaline phosphatase reaction has been detected in the oosome material (Tawfik, 1957) and unspecifically in the posterior pole plasm (Bhuiyan and Shafiq, 1959). The ultrastructure of the oosome material has been investigated in different *Drosophila* species (Mahowald, 1962, 1968b; Ullmann, 1965), in the fly *Coelopa* (Schwalm *et al.*, 1970), in the gall midges *Wachtiella* and *Miastor* (Wolf, 1967, 1969a; Mahowald, 1968a, 1971c), and in the hymenopteran *Pimpla* (Schneider, cited by Meng, 1970). In the mature egg, this electron-dense material consists of several bodies from about 0.5 μm to over 1 μm in diameter *(Drosophila, Coelopa)* or of what seems to be a network *(Wachtiella, Miastor)*. No membranes surround these structures. Their substructure is fibrillar or granular. In *Drosophila* and *Miastor* it has been shown that the oosome material undergoes a series of characteristic ultrastructual changes during early development (Counce, 1963; Mahowald, 1968a,b, 1971c). In part, these changes are species-specific. During early cleavage the oosome material fragments into smaller units and attains its most fragmented state when the cleavage nuclei reach the posterior pole plasm. When the pole cells have stopped dividing, reaggregation occurs. A similar, but in part different, pattern has been described in *Coelopa* (Schwalm *et al.*, 1970).

Two interesting observations in *Drosophila* give some clues to how the polar granules exert their influence (Mahowald, 1968b, 1971b,c). First, the RNA of the polar granules is no longer detectable after pole-cell formation. Second, clusters of ribosomes are attached to the periphery of the polar granules when the granules are fragmented before and during pole-cell formation. Mahowald has postulated that the polar granules consist of masked mRNA protected by proteins and stored during oogenesis. During the critical period before and during pole-cell formation, specific proteins are transcribed from this mRNA and these proteins are responsible for the effect of the polar granules. Although direct evidence is lacking as yet, this is indeed an attractive working hypothesis. Stable forms of mRNA are known in other systems (see Spirin, 1966; cf. Section II, B, 2). Germ-cell determining factors assembled in structures similar to polar granules may exist also in amphibian eggs (see Mahowald and Hennen, 1971).

In *Drosophila* the oosome material has been followed in the germ line during the life cycle (Counce, 1963; Mahowald, 1971a,c). When the pole cells are transformed into primordial germ cells, the aggregated polar granules (see above) again fragment and become attached to the nuclear envelope as fibrous bodies presumably representing the protein part of the polar granules. Such bodies are connected to the envelopes of the germ-line nuclei up to the start of oogenesis. More of this fibrous material is probably synthesized, since its concentration does not decrease, while the primordial germ cells grow in number during postembryonic development. The fibrous bodies are not found in the young oocyte, but they are abundant in the nurse cells. The oocyte and its nurse cells are descendants of the same oogonium. Presumably RNA becomes attached to the fibrous bodies in the nurse cells. This material is then probably transported to the posterior pole of the egg, where it forms the polar granules. Accumulation of nurse-cell RNA in the oosome region has been detected in *Pimpla* (Meng, 1968, 1970). The idea that the oosome material is continuously present in the germ line agrees well with the concept of a stable germ line shielded from the numerous differentiating impulses to which the soma is subjected.

III. Postembryonic Development

In different animal groups, where during postembryonic development one organization type has to be changed for another, a transformation through some kind of metamorphosis from the larval to the adult body is necessary. This may take place when a stage adapted for active or passive dispersion is succeeded by a stage adjusted to sedentary life, but metamorphosis occurs especially when during the development one type of nutritional intake replaces another. In the latter case the larval life is usually characterized by excessive growth. The insects are good examples of this. When the juvenile form has a demand for the same food as the adult the postembryonic changes are only gradual through a series of moltings. If there are great differences between the larval and adult requirements for nutriment and habitat, the corresponding difference in the organization type of the larva and imago has to be covered by some rather profound processes of metamorphosis. In this case the larva represents a kind of double organism. One part of it, the larval body, will grow and function. Another part, the imaginal anlagen, will grow very little and remain in a quiescent state until metamorphosis. Then they exhibit a rapid growth and differentiation takes place in a way that may be regarded as a postponed embryonic development. Thus, in insects, no adequate distinction can be made between embryonic and postembryonic development.

The mechanism by which the continued cellular differentiation may be directed during the postembryonic development in insects seems to be well established through observations on the "puffs" in polytene chromosomes in Diptera, reviewed by Beermann (1959), Kroeger and Lezzi (1966), and Ashburner (1970). These puffs appear within euchromatic loci and indicate a temporary gene activity. The pattern of puffing is characteristic for each type of cell and each type of function in a given individual. These localized gene activities represent also a localized synthesis of DNA (Ficq and Pavan, 1958). Some general aspects upon the gene–physiological basis for differentiation in insects are discussed by Hadorn (1950).

Of importance to the understanding of the pattern of differentiation during the postembryonic development in insects is an acquaintance with the regenerative capacity. A survey of this phenomenon could very well have been included here. However, four comprehensive articles about this problem have appeared, three concerning regeneration in insects (Bodenstein, 1953, 1962; Lawrence, 1970), and one concerning regeneration in Crustacea (Bliss, 1960).

Growth, molting, and metamorphosis are hormonally controlled. (The endocrine control is dealt with in Chapter 5 of this volume.) Hormonal control represents a trigger mechanism by which, in a still unknown manner, certain kinds of physiological reactions are initiated or blocked. Consequently, these physiological processes have their distinct qualities irrespective of whether they are hormonally controlled or not. Thus the physiological courses of events can very well be described and discussed without considering how they are actually switched on or off.

A. GROWTH

Within the egg as a whole there is no growth. Only a kind of "inner growth" occurs in the egg representing a transformation of stored yolk components into active protoplasm. The growth during insect development is restricted to the larval development and during this feeding period there will be deposited all the mass necessary for the final adult. In most organisms growth occurs through cell multiplication. The difference in size between the juvenile and the full-grown animal is due to a difference in number of cells and not to a different average size of their single cells. This can be observed not only during the life cycle of the individual but also as a difference between small and large species belonging to the same organization type. The organs of the smaller species are made up of a smaller number of cells than in the larger species (Rensch, 1948). Thus the differentiation of smaller species is completed at an earlier stage of growth than in larger ones. However, in the insect larva, the general principle of growth by cell multiplication is modified. In endopterygote groups the growth of many organs may be attained through an enormous enlargement of the single cells. Often, but not obligatorily, this growth by increase in the dimensions of the cells concerns the specific larval organs which undergo breakdown at metamorphosis (Trager, 1935; Wigglesworth, 1954). The growth of the cell is not restricted to the cytoplasm but also involves a growth of the nucleus. A very high degree of polyploidy is thereby sometimes attained. In the polyploid nuclei of most insects a complete separation of the chromosomes is retained, while in dipteran larvae the polyploidization brings about the well-known polytenization. A general survey of the cytochemistry of the giant chromosomes is given by Alfert (1954) and Ashburner (1970). During continued development a somatic reduction of chromosome groups may occur as a normal phenomenon (Berger, 1938). More often, the larval high-ploid tissues are entirely broken down (Kramer, 1959). The absolute growth of the imaginal anlagen during the larval development is only slight (Novák, 1956). Also the principle for the growth may be different, e.g., in Diptera, where the larval growth occurs through enlargement of the cells, the imaginal discs grow by cell multiplication (Bodenstein, 1950).

1. Some Principles of Growth during Molting

The postembryonic growth of different insect species is characterized by series of a varied number of moltings. Thus the growth in length or area will be discontinuous owing to the rigidity of the cuticle, while increase in weight or mass may represent more or less continuous S-shaped curves, even if a certain discontinuity may appear due, for instance, to a changed intake of nourishment or water around the molting periods. In some insects, as in the *Rhodnius* larva, an outburst of mitosis in the epiderm is observed to occur preceeding a renewed growth (Wigglesworth, 1948). Whereas the molting affects the growth of the body wall, the growth of the inner organs is rather unaffected.

The apparently discontinuous growth of the epiderm has been the object for some analyses and certain "laws" for growth have been founded. One such empirical law is termed "Dyar's rule" and says that the growth through moltings proceeds as a geometrical progression, where all steps in the increase of the dimensions are represented by the same ratio, which is constant for the given species. This rule seems to be a fairly good approximation for the growth in all insect groups and is of practical importance for the description of the process of growth through moltings. The so-called "Przibram's rule" represents an attempt to extend Dyar's rule, stating that the progression factor of the length should always be the same, that is, $1.26 = \sqrt[3]{2}$, because an ecdysis is assumed to occur only after doubling of the mass of cells. Przibram's rule represents a definite overestimation and should be principally rejected. Within groups of insects where species have the same number of molting stages, as, for example, Hemiptera (Heteroptera) with five ecdyses constantly, the progression factor will not be the same for all species. The greater the individual size of the species, the greater the progression factor will be because it has been stated that the total growth itself has a direct, positive larger insects have relatively small offspring, which grow relatively much, while smaller insects of the same organization type have relatively large offspring which grow relatively little.

For still another reason the rule of Przibram cannot be valid; it presupposes to some extent the existence of a harmonic, isogonic growth. On the contrary, insect growth is disharmonic and heterogonic, which means that during the continuous growth there will appear a successive change in the body proportions. An approximate but useful expresson for the heterogonic growth can be obtained from the formula of Huxley: $y = kx^{\alpha}$, where x is equal to the dimension of the whole, y that of the part, α is the growth constant (in heterogonic growth greater or less than unity), and k a factor of proportionality (Huxley, 1932). By the use of this growth constant it can be shown that even during the gradual postembryonic development of the most primitive insects, Collembola, changes in proportionality occur and centers of growth along the body can be observed (Fig. 7) (Agrell, 1948b). Thus, the so-called anterioposterior growth is greatly modified. As regards the growth of appendages during the same development, the principles of growth are similar in different parts of the individual but may deviate in different groups of species (Agrell, 1948b). Also it was shown that smaller species which grow less undergo greater changes in proportionality during their individual growth than the bigger ones. This can also be seen from Fig. 7. The sum of the black areas represents the sum of the deviations of the α constant for all body segments from unity, that is from isogonic growth, and is thus a measure of the magnitude of heterogonic growth. The smaller the species the greater this total change in body proportions will be.

Not only the morphological changes are heterogonic during insect growth; chemical growth is also found to be heterogonic and to show a corresponding conformity to law, which has been observed in other animal groups (Tessier, 1931).

The period of larval development may not be regarded as exclusively a period of overall growth. Certain abdominal muscles in *Rhodnius* undergo a cycle of development and involution during each molting period in a manner which has some resemblance to a repeated metamorphosis (Wigglesworth, 1956a). Similar cyclical changes were observed in locust larvae (Hill and Goldsworthy, 1968). A cooperation between two organ systems, between the hemocytes and the thoracic glands, for the proper progress of molting is demonstrated in the *Rhodnius* larva (Wigglesworth, 1956b). A similar interdependence in *Drosophila* between lymph-gland cells and imaginal buds (Shatoury and Waddington, 1957)

and between hemocytes and epidermal cells (Whitten, 1969) has been
observed.

An interesting approach to the problem of an inherent growth control
during molting has been made by studying the regeneration of bristle

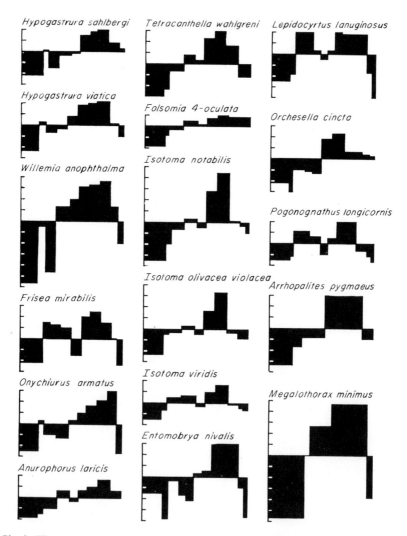

Fig. 7. The growth gradient along the body of some species of Collembola. Vertical
axes denote the magnitude of the growth constant α. Horizontal axes placed at $\alpha=1$
denote the sequence of body segments; from left to right: head, prothorax, etc., up to
and including the sixth abdominal segment. From Agrell (1948b).

plaques in the *Rhodnius* larva (Wigglesworth, 1954). Each plaque seems to inhibit the emergence of a new plaque within a certain distance of itself. The hypothesis is advanced that there is a competition between the plaques within each certain area for essential substances necessary for the plaque formation. Thus, morphogenesis in the insect is regarded as a matter of chemical self-regulation within the epidermis. The theory is substantiated by some morphogenetic effects induced in normal or mutant insect forms (reviewed by Lawrence, 1970).

2. Metabolism during Growth and Molting

The oxygen consumption calculated on a per weight basis decreases in time with growth during larval development (Chen, 1951; Slăma, 1957; Pouvreau, 1968). This is an expression of the general decrease in metabolic rate following an increase in size. The metabolic intensity may vary rhythmically during molting, demonstrating peaks at each molt (Edwards, 1953; Zwicky and Wigglesworth, 1956; Ito and Seki, 1954). This may reflect the nutritional stage of the larva but may also be an indication of a rhythmically changed basal metabolism caused by morphological changes (Wigglesworth, 1956a). The rate of cyanide-insensitive oxygen uptake is high in the molting period (Ito and Seki, 1954).

During the larval growth of endopterygote insects there is a steady accumulation of fat and glycogen (Strauss, 1911; Busnel, 1937; Melampy and Olsan, 1940; Babers, 1941; Demyanovsky and Zubova, 1957; Russo-Caia, 1960). In the sheep blowfly no increase in glycogen concentration was found (Rainey, 1938). In the honey bee larva, the respiratory quotient is high and above unity, indicating a conversion of carbohydrate into fat (Kahn and Lavrova, 1937; Melampy and Willis, 1939). A differential change in triglycerides compared to phospholipids (structural lipids) was observed in different insect larvae (Wimer and Lumb, 1967; Beaudoin *et al.*, 1968; Castillón *et al.*, 1971; Lipsitz and McFarlane, 1971). The total nitrogen content should follow the growth curve. The concentration of free ninhydrin-positive substances is constant during the larval development of *Culex* (Chen, 1958), but decreases during the same period in *Drosophila* (Benz, 1955), as was also found for a butterfly larva (Ganti and Shanmugasundaram, 1963). A systematic variation in the concentration of free amino acids was found during growth and molting of cockroaches (Jarnicka-Stanios, 1967). A net synthesis of some amino acids is demonstrated during the growth of the silkworm larva (Fukuda *et al.*, 1961). The [^{14}C]amino acid incorporation in blowfly larvae was studied by Howells *et al.* (1967). An elimination of ammonia should occur in the house fly larva (Russo-Caia, 1960). The relative amount of the two nucleic acids decreases during larval development of the silkworm and the house fly (Wyatt, 1959; Russo-Caia, 1960). A rapid accumulation of uric acid occurs during late larval development in the rice stem borer (Tojo and Hirano, 1968). The composition of the molting fluid differs from that of hemolymph (Katzenellenbogen and Kafatos, 1970).

Variation in enzyme activity during the larval growth period has been the object of scattered research interest. Uricase is present in the larva of the blowfly, but disappears suddenly at pupation (Brown, 1938). The activity of succinic oxidase is high in the mealworm larva for a period after hatching from the egg but then decreases rapidly (Ludwig and Barsa, 1956). In a study of proteolytic, lipolytic, and amylolytic activity during the larval development of the house fly, Russo-Caia (1960) found that tryptic activity disappears at metamorphosis. Different dehydrogenases were studied during larval growth in *Drosophila* (Rechsteiner, 1970), transaminases in *Musca* (McAllen and Chefurca, 1961), acetylcholine and acetylcholine esterase in a moth (Grzelak *et al.*, 1970), ATPase activities in *Bombyx* (Yabe, 1962), and β-glucuronidase activity in blowflies (Varute and Sawant, 1971a,b). The specific activity of phospholipase A in larvae of *Culex* decreases with growth (Rao and Subrahmanyam, 1970). Glutamyl transpeptidase activity shows a peak at the end of the larval period of *Musca* (Bodnaryk and Skillings, 1971). Chitin synthesis was studied by Porter and Javorsky (1965). Soluble fat-body proteins increase during larval development of the corn borer (Chippendale, 1970b), indicating an active protein synthesis. In the same beetle it was found that the larval midgut and fat-body cells have the potential to synthesize the two major hemolymph proteins (Chippendale, 1970b). The successive appearance of tissue antigens during the development of mosquito larvae was observed by Zaman and Chellappah (1963).

In immediate relation to the molting process some biochemical changes may occur in addition to the mentioned cycling in respiratory intensity. Thus, during ecdysis, a decrease of the caloric value of oxygen takes place in the silkworm larva (Balzam, 1933) and the ratio Na^+/K^+ increases in the hemolymph of the locust (Hoyle, 1956). Many biochemical parameters were found to vary cyclically in time with the molting of the locust (Hill and Goldsworthy, 1968). Also it has been found that during molting in the silkworm larva about 20–25% of the lipids are consumed, phospholipids are synthesized, and after the molt inorganic phosphate is liberated from phosphorylated esters (Niemierko *et al.*, 1956). The mitotic activity at the last, metamorphic, molt in the milkweed bug studied by autoradiography showed three steps of differentiated divisions (Lawrence, 1968). The G1 phase was very long; the G2 was absent; and the S phase and prophase overlapped.

The reported biochemical variations, which appear around each molt, support the idea of larval development being a definitely discontinuous process. Ecdysis seems to be followed by profound metabolic changes and the growth process, at least of the epidermis, may also be almost as discontinuous as is indicated by the measurements of the stepwise increase in size of the body parts.

B. METAMORPHOSIS

During embryonic development some imaginal characters are determined. The irreversible mapping out of the future imaginal body is not thereby completed, but will continue during the larval development in the epiderm (Wigglesworth, 1940; Yosii, 1954) and even within the imaginal discs (Bodenstein, 1941; Vogt, 1946; Henke *et al.*, 1946; Hadorn, 1948, 1966; Pantelouris and Waddington, 1955). However, the visible differentiation of the imaginal primordia will appear only at the final onset of metamorphosis.

Metamorphosis is a very complicated affair to deal with, not only because it represents in its most advanced state such a profound conversion of the living system, but also because there exist within the insect groups so many gradations in the transforming changes, when the larva develops into the imago. The general nature of insect metamorphosis is discussed in some comprehensive reviews dealing either primarily with the morphological and phylogenetic aspects (e.g., Snodgrass, 1954), or mainly with the physiological implications (Richards, 1937; Bodenstein, 1953; Wigglesworth, 1954). Hinton (1971) discusses the comparative aspects of the metamorphic stages.

1. Histolysis and Histogenesis

When the insect larva is transformed into an adult, this can occur in a more or less drastic way. In the more primitive insect groups, all the larval organs may represent the corresponding imaginal organs after only small and continuously proceeding changes, termed ametabolous or paurometabolous development. However, the last molt will represent a greater degree of transformation than the preceding ones. On the other hand, in the more advanced groups the organization type of the larva may be so divergent from that of the adult that only few of the the larval organs can be used for the imaginal life and more or less radical transformations are necessary. These occur mainly during the pupal stage and consequently two molts are necessary for the imaginal change. This development is called holmetabolous and characterizes the Endopterygota. The Exopterygota assume a somewhat intermediate position in this respect with their hemimetabolous development. Thus, this transformation of the larva to the imago represents a varied degree of histolysis of larval tissues and a corresponding degree of histogenesis of the imaginal organs. The histolysis should represent a programmed cell death, a hormonally induced and neurologically activated cytolytic mechanism (Lockshin and Williams, 1965; Lockshin, 1971). The interaction of phagocytes should be only secondary (Evans, 1936; Crossley, 1968; Akai, 1969). A nutritive connection between phagocytes and epidermal cells has been suggested (Whitten, 1969). Molting and metamorphosis as a whole may also be under nervous control (Wigglesworth, 1934; Edwards, 1966).

The epidermis determines the principal shape of the insect, and its morphogenetic changes are therefore of special interest. If we take the well-studied *Rhodnius* as an example of a gradual development, it is clear that even in this case the development is not continuous, but cyclical. The epidermal cells pass through waves of mitotic activity in time with the molts and associated with cytoplasmic changes. Also, chromatolysis occurs and is most pronounced at the last ecdysis when the pre-imaginal larva changes into the imago. However, the larval epidermis is taken over, on a large scale, by the adult. Even when a pupal stage fills the gap in incompatibility between the larva and the pupa, the larval epiderm may still be used to a great extent in the imaginal body. This should be the case also in such advanced groups as Coleoptera and Lepidoptera. The larval epidermis retains the potential for renewed growth and further differentiation, which may be tremendously enhanced within certain areas and lead to very rapid changes in form. However, it is difficult to decide whether these centers of imaginal growth within the larval epidermis actually belong to the true larval tissue. In any case, a differentiated histolysis of the larval epidermis at metamorphosis is not observed, with the exception of the special larval appendages. In those insect groups which have the most advanced type of metamorphosis, the Hymenoptera and Diptera, an actual replacement of larval epidermis by imaginal tissue takes place (Hinton, 1963). The imaginal primordia may have existed during the entire larval stage in the form of the so-called imaginal discs, but their differentiation has been hormonally depressed. They represent the main parts of the head and of the body appendages and appear as strange invaginated pocket structures, which evaginate and converge as the result of a sudden imaginal differentiation. Also in the abdominal epidermis centers of growth are observed, which may depict a kind of less delimited imaginal discs. In Lepidoptera imaginal wing buds exist, but the legs should not have their origin from preexisting imaginal discs (Kuske *et al.*, 1961). Through genetic marking with X rays it has been found that the imaginal discs of *Drosophila* (leg, wing, and antennal discs) are initiated very early as 10–20 cells, which show a mitotic arrest during embryogenesis (Bryant and Schneiderman, 1969; Bryant, 1970; Postlethwait and Schneiderman, 1971). During the growth of the larval tissues through cell and nuclear enlargement, the imaginal discs grow exponentially through cell multiplication about in time with the larval growth (Lewerenz, 1961). The clonal growth pattern, which forms the foundation for further determination, appears as a result of oriented cell divisions and not of cell migration. Also in Hymenoptera and Lepidoptera with less distinct imaginal anlagen, the clonal growth pattern should depend upon oriented cell divisions (Whiting, 1939; Yagi and Saitoh, 1955). For the eye imaginal discs of the mosquito *Aedes* it was observed that a mitotic wave preceeds a differentiation wave (White, 1961).

When the imaginal discs have stopped growing, a differentiation arrives, visible as a formation of endoplasmic reticulum and an attachment of ribosomes onto it (Agrell, 1968). These larval imaginal discs demonstrate a complete continuity of the membrane system in their cells: nuclear envelope, endoplasmic reticulum, Golgi apparatus, and mitochondrial membranes (Agrell, 1966). Later the organ-specific differentiation becomes visible (Waddington, 1962; Wehman, 1969).

The imaginal discs may undergo so-called transdetermination. After long-term cultivation in adult hosts and later transference to metamorphosing larvae, one type of imaginal disc may form structures characterizing other types of discs. This indicates that under these experimental conditions the determination of imaginal primordia is not irreversible (reviewed by Hadorn, 1966).

Because of the often very great difference in organization between the larva and imago, the muscles, in particular, are those inner organs which are most affected by metamorphosis. Some kind of muscular degeneration and consecutive regeneration occur in all insect groups at the larval–imaginal shift. In less advanced groups these changes are qualitatively and quantitatively faint and represent only cytoplasmic rearrangements within one and the same cell, while in higher groups a complete exchange of larval and imaginal muscles may take place through profound processes of histolysis and histogenesis. However, it is discussed to what extent imaginal muscles develop *de novo* from imaginal myoblasts or are reorganized from nuclei within the larval muscle cells.

Specific larval organs representing adaptations to the larval feeding habits or other demands upon the environment always degenerate. The fat body, often the largest organ, by far, in the larva, belongs to these specific larval organs. It represents a tissue for storage of nutriments and is consistently histolyzed during advancing metamorphosis and its contents are utilized for the imaginal growth. A reorganization of the imaginal fat body from the nuclei of the cytolyzed larval fat-body cells, as has been proposed by Teunissen (1937), seems unlikely. However, it has been demonstrated that the brain hormone may induce nuclear activation and structuralization of mitochondria and endoplasmic reticulum in lepidopteran fat-body cells (Ishizaki, 1963). Among the insect groups, the transformation of the alimentary canal, as the muscular changes, exhibits smooth transitions. The imaginal gut may develop from a simple renewal of the developmental activity of the larval cells, but it may also to a great extent represent a new formation, as in Hymenoptera and Diptera, where the imaginal intestine is reorganized from anterior and posterior imaginal rings. Some organs are not very much affected by histolysis during the metamorphosis, e.g., the nervous, tracheal, and blood-vessel systems and the Malpighian tubules.

Structural changes in different organs during metamorphosis have been recently studied in intestine (Janda and Krieg, 1969; Judy and Gilbert, 1969), silkgland (Matsuura *et al.*, 1968; Kafatos and Feder, 1968), muscles (Crossley, 1968), fat body (Ishizaki, 1965; Walker, 1966), and nervous system (Heywood, 1965; Edwards, 1969, a review).

The morphological changes at the transition from larval to adult life have been the object of thorough investigations for most insect groups (see the following references): Hemiptera, Wigglesworth (1954); Megaloptera, Ochsé (1944); Coleoptera, Poyarkoff (1910) and Murray and Tiegs (1935); Trichoptera, Haller (1948); Lepidoptera, Hufnagel (1918); Hymenoptera, Anglas (1901), Perez (1912), and Tiegs (1922); Diptera, Perez (1910), Snodgrass (1924), and Robertson (1936); general, Etkin and Gilbert (1968).

2. Metabolic Changes during Metamorphosis

The biochemistry of insect metamorphosis has been the object of many investigations and the results also allow some comparisons with structural changes. Some of these investigations deal especially with the metabolism at diapause, which as a temporary arrest in the development is characterized by a lowered metabolism. As some comprehensive reviews have been published about the metabolic aspects of diapause, this phenomenon will not be treated separately in this chapter, but we shall consider those results which may be important to the understanding of the processes of metamorphosis in general. For the rest, the reader is referred to the reviews in question, Lees (1955, 1956) and Harvey (1962).

The interest in insect biochemistry has to a great extent been directed toward studies on the composition of the hemolymph, also concerning metamorphosis, and a vast material has been rapidly collected (reviewed by Wyatt, 1961). It may be difficult to understand this specialized assiduousness. Analyses of blood samples may be very useful as a practical and necessary tool for diagnosis in the hospitals, because the physiological background for the measured changes in the human blood composition has been so thoroughly worked out. However, the insect hemolymph, as the blood in other animals, may or may not reflect important metabolic changes within different tissues, but the way in which this occurs in the insect body is at present almost completely unknown. Thus, the results from the analyses of the insect hemolymph are very difficult to evaluate in causal connections, even if they can be explicit in themselves, and these results will be used in a very restrictive sense in the following section.

For reviews about chemical changes during metamorphosis, see Needham (1929), Buck (1953), Rockstein (1957), Gilbert and Schneiderman (1961), Fast (1964), Karlson and Sekeris (1964), Chen (1966), and Gilbert (1967).

a. General Metabolism and Energy Utilization. The energy metabolism represented by the oxygen consumption, carbon dioxide production, or heat production during the period of metamorphosis is more or less U-shaped. All investigations agree in this respect: Coleoptera, Krogh (1914) and Ludwig (1931); Lepidoptera, Heller (1926a), Taylor (1927), Crescitelli (1935), Squire (1936), Schwan (1940), Bell (1940), and Ito (1954); Hymenoptera, Bodine and Evans (1932), Kahn and Lavrova (1937), Melampy and Willis (1939), and Slăma (1957); Diptera, Tangl (1909), Taylor (1927), Frew (1929), Poulson (1935), and Agrell (1952) (Fig. 8).

Thus, insect metamorphosis is characterized by a decrease in metabolic activity followed by a successive restitution of this activity. A close and adequate correlation between the U-shaped metabolic curve and the processes of histolysis and histogenesis has been demonstrated for the fly pupa (Fig. 9H) (Agrell, 1949c). In lethal *Drosophila* mutants, which have a disturbed morphogenesis, the respiratory activity will not increase (Chen, 1951). Organs *in vitro* demonstrate less U-shaped respiratory curves than the intact animal (Fourche and Ambrosioni, 1969). It is suggested that the respiratory rate to some extent depends upon regulato-

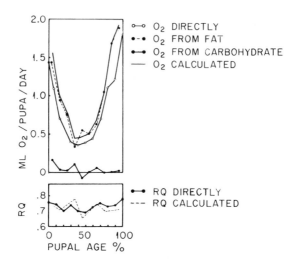

Fig. 8. The oxygen consumption and respiratory quotient during metamorphosis of the fly *Calliphora erythrocephala* directly measured on living pupae and calculated from estimations of the gradual disappearance of fat and carbohydrate. From Agrell (1952).

ry mechanisms requiring the integration of the whole organism (Fourche, 1969).

The fall in respiratory intensity may appear even before the moment of pupation during the prepupal period, when the larva has stopped feeding, as in the honey bee (Melampy and Willis, 1939). In this respect there are marked differences between queen, worker, and drone (Melampy and Willis, 1939; Kahn and Lavrova, 1937), probably because of their different types of nourishment. A pupal diapause does not affect the principal course of the respiratory curve; only the period of low metabolism is prolonged (Heller, 1926a; Bodine and Evans, 1932; Agrell, 1948b; Waku, 1957).

The respiratory quotient has also been measured during metamorphosis in most of the works cited above. They all agree in reporting respiratory quotients (RQ's) around 0.7 indicating a utilization of fat during the pupal life. In the honey bee pupa higher RQ values may denote complications and again there are differences between the casts. During diapause in Lepidoptera, seemingly very low RQ values can be measured, down to 0.1. The main reason for these should be cyclic gigantic outbursts of CO_2, a phenomenon which seems to be widespread in all insects under conditions when the oxygen supply is high relative to demand (Buck and

Keister, 1958). However, some kind of retention of carbon dioxide may not be the whole explanation. Thus it must taken into consideration that the interburst RQ has a negative thermal coefficient during diapause as well as during latent development and assumes a series of constant levels at each developmental step (Agrell, 1947a).

Direct measurement of the utilization during the pupal life of the energy store accumulated in the larva underlines the importance of a fat utilization (Rudolfs, 1926, 1929; Needham, 1929; Evans, 1932; Becker, 1934; Haub and Hitchcock, 1941; Demyanovsky and Zubova, 1957; Russo-Caia, 1960; Villeneuve and Lemonde, 1963). Unsaturated fatty acids should only be little used for energy production (Schmidt, 1963; D'Costa and Birth, 1966). Studies of phospholipids, the structural fats, show a changed pattern during development (Beaudoin et al., 1968) and the relative amount of phospholipids increases with adult development (Castillón et al., 1971). In the fly pupa, the directly observed oxygen consumption was compared to the one calculated from the measured values of fat and carbohydrate decomposition (Agrell, 1952), and a complete correspondence between the measured and calculated respiratory curves was found (Fig. 8). Thus the main fuel during the pupal development in this insect is fat, supplemented by a small amount of carbohydrate. Very little labeled glucose was respired during imaginal development of *Lucilia* (Crompton and Polakis, 1969). It may be noted that these curves (Fig. 8) indicate a conversion of fat into carbohydrate when the metabolism is at its lowest (as is also suggested by Haub and Hitchcock, 1941). In other insects the proportion of fat to carbohydrate utilization may be different, and no interconversion of [^{14}C]palmitate or [^{14}C]acetate into carbohydrate was found during lepidopteran metamorphosis (Chino and Gilbert, 1965). The fat to carbohydrate ratio may be different also in related species (Heller, 1926b). In all events the utilization of carbohydrate is high in the honey bee pupa (Strauss, 1911; Melampy and Olsan, 1940). The amount of low molecular reducing substances may vary in some U-shaped fashion during the period of metamorphosis (Crescitelli and Taylor, 1935; Agrell, 1952; Del Vecchio, 1955b; Czoppelt and Rembold, 1970; Tate and Wimer, 1971). Glycogen and trehalose may be synthesized at the expense of each other (Schmidt and Mathur, 1967; Tate and Wimer, 1971). A marked utilization of citrate may occur during metamorphosis (Levenbook and Hollis, 1961; Pant and Sharma, 1967). An observed rhythm of glycogen variation during the metamorphosis of *Calliphora* may reflect a redistribution of carbohydrates from the fat-body cells to differentiating tissues (Lindh,

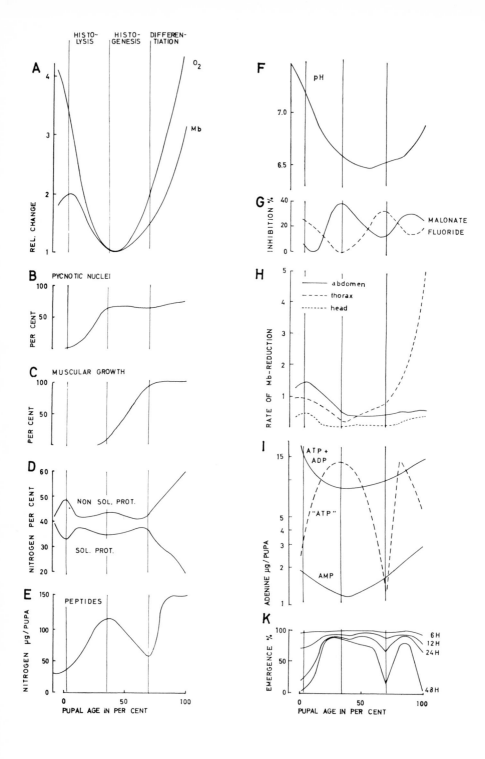

1967). Comprehensive summaries of the earlier literature on the carbohydrate metabolism of insects are given by Babers (1941), Rockstein (1957), and Wyatt (1967).

Investigations of the nitrogen metabolism indicate a constancy in the amount of total nitrogen during the pupal life. No excretion of ammonia occurs (Frew, 1929; Evans, 1932, 1934; Agrell, 1952; Del Vecchio, 1955a). The main excretory product during the pupal life is uric acid, which accumulates (Brown, 1938; Brighenti, 1940; Bernard and Fixler, 1963; Birt and Christian, 1969; Tojo, 1971), especially during histolysis (Russo-Caia, 1960). In spite of the radical processes of histolysis and histogenesis in the pupa there are only comparatively small changes in the total amount of protein and low molecular nitrogen compounds irrespective of the insect group (Heller, 1932; Agrell, 1949a, 1951, 1952; Benz, 1955; Chen and Kühn, 1956; Chen, 1958; Lennie and Birt, 1965; Mitlin et al., 1966; Levenbook, 1962; Levenbook and Dinamarca, 1966; Pant and Lal, 1970). However, single amino acids may vary rhythmically during metamorphosis. The nitrogen metabolism is not reflected in the U-shaped respiratory curve and makes no observable con-

---

Fig. 9. Schematic representation of some biochemical changes during the pupal life of one and the same insect species, the fly *Calliphora erythrocephala*. From Agrell (1952, 1961). (A) The change of oxygen consumption and methylene blue reducing capacity (Mb). U-shaped curves were also found for different single apoenzymes: malic, succinic, glutamic, citric, and L-amino acid dehydrogenases, and to a certain extent also for lactic acid dehydrogenase. (B) Histolysis illustrated by the increase in amount of pycnotic nuclei. (C) Histogenesis illustrated by the growth of the imaginal thoracic muscles. (D) Differentiation illustrated by the conversion of soluble into nonsoluble proteins. During the same period the number of mitochondria increases rapidly. (E) The change in amount of peptides. The same curve is obtained whether the peptides are defined as TCA-soluble and alcohol-insoluble nitrogen or as the difference between phosphotungstic acid and TCA-precipitable nitrogen. The same course was found for the phosphates which were difficult to hydrolyze. (F) The variation in tissue pH. (G) The inverse inhibitory action of malonate and fluoride upon methylene blue respiration. The lactic acid content in the pupa varies with the fluoride inhibition. The increase in spontaneous Mb reduction after saturation with different donors varies with the malonate inhibitions (i.e., succinate, fumarate, malate, acetate, and lactate). (H) The change in methylene blue reducing capacity in different sections of the pupa demonstrating that the decreasing part of the metabolic curve corresponds to histolysis of the larval tissues and that the rising part is almost entirely concerned with the formation of the imaginal muscles, principally in the thorax. The same distribution was found for single apodehydrogenases, i.e., malic, succinic, glutamic, citric dehydrogenases, and to a certain extent also for lactic dehydrogenase. (I) The variation in amounts of adenosine phosphates. The ATP probably includes some UTP or some other energy-rich nucleotide phosphate. (The ATPase activity varies in a U-shaped fashion.) (K) The varied sensitivity to 6–48 hours anaerobiosis evaluated as percent emerged flies.

tribution to the energy metabolism. An interpretation of this curve as dependent upon the amino acid oxidation, attributed to Agrell by Buck
(1953), has never been made. The changes between structural and non-
structural proteins or between proteins and peptides are obvious (Evans,
1932; Agrell, 1952; Del Vecchio, 1955a) and seem actually to reflect
morphological processes (Fig. 9D). From Fig. 9A,C it can be seen that
respiration increases in spite of completed histogenesis. The increase in
structural protein (Fig. 9D) seems related to the respiratory increase. An
intense formation of muscle mitochondria was observed to occur in paral-
lell (Agrell, 1952) as was also an incorporation of protein into the muscle mitochondria at the expense of soluble proteins (Lennie and Birt,
1967). Therefore, this later part of the metamorphosis should represent
differentiation during which period the efficiency of the respiratory system increases.

The electrophoretic pattern of pupal proteins in *Calliphora*, as well as
the behavior of different protein fractions, indicates a possible splitting
and subsequent synthesis in time with histolysis–histogenesis (Agrell,
1952). A peptide fraction shows a marked parallellism to the morphological changes (Fig. 9E) (Agrell, 1961). New fractions of soluble proteins
may arrive during metamorphosis (Stamm, 1962; Laufer, 1963; Patel,
1971). A specific migration of hemolymph proteins into the tissues of the
butterfly prepupa has been observed (Loughton and West, 1965; Chippendale, 1970a, 1971).

There may be a rapid turnover from larval to imaginal protein, but the
question remains as to what extent the larval proteins are broken down
(Agrell, 1952). Tracer studies on butterfly pupae indicate a high incorporation of amino acids in the imaginal tissues (Skinner, 1960). In Diptera
the incorporation was demonstrated to be U-shaped during the metamorphosis (Dinamarca and Levenbook, 1966; Howells *et al.*, 1967; Sekeris
et al., 1968). (Some further aspects on protein synthesis will be discussed in Section III, B, 2, b.)

Concerning phosphorus metabolism, a comparison has been made between some measurements of the phosphorus content in different pupal
and imaginal organs in butterfly pupae (Heller, 1936) in which a low
amount of energy-rich phosphate was indicated in the pupa. One insect
has been the object of a more thorough investigation of the variation of
phosphorous compounds during the period of metamorphosis, the fly
Calliphora erythrocephala, about which two almost parallel publications
exist (Agrell, 1952; Levenbook, 1953). These results coincide for the
most part. The two mentioned investigations agree in demonstrating inorganic P as varying along a ∩ curve and the easily hydrolyzable phos-

phates along U curves. The lipid P as a whole does not vary much during the pupal life. Agrell (1952) has divided this P fraction into two parts; one alcohol-soluble and the other alcohol–ether-soluble. They show a mutual inverse variation, the former ∩-, the latter U-shaped. (A similar separation of the RNA_P in fractions will be dealt with below.) The only discrepancy between the results of Levenbook and Agrell occurs in respect to the total amount of the trichloroacetic acid–soluble P (TCA-soluble P). This does not vary during development according to Levenbook, but shows a marked parallellism with histolysis, histogenesis, and differentiation according to Agrell. The lack in consistency concerns the phosphate which is difficult to hydrolyze, where Levenbook reports an average value which is about five times lower than that reported by Agrell, while the other P fractions correspond in amount. The phosphates which are difficult to hydrolyze vary in exactly the same manner as a TCA-soluble peptide fraction and this phosphorus fraction may thus represent a phosphorus-containing peptide or a complex-linked glucose amino phosphate, possibly some kind of a chitin precursor (Agrell, 1952). The chitin formation in endopterygotes occurs consistently in two steps, one for pupal and the other for imaginal chitin (Agrell, 1952; Cerkasov and Seifert, 1960).

The energy-rich phosphates have been further analyzed by Agrell (1952); it was shown that the total amount of nucleotide phosphates, as well as of arginine phosphate (Pettersson, 1955), follows a U-shaped curve, while the actual amount of ATP seems to be largely independent of the catabolic intensity and also of the ATPase activity (Fig. 9I). The regulatory factor must be the processes of synthesis. The limiting role of available ATP for the energy metabolism was further substantiated by experiments on the sensitivity of the pupae to anaerobiosis (Agrell, 1952) (Fig. 9K). Thus the level of immediately available energy in the pupa is not an uncomplicated reflection of the general energy production. The levels of other energy-rich di- and triphosphates, such as UTP, UDP, GTP, GDP, and CTP, do not vary along U-shaped curves but rather along ∩ curves (Tojo and Hirano, 1967).

In some insects the pH in the pupal tissues varies in a U-shaped manner (Fig. 9F) (Ludwig, 1934; Agrell, 1947b). This change in pH does not depend upon a varied accumulation of lactic acid but may be caused by some decomposition product from the nucleotide metabolism, e.g., inosinic acid (Agrell, 1952). Observations on the buffer capacity in the pupal tissues indicate that the variations in this capacity are related to changes in activity of the dehydrogenase system (Agrell, 1948a).

During the pupal stage there is some decrease in weight produced by emittance of water (and carbon dioxide) (Agrell, 1947a, 1952). An observed U-shaped change in the ratio of water to dry matter may indicate a varied capacity of the pupal tissues to retain water (Agrell, 1952). The gut is suggested to have an osmoregulatory function during metamorphosis (Fyhn and Saether, 1970).

b. *Intermediate Metabolism.* Of special interest for the understanding of the U-shaped change in metabolism during the pupal life are statements of the variation in activity of the respiratory enzymes. Thus Wolsky (1941) indicated and Agrell (1948a, 1952) confirmed that the spontaneous dehydrogenase activity varies in the same U-shaped manner as the respiratory curve in fly pupae (Fig. 9A). If one considers the dilution effect in the *in vitro* system, as well as possible muscular activities of larval and imaginal origin, the correspondence should be complete (Agrell, 1961). Later it was shown that the activity of a number of more important isolated respiratory enzymes also varies in U-shaped fashion (Agrell, 1949b, 1952, 1961). Other investigations also demonstrate a more or less U-shaped variation for different dehydrogenases, although for some species and enzymes the U-shaped course may be less obvious (Ito, 1955; Ludwig and Barsa, 1955, 1956, 1958, 1959; Sulkowski and Wojtczak, 1958; Jones, 1964; Rousell, 1967; Crompton and Birt, 1969; Rechsteiner, 1970; Ursprung *et al.*, 1970). Direct observations on citrate showed a change in turnover and a formation of glutamate, which were U-shaped (Levenbook, 1966). The terminal oxidases, the cytochrome system, also vary in a U-shaped manner (Wolsky, 1938; Williams, 1951; Bodenstein and Sacktor, 1952; Ludwig, 1953; Ito, 1954; Ludwig and Barsa, 1955; Sulkowski and Wojtczak, 1958; Jones, 1964; Rousell, 1967). Thus, the general conclusion can be drawn that the course of the U-shaped metabolic curve is produced by a corresponding change in activity of the oxidative enzymes. It is difficult to decide if these changes in activity imply a decomposition of the enzyme protein, even if a close correspondence was found for histolysis and histogenesis and the variations in activity of single dehydrogenases (Agrell, 1949c). However, as mentioned above, the general course of protein synthesis during metamorphosis is U-shaped.

The intermediate respiratory metabolism during metamorphosis has also been studied through experiments with adequate inhibitors. An inhibition of the glycolytic system by fluoride and iodoacetate was followed during the development of fly pupae (Fig. 9G) (Agrell, 1961). The magnitude of this inhibition proceeds, to a certain extent, along a U-shaped course and the fluctuation of directly estimated lactic acid showed corresponding changes. The spontaneous dehydrogenase activity obtained after addition of different donors strongly indicates that the quantitative variation of these metabolites is also similar. The inhibition of succinic dehydrogenase, and, therefore, of the tricarboxylic acid cycle by malonate, showed the reversed course in all details (Fig. 9G). In this way, the interdependence of the two systems was indicated and further substantiated by the malonate inhibitions after anaerobiosis (Agrell, 1961). Because glycolysis is a prerequisite for the activity of the tricarboxylic acid cycle, the conclusion may be drawn that the glycolytic system is an important bottleneck in the respiratory metabolism during metamorphosis.

The developmental changes of terminal oxidases have also been objects for experiments employing inhibitors. In diapausing butterfly pupae, the respiration was insensitive to such cytochrome oxidase inhibitors as cyanide, azide, and carbon monoxide. This insensitivity was shown to depend upon a large excess of cytochrome oxidase relative to cytochrome c in many of the pupal tissues (Kurland and Schneiderman, 1959; Gilbert and Schneiderman, 1961). Likewise, in *Drosophila* pupae a lowered sensitivity to carbon monoxide was found when respiration was at its lowest by Wolsky (1938). In nondiapausing *Bombyx* pupae the cyanide-insensitive oxygen uptake was the reverse of the normal respiration according to Ito (1954). An interesting localized effect of carbon monoxide has been studied on *Drosophila* pupae by combination with pointwise illumination by Wolsky (1937).

In addition to these respiratory enzymes some other types of enzymatic activities have been followed during the pupal life, viz., catalase, Fink (1930); tyrosinase, Ohnishi (1953); phenol oxidase, Wojtczak (1956) and Jones and Wilson (1959); alkaline and acid phosphatase, Yao (1950), Russo-Caia (1960), and Treves *et al.* (1970); lipase, Agrell (1951) and Russo-Caia (1960); amylase, Russo-Caia (1960); esterases, Pantelouris and Downer (1969); β-glucuronidase, Hegdekar and Smallman (1969) and Varute and Sawant (1971a,b); transaminase, McAllen and Chefurca (1961); pyrophosphatase, Finch and Birt (1962); phosphatidase, Hirano and Gilbert (1967). The variation of the activity of some of these enzymes during metamorphosis may be U-shaped. For nucleases it was observed that at the onset of metamorphosis a marked change in the enzyme pattern arrives, possibly representing a shift from a larval to an imaginal nuclease (Himeno *et al.*, 1968; Boyd and Boyd, 1970). Concerning ATPase, it has been shown for the fly *Calliphora* and *Bombyx* that the activity of this enzyme varies along a U-shaped curve during the period of metamorphosis (Agrell, 1952; Russo-Caia, 1960; Yabe, 1962). The regeneration starts first when the final amount of muscular tissue is already reached (Agrell, 1952; Yabe, 1962). Thus the ATPase activity seems related to the function rather than to the amount of myosin. This has been directly confirmed for the house fly pupa through simultaneous measurements of myosin content and ATPase activity (Maruyama, 1954). In the honey bee pupa, where the processes of histolysis and histogenesis are less pronounced, the increases in ATPase activity and myosin content are more parallel (Maruyama, 1957). Studies of acetylcholine esterase activity demonstrated a close correlation to morphological differentiation (Lee and Fan, 1966; Mansingh and Smallman, 1967; Shappirio et al., 1967; Grzelak et al., 1970). However, no correlation between electrical and enzyme activities was found (Tyshtchenko and Mandelstam, 1965). The cholinergic system during development is reviewed by Smallman and Mansingh (1969). Multiple forms of dehydrogenases, hydrolases, and esterases have been observed in insects (Laufer, 1961; Agrell and Kjellberg, 1965; Eguchi and Tatsuyoshi, 1965; Eguchi, 1968). A stage and tissue specificity in the enzyme pattern has been observed.

Of interest in the understanding of histolysis and histogenesis are changes in proteinase activity. These were followed during the development of fly pupae by Agrell (1951), Russo-Caia (1960), and by Birth and Christian (1969). It was shown that the only existing tissue proteinase was of the peptic type. The activity shows only a small variation during development when measured at constant pH, as does that of dipeptidase. These changes were definitely not U-shaped. However, the tissue pH showed a marked U-shaped change and therefore the proteolytic activity in the living tissues may possibly operate along a ∩-shaped curve with time during histolysis and histogenesis, even if the actual amino acid level varies only faintly in relation to the measured enzymatic activity (Agrell, 1949a, 1951). As has been mentioned immediately above, the change in pH, in turn, could effect the changes in the energy metabolism itself. Moreover, the proteolytic activity may not be the only factor managing these processes; a thermolabile membranolytic factor, which follows a ∩-shaped curve, must also be taken into consideration (Agrell, 1951). For butterfly pupae there are some observations that the proteolytic activity should accumulate in lysosomes (Lockshin and Williams, 1965; Matsuura et al., 1968). For dipteran pupae only lysosomes containing acid phosphatase are reported (Rasch and Gawlik, 1964; Hegdekar and Smallman, 1967). The observation that histolysis can be blocked after puromycin or actinomycin D administration (Lockshin, 1969) confirms an older statement that histolysis is an active process which requires the intact homeostasis of the pupae for its fulfillment (Agrell,

1952). This conclusion was drawn from experiments where the changes in dehydrogenases were followed during and after anaerobiosis.

The problems of protein synthesis are intimately related to the metabolism of the nucleic acids, but there are very few investigations of this metabolism for the metamorphosis period. Some values for the silkworm are plotted by Wyatt (1959), who also reports increased incorporation of ^{32}P in RNA of wing buds at a certain stage. Moreover, barbituric acid and ribonuclease interfere with the RNA metabolism of epidermal cells during the development of the giant silk moth (Blaustein and Schneiderman, 1960).

The total amount of DNA and RNA varies only little during the period of metamorphosis: *Calliphora,* Agrell (1964b) (Fig. 10); *Tribolium,*

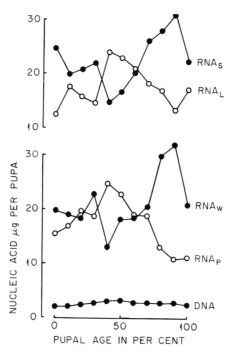

Fig. 10. The variation in amount of DNA and different types of RNA during metamorphosis of the fly *Calliphora erythrocephala.* Upper diagram: the results from estimations by the Ogur and Rosen technique. RNA$_S$, acid-stable RNA; RNA$_L$, acid-labile RNA. Lower diagram: the results from estimation by the Kirby technique. RNA$_W$, RNA in water phase; RNA$_P$, RNA in the phenol phase. The estimations of RNA were made both on UV absorption and phosphorus content. DNA was estimated with diphenylamine reagent. From Agrell (1952, 1964b).

Devi *et al.* (1963) ; *Aedes,* Lang *et al.* (1965) ; *Philosamia,* Takahashi
(1966). For some unknown reason Price (1965) reports a precipitous fall
of both DNA and RNA in *Calliphora* during the imaginal development.
However, different tissues may have different temporal patterns for DNA
and RNA synthesis, which to some extent can be correlated with morphological changes (*Crecropia,* Linzen and Wyatt, 1964 and Krishnakumaran
et al., 1967; *Rynchosciara,* Mattingly and Parker, 1968; *Tenebrio,* Chase,
1970). The mitochondrial DNA and RNA seem to vary along a U-
shaped curve (Lennie *et al.,* 1967). An increased incorporation of thym-
idin was found during imaginal growth and differentiation in *Cecropia*
(Bowers and Williams, 1964). The incorporation of amino acids into
protein was found to follow a U-shaped curve during the metamorphosis
(Dinamarca and Levenbook, 1966; Sekeris *et al.,* 1968). A connection
between methylation of tRNA and a regulation of protein synthesis is
presented by Baliga *et al.* (1965) for *Tenebrio.* It has been found that
two RNA fractions vary inversely during the metamorphosis of *Calliphora.* One fraction is phenole extractable and easily eluted by acid. The
other fraction is water extractable and less easily eluted by acid (Fig. 10)
(Agrell, 1964b). The first fraction should represent nuclear and metabolic RNA, the second ribosomal RNA (Georgiev, 1967). The inverse mir-
rorlike changes of ribosomal and nuclear RNA may indicate a varied
liberation of ribosomal RNA from the nucleus. The distribution of the two
types of RNA was very much the same in the histolysis center (the hind
pupal part) and in the histogenesis center (the anterior pupal part)
(Agrell, 1952). This should denote that the histolyzing fat-body tissue
can also provide an RNA synthesis. An analysis of the qualitative and
quantitative variations of the basic proteins during metamorphosis of *Calliphora* indicated that most of the basic proteins should be associated
with ribosomal RNA (Agrell and Lindh, 1966) and also that with advancing metamorphosis a shift from low molecular to high molecular basic
proteins occurs. Conversely polyamines seem to be preferentially associated to the nuclear RNA in *Calliphora* pupae (Heby, 1972).

We may regard the insect pupa as a very complicated, closed system,
where mutually counteractive processes are balanced and joined into a
harmonious sequence. The functional cessation of the larval tissues and
the first development of the imaginal epidermis is dependent upon a
changed hormonal balance. In spite of the high amount of fat and carbohydrate, which is far from consumed at the emergence of the imago,
there is a marked decrease in the total metabolism during the early pupal
life followed by a later steep increase. Thus there must exist bottlenecks
in the intermediate metabolism representing temporary limitations in the

availability of the stored energy. The most important limiting factors for the respiratory metabolism during metamorphosis seem to exist within the glycolytic system, which is a prerequisite for fat metabolism as well as for the tricarboxylic acid cycle. During histolysis there appears to be an interplay between the disturbed energy metabolism, an accumulation of acid metabolites, and an activation of proteolytic and membranolytic factors, all of which retroact upon the enzymatic level and lead to further decreased metabolism. The result is histolysis of the larval body, which in Fig. 9B is represented as the increase in number of pycnotic nuclei. Histolysis seems to be an active process which needs the intact set of, e.g., respiratory enzymes, for its progression. Organic material necessary for the imaginal tissues is thus eventually set free and the principal imaginal growth will begin. Imaginal growth, i.e., histogenesis, is found to occur in the fly pupa during a limited period only (Fig. 9C) and is succeeded by a period of differentiation when structural changes are initiated at the cellular level, such as incorporation of soluble into nonsoluble protein and an intense formation of mitochondria so that the respiratory efficiency is further promoted (Fig. 9A) .

IV. Prospects for Future Work in the Physiology and Biochemistry of Insect Development

From the foregoing, it is obvious that our understanding of causal relationships in developmental physiology of insects is far from complete. In the field of physiological chemistry as one example, it is evident already from the extensive review by Gilmour (1960) that general insect biochemistry is ahead of the biochemistry of insect development. The developmental changes on structural as well as functional levels, cellular as well as supracellular, are likewise far from understood. For many important problems even the most elementary data are lacking.

The writing of a treatment such as has been presented above inevitably arouses the desire in the minds of the authors for more information along certain lines. A review of some of these desiderata for further work in the field of developmental physiology of insects may be appropriate in a treatment of a specific area such as this.

It has been emphasized above that, in regard to the embryonic as well as the postembryonic development, insects taken as a group exhibit a continuous series of physiological transformations. This includes the most fundamental courses of events, e.g., the regulatory capacity of the egg and the degree of metamorphosis. At the same time, the developing insect individual represents an organism which should demonstrate a pronounced interplay between the structure and function of its parts. Therefore, what may be more generally desired for future works are considerations of a comparative nature, irrespective of the field with which the investigations are dealing. This can only be accomplished if the individual scientist were to extend his particular approach, for instance, to several interdependent enzymes or metabolites, to different tissues, and especially if one and the same investigation with its distinct methods and experimental design could be expanded to comprise material from different taxonomic groups. A very desirable approach, also, would be a combination of different methods applied to the same material, e.g., parallel use of cytochemical and biochemical techniques or experiments involving surgical procedures accompanied by cytological observations of nuclear and cytoplasmic changes.

The structure of the developing insect egg is still incompletely known. Here, further electron microscopic observations are especially needed in order to make possible an understanding of the relationship between the embryonic determinations and the quality and quantity of the periplasm. The syncytial connections within the egg, as well as nuclear multiplications in conjunction with cytoplasmic growth and utilization of yolk material, need to be studied by similar means. Further investigation on nuclear migration and on mitotic gradients are also needed.

Additional cytochemical observations are necessary to localize such components of the ovum as nucleic acids and enzymes and, if possible, to reveal a chemical pattern which can be causally connected to the determinative events in the ooplasm. Further biochemical and autoradiographic studies on the synthesis of DNA, of the different types of RNA, and of proteins are also needed. The function of the cytoplasmic DNA is still unclear. Comparative biochemical studies should be made on various representative eggs of varying regulative capacity. Also the interdependence between the glycolysis and the tricarboxylic acid cycle during embryogenesis, as well as the alternative glycolytic pathways and the utilization of different terminal oxidases, need to be further investigated. The same can be said about the intermediate metabolism of lipids and proteins and of the metabolism of the energy-rich phosphates. Additional studies on the mechanisms of the morphogenetic movements are also desirable. The role of inductional processes, especially during the later embryonic stages, of more determinative eggs should be further clarified. There is a need for continued studies on the cellular basis for differentiation, e.g., through further observations on the action spectrum of irradiation, both for nuclear and cytoplasmic damages. Continued work in the field of cell and embryo culture may also shed some light on the process-es of differentiation. An improvement of the methods of nuclear trans-plantation is highly desirable.

Thus, some initial attempts have been made to apply the advanced methods of developmental physiology and biochemistry in the field of in-sect embryogenesis. It is not an unreasonable hope that the nature of the causal interactions, which have been demonstrated by the classical meth-ods, will be further clarified by the application of these modern tech-niques.

As for postembryonic development, cytochemical and biochemical studies are needed on the nature of growth by cell multiplication as com-pared to growth by cell enlargement. Further observations are also highly desirable on the relationship between structural and biochemical (cyto-chemical) changes during histolysis and histogenesis, especially with an open mind for comparative aspects of such changes. In this connection, further studies on the degradation and synthesis of proteins should be made through whatever techniques possible, especially with immunologi-cal techniques, if feasible. As in the case of embryonic development, further information concerning alternative glycolytic pathways during metamorphosis is needed, especially from the isoenzymic point of view; similar information would be highly desirable for different terminal oxi-dases. Interrelationships between the intermediate metabolism of carbo-hydrates, fats, and proteins should be further clarified, preferably on the organ level. The importance of different types of RNA in histogenesis and differentiation has been virtually.unexplored and much additional infor-mation is needed concerning the metabolism of nucleotides and of the energy-rich phophates in these processes.

The future of this whole area of investigation is as rich and promising as the variety and versatility of insectan material available to the experi-mental embryologist. With the ever-growing interest of the biochemist and biophysicist in this field of insect biology, we can anticipate an in-creasing understanding of the truly fundamental mechanisms underlying insect development.

References

Achazi, R. K. (1969). *Zool. Anz., Suppl.* 32, 249.

Achazi, R. K., and Duspiva, F. (1971). *Wilhelm Roux' Arch. Entwicklungsmech. Organismen* 168, 195.

Achtelig, M., and Krause, G. (1971). *Wilhelm Roux' Arch. Entwicklungsmech. Organis-men* 167, 164.

Agrell, I. (1947a). *Ark. Zool.* [1] **39A**, No. 10.

Agrell, I. (1947b). *Acta Physiol. Scand.* **14**, 317.

Agrell, I. (1948a). *Acta Physiol. Scand.* **16**, 9.

Agrell, I. (1948b). *Ark. Zool.* [1] **41A**, No. 12.

Agrell, I. (1949a). *Acta Physiol. Scand.* **18**, 247.

Agrell, I. (1949b). *Acta Physiol. Scand.* **18**, 355.

Agrell, I. (1949c). *Nature (London)* **167**, 283.

Agrell, I. (1951). *Acta Physiol. Scand.* **23**, 179.

Agrell, I. (1952). *Acta Physiol. Scand.* **28**, 306.

Agrell, I. (1961). *Symp. Genet. Biol. Ital.* **8**, 563.

Agrell, I. (1962). *Ark. Zool.* [2] **15**, No. 7.

Agrell, I. (1964a). *In* "Synchrony in Cell Division and Growth" (E. Zeuthen, ed.), p. 39. Wiley (Interscience), New York.

Agrell, I. (1964b). *In* "The Physiology of Insecta" (M. Rockstein, ed.), Vol. 1, p. 91. Academic Press, New York.

Agrell, I. (1966). *Z. Zellforsch. Mikrosk. Anat.* **72**, 22.

Agrell, I. (1968). *Z. Zellforsch. Mikrosk. Anat.* **88**, 365.

Agrell, I., and Kjellberg, B. (1965). *Comp. Biochem. Physiol.* **16**, 515.

Agrell, I., and Lindh, N. O. (1966). *Comp. Biochem. Physiol.* **19**, 691.

Akai, H. (1969). *Jap. J. Appl. Entomol. Zool.* **13**, 17.

Alfert, M. (1954). *Int. Rev. Cytol.* **3**, 131.

Allais, J. P., Bergerard, J., Etienne, J., and Polonovski, J. (1964). *J. Insect Physiol.* **10**, 753.

Allen, T. H. (1940). *J. Cell. Comp. Physiol.* **16**, 149.

Anderson, D. T. (1962). *Acta Zool. (Stockholm)* **43**, 221.

Anderson, D. T. (1963). *J. Embryol. Exp. Morphol.* **11**, 339.

Anderson, D. T. (1964). *J. Embryol. Exp. Morphol.* **12**, 65.

Anderson, D. T. (1966). *Annu. Rev. Entomol.* **11**, 23.

Anglas, M. J. (1901). *Bull. Sci. Fr. Belg.* [5] **34**, 363.

Ashburner, M. (1970). *Advan. Insect Physiol.* **7**, 1.

Babcock, K. L., and Rutschky, C. W. (1961). *Ann. Entomol. Soc. Amer.* **54**, 156.

Babers, F. H. (1941). *J. Agr. Res.* **62**, 509.

Baliga, B. S., Srinivasan, P. R., and Borch, E. (1965). *Nature (London)* **208**, 555.

Balzam, N. (1933). *Acta Biol. Exp. (Warsaw)* **8**, 59.

Banerjee, B. (1964). *Naturwissenschaften* **51**, 445.

Bantock, C. R. (1961). *Nature (London)* **190**, 466.

Bantock, C. R. (1970). *J. Embryol. Exp. Morphol.* **24**, 257.

Beaudoin, A. R., Villeneuve, J. L., and Lemonde, A. (1968). *J. Insect Physiol.* **14**, 831.

Becker, M. (1934). *Biochem. Z.* **272**, 227.

Beermann, W. (1959). *In* "Developmental Cytology" (D. Rudnick, ed.), p. 83. Ronald Press, New York.

Beermann, W. (1960). *Chromosoma* **11**, 263.

Bell, J. (1940). *Physiol. Zool.* **13**, 73.

Benz, G. (1955). *Jahresber. Schweiz. Ges. Vererb. Forsch.* **15**, 498.

Berger, C. A. (1938). *Contrib. Embryol.* **27**, 209.

Bernard, G. R., and Fixler, D. E. (1963). *Physiol. Zool.* **36**, 244.

Bhuiyan, N. I., and Shafiq, S. A. (1959). *Exp. Cell Res.* **16**, 427.

Bier, K. (1954). *Biol. Zentralbl.* **73**, 170.

Bier, K. (1967). *Naturwissenschaften* **54**, 189.

Bier, K. (1970). *Zool. Anz., Suppl.* **33**, 7.

Birt, L. M., and Christian, B. (1969) . *J. Insect. Physiol.* **15**, 711.

Blaustein, M. P., and Schneiderman, H. A. (1960). *J. Insect Physiol.* **5**, 143.

Bliss, D. E. (1960). *In* "The Physiology of Crustacea" (T. H. Waterman, ed.), Vol. 1, p. 561. Academic Press, New York.

Bock, E. (1942). *Wilhelm Roux' Arch. Entwicklungsmech. Organismen* **141**, 159.

Bodenstein, D. (1941). *J. Exp. Zool.* **87**, 31.

Bodenstein, D. (1950). *In* "Biology of Drosophila" (M. Demerec, ed.), p. 275. Wiley, New York.

Bodenstein, D. (1953). *In* "Insect Physiology" (K. D. Roeder, ed.), p. 780. Wiley, New York.

Bodenstein, D. (1955). *In* "Analysis of Development" (B. H. Willier, P. Weiss, and V. Hamburger, eds.), p. 337. Saunders, Philadelphia, Pennsylvania.

Bodenstein, D. (1962). *Symp. Genet. Biol. Ital.* **9**.

Bodenstein, D., and Sacktor, B. (1952). *Science* **116**, 299.

Bodine, J. H. (1929). *Physiol. Zool.* **2**, 459.

Bodine, J. H., and Allen, T. H. (1941). *J. Exp. Zool.* **88**, 343.

Bodine, J. H., and Boell, E .J. (1935). *Proc. Iowa Acad. Sci.* **42**, 210.

Bodine, J. H., and Boell, E. J. (1936). *J. Cell. Comp. Physiol.* **8**, 357.

Bodine, J. H., and Boell, E. J. (1937). *Physiol. Zool.* **10**, 245.

Bodine, J. H., and Evans, T. C. (1932). *Biol. Bull.* **63**, 235.

Bodine, J. H., and Fitzgerald, L. R. (1948a). *Physiol. Zool.* **21**, 93.

Bodine, J. H., and Fitzgerald, L. R. (1948b). *J. Exp. Zool.* **109**, 187.

Bodine, J. H., and Wolkin, J. E. (1934). *Physiol. Zool.* **7**, 464.

Bodine, J. H., Ray, O. M., Allen, T. H., and Carlson, L. (1939). *J. Cell. Comp. Physiol.* **14**, 173.

Bodine, J. H., Teffert, W. A., West, W. L., and Pyle, Z. P. (1954). *Physiol. Zool.* **27**, 263.

Bodnaryk, R. P., and Skillings, J. R. (1971). *Insect Biochem.* **1**, 467.

Boell, E. J. (1935). *J. Cell. Comp. Physiol.* **6**, 369.

Boell, E. J. (1955). *In* "Analysis of Development" (B. H. Willier, P. Weiss, and V. Hamburger, eds.), p. 520. Saunders, Philadelphia, Pennsylvania.

Boell, E. J., and Poulson, D. F. (1939). *Anat. Rec.* **75**, Suppl., 65.

Bowers, B., and Williams, C. M. (1964). *Biol. Bull.* **126**, 205.

Boyd, J. B., and Boyd, H. (1970). *Biochem. Genet.* **4**, 447.

Brauer, A., and Newman, T. (1959). *Trans. Ky. Acad. Sci.* **20**, 51.

Brauer, A., and Taylor, A. C. (1936). *J. Exp. Zool.* **73**, 127.

Briggs, R., and King, T. J. (1957). *J. Morphol.* **100**, 269.

Brighenti, A. (1940). *Boll. Soc. Ital. Biol. Sper.* **15**, 198.

Brown, A. W. A. (1938). *Biochem. J.* **32**, 895 and 903.

Bryant, P. J. (1970). *Develop. Biol.* **22**, 389.

Bryant, P. J., and Schneiderman, H. A. (1969) . *Develop. Biol.* **20**, 263.

Buck, J. B. (1953). *In* "Insect Physiology" (K. D. Roeder, ed.), p. 191. Wiley, New York.

Buck, J. B., and Keister, M. (1958). *J. Insect Physiol.* **1**, 327.

Bull, A. L. (1966). *J. Exp. Zool.* **161**, 221.

Bunde, D. E., and Pepper, J. H. (1968). *J. Insect Physiol.* **14**, 1635.

Burkholder, J. R. (1934). *Physiol. Zool.* **7**, 247.

Busnel, R. G. (1937). *C. R. Acad. Sci.* **205**, 1177.
Campbell, F. L. (1959). *In* "Physiology of Insect Development," p. 167. Univ. of Chicago Press, Chicago, Illinois.
Carlson, L. D. (1941). *Biol. Bull.* **81**, 375.
Castillón, M. P., Catalán, R. E., Municio, A. M., and Suarez, A. (1971). *Comp. Biochem. Physiol.* **38B**, 109.
Cerkasov, J., and Seifert, J. (1960). *Acta Soc. Zool. Bohemslov.* **60**, 130.
Chase, A. M. (1970). *J. Insect Physiol.* **16**, 865.
Chen, P. S. (1951). *Z. Indukt. Abstamm.-Vererbungsl.* **84**, 38.
Chen, P. S. (1958). *J. Insect Physiol.* **2**, 38.
Chen, P. S. (1966). *Advan. Insect Physiol.* **3**, 53.
Chen, P. S., and Briegel, H. (1965). *Comp. Biochem. Physiol.* **14**, 463.
Chen, P. S., and Kühn, A. (1956). *Z. Naturforsch.* B **11**, 305.
Chino, H. (1956). *Annot. Zool. Jap.* **30**, 106.
Chino, H. (1957). *Embryologia* **3**, 295.
Chino, H. (1958). *J. Insect Physiol.* **2**, 1.
Chino, H. (1961). *J. Insect Physiol.* **6**, 231.
Chino, H. (1963). *Arch. Biochem. Biophys.* **102**, 400.
Chino, H., and Gilbert, L. I. (1965). *J. Insect Physiol.* **11**, 287.
Chino, H., and Yushima, T. (1954). *Zool. Mag.* **63**, 185.
Chippendale, G. M. (1970a). *J. Insect Physiol.* **16**, 1057.
Chippendale, G. M. (1970b). *J. Insect Physiol.* **16**, 1909.
Chippendale, G. M. (1971). *Insect Biochem.* **1**, 122.
Coleman, A. E. (1959). *Trans. Ky. Acad. Sci.* **20**, 59.
Colombo, G., Benassi, C. A., Allegri, G., and Longo, E. (1962). *Comp. Biochem. Physiol.* **5**, 83.
Counce, S. J. (1956). *Z. Indukt. Abstamm.- Vererbungsl.* **87**, 443.
Counce, S. J. (1959). *Anat. Rec.* **134**, 546.
Counce, S. J. (1961). *Annu. Rev. Entomol.* **6**, 295.
Counce, S .J. (1963). *J. Morphol.* **112**, 129.
Counce, S. J. (1966). *Ann. N.Y. Acad. Sci.* **139**, 65.
Counce, S. J., and Selman, G. G. (1955). *J. Embryol. Exp. Morphol.* **3**, 121.
Crescitelli, F. (1935). *J. Cell. Comp. Physiol.* **6**, 351.
Crescitelli, F., and Taylor, I. R. (1935). *J. Biochem.* **108**, 349.
Crompton, M., and Birt, L. M. (1969) . *J. Insect. Physiol.* **15**, 1119.
Crompton, M., and Polakis, S. E. (1969). *J. Insect Physiol.* **15**, 1323.
Crossley, A. C. (1968). *J. Insect Physiol.* **14**, 1389.
Czoppelt, C., and Rembold, H. (1970). *J. Insect Physiol.* **16**, 1249.
Das, C. C., Kaufmann, B. P., and Gay, H. (1964). *J. Cell Biol.* **23**, 423.
Davis, C. W. C. (1970). *Aust. J. Zool.* **18**, 125.
Davis, C. W. C., Krause, J., and Krause, G. (1968). *Wilhelm Roux' Arch. Entwicklungsmech. Organismen* **161**, 209.
D'Costa, M. A., and Birth, L. M. (1966). *J. Insect Physiol.* **12**, 1377.
Del Vecchio, R. J. (1955a). *J.N.Y. Entomol. Soc.* **63**, 141.
Del Vecchio, R. J. (1955b). *J.N.Y. Entomol. Soc.* **63**, 9.
Demyanovsky, S. Y., and Zubova, V. A. (1957). *Biochemistry (USSR)* **21**, 698.
Devi, A., Lemonde, A., Srivastava, U., and Sarkar, N.K. (1963). *Exp. Cell Res.* **29**, 443.
Dinamarca, M. L., and Levenbook, L. (1966). *Arch. Biochem. Biophys.* **117**, 110.
Du Bois, A. W. (1936). *Rev. Suisse Zool.* **45**, 1.

Du Praw, E. J. (1963). *Proc. Int. Congr. Zool., 16th, 1963* Vol. II, p. 238.
Durand, M. C. (1955). *C. R. Acad. Sci.* 241, 1340.
Durand, M. (1958). *Exp. Cell Res.* 15, 257.
Durand, M. (1961). *Bull. Biol. Fr. Belg.* 95, 28.
Duspiva, F. (1969). *Naturwiss. Rundsch.* 22, 191.
Dutrieu, J. (1961). *C. R. Acad. Sci.* 252, 347.
Eastham, L. (1928). *Quart. J. Microsc. Sci.* 71, 353.
Edwards, G. A. (1953). *In* "Insect Physiology" (K. D. Roeder, ed.), p. 96. Wiley, New York.
Edwards, J. S. (1966). *J. Insect Physiol.* 12, 1423.
Edwards, J. S. (1969). *Advan. Insect Physiol.* 6, 97.
Eguchi, M. (1968). *Appl. Entomol. Zool.* 3, 189.
Eguchi, M., and Tatsuyoshi, S. (1965). *J. Insect Physiol.* 11, 1145.
Etkin, W., and Gilbert L. I., eds. (1968). "Metamorphosis, a Problem in Developmental Biology." Appleton, New York.
Eudy, W. W., and Dobrogosz, W. J. (1970). *Comp. Biochem. Physiol.* 35, 567.
Evans, A. C. (1932). *J. Exp. Biol.* 9, 314.
Evans, A. C. (1934). *J. Exp. Biol.* 11, 397.
Evans, A. C. (1936). *Proc. Roy. Entomol. Soc. London* 11, 52.
Ewest, A. (1937). *Wilhelm Roux' Arch. Entwicklungsmech. Organismen* 135, 689.
Fast, P. G. (1964). *Mem. Entomol. Soc. Can.* 37, 1.
Favard-Séréno, C., and Durand, M. (1963). *Develop. Biol.* 6, 206.
Ficq, A., and Pavan, C. (1958). *Nature (London)* 180, 983.
Finch, L. R., and Birt, L. M. (1962). *Comp. Biochem. Physiol.* 5, 59.
Fink, D. E. (1925). *J. Gen. Physiol.* 7, 527.
Fink, D. E. (1930). *J. Agr. Res.* 41, 691.
Fitzgerald, L. R. (1949). *J. Exp. Zool.* 110, 461.
Forrest, H. S., Menaker, M., and Alexander, J. (1966). *J. Insect Physiol.* 12, 1411.
Forrest, H. S., Harris, S. E., and Morton, L. J. (1967). *J. Insect Physiol.* 13, 359.
Fourche, J. (1969). *Bull. Biol. Fr. Belg.* 103, 225.
Fourche, J., and Ambrosioni, J. C. (1969). *Z. Vergl. Physiol.* 62, 348.
Frew, J. G. H. (1929). *Brit. J. Exp. Biol.* 6, 205.
Fukuda, T., Duchâteau-Bosson, G. H., and Florkin, M. (1961). *Arch. Int. Physiol. Biochim.* 69, 701.
Furneaux, P. J. S., and McFarlane, J. E. (1965a). *J. Insect Physiol.* 11, 591.
Furneaux, P. J. S., and McFarlane, J. E. (1965b). *J. Insect Physiol.* 11, 631.
Fyhn, H. J., and Saether, T. (1970). *J. Insect Physiol.* 16, 263.
Gadallah, A. I., Kilgore, W. W., and Painter, R. R. (1970a). *J. Insect Physiol.* 16, 1245.
Gadallah, A. I., Kilgore, W. W., and Painter, R. R. (1970b). *J. Econ. Entomol.* 63, 1777.
Gadallah, A. I., Kilgore, W. W., and Painter, R. R. (1971a). *Insect Biochem.* 1, 302.
Gadallah, A. I., Kilgore, W. W., and Painter, R. R. (1971b). *J. Econ. Entomol.* 64, 371.
Gadallah, A. I., Kilgore, W. W., Marei, N., and Painter, R. R. (1971c). *Insect Biochem.* 1, 385.
Gaeta, I., and Zappanico, A. (1959). *Ric. Sci.* 29, Suppl., 788.
Ganti, Y., and Shanmugasundaram, E. R. B. (1963). *J. Exp. Zool.* 152, 1.
Gauss, U., and Sander, K. (1966). *Naturwissenschaften* 53, 182.
Geigy, R. (1932). *Wilhelm Roux' Arch. Entwicklungsmech. Organismen.* 125, 406.
Georgiev, G. P. (1967). *Progr. Nucl. Acid Res. Mol. Biol.* 6, 259.
Geyer-Duszyńska, I. (1959). *J. Exp. Zool.* 141, 391.

Geyer-Duszyńska, I. (1961). *Chromosoma* **12**, 233.

Geyer-Duszyńska, I. (1966). *Chromosomes Today, Proc. Oxford Chromosome Cont., 1st, 1964* Vol. 1, p. 174.

Geyer-Duszyńska, I. (1967). *Rev. Suisse Zool.* **74**, 614.

Gilbert, L. I. (1967). *In* "Comprehensive Biochemistry" (M. Florkin and E. H. Statz, eds.). Elsevier, Amsterdam.

Gilbert, L. I., and Schneiderman, H. A. (1961). *Amer. Zool.* **1**, 11.

Gill, K. S. (1963). *J. Exp. Zool.* **152**, 251.

Gill, K. S. (1964). *J. Exp. Zool.* **155**, 91.

Gilmour, D. (1960). "Biochemistry of Insects." Academic Press, New York.

Gloor, H. (1947). *Rev. Suisse Zool.* **54**, 637.

Goldman, A. S., and Setlow, R. B. (1956). *Exp. Cell Res.* **11**, 146.

Grellet, P. (1971a). *J. Insect Physiol.* **17**, 1533.

Grellet, P. (1971b). *Wilhelm Roux' Arch. Entwicklungsmech. Organismen* **167**, 243.

Grzelak, K., Lassota, Z., and Wroniszewska, A. (1970). *J. Insect Physiol.* **16**, 1405.

Günther, J. (1971). *Zool. Jahrb., Abt. Anat. Ontog. Tiere* **88**, 1.

Gurdon, J. B. (1964). *Advan. Morphog.* **4**, 1.

Hadorn, E. (1948). *Folia Biotheor. Leiden* **3**, 109.

Hadorn, E. (1950). *Rev. Suisse Zool.* **57**, Suppl. 1, 115.

Hadorn, E. (1966). *In* "Major Problems in Developmental Biology" (M. Locke, ed.), p. 85. Academic Press, New York.

Haget, A. (1953). *Bull. Biol. Fr. Belg.* **87**, 123.

Haget, A. (1963). *Proc. Int. Congr. Zool., 16th, 1963* Vol. II, p. 261.

Haller, P. H. (1948). *Mitt. Schweiz. Entomol. Ges.* **21**, 301.

Hansen-Delkeskamp, E. (1968). *Wilhelm Roux' Arch. Entwicklungsmech. Organismen* **161**, 23.

Hansen-Delkeskamp, E. (1969). *Wilhelm Roux' Arch. Entwicklungsmech. Organismen* **162**, 114.

Hansen-Delkeskamp, E., Sauer, H. W., and Duspiva, F. (1967). *Z. Naturforsch. B* **22**, 540.

Harris, S. E., and Forrest, H. S. (1967a). *Science* **156**, 1613.

Harris, S. E., and Forrest, H. S. (1967b). *Proc. Nat. Acad. Sci. U.S.* **58**, 89.

Harris, S. E., and Forrest, H. S. (1970). *Develop. Biol.* **23**, 324.

Harris, S. E., and Forrest, H. S. (1971). *J. Insect Physiol.* **17**, 303.

Harvey, W. R. (1962). *Annu. Rev. Entomol.* **7**, 57.

Haub, J. G., and Hitchcock, F. A. (1941). *Ann. Entomol. Soc. Amer.* **34**, 17, 26, and 32.

Heby, O. (1972). *Insect Biochem.* **2**, 13.

Hegdekar, B. M., and Smallman, B. N. (1967). *Can. J. Biochem.* **45**, 1202.

Hegdekar, B. M., and Smallman, B. N. (1969). *Can. J. Zool.* **47**, 45.

Hegner, R. W. (1909). *J. Exp. Zool.* **6**, 507.

Hegner, R. W. (1911). *Biol. Bull.* **20**, 237.

Heinig, S. (1967). *Zool. Jahrb., Abt. Anat. Ontog. Tiere* **84**, 425.

Heller, J. (1926a). *Biochem. Z.* **169**, 208.

Heller, J. (1926b). *Biochem. Z.* **172**, 59.

Heller, J. (1932). *Biochem. Z.* **255**, 205.

Heller, J. (1936). *C. R. Soc. Biol.* **121**, 414.

Henke, K. E., Schatz, E., and Schwenk, H. (1946). *Nachr. Ges. Wiss. Goettingen* **1**, 5.

Herbst, E. J., and Dion, A. S. (1970). *Fed. Proc., Fed. Amer. Soc. Exp. Biol.* **29**, 1563.

Heymons, R. (1895). "Die Embryonalentwicklung von Dermapteren und Orthopteren." Fischer, Jena.

Heywood, R. B. (1965), *J. Insect Physiol.* **11**, 413.

Hill, D. L. (1945). *J. Cell. Comp. Physiol.* **25**, 205.

Hill, L., and Goldsworthy, G. J. (1968). *J. Insect Physiol.* **14**, 1085.

Himeno, M., Morishima, I., Sakai, F., and Onodera, K. (1968). *Biochim. Biophys. Acta* **167**, 575.

Hinton, H. E. (1963). *Sci. Progr. (London)* **51**, 306.

Hinton, H. E. (1969). *Annu. Rev. Entomol.* **14**, 343.

Hinton, H. E. (1971). *Proc. Roy. Entomol. Soc. London* **35**, 55.

Hirano, C., and Gilbert, L. I. (1967). *J. Insect Physiol.* **13**, 163.

Horikawa, M., and Fox, A. S. (1964). *Science* **145**, 1437.

Howells, A. J., Birt, L. M., and Finch, L. R. (1967) . *J. Insect Physiol.* **13**, 1221.

Howland, R. B., and Child, G. P. (1935). *J. Exp. Zool.* **70**, 415.

Hoyle, G. (1956). *Nature (London)* **178**, 1236.

Hudson, B. W., Bartel, A. H., and Craig, R. (1959). *J. Insect Physiol.* **3**, 63.

Huettner, A. F. (1923). *J. Morphol.* **37**, 385.

Hufnagel, A. (1918). *Arch. Zool. Exp. Gen.* **57**, 47.

Huxley, J. (1932). "Problems of Relative Growth." Methuen, London.

Idris, B. E. M. (1960). *Wilhelm Roux' Arch. Entwicklungsmech. Organismen* **152**, 230.

Illmensee, K. (1968). *Nature (London)* **219**, 1268.

Illmensee, K. (1970). *Naturwissenschaften* **57**, 550.

Imaizumi, T. (1958). *Cytologia* **23**, 286.

Ishizaki, H. (1963). *Exp. Cell Res.* **31**, 606.

Ishizaki, H. (1965). *J. Insect Physiol.* **11**, 845.

Ito, T. (1954). *Bull. Sericult. Exp. Sta., Tokyo* **14**, 263.

Ito, T. (1955). *Annot. Zool. Jap.* **28**, 1.

Ito, T., and Seki, M. (1954). *Acta Sericol.* **9**, 1.

Ito, T., Shigematsu, H., and Horie, Y. (1954). *Jap. J. Appl. Entomol. Zool.* **19**, 49.

Jacob, J., and Sirlin, J. L. (1959). *Chromosoma* **10**, 210.

Janda, V., and Krieg, P. (1969). *Z. Vergl. Physiol.* **64**, 288.

Jarnicka-Stanios, H. (1967). *Ann. Univ. Mariae Curie-Sklodowska, Sect. C* **22**, 27.

Jazdowska-Zagrodzińska, B. (1966). *J. Embryol. Exp. Morphol.* **16**, 391.

Johannsen, O. A., and Butt, F. H. (1941). "Embryology of Insects and Myriapodes." McGraw-Hill, New York.

Jones, B. M., and Wilson, R. S. (1959). *Biol. Bull.* **117**, 482.

Jones, C. R. (1964). *J. Cell. Comp. Physiol.* **63**, 65.

Judy, K. J., and Gilbert, L. I. (1969). *Ann. Entomol. Soc. Amer.* **62**, 1438.

Jung, E. (1966a). *Z. Morphol. Oekol. Tiere* **56**, 444.

Jung, E. (1966b). *Wilhelm Roux' Arch. Entwicklungsmech. Organismen* **157**, 320.

Jung, E. (1971). *Wilhelm Roux' Arch. Entwicklungsmech. Organismen* **167**, 299.

Jung, E., and Krause, G. (1967). *Wilhelm Roux' Arch. Entwicklungsmech. Organismen* **159**, 89.

Jura, C. (1957). *Zool. Pol.* **8**, 177.

Jura, C. (1964). *Acta Biol. Cracov., Ser. Zool.* **7**, 59, 89.

Jura, C. (1965). *Acta Biol. Cracov., Ser. Zool.* **8**, 141.

Jura, C. (1967). *Acta Biol. Cracov., Ser. Zool.* **10**, 97.

Jura, C., Krzysztofowicz, A., and Weglarska, B. (1957). *Zool. Pol.* **8**, 201.

Jura, C., Krzysztofowicz, A., and Weglarska, B. (1958). *Zool. Pol.* **9**, 3.

Kafatos, F. C., and Feder, N. (1968). *Science* **161**, 470.

Kahle, W. (1908). *Zoologica (Stuttgart)* **21**, 1.

Kahn, I. L., and Lavrova, N. P. (1937). *Wiss. Ber. Mosk. Staatsuniv.* **11, 3**.

Kalthoff, K. (1970a). *Zool. Anz., Suppl.* **33**, 59.

Kalthoff, K. (1970b). *Verh. Deut. Zool. Ges., Koeln* p. 61.

Kalthoff, K. (1971a). *Develop. Biol.* **25**, 119.

Kalthoff, K. (1971b). *Wilhelm Roux' Arch. Entwicklungsméch. Organismen* **168**, 85.

Kalthoff, K. (1971c). *Wilhelm Roux' Arch. Entwicklungsmech. Organismen* **168**, 63.

Kalthoff, K., and Sander, K. (1968). *Wilhelm Roux' Arch. Entwicklungsmech. Organismen* **161**, 129.

Karlson, P., and Sekeris, C. E. (1964) . *Comp. Biochem.* **6**, 221.

Katzenellenbogen, B. S., and Kafatos, F. C. (1970). *J. Insect Physiol.* **16**, 2241.

Kilgore, W. W., and Painter, R. R. (1964). *Biochem. J.* **92**, 353.

King, R. C. (1960). *Growth* **24**, 265.

King, R. C., Bentley, R. M., and Aggarwal, S. K. (1966). *Amer. Natur.* **100**, 365.

Kinsella, J. E. (1966a). *Comp. Biochem. Physiol.* **19**, 291.

Kinsella, J. E. (1966b). *Can. J. Biochem.* **44**, 247.

Kinsella, J. E. (1966c). *Comp. Biochem. Physiol.* **17**, 635.

Kinsella, J. E. (1966d). *J. Insect Physiol.* **12**, 435.

Kinsella, J. E., and Smyth, T., Jr. (1966). *Comp. Biochem. Physiol.* **17**, 237.

Koch, P. (1964). *Wilhelm Roux' Arch. Entwicklungsmech. Organismen* **155**, 549.

Koch, P. (1966). *Zool. Anz., Suppl.* **29**, 251.

Koch, P., and Heinig, S. (1968). *Wilhelm Roux' Arch. Entwicklungsmech. Organismen* **161**, 241.

Kozhanchikov, I. V. (1940). *C. R. Acad. Sci.* **27**, 80.

Kramer, V. (1959). *Z. Morphol. Oekol. Tiere* **48**, 169.

Krause, G. (1934). *Wilhelm Roux' Arch. Entwicklungsmech. Organismen* **132**, 115.

Krause, G. (1939). *Biol. Zentralbl.* **59**, 495.

Krause, G. (1958a). *Zool. Anz., Suppl.* **21**, 396.

Krause, G. (1958b). *Ergeb. Biol.* **20**, 159.

Krause, G. (1963). *Zool. Anz., Suppl.* **26**, 190.

Krause, G., and Krause, J. (1956). *Zool. Jahrb., Abt. Anat. Ontog. Tiere* **75**, 481.

Krause, G., and Krause, J. (1964). *Wilhelm Roux' Arch. Entwicklungsmech. Organismen* **155**, 451.

Krause, G., and Krause, J. (1965). *Z. Naturforsch. B* **20**, 334.

Krause, G., and Krause, J. (1971). *Wilhelm Roux' Arch. Entwicklungsmech. Organismen* **167**, 137.

Krause, G., and Sander, K. (1962). *Advan. Morphog.* **2**, 259.

Kroeger, M., and Lezzi, M. (1966). *Annu. Rev. Entomol.* **11**, 1.

Krogh, A. (1914). *Z. Allg. Physiol.* **16**, 178.

Krishnakumaran, A., Berry, S. J., Oberlander, H., and Schneiderman, H. A. (1967) . *J. Insect Physiol.* **13**, 1.

Kunz, W. (1970). *Verh. Deut. Zool. Ges., Koeln* p. 42.

Kunz, W., Trepte, H.-H., and Bier, K. (1970). *Chromosoma* **30**, 180.

Kurland, C. G., and Schneiderman, H. A. (1959). *Biol. Bull.* **116**, 136.

Kuske, G., Penner, M. L., and Piepho, H. (1961). *Biol. Zentralbl.* **80**, 347.

Küthe, H.-W. (1966). *Wilhelm Roux' Arch. Entwicklungsmech. Organismen* **157**, 212.

Lagowski, J. M., and Forrest, H. S. (1967). *Proc. Nat. Acad. Sci. U.S.* **58**, 1541.

Lang, C. A., Lau, H. Y., and Jefferson, O. J. (1965) . *Biochem. J.* **95**, 372.

Laufer, H. (1961). *Ann. N.Y. Acad. Sci.* **94**, 825.

Laufer, H. (1963). *Ann. N.Y. Acad. Sci.* **103**, 1137.

Lawrence, P. A. (1968). *J. Cell Sci.* **3**, 391.
Lawrence, P. A. (1970). *Advan. Insect Physiol.* **7**, 197.
Lee, T., and Fan, S. (1966). *Acta Enzymol. Sinica* **15**, 91.
Lees, A. D. (1955). "The Physiology of Diapause in Arthropods," Cambridge Monogr. Exp. Biol. Cambridge Univ. Press, London and New York.
Lees, A. D. (1956). *Annu. Rev. Entomol.* **1**, 1.
Lennie, R. W., and Birt. L. M. (1965) . *J. Insect Physiol.* **11**, 1213.
Lennie, R. W., and Birt, L. M. (1967) . *Biochem. J.* **102**, 338.
Lennie, R. W., Gregory, D. W., and Birth, L. M. (1967). *J. Insect Physiol.* **13**, 1745.
Leonardi, M. C. (1956). *Rend. Inst. Lomb. Sci. Lett., Ser. 3* **90**, 573.
Lesseps, R. J. (1965). *Science* **148**, 502.
Levenbook, L. (1953). *J. Cell. Comp. Physiol.* **41**, 313.
Levenbook, L. (1962). *J. Insect Physiol.* **8**, 559.
Levenbook, L. (1966). *Acta Biochim. Pol.* **13**, 405.
Levenbook, L., and Dinamarca, M. L. (1966). *J. Insect Physiol.* **12**, 1343.
Levenbook, L., and Hollis, V. W., Jr. (1961). *J. Insect Physiol.* **6**, 52.
Levenbook, L., Travaglini, E., and Schultz, J. (1953). *Anat. Rec.* **117**, 585.
Lewerenz, G. (1961). *Deut. Entomol. Z.* [N.S.] **8**, 22.
Lewis, E. B. (1963). *Amer. Zool.* **3**, 33.
Lindh, N. O. (1967). *Comp. Biochem. Physiol.* **20**, 209.
Linzen, B., and Wyatt, G. R. (1964). *Biochim. Biophys. Acta* **87**, 188.
Lipsitz, E. Y., and McFarlane, J. E. (1970). *Comp. Biochem. Physiol.* **34**, 699.
Lipsitz, E. Y., and McFarlane, J. E. (1971). *Insect Biochem.* **1**, 446.
Lockshin, R. A. (1966). *Science* **154**, 775.
Lockshin, R. A. (1969). *J. Insect Physiol.* **15**, 1505.
Lockshin, R. A. (1971). *J. Insect Physiol.* **17**, 149.
Lockshin, R. A., and Williams, C. M. (1965). *J. Insect Physiol.* **11**, 831.
Loughton, B. G., and West, A. S. (1965). *J. Insect Physiol.* **11**, 919.
Lu, K. H., and Bodine, J. H. (1953). *Physiol. Zool.* **26**, 242.
Ludwig, D. (1931). *J. Exp. Zool.* **60**, 309.
Ludwig, D. (1934). *Ann. Entomol. Soc. Amer.* **27**, 429.
Ludwig, D. (1953). *J. Gen. Physiol.* **36**, 751.
Ludwig, D., and Barsa, M. C. (1955). *J. N. Y. Entomol. Soc.* **63**, 161.
Ludwig, D., and Barsa, M. C. (1956). *Ann. Entomol. Soc. Amer.* **49**, 103.
Ludwig, D., and Barsa, M. C. (1958). *Ann. Entomol. Soc. Amer.* **51**, 311.
Ludwig, D., and Barsa, M. C. (1959). *J. N. Y. Entomol. Soc.* **67**, 151.
Ludwig, D., and Ramazzotto, L. J. (1965). *Ann. Entomol. Soc. Amer.* **58**, 543.
Ludwig, D., and Rothstein, F. (1952). *Physiol. Zool.* **25**, 263.
Ludwig, D., and Wugmeister, M. (1955). *J. Cell. Comp. Physiol.* **45**, 157.
Lüscher, M. (1944). *Rev. Suisse Zool.* **51**, 531.
McAllen, J. W., and Chefurca, W. (1961). *Comp. Biochem. Physiol.* **2**, 290.
McFarlane, J. E. (1966). *J. Insect Physiol.* **12**, 1567.
McFarlane, J. E., and Hogan, T. W. (1966). *J. Insect Physiol.* **12**, 1265.
Mahowald, A. P. (1962). *J. Exp. Zool.* **151**, 201.
Mahowald, A. P. (1963a). *Exp. Cell Res.* **32**, 457.
Mahowald, A. P. (1963b). *Develop. Biol.* **8**, 186.
Mahowald, A. P. (1968a). *J. Cell Biol.* **39**, 84a.
Mahowald, A. P. (1968b). *J. Exp. Zool.* **167**, 237.
Mahowald, A. P. (1971a). *J. Exp. Zool.* **176**, 329.

Mahowald, A. P. (1971b). *J. Exp. Zool.* **176**, 345.

Mahowald, A. P. (1971c). *In* "Origin and Continuity of Cell Organelles" (J. Reichert and H. Ursprung, eds.), p. 158. Springer-Verlag, Berlin and New York.

Mahowald, A. P., and Hennen, S. (1971). *Develop. Biol.* **24**, 37.

Mahr, E. (1957). *Naturwissenschaften* **44**, 226.

Mahr, E. (1960a). *Z. Morphol. Oekol. Tiere* **49**, 263.

Mahr, E. (1960b). *Wilhelm Roux' Arch. Entwicklungsmech. Organismen* **152**, 263.

Mahr, E. (1961). *Zool. Anz., Suppl.* **24**, 99.

Mansingh, A., and Smallman, B. N. (1967). *J. Insect Physiol.* **13**, 861.

Maruyama, K. (1954). *Biochim. Biophys. Acta* **14**, 284.

Maruyama, K. (1957). *Z. Vergl. Physiol.* **40**, 451.

Maschlanka, H. (1938). *Wilhelm Roux' Arch. Entwicklungsmech. Organismen* **137**, 714.

Matsuura, S., Morimoto, T., Nagata, S., and Tashiro, Y. (1968). *J. Cell Biol.* **38**, 589.

Mattingly, E., and Parker, C. (1968). *J. Insect Physiol.* **14**, 1077.

Maul, V. (1967). *Zool. Jahrb., Abt. Anat. Ontog. Tiere* **84**, 63.

Maul, V. (1970a). *J. Morphol.* **130**, 247.

Maul, V. (1970b). *Zool. Anz., Suppl.* **33**, 53.

Mehrotra, K. N. (1960). *J. Insect Physiol.* **5**, 129.

Melampy, R. M., and Olsan, R. D. (1940). *Proc. Soc. Exp. Biol. Med.* **45**, 754.

Melampy, R. M., and Willis, E. R. (1939). *Physiol. Zool.* **12**, 302.

Melander, Y. (1963). *Hereditas* **49**, 91.

Melvin, R. (1928). *Biol. Bull.* **55**, 135.

Meng., C. (1968). *Wilhelm Roux' Arch. Entwicklungsmech. Organismen* **161**, 162.

Meng, C. (1970). *Wilhelm Roux' Arch. Entwicklungsmech. Organismen* **165**, 35.

Mitlin, N., Mauldin, J. K., and Hedin, P. A. (1966). *Comp. Biochem. Physiol.* **19**, 35.

Moloo, S. K. (1971). *J. Insect Physiol.* **17**, 1489.

Moser, J. G., Bode, H. J., Nünemann, H., Collatz, S., Feldhege, A., and Herzfeld, A. (1970). *Verh. Deut. Zool. Ges., Koeln* p. 56.

Moulinier, M. C. (1957). *C. R. Acad. Sci.* **245**, 1657.

Muckenthaler, F. A., and Mahowald, A. P. (1966). *J. Cell Biol.* **28**, 199.

Mukerji, R. N. (1930). *Proc. Roy. Soc., Ser. B* **106**, 131.

Müller, K. (1938). *Z. Wiss. Zool. Abt. A* **151**, 192.

Mulnard, J. (1947). *Arch. Biol.* **58**, 289.

Mulnard, J. (1954). *Arch. Biol.* **65**, 261.

Murray, F. U., and Tiegs, O. W. (1935). *Quart. J. Microsc. Sci.* **77**, 405.

Needham, D. M. (1929). *Biol. Rev.* **4**, 307.

Needham, J. (1931). "Chemical Embryology." Cambridge Univ. Press, London and New York.

Netzel, H. (1965). *Wilhelm Roux' Arch. Entwicklungsmech. Organismen* **156**, 88.

Netzel, H. (1968). *Wilhelm Roux' Arch. Entwicklungsmech. Organismen* **160**, 119.

Nicklas, R. B. (1959). *Chromosoma* **10**, 301.

Niemierko, S., Wlodawer, P., and Wojtczak, A. F. (1956). *Acta Biol. Exp. (Warsaw)* **17**, 255.

Nigon, V., and Daille, J. (1958). *Biochim. Biophys. Acta* **29**, 246.

Nigon, V., and Gillot, S. (1964). *Exp. Cell Res.* **33**, 29.

Nitschmann, J. (1959). *Zool. Anz., Suppl.* **22**, 370.

Novák, V. J. A. (1956) . *Beitr. Entomol.* **6**, 205.

Nünemann, H., and Moser, J. G. (1970). *Zool. Anz., Suppl.* **33**, 113.

Ochsé, W. (1944). *Rev. Suisse Zool.* **51**, 1.

Ohnishi, E. (1953). *Jap. J. Zool.* **11**, 69.

Okada, E., and Waddington, C. H. (1959). *J. Embryol. Exp. Morphol.* **7**, 583.

Okada, M. (1970). *Sci. Rep. Tokyo Kyoiku Daigaku, Sect. B* **14**, 95.

Overton, J., and Raab, M. (1967). *Develop. Biol.* **15**, 271.

Painter, R. R., and Kilgore, W. W. (1967). *J. Insect Physiol.* **13**, 1105.

Painter, T. S. (1959). *Proc. Nat. Acad. Sci. U. S.* **45**, 897.

Pant, R., and Agrarval, H. C. (1965). *J. Insect Physiol.* **11**, 387.

Pant, R., and Lal, D. M. (1970). *Indian J. Biochem.* **7**, 57.

Pant, R., and Sharma, S. C. (1967). *Indian J. Exp. Biol.* **5**, 181.

Pantelouris, E. M., and Downer, R. G. H. (1969). *J. Insect Physiol.* **15**, 2357.

Pantelouris, E. M., and Waddington, C. H. (1955). *Wilhelm Roux' Arch. Entwicklungsmech. Organismen* **147**, 539.

Patel, N. G. (1971). *Insect Biochem.* **1**, 391.

Pauli, M. E. (1927). *Z. Wiss. Zool., Abt. A* **129**, 481.

Perez, C. (1910). *Arch. Zool. Exp. Gen.* **4**, 1.

Perez, C. (1912). *Mem. Acad. Roy. Belg., Cl. Sci.* **3**, 1.

Pettersson, I. (1955). *Acta Physiol. Scand.* **34**, 116.

Pflugfelder, O. (1952). 'Entwicklungsphysiologie der Insekten." Akad. Verlagsges, Leipzig.

Philiptschenko, J. (1912). *Z. Wiss. Zool., Abt. A* **103**, 519.

Porter, C. A., and Javorsky, E. G. (1965). *J. Insect Physiol.* **11**, 1151.

Postlethwait, J. H., and Schneiderman, H. A. (1971). *Develop. Biol.* **24**, 477.

Poulson, D. F. (1935). *Z. Vergl. Physiol.* **22**, 466.

Poulson, D. F. (1940). *J. Exp. Zool.* **83**, 271.

Poulson, D. F. (1947). *Proc. Nat. Acad. Sci. U.S.* **33**, 182.

Pouvreau, A. (1968). *Ann. Abeille* **11**, 5.

Poyarkoff, E. (1910). *Arch. Anat. Microsc. Morphol. Exp.* **12**, 333.

Price, G. M. (1965). *J. Insect Physiol.* **11**, 869.

Price, R. D. (1958). *Ann. Entomol. Soc. Amer.* **51**, 600.

Quickenden, K. L. (1970). *J. Insect Physiol.* **16**, 171.

Rabinowitz, M. (1941). *J. Morphol.* **69**, 1.

Rainey, R. C. (1938). *Ann. Appl. Biol.* **25**, 822.

Randall, D. D., and Derr, R. F. (1965). *J. Insect Physiol.* **11**, 329.

Rao, R. M., and Subrahmanyam, D. (1970). *Arch. Biochem. Biophys.* **140**, 443.

Rasch, E. M., and Gawlik, S. (1964). *J. Cell Biol.* **23**, 252.

Ray, O. M. (1937) . *Anat. Rec.* **70**, Suppl., 1 and 80.

Rechsteiner, M. C. (1970). *J. Insect Physiol.* **16**, 1179.

Reith, F. (1925). *Z. Wiss. Zool., Abt. A* **126**, 181.

Reith, F. (1931). *Z. Wiss. Zool., Abt. A* **139**, 664.

Reith, F. (1933). *Wilhelm Roux' Arch. Entwicklungsmech. Organismen* **127**, 283.

Reith, F. (1936). *Z. Wiss. Zool., Abt. A* **147**, 77.

Rempel, J. G., and Church, N. S. (1965). *Can. J. Zool.* **43**, 915.

Rensch, B. (1948). *Evolution* **2**, 218.

Richards, A. G. (1937). *J. N. Y. Entomol. Soc.* **45**, 149.

Richards, A. G., and Miller, A. (1937). *J. N. Y. Entomol. Soc.* **45**, 1.

Riemann, J. G. (1965). *Biol. Bull.* **129**, 329.

Robbie, W. A. (1941). *J. Cell. Comp. Physiol.* **17**, 369.

Robbie, W. A., Boell, E. J., and Bodine, J. H. (1938). *Physiol. Zool.* **11**, 54.

Roberts, R. B., and Smith, H. W. (1971). *Ann. Entomol. Soc. Amer.* **64**, 693.

Robertson, C. W. (1936). *J. Morphol.* **59**, 351.

Rockstein, M. (1957). *Annu. Rev. Entomol.* **2**, 19.

Roemhild, G. (1965). *Physiol. Zool.* **38**, 213.

Roemhild, G. (1968). *J. Insect Physiol.* **14**, 1035.

Roonwal, M. L. (1936). *Phil. Trans. Roy. Soc. London, Ser. B* **226**, 391.

Rothstein, F. (1952). *Physiol. Zool.* **25**, 171.

Rousell, P. G. (1967). *J. N. Y. Entomol. Soc.* **75**, 119.

Rudolfs, W. (1926). *J. N. Y. Entomol. Soc.* **34**, 249.

Rudolfs, W. (1929). *J. N. Y. Entomol. Soc.* **37**, 17.

Russo-Caia, S. (1960). *Ric. Sci.* **30**, Suppl., No. 12.

Rutschky, C. W., and Joseph, S. R. (1957). *Proc. Pa. Acad. Sci.* **31**, 131.

Salkeld, E. H. (1964). *Can. Entomol.* **96**, 389.

Salkeld, E. H. (1965). *Can. J. Zool.* **43**, 593.

Salkeld, E. H., and Hudson, A. (1964). *Can. Entomol.* **96**, 147.

Salt, R. W. (1961). *Annu. Rev. Entomol.* **6**, 55.

Sander, K. (1959). *Wilhelm Roux' Arch. Entwicklungsmech. Organismen* **151**, 430 and 660.

Sander, K. (1962). *Zool. Anz., Suppl.* **25**, 315.

Sander, K. (1968). *Zool. Anz., Suppl.* **31**, 81.

Sander, K. (1971). *Wilhelm Roux' Arch. Entwicklungsmech. Organismen* **167**, 336.

Sander, K., and Vollmar, H. (1967). *Nature (London)* **216**, 174.

Sander, K., Herth, W., and Vollmar, H. (1970). *Zool. Anz., Suppl.* **33**, 46.

Sauer, G. (1962). *Zool. Anz., Suppl.* **25**, 323.

Sauer, H. W. (1964). *Zool. Anz., Suppl.* **27**, 480.

Sauer, H. W. (1966). *Z. Morphol. Oekol. Tiere* **56**, 143.

Sauer, H. W. (1970) . *Verh. Deut. Zool. Ges., Koeln* p. 47.

Sauer-Löcher, E. (1954). *Wilhelm Roux' Arch. Entwicklungsmech. Organismen* **147**, 302.

Schanz, G. (1966). *Zool. Anz., Suppl.* **29**, 188.

Schlottmann, L. L., and Bonhag, P. F. (1956). *Univ. Calif., Berkeley, Publ. Entomol.* **11**, 351.

Schmidt, G. H. (1963). *Naturwissenschaften* **50**, 375.

Schmidt, G. H., and Mathur, M. (1967). *Entomol. Exp. Appl.* **10**, 421.

Schnetter, M. (1934a). *Z. Morphol. Oekol. Tiere* **29**, 114.

Schnetter, M. (1934b). *Wilhelm Roux' Arch. Entwicklungsmech. Organismen* **131**, 285.

Schnetter, W. (1965). *Wilhelm Roux' Arch. Entwicklungsmech. Organismen* **155**, 637.

Schnetter, W. (1967). *Zool. Anz., Suppl.* **30**, 494.

Schnetter, W. (1970). *Zool. Anz., Suppl.* **33**, 108.

Schubiger, M., and Schneiderman, H. A. (1971) . *Nature (London)* **230**, 185.

Schwalm, F. E. (1965). *Z. Morphol. Oekol. Tiere* **55**, 915.

Schwalm, F. E. (1969). *Wilhelm Roux' Arch. Entwicklungsmech. Organismen* **162**, 41.

Schwalm, F. E., Simpson, R., and Bender, H. A. (1970). *Wilhelm Roux' Arch. Entwicklungsmech. Organismen* **166**, 205.

Schwan, H. (1940). *Ark. Zool.* [1] **32A**, No. 9.

Scriba, M. E. L. (1963). *Zool. Anz., Suppl.* **26**, 92.

Scriba, M. E. L. (1964). *Zool. Jahrb., Abt. Anat. Ontog. Tiere* **81**, 435.

Scriba, M. E. L. (1967). *Wilhelm Roux' Arch. Entwicklungsmech. Organismen* **159**, 314.

Sehl, A. (1931). *Z. Morphol. Oekol. Tiere* **20**, 533.

Seidel, F. (1929). *Wilhelm Roux' Arch. Entwicklungsmech. Organismen* **119**, 322.

Seidel, F. (1934). *Wilhelm Roux' Arch. Entwicklungsmech. Organismen* **131**, 135.
Seidel, F. (1961). *Zool. Anz., Suppl.* **24**, 121.
Seidel, F. (1964). *Zool. Anz., Suppl.* **27**, 121.
Seidel, F. (1966). *Zool. Anz., Suppl.* **29**, 166.
Seidel, F., Bock, E., and Krause, G. (1940). *Naturwissenschaften* **28**, 433.
Sekeri, K. E., Sekeris, C. E., and Karlson, P. (1968). *J. Insect Physiol.* **14**, 425.
Shappirio, D. G., Eichembaum, D. M., and Locke, D. R. (1967). *Biol. Bull.* **132**, 108.
Shatoury, H. H., and Waddington, C. H. (1957). *J. Embryol. Exp. Morphol.* **5**, 122.
Shaw, E. I. (1955). *Exp. Cell Res.* **9**, 489.
Shieldo, G., and Sang, J. H. (1970). *J. Embryol. Exp. Morphol.* **23**, 53.
Shulov, A., Pener, M. P., Kuk-Meiri, S., and Lichtenstein, N. (1957). *J. Insect Physiol.* **1**, 279.
Skinner, D. M. (1960). *Anat. Rec.* **138**, 383.
Slǎma, K. (1957). *Acta Soc. Zool. Bohemoslo.* **21**, 289.
Slifer, E. H. (1930). *Physiol. Zool.* **3**, 501.
Slifer, E. H. (1931). *J. Morphol.* **51**, 613.
Slifer, E. H. (1932a). *Biol. Zentralbl.* **52**, 223.
Slifer, E. H. (1932b). *Physiol. Zool.* **5**, 448.
Slifer, E. H. (1937). *Quart. J. Microsc. Sci.* **79**, 493.
Smallman, B. N., and Mansingh, A. (1969). *Annu. Rev. Entomol.* **14**, 387.
Smith, R. L., and Forrest, H. S. (1969). *J. Insect Physiol.* **15**, 953.
Smith, R. L., and Forrest, H. S. (1971). *Develop. Biol.* **25**, 502.
Snodgrass, R. E. (1924). *J. Agr. Res.* **28**, 1.
Snodgrass, R. E. (1954). *Smithson. Misc. Collect.* **122**, No. 9.
Spirin, A. S. (1966). *Curr. Top. Develop. Biol.* **1**, 1.
Squire, F. A. (1936). *Bull. Entomol. Res.* **27**, 381.
Stamm, D. (1962). *Rev. Espan. Fisiol.* **18**, 53.
Staudenmayer, T. (1955). *Z. Vergl. Physiol.* **37**, 416.
Strasburger, E. H. (1934). *Z. Wiss. Zool., Abt. A* **145**, 625.
Strauss, J. (1911). *Z. Biol.* **56**, 347.
Sulkowski, E., and Wojtczak, L. (1958). *Acta Biol. Exp. (Warsaw)* **18**, 239.
Svoboda, J. A., Pepper, J. H., and Baker, G. L. (1966). *J. Insect Physiol.* **12**, 1549.
Taege, M. (1963). *Deut. Entomol. Z* [N.S.] **10**, 335.
Tahmisian, T. N. (1943). *J. Exp. Zool.* **92**, 199.
Takahashi, S. (1966). *J. Insect Physiol.* **12**, 789.
Takami, I. (1943). *Zool. Mag.* **54**, 23.
Tangl, F. (1909). *Arch. Gesamte Physiol. Menschen Tiere* **130**, 1.
Tate, L. G., and Wimer, L. T. (1971). *Insect Biochem.* **1**, 199.
Tawfik, M. F. S. (1957). *J. Insect Physiol.* **1**, 286.
Taylor, I. R. (1927). *J. Morphol.* **44**, 313.
Telfer, W. H. (1965). *Annu. Rev. Entomol.* **10**, 161.
Tessier, G. (1931). *Trav. Sta. Biol. Roscoff* **9**, 29.
Teunissen, J. H. (1937). *Cytologia, Fuji Jubilee* p. 836.
Thompson, V., and Bodine, J. H. (1938). *J. Cell. Comp. Physiol.* **12**, 247.
Tiegs, O. W. (1922). *Trans. Phil. Soc. S. Aust.* **46**, 319.
Tiegs, O. W., and Murray, F. U. (1937). *Quart. J. Microsc. Sci.* **80**, 185.
Tojo, S. (1971). *Insect Biochem.* **1**, 249.
Tojo, S., and Hirano, C. (1967). *Appl. Entomol. Zool.* **2**, 93.
Tojo, S., and Hirano, C. (1968). *J. Insect Physiol.* **14**, 1121.

Trager, E. (1935). *J. Exp. Zool.* **71**, 489.

Travaglini, E. C., Levenbook, L., and Schultz, J. (1958). *Exp. Cell Res.* **15**, 62.

Treves, C., Nassi, P., Cappugi, G., Vanni, P., and Ramponi, G. (1970). *Comp. Biochem. Physiol.* **34**, 61.

Trowbridge, C., and Bodine, J. H. (1940). *Biol. Bull.* **79**, 452.

Truckenbrodt, W. (1965). *Wilhelm Roux' Arch. Entwicklungsmech. Organismen* **156**, 101.

Tuft, P. H. (1949). *Exp. Cell Res., Suppl.* **1**, 545.

Tyshtchenko, V. P., and Mandelstam, J. E. (1965). *J. Insect Physiol.* **11**, 1233.

Ullmann, S. L. (1965). *J. Embryol. Exp. Morphol.* **13**, 73.

Urbani, E., and Bellini, L. (1959). *Ric. Sci.* **29**, 1725.

Urbani, E., and Rossi, M. (1959). *Atti. Accad. Naz. Lincei, Cl. Sci. Fis., Mat. Natur., Bend.* [8] **26**, 54.

Ursprung, H., Sofer, W. H., and Burroughs, N. (1970). *Wilhelm Roux' Arch. Entwicklungsmech. Organismen* **164**, 201.

Vanderberg, J. P. (1963). *Biol. Bull.* **125**, 556.

Varute, A. T., and Sawant, V. A. (1971a). *Insect Biochem.* **1**, 327.

Varute, A. T., and Sawant, V. A. (1971b). *Comp. Biochem. Physiol.* **38B**, 211.

Verma, G. N. (1965). *Indian J. Entomol.* **27**, 144.

Villeneuve, J. L., and Lemonde, A. (1963). *Arch. Int. Physiol. Biochim.* **71**, 143.

Vogt, M. (1946). *Biol. Zentralbl.* **65**, 238.

von Borstel, R. C. (1957). *Publ. Amer. Ass. Advan. Sci.* **48**, 175.

von der Crone-Gloor, U. (1959). *J. Insect Physiol.* **3**, 50.

von Kraft, A. (1960). *Zool. Jahrb., Abt. Anat. Ontog. Tiere* **78**, 485.

Waddington, C. H. (1962). *J. Cell Comp. Physiol.* **60**, 93.

Waku, Y. (1957). *Sci. Rep. Tohoku Univ., Ser. 4* **23**, 143.

Walker, P. A. (1966). *J. Insect Physiol.* **12**, 1009.

Wegener, G., Kläner, S., and Sauer, H. W. (1971). *Wilhelm Roux' Arch. Entwicklungsmech. Organismen* **167**, 118.

Wehman, H. J. (1969). *Wilhelm Roux' Arch. Entwicklungsmech. Organismen* **163**, 375.

Weygoldt, P. (1960). *Zool. Anz.* **164**, 381.

White, M. J. D. (1950). *Tex., Univ., Publ.* **5007**.

White, R. H. (1961). *J. Exp. Zool.* **148**, 223.

Whiting, A. R. (1939). *Proc. Amer. Phil. Soc.* **80**, 65.

Whitten, J. M. (1969). *J. Insect Physiol.* **15**, 763.

Wigglesworth, V. B. (1934). *Quart. J. Microsc. Sci.* **77**, 191.

Wigglesworth, V. B. (1940). *J. Exp. Biol.* **17**, 180.

Wigglesworth, V. B. (1948). *Biol. Rev.* **23**, 408.

Wigglesworth, V. B. (1954). "The Physiology of Insect Metamorphosis." Cambridge Univ. Press, London and New York.

Wigglesworth, V. B. (1956a). *Quart. J. Microsc. Sci.* **97**, 465.

Wigglesworth, V. B. (1956b). *Ann. Sci. Nat. Zool. Biol. Anim.* [12] **18**, 139.

Williams, C. M. (1951). *Fed. Proc., Fed. Amer. Soc. Exp. Biol.* **10**, 546.

Williams, M. (1936). *Physiol. Zool.* **9**, 231.

Wilson, E. B. (1953). "The Cell in Development and Heredity." Macmillan, New York.

Wimer, L. T., and Lumb, R. H. (1967). *J. Insect Physiol.* **13**, 889.

Wojtczak, L. (1956). *Acta Biol. Exp. (Warsaw)* **17**, 205.

Wolf, R. (1967). *Wilhelm Roux' Arch. Entwicklungsmech. Organismen* **158**, 459.

Wolf, R. (1969a). *Wilhelm Roux' Arch. Entwicklungsmech. Organismen* **162**, 121.

Wolf, R. (1969b). *Wilhelm Roux' Arch. Entwicklungsmech. Organismen* **163**, 40.

Wolf, R., and Krause, G. (1971). *Wilhelm Roux' Arch. Entwicklungsmech. Organismen* **167**, 266.

Wolsky, A. A. (1937). *Nature (London)* **139**, 1069.

Wolsky, A. A. (1938). *J. Exp. Biol.* **15**, 225.

Wolsky, A. A. (1941). *Science* **94**, 48.

Wolsky, A. A. (1949). *Proc. Nat. Inst. Sci. India* **15**, 67.

Wyatt, G. R. (1959). *Proc. Int. Congr. Biochem., 4th, 1958* Vol. 12, p. 161.

Wyatt, G. R. (1961). *Annu. Rev. Entomol.* **6**, 75.

Wyatt, G. R. (1967). *Advan. Insect Physiol.* **4**, 282.

Yabe, I. (1962). *Jap. J. Zool.* **13**, 375.

Yagi, N., and Saitoh, K. (1955). *Jap. J. Zool.* **11**, 345.

Yajima, H. (1960). *J. Embryol. Exp. Morphol.* **8**, 198.

Yajima, H. (1964). *J. Embryol. Exp. Morphol.* **12**, 89.

Yajima, H. (1970). *J. Embryol. Exp. Morphol.* **24**, 287

Yao, T. (1950). *Quart. J. Microsc. Sci.* **91**, 79 and 89.

Yosii, R. (1954). *Biol. Zentralbl.* **64**, 305.

Yushima, T. (1957). *J. Econ. Entomol.* **50**, 440.

Zalokar, M. (1971). *Proc. Nat. Acad. Sci. U.S.* **68**, 1539.

Zaman, V., and Chellappah, W. T. (1963). *Exp. Parasitol.* **13**, 108.

Zeuthen, F. (1951). *Pubbl. Sta. Zool. Napoli* **23**, Suppl., 47.

Zwicky, K., and Wigglesworth, V. B. (1956). *Proc. Roy. Entomol. Soc. London, Ser. A* **31**, 10.

Chapter 5

PHYSIOLOGY OF GROWTH AND DEVELOPMENT: ENDOCRINE ASPECTS*

Lawrence I. Gilbert and David Shaw King

I. Introduction 250
II. The Endocrine Glands: Structure and General Functions 252
    A. Brain (Neurosecretion) 252
    B. Corpora Cardiaca 257
    C. Corpora Allata 257
    D. Prothoracic Glands 259
    E. Oenocytes 262
III. Endocrine Gland Interactions 262
    A. Brain Activation 263
    B. Prothoracic Gland Activation 265
    C. Regulation of the Corpora Allata 266
    D. Corpora Allata–Prothoracic Gland Interactions 267
IV. The Molting Hormone—Chemistry and Metabolism 271
    A. Occurrence 271
    B. Chemistry 274
    C. Extraction, Isolation, and Analysis 280
    D. Structure-Activity Correlations 282
    E. Biosynthesis 284
    F. Inactivation 287
V. The Juvenile Hormone—Chemistry and Metabolism 288
    A. Occurrence 288

* Original work from the laboratory of L. I. Gilbert was supported by Grant AM-02818 from the National Institute of Arthritis and Metabolic Diseases, N.I.H., and by Grant GB-27574 from the National Science Foundation.

249

B. Chemistry 292
C. Extraction, Isolation, and Analysis 295
D. Structure-Activity Correlations 296
E. Biosynthesis 297
F. Inactivation 298
VI. The Action of Insect Hormones 299
A. Hormone Transport 300
B. Recognition of Target Cells 303
C. Effects at Tissue, Cell, and Biochemical Levels 306
D. Effects Close to Site of Action 335
VII. Conclusions 353
References 354

I. Introduction

In the earlier version of this chapter (Gilbert, 1964), we had just learned of the tentative structure of α-ecdysone and, in considering the chemical nature of insect growth hormones in the conclusions, we stated that "structural determination and chemical synthesis of these substances is most probable in the next few years." In the area of insect endocrinology, chemical investigations of insect hormones, especially since 1963, have been extremely productive and have, in fact, led to the possibility of insect control by hormone analogues. In terms of hormone action, our last review concluded by stating that "the mechanism of action of no insect hormone is known with certainty" and although this statement still remains essentially correct 8 years later, data have been gathered on hormone action that will no doubt serve as a framework for future breakthroughs.

Although the exact details of endocrine gland regulation remain a matter for conjecture, there is an accumulating quantity of evidence suggesting the presence of positive feedback mechanisms, and we still do not fully understand how the endocrine glands are turned off.

We intend to use small portions of the original review in the first edition of this volume as a substratum upon which to reconstruct events occurring in the last 8 years. Therefore, with some exceptions, we will discuss chiefly that work reported subsequent to 1964 and, because of the literal deluge of reported experiments, we cannot discuss even for the period since 1964 all relevant published material (bursicon, diapause hormone, etc.).

Eight years ago, one could confidently picture the classical scheme of endocrine control of molting and metamorphosis in holometabolous insects in the following manner: The temporal sequence of the molting process as well as the qualitative expression of the molt (whether it is larval–larval, larval–pupal, or pupal–adult) is under endocrine control. The main endocrine axis in holometabolous insects consists of the brain and associated head glands innervated by the brain (corpora allata and corpora cardiaca) and two glands composed of lobulated cells with polymorphonuclei situated in the prothorax, the prothoracic glands. Clusters of neurosecretory cells in the brain produce a brain hormone which in many cases enters the corpora cardiaca, perhaps to be modified, and finally enters the hemolymph of the animal where it presumably stimulates the synthesis and/or release of the insect molting hormone (MH, or its precursor) from the prothoracic glands. The brain hormone is thus a trophic hormone and it is MH that actually initiates the molting process. The corpora allata secrete the juvenile hormone (JH) which modifies the expression of the molt. JH must act in conjunction with MH, as it usually exerts its effect only after the molting process has been initiated. When a relatively high titer of JH is present, the result is a larval–larval molt. When the concentration of JH is less, the molt is from larva to pupa, while in the absence of JH, a pupal–adult molt ensues. Thus, JH is a modifying agent that favors the synthesis of larval structures and opposes adult differentiation. More than four decades of surgical experiments and cytological examinations have led to the scheme of the endocrine control of metamorphosis presented above.

As one example of the many histological studies conducted on the insect's endocrine glands, let us briefly consider the results on the lepidopteran *Cerura vinula* (Hintze, 1968). During each larval instar, the brain neurosecretory cells, cells of the prothoracic glands, and those of the corpora allata undergo phases of secretory activity with the activity of the corpora allata decreasing during the last larval instar. The first metamorphic molt is characterized by active brain neurosecretory cells from the third day of the last larval instar until after pupation, while the prothoracic glands appear active from the third day until apolysis, some 6 days after spinning of the cocoon. These observations, as well as many others, are consistent with the classical scheme of endocrine control of growth and development discussed above. As will be seen subsequently, we are not now as confident of the details of the above scheme and the suggestion "that the prothoracic glands secrete a precursor to the true molting hormone and that metabolic conversion to the true hormone takes place in other abdominal tissues or within cytoplasm of the target cells" (Gilbert, 1964) may well be true (see Section V, B). In any event, the classical scheme will be utilized here as a basis for discussion.

II. The Endoctrine Glands: Structure and General Functions

A. BRAIN (NEUROSECRETION)

On the basis of experiments on larvae of the gypsy moth *(Porthetria dispar)*, Kopec (1917, 1922) first suggested that insect metamorphosis was humorally controlled. When these animals were deprived of their brains 10 days or more after the final larval molt, pupation occurred and brainless but otherwise normal moths emerged. However, if the brain was extirpated prior to the tenth day, the caterpillars failed to pupate although they survived for a long time. Kopec found that if he divided the larva into two blood-tight compartments by a ligature posterior to the thorax, both portions pupated simultaneously if tied off after the tenth day, but only the anterior portion pupated if the ligatures were applied prior to this critical period. He concluded from this that the brain liberates some substance into the blood which is essential for pupation and that it is released on about the tenth day after the final larval molt.

About 15 years after Kopec's work, Wigglesworth (1934) showed that decapitation of a *Rhodnius* larva within 3–5 days after feeding prevented molting, but that decapitation after this period did not. He concluded that there is a factor within the head which initiates molting and that this factor is found in the blood before the third day after feeding. He subsequently demonstrated that the site of hormone production in the head was indeed the protocerebrum (Wigglesworth, 1940). The critical role of the brain in molting has been consistently verified (Caspari and Plagge, 1935; Fraenkel, 1935; Bodenstein, 1936, 1938; Kühn and Piepho, 1936; Bounhiol, 1938; Schmieder, 1942; Williams, 1952a,b).

Hanström (1938) identified large neurosecretory cells in the brain of *Rhodnius.* Wigglesworth (1940) excised this portion of the brain from *Rhodnius* larvae at the time of the critical period and implanted it into permanent larvae which had been decapitated soon after feeding. This caused the decapitated larvae to molt. He found that no other part of the brain nor any other part of the nervous system had this effect. The same type of cell has been found in all other species of insects thus far studied (Gabe, 1954; Scharrer and Scharrer, 1954; Gersch, 1960, 1961a,b, 1962; Van der Kloot, 1960, 1962; Bern, 1962).

A basic tenet of insect endocrinology is that the brain acts as an endocrine gland and is unquestionably involved in the control of other endocrine centers. This statement has been strengthened over the last 8 years by numerous research findings from the morphological to the biochemical level. By a variety of surgical regimens, staining reactions, and autoradiographic techniques, it has been demonstrated that brain neurosecretory cell activity can sometimes be positively correlated with the onset of the molting cycle which is initiated by brain hormone activation of the prothoracic glands. However, in some cases one cannot correlate cycles of neurosecretory cell activity with physiological processes. This may in part be due to "reservoirs" of neurosecretory material within the neuropile that accomodate large variations in the amount of material within the neurosecretory system and, at least in the locust, explains the absence of definitive cycles of stainable content within the perikarya of the median neurosecretory cells of the brain (Highnam and West, 1971). One notable exception to the classical scheme is the finding that renewed secretion by the brain is not always needed for each molt. In the tobacco hornworm *(Manduca sexta)*, for example, extirpation of the brain from newly pupated diapausing insects did not appear to interfere with subsequent development to the adult. Further, when fourth and fifth instar larvae were deprived of their brains, a significant percentage of larvae went on to pupate, entered diapause, and subsequently underwent pupal–adult development (K. Judy, 1972). Thus, at least in *M. sexta,* brain neurosecretory cell activity is not essential for the molting process. [Could a product of the neurosecretory cells of the ventral nerve cord substitute for the brain hormone in this instance as has been suggested by M. Gersch (personal communication)?] Despite these unresolved questions, the role of the brain hormone in the molting process of many insects is a vital one and insect neurosecretory cells appear to play important roles in many other physiological processes as well.

Evidence has been presented for neurosecretory control of regeneration, reproduction, protein metabolism, carbohydrate metabolism, lipid metabolism, cell respiration, excretion, color change, behavior, cardiac rhythmicity, sclerotization, circadian rhythms, and neuroendocrine integration (see Scharrer and Weitzman, 1970). It should be pointed out, however, that some of the processes referred to above are regulated by neurosecretory cells in regions of the nervous system other than the brain. The number of neurosecretory cells in an insect brain varies from insect to insect, but more importantly is usually judged on the basis of staining reactions. Several studies have demonstrated that the staining reaction varies with the physiological state and developmental stage of the insect, and a depleted cell may easily be overlooked. By examining larval, pupal, and adult states of the Cecropia silkworm, a composite map of brain neurosecretory cells was made which revealed the presence of 8 large medial A cells, 8 small medial A cells, 4 deep medial A cells, 4 posterior A cells, 10 lateral A cells, 4 lateral B cells, and 4 medial B cells (the A and B designations made on the basis of staining reactions) (Herman and Gilbert, 1965; see, also, Hinks, 1971). In some insects at least, it is the B cells which join the corpora cardiaca, while the A cells innervate the wall of the aorta which may be considered a neurohemal organ (e.g., Dogra, 1967; Unnithan et al., 1971).

In our earlier review, the neuronal properties of the neurosecretory cell were dealt with in some detail, the conclusion being that they do share many electrical properties with nonneurosecretory neurons. There is now direct evidence that insect neurosecretory cells can conduct action potentials with relatively slow conduction velocity (Gosbee et al., 1968). The presumed causal relationship between electrical activity and the cholinergic system with brain hormone production and release has been quietly laid to rest (Mansingh and Smallman, 1967). There has been a virtual plethora of studies on the ultrastructure of neurosecretory cells and in general the cells contain granules of about 1000–1500 Å in diameter or 2000–3000 Å depending on the cell, species, and perhaps physiological state (e.g., Bloch et al., 1966; Scharrer, 1963, 1968; Smith and Smith, 1966). It is generally agreed that the active principles of neurosecretory cells are peptides or small proteins and that these are carried by larger proteins, the packaging occurring in the Golgi (see Gilbert, 1964). With the neurosecretory cells of the brain of Calliphora, it was possible to make a granule-to-granule comparison with the light microscope (dark field) and the electron microscope, the results demonstrating that minute granules seen in the unstained cells under the compound microscope are indeed the elementary granules observed under the electron microscope (Bloch et al., 1966). One important question relates to the regulation and mechanism of synthesis and release of neurosecretion in insect cells and the following discussion will also pertain to aspects of corpora cardiaca physiology as well as to the brain hormone.

The primary stimuli for the synthesis and/or release of the neurosecretory substances are environmental (photoperiod, temperature change, nutrition, pressure, etc.), and it is reasonable to accept the fact that they stimulate sensory neurons which then pass information to the central nervous system where integration and action take place. Once the active material is synthesized and packaged, however, how does it find its way to the target tissue? For the brain hormone, it is generally assumed that the humoral factor passes via neurosecretory axons to the corpora cardi-

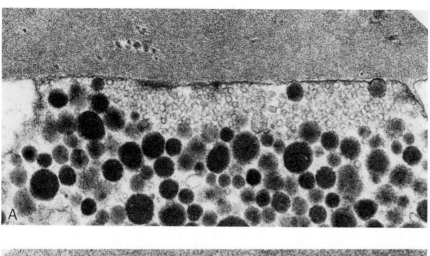

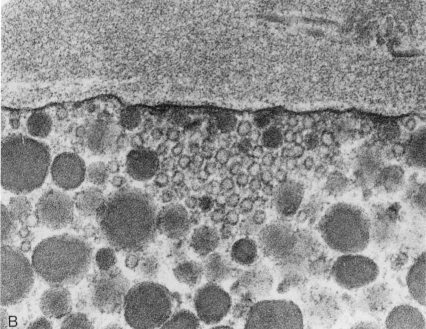

Fig. 1. Sites of release of neurosecretory substance facing extracellular stroma in corpus cardiacum of adult female *L. maderae.* Note A-type dark neurosecretory granules, small "clear" and few dense-core vesicles pressing against axolemma. (A) × 43,700 (B) × 66,600. From Scharrer (1968).

aca where it may be altered and then is released into the hemolymph. However, there is accumulating evidence that other neurosecretory cells may pass their contents directly to target tissues innervated by these cells (e.g., Johnson and Bowers, 1963) and through specialized channels (e.g., Whitten, 1964).

If indeed neurosecretory material is released into the general circulation, and experimental evidence suggests that it is (Kater, 1968; Normann and Duve, 1969), how does it escape the confines of the nervous system? Recent studies with the electron microscope suggest several mechanisms of discharge (Scharrer and Weitzman, 1970; Maddrell, 1970). For example, it appears that the substance is discharged at specialized areas of the axon (synaptoids) not restricted to axon termination (Schrarrer, 1968) (Fig. 1). It is of interest that these areas of release appear to be formed on demand when the cell is induced to secrete its hormone (Scharrer and Kater, 1969). In some insects, the membrane surrounding the neurosecretory granule may fuse with the axolemma and the contents extrude (exocytosis) into the extracellular space through stroma channels (Normann, 1965, 1969; Smith and Smith, 1966; Smith, 1970). This mechanism of release is consistent with current theories of release of transmitter substances at the neuromuscular junction and at synapses in the central nervous system. If exocytosis is the primary mechanism, one would have to conclude that the synaptoid areas of the axon are a *result* of exocytosis and represent vesicles made up of excess membrane which in turn resulted from the fusion of neurosecretory granule membrane and axolemma (Normann, 1969). As pointed out by Maddrell (1970) and by Scharrer and Weitzman (1970), however, exocytosis has been seen only in a few insects (perhaps due to fixation problems; see H. Schooneveld, discussion in Maddrell, 1970) and no *general* conclusions can be reached regarding the release of neurosecretion in insects.

Although cytological studies have generally supported the concept that brain neurosecretory material is released during the first several days of the molting cycle, presumably to ultimately stimulate the prothoracic glands, more recent studies suggest roles for these cells in addition to prothoracic gland activation. In *Rhodnius,* for example, some neurosecretory cells exhibit activity at the time of ecdysis as well, perhaps due to bursicon release, and may synchronize pre-ecdysial behavior, vesicle involution, dermal gland secretion, etc. (e.g., Steel and Harmsen, 1971). It is also possible that a brain hormone is released that has coordinating functions in the contraction of the last instar fly larva to form the barrel-shaped puparium as well as in the subsequent tanning of the puparium (Zdarek and Fraenkel, 1969).

B. CORPORA CARDIACA

Earlier experiments have demonstrated that the corpora cardiaca act as neurohemal organs receiving the brain hormone (or brain hormone precursor) (Gilbert, 1964). Most of the work in recent years has been devoted to studying the micromorphology of these structures and their function in regulating physiological events other than those concerned with the molting process.

In discussing their cytology, it should be recognized that profound species differences exist and that there is no single generalized corpus cardiacum. In addition to receiving neurosecretory axons from the brain, the corpus cardiacum contains parenchymal secretory cells resembling neurons in their properties and glia-like interstitial cells in *Leucophaea* (Scharrer, 1963). As seen by Unnithan *et al.* (1971), the parenchymal cells of *Oncopeltus* are of two types arranged in clusters and in some cases surrounded by interstitial cell cytoplasm. The processes of the parenchymal cells run interiorly and form a plexus close to the aorta and corpus allatum. One type of parenchymal cell contains granules of a mean diameter of 2000 Å while the second contains granules of slightly smaller size (1500 Å mean diameter). In this insect, the corpus cardiacum has intrinsic secretory cells, but neurons from the brain traverse the structure rather than terminating in it so that the corpus cardiacum cannot be considered to be a neurohemal organ in the usual sense (see, also, Normann, 1965). Ultrastructural analyses of the corpora cardiaca of *Leucophaea* (Scharrer, 1963), *Calliphora* (Normann, 1965), and *Carausius* (Smith and Smith, 1966) all indicate the presence of intrinsic neurosecretory cells and suggest that this structure is the site of release of intrinsic and extrinsic neurosecretion.

C. CORPORA ALLATA

From a historical point of view, one might say that the field of insect endocrinology was founded in 1913 when Nabert, after studying many insects of several orders, stated that the corpora allata were glandular and exhibited periodic internal secretions. In 1918, on the basis of a thorough histological investigation of several species of Lepidoptera, Ito (1918) concluded that the corpora allata were indeed organs of internal secretion, and that they functioned actively in the adult moths. In the Lepidoptera, the corpora allata are paired globular bodies, whereas in many other orders of insects they are fused into a single median mass beneath the aorta. In the Diptera, the corpora allata contribute to the structure of the ring gland.

On the basis of surgical experiments on *Rhodnius,* Wigglesworth (1934) concluded that there was an "inhibitory factor" present in larvae during the first four instars which prevented them from molting into adults, and believed that this "inhibitory factor" was produced in small quantities in the head region. Wigglesworth's classic paper on the function of the corpus allatum in the growth of *Rhodnius* appeared in 1936. In it he showed that the corpus allatum is the source of the inhibitory hormone which prevents metamorphosis in young larvae. Fifth instar larvae with corpora allata from young larvae implanted in their abdomens molted into sixth and in some cases seventh instar larvae. Wigglesworth concluded that the character of each larval instar is determined by the corpus allatum which limits the degree of differentiation toward the adult and suggested that the hormone from the corpus allatum be named the juvenile hormone (JH).

In recent years there have been several studies on the ultrastructure of the corpora allata (Waku and Gilbert, 1964; Scharrer, 1964; Thomsen and Thomsen, 1970; Tombes and Smith, 1970; Odhiambo, 1966 ; King *et al.,* 1966; Joly *et al.,* 1968). In general, when the corpora allata are examined at any active stage, the cells composing the glands are what one would expect of cells engaged in active synthesis. In the Cecropia silkmoth, for example, the pupal corpora allata are inactive while the male adult glands are secreting copious quantities of JH (Gilbert and Schneiderman, 1961). The micromorphological study of the glands of this insect by Waku and Gilbert revealed that almost every cell organelle studied exhibited morphological alterations during the pupal–adult transformation and, in general, was more highly structured in the adult glands. For example, mitochondria in the young adult cells show not only a remarkable increase in number from the pupal glands, but also contain many closely packed cristae in a highly electron-dense matrix.

The cell boundaries or plasma membranes of the cells of the corpora allata are characterized by their complicated outlines replete with countless processes and invaginations, resulting in compartmentalization of the peripheral cytoplasm. A thick basement membrane not only covers the entire corpus allatum, but penetrates deeply into the space between adjacent cells, especially in the case of the pupa. Scharrer (1964) emphasized the change in the cell boundaries during the course of activation of the corpus allatum in *Leucophaea.* She found that the cell boundaries in the inactive gland were very much folded and interdigitated but those in the active gland were straightened as a result of cytoplasmic proliferation.

Since the corpora cardiaca contain many neurosecretory neurons (that most likely originate in the brain) and communicate directly with the corpora allata, it is not surprising that the corpora allata contain many neurosecretory nerve fibers. Since some of these neurosecretory axons penetrate deeply between the cells of the corpora allata and have intimate contact with these cells by virtue of the loss of covering sheaths, these axons may well regulate the release of JH.

Of special interest was Scharrer's (1971) observation that structured bodies originate in the Golgi, then aggregate in the cytoplasm of corpora allata cells, and are then released into the extracellular compartment where they may enter the hemolymph. This material may be analogous to the electron-dense bodies in the active Cecropia corpora allata (Waku and Gilbert, 1964) and are possibly carriers of the cell's active secretion (i.e., JH). Studies on the corpora allata of the fly *C. erythrocephala* by Thomsen and Thomsen (1970) reveal the presence of many lipid droplets in the active gland. They suggest as a working hypothesis that the lipoidal JH (see Section V, B) or its precursor is synthesized in the tubules of the agranular endoplasmic reticulum and collected in membrane-bound vacuoles. Disintegration of the vacuolar membranes causes release of the contents into the cytoplasm where it appears as lipid droplets. The droplets may then be liberated into the hemolymph via the surface of the gland or through the intercellular channels postulated by Scharrer (1964). Although at first glance this hypothesis is very attractive because of the lipoidal nature of JH, similar lipid droplets were not observed in the very active glands of the adult male Cecropia moth (Waku and Gilbert, 1964), and the association of JH with hemolymph lipoprotein (Section VI, A, 3) suggests that JH may be released from the corpora allata as a lipoprotein conjugate and would therefore not be seen as lipid droplets in the corpora allata. In general then, ultrastructural examination of the corpora allata has given us some important information, but the secretory product of these glands has yet to be unequivocally identified under the electron microscope.

D. PROTHORACIC GLANDS

In a detailed embryological study of the commercial silkworm, Toyama (1902) identified the prothoracic glands as epithelial invaginations of the labial segment of the head. He described them as being composed of loosely connected lobulated cells of great size, extending from the head into the thorax, and suggested that they might be glandular in nature. Ke (1930) studied these organs in several lepidopteran larvae and named them the prothoracic glands (see, also, Lee, 1948). Glands with a similar function and location in the body have been described in the Orthoptera

(Scharrer, 1948; Bodenstein, 1953), Hymenoptera (Williams, 1948), Odonata (Cazal, 1947, 1948), Hemiptera (Wigglesworth, 1952), Coleoptera (Stellwag-Kittler, 1954), Mecoptera (Sellier, 1951), and in the Diptera, where they make up part of the ring gland (Possompès, 1949a,b). In some orders they are called thoracic or peritracheal glands (Pflugfelder, 1958). Extirpation of the prothoracic glands is very difficult owing to their diffuse nature, except in the cockroach where they form a compact mass (Chadwick, 1956).

Hachlow (1931) presented the first evidence that there was an organ located in the thorax of insects which was essential for development. By the use of ligation and surgical techniques, he showed that if the pupal thorax was removed from other segments of the body, those segments did not initiate adult development. These results were later confirmed by Bodenstein (1938). However, it was the classic experiments of Fukuda (1940a,b, 1941, 1944) which were to reveal the function of the prothoracic glands. In a series of ingenious ligation experiments on the larvae of *Bombyx mori,* Fukuda found that only the region of the body which contained prothoracic glands could pupate. He further demonstrated that a compartment without prothoracic glands would pupate if active prothoracic glands were implanted into it. Fukuda concluded that at a critical period after feeding the prothoracic glands secreted a principle into the blood which induced pupation. Following this, Piepho (1942) suggested that, since the brain and the prothoracic glands were both needed in the molting of Lepidoptera, perhaps the brain–prothoracic gland relationship was similar to that of the pituitary and thyroid of vertebrates. Williams (1946, 1947, 1948, 1951, 1952a,b), in a series of important experiments on pupae of *H. cecropia,* found that implantation of one or several chilled brains into an isolated pupal abdomen which contains no prothoracic glands had no effect, but that implantation into an isolated pupal abdomen of a chilled brain along with several pairs of prothoracic glands caused the abdomen to molt. Thus, Williams demonstrated that the prothoracic glands when stimulated by brain hormone secrete a substance essential for molting.

Although we have generally accepted the postulate that the brain hormone activates the prothoracic glands to secrete the molting hormone (MH), the possibility now exists that the prothoracic glands may not be the source of MH (Section IV). Nevertheless, they appear essential for the molting process and for descriptive purposes will be discussed here (see Herman, 1967, for a detailed survey).

Light microscopical examination of the glands of the Cecropia silk-

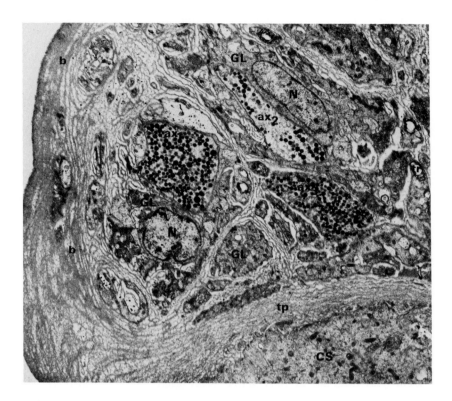

Fig. 2. Neurosecretory fibers associated with the prothoracic glands of *B. mori.* CS, secretory cell; tp, tunica propria; tr, tracheole; ax, axons; GL, glial cell; b, basal membrane; N, nucleus. × 5200. From Beaulaton (1968).

moth (Herman and Gilbert, 1966) revealed the presence of about 250 large cells with polymorphic nuclei in each of the paired glands. These cells vary in size from 47 × 22 μm in a fourth instar larva to about double that size in a young pharate adult. It appears that the glands are innervated by neurons containing neurosecretory droplets as is also the case with *Leucophaea* (Scharrer, 1964), *Calliphora* (Normann, 1965), *Tenebrio* (Romer, 1971a), *Antheraea,* and *Bombyx* (Beaulaton, 1968) (Fig. 2). Not only are the glands linked with the prothoracic ganglia and interganglionic connectives, but also with the subesophageal ganglion (Hintze-Podufal, 1970). Prior to and after each period of apparent secretory activity, the cells are smaller and contain relatively regular nuclei, small nucleoli, little cytoplasm, and few, if any, vacuoles. Initial secretory activity the appearance by nuclear and nucleolar volume increases that precede the appearance of nuclear vacuoles and enhanced nuclear irregularity. An increase in cytoplasmic volume and vacuolation then occurs concomitantly with a decrease in nuclear vacuolation. Cells at the height of their secretory activity are characterized by maximal cytoplasmic vacuolation, nuclear irregularity, and vacuolation of the striated border. Subsequently, glandular activity progressively diminishes. Maximal gland activity in Cecropia occurs prior to and during the first visible signs of epidermis retraction in each stage, and thus correlates well with the widely accepted role of ecdysone in causing apolysis and secretion of a new cuticle.

As pointed out previously (Herman and Gilbert, 1966; Herman, 1967), two distinct groups of insects can be recognized in regard to the type of prothoracic gland. Cecropia is in the first group, having glands composed of relatively few, but typically large, polyploid cells in various regions of the thorax. In Orthoptera and several other groups, the glands are typically compact organs located in the head (see Herman and Gilbert, 1966, for discussion of the misnomer "prothoracic glands"). Other insects (e.g., termites) appear to be intermediate and have glands with both cephalic and thoracic regions.

E. Oenocytes

Oenocytes undergo cyclical activity coordinated with molting in the Cecropia larva and pupa and have glandular homologues in all holometabolous insects (Harmsen and Beckel, 1960). Although it has been suggested that oenocytes can synthesize MH (Locke, 1969; Romer, 1971b; Weir, 1970), there is no conclusive evidence for this assumption (see Section IV, E).

III. Endocrine Gland Interactions

Although this section on endocrine gland interaction will attempt to delineate our present knowledge of endocrine gland control, by necessity some of the effects of hormones will also be discussed here. For example, when we consider activation of the prothoracic glands, we are in fact dealing with the action of the brain hormone, juvenile hormone (JH), and molting hormone (MH). Therefore, these data will not be included in Section VI on the action of insect hormones. Except for some well-established dogmas, the area of endocrine gland interactions is probably in the most confused state of any area of insect endocrinology. This is due in part to obvious species differences which make generalizations difficult and to the still unsettled question regarding the cytological parameters defining an active or inactive gland (e.g., Joly, 1967; Lea and Thomsen, 1969). A further complication is that the insect endocrine glands appear to undergo a circadian rhythm of activity. For example, in *Drosophila* larvae, the nuclei of the neurosecretory cells of the brain and the nuclei of cells constituting the corpora allata and prothoracic glands show a bimodal pattern in diameter size during 24 hours with maxima occurring 3 hours before dawn and dark (Rensing *et al.*, 1965; see, also, Dutkowski *et al.*, 1971). From this, the obvious conclusion is that in order to precisely correlate developmental or biochemical events with cytological parameters of the endocrine gland, one should conduct all experiments at the same time of day. The possibility of monthly and annual cycles of activity cannot be ruled out in long-lived insects. Many of the studies regarding control of the corpora allata during oogenesis have been recently summarized (Engelmann, 1971) and are discussed in Chapter 3 of this volume.

A. BRAIN ACTIVATION

Although we think of a brain hormone that initiates the complex series of events culminating in the molt, it should be kept in mind that there are probably several brain hormones (e.g., eclosion hormone, Section VI, C) and that these too may originate in neurosecretory cells located in the pars intercerebralis. It is therefore quite possible that some investigators have cytologically staged the phase of activity of a group of neurosecretory cells and inadvertently measured an unrelated physiological parameter.

The previous review (Gilbert, 1964) discussed the role of environmental and nutritional factors in inducing brain competence via sensory receptors such as the eyes, and proprioceptors such as those in the abdomen of *Rhodnius*. There are likely a myriad of factors that can activate the brain both by nervous and humoral means. In *Galleria* larvae, for example, crowded or restricted animals have a delay in pupation, and a variety of studies suggest that mechanoreceptors act via the nervous system to inhibit brain neuroendocrine activity (Edwards, 1966; Sehnal and Edwards, 1969; Woolever and Pipa, 1970; Pipa, 1971). New evidence suggests that injury can activate the brain. When last instar *Galleria* larvae are injured less than 1 day after the larval molt, an additional larval molt is induced (Krishnakumaran, 1972). However, injury later in the instar only delays the ensuing pupal molt. In a series of implantation and extirpation maneuvers involving the brain, Krishnakumaran showed that brains from injured larvae had prothoracotropic activity and elicited a supernumerary larval molt even when the host was at a stage having no detectable amounts of JH. Although the author suggests that the isolated, implanted brain is therefore capable of turning on the host's corpora allata, it may be that the brain activates the prothoracic glands which in turn stimulate the corpora allata to produce JH (see Section III, D).

An example of humoral control of brain neurosecretory cell activity is the study by Lea and Thomsen (1969), who measured the activity (changes in nuclear and nucleolar volume) of the median neurosecretory cells of *Calliphora* adults during sugar and meat feeding. Their data from allatectomy and implantation experiments reveal that neurosecretory cell activity (synthesis of neurosecretory granules) is controlled by a hormone from the corpora allata. The effects do not appear to be indirectly mediated via the ovaries or nutritional state and, as the authors point out, other processes claimed to be controlled by the corpora allata on the basis of surgical manipulations may, in fact, be directly controlled by a brain hormone and only indirectly regulated by the corpora allata. Support for this assumption comes from the studies of K. B. Davey (personal communication) who showed that injection of JH into *Rhodnius* turns on brain neurosecretory cells (see, also, Herman and Gilbert, 1966).

In regard to neurosecretion, there is increasing evidence that neurosecretory material is transported to target tissues in a closed system rather than being transported in the hemolymph. In *Periplaneta americana,* for example, electron microscopic observation and physiological studies reveal that nerves from the corpora cardiaca carry neurosecretory material (heart accelerating factor) directly to the aorta (Johnson and Bowers, 1963). In *Rhodnius* a similar phenomenon has been reported where abdominal nerves appear to carry neurosecretory material to the epidermis suggesting localized endocrine control of the epidermis (Maddrell, 1965). Whitten's (1964) morphological study of several flies presents an alternative to both hemolymph-borne secretion and neuronal transport in that she presents cogent circumstantial evidence for the direct transport of secretory products from the cells of origin to target cells by way of channels in the continuous connective tissue membranes. The basement membranes under this view are intimately concerned with intercellular transport of cellular secretory products. Notwithstanding the above, the fact that implanted brains and other endocrine glands are hormonally effective still leaves a major role for the hemolymph in hormone transport (see also Section VI, A). However, if some factors are transported via nerves and connective tissue, are they still hormones according to the classical definition?

B. Prothoracic Gland Activation

The classical experiments in insect endocrinology established that, with some exceptions, removal of the prothoracic glands prevented molting while implantation of active prothoracic glands elicited molting (Gilbert, 1964). Although they have long been considered the sole source of MH, their exact role in ecdysone production is open to question at this time (Section IV, E). Temporal correlations between the periodic activity of the brain and prothoracic glands have now been made in many insects of diverse orders. The cytological studies discussed previously suggesting innervation of the prothoracic glands by ordinary neurons and neurosecretory neurons (e.g., Srivastava and Singh, 1968) indicate some nervous and localized hormonal control as well. It may be that regulation of the prothoracic glands in the normal insect is at least in part mediated by nervous impulses or by local regulation at the neuroendocrine level. The nervous system may act as a sensor and nerves may inhibit the prothoracic glands when MH has reached a critical level. This would imply that activation is by humoral means and that the turning off of the glands is by inhibiting impulses from the central nervous system. This is in accord with the observations of Possompès (1953) that the prothoracic glands only function *normally* when nervous connections are intact. Further, there is some suggestive evidence that the brain (lateral group of neurosecretory cells of the protocerebrum) of locusts may also produce a hormone that inhibits the activity of the prothoracic glands (Carlisle and Ellis, 1968).

It is well known from cytological studies that active prothoracic glands display a cytoplasmic countenance indicative of increased RNA synthesis. This has been confirmed by autoradiographic analysis of [^{3}H]uridine incorporation into the RNA of cells comprising the prothoracic glands of several saturniid silkworms (Oberlander et al., 1965). It was shown that the highest level of incorporation occurred in larval glands, while in the diapausing pupa RNA synthesis is essentially absent. When brain hormone is secreted to initiate adult development, RNA synthesis again increases in the prothoracic glands as would be expected. To demonstrate that the brain hormone acts directly on the prothoracic glands, active brains were incubated *in vitro* with inactive prothoracic glands and RNA synthesis in the cells of the prothoracic glands was shown to be stimulated while control ganglia were ineffective. Using gallocyanin coloration and cytophotometry, Gersh and Stürzebecher (1970) demonstrated that cockroach prothoracic glands respond to an active brain of a lepidopteran as well as to cockroach brain and corpora cardiaca extracts by increased rates of RNA synthesis. This not only confirms the idea that RNA synthesis is indicative of prothoracic gland activation, but that the brain hormone acts between insect orders. However, little is really known at the biochemical level about the action of the brain hormone and, as pointed out in the 1964 review, we have essentially no knowledge of how the prothoracic glands are turned off (however, see Section III, D).

C. REGULATION OF THE CORPORA ALLATA

Our discussion of the micromorphology of the corpora allata [the source of JH (see Section V, E)] revealed the presence of ordinary neurons and neurosecretory neurons (see, also, Odhiambo, 1966c) in the corpora allata that had originated in the brain. Electrocoagulation of the C cells of the pars intercerebralis of *L. migratoria* causes a cessation of activity in the corpora allata (Joly *et al.*, 1968). This implies both nervous and local humoral regulation of the corpora allata, although there have been several reports in the literature where implanted glands resting free in the hemocoel undergo cyclical variations in activity, sometimes behaving as if they were in their normal positions.

Much of the data accumulated on corpora allata regulation is derived from studies on adult insects where egg maturation is JH-dependent (see Chapter 3 of this volume). In general, however, in those adults it appears that the corpora allata are activated by the nutritional state of the hemolymph which in turn may be regulated by brain hormone or JH. Other factors such as mating or parturition can also result in active corpora allata by acting via the central nervous system. In addition, in some viviparous cockroaches the brood sac apparently releases a humoral agent which influences neurons in the central nerve cord and brain; the brain then apparently inhibits the corpora allata by nervous means (Engelmann, 1965).

A novel idea has been advanced by Joly *et al.* (1969) who studied the effects of implanting corpora allata from various stages of the locust on the host's corpora allata as well as the implant at the ultrastructural level. They found that active corpora allata of young female adults become inactive when implanted into old larvae that normally have inactive glands, while the implantation of inactive corpora allata into a locust having active glands appears to activate the implanted corpora allata. Since specific neurosecretory cells in the pars intercerebralis of the locust had been shown to "inhibit" the action of the corpora allata, these French workers also examined the ultrastructure of the corpora allata of young adults whose neurosecretory cells had been destroyed at the beginning of the last larval instar. The corpora allata of these animals were not active, as judged by ultrastructural criteria, so that the brain neurosecretory cells were probably not directly inhibiting the corpora allata by nervous means. They conclude from this circumstantial evidence that the secretion of the neurosecretory cells of the pars intercerebralis acts by inactivating *circulating* JH rather than by inhibiting the corpora allata. This implies that brain hormone in these insects can induce the synthesis of enzymes which break down JH or perhaps modify the target tissues so that they are refractory to circulating JH (see, however, Section VI, D). It is obvious that this work must be extended to the biochemical level and to other insect species since the hypothesis has wide ramifications for our views of endocrine gland interactions.

The nature of the signals that cause the brain to stimulate the corpora allata in young insects is probably environmental (photoperiod, temperature, humidity, etc.). The evidence for this is largely indirect, as for example the research on the effects of ocellar cauterization on the cytological appearance of the corpora allata of cockroaches (Brousse-Gaury, 1970). When one ocellus is destroyed, the distribution of neurosecretory material in the corpus cardiacum is altered, followed by definitive histological changes in the corpora allata. This finding suggests that the corpora allata may be controlled by neurosecretory cells of the brain which are in turn regulated by nervous impulses generated from the ocellus.

D. Corpora Allata–Prothoracic Gland Interactions

1. Stimulation

In 1959, three laboratories almost simultaneously presented data indicating that material from the corpora allata was capable of simulating the prothoracic glands. Implantation of corpora allata into *Philosamia cynthia ricini* pupae debrained for at least 2 months caused these pupae to develop (Ichikawa and Nishiitsutsuji-Uwo, 1959). When the donor was a larva or adult, the brainless pupa molted into a pupal–adult intermediate, which would indicate the presence of juvenile hormone. Implantation of pupal corpora allata caused the host pupae to molt into normal adults, presumably owing to the absence of JH and to the presence of a prothoracic gland activator. They interpret their results as revealing that the corpora allata can store brain hormone, accounting for the prothoracic gland stimulation, and also produce JH in the larval and adult stages. Similar results were obtained by Williams (1959), using brainless, diapausing saturniids as hosts for implanted adult *H. cecropia* corpora allata. He found that these implanted corpora allata induced development in brainless pupae but not in isolated abdomens devoid of prothoracic glands. Williams (1961) emphasized that the pupal corpora allata are without trophic activity, in contrast to the report of the Japanese workers. He suggested that the adult corpora allata are secreting a trophic factor which may or may not be identical with JH also secreted at this stage. Thus, one view indicates storage of brain hormone by the corpora allata, and the other that the corpora allata secrete a substance which mimics brain hormone.

Using JH extracts prepared from adults of *H. cecropia* or *Samia cynthia* (see Section V), Gilbert and Schneiderman (1959) obtained results consistent with those of Williams (1961). They found that pupae receiving large injections of crude extract molted very promptly into pupal–adult intermediates. Thus, results of more than 800 injections disclosed that pupae receiving more than 50 mg of ether extracts of JH molted into second pupae or pupalike intermediates within 10–15 days after being placed at 25°C. This precocious molting suggested that JH (or some other constituent of the extract) hastened the molt. Injection of like amounts into diapausing pupae gave similar results. In all cases, the ether extracts terminated pupal diapause. Because this effect could have been due to stimulation of the brain, a series of experiments were conducted on brainless diapausing pupae. Again molting occurred, which indicated that these extracts stimulated the prothoracic glands. The possibility still existed that these extracts contained ecdysone and that this reacted directly with the pupal tissues to initiate development. This possibility was tested by injecting a large series of isolated pupal abdomens of *S. cynthia* and *A. polyphemus* with 80–300 mg of ether extract. However, none of these preparations ever initiated development, although many survived as long as 4 months.

The possibility existed at that time that the JH extracts were contaminated with brain hormone, but it has since been established that pure JH does, in fact, stimulate molting in debrained diapausing pupae as do a host of synthetic mimics of JH (Meyer, 1971). The fact that active corpora allata as well as JH and several JH mimics can break diapause at other stages in the life cycle (de Wilde and de Boer, 1961; Bowers and Blickenstaff, 1966) supports the previous data on the prothoracotropic action of JH.

To further investigate the interaction between prothoracic gland and corpora allata, a series of experiments was conducted on saturniid pupae whereby the corpora allata and prothoracic glands were analyzed autoradiographically for nuclear RNA synthesis after being exposed *in vivo* to quantities of pure β-ecdysone (MH) and pure Cecropia JH (Siew and Gilbert, 1971). The results of these experiments revealed that the injection of β-ecdysone into nondeveloping pupae had a profound stimulatory effect on the animal's prothoracic glands within 3 hours after injection and is consistent with the surgical data suggesting a positive feedback relationship between MH and the prothoracic gland (Gilbert, 1964). In addition, the corpora allata were also activated by β-ecdysone injection, but the peak of activity lagged the prothoracic gland peak. Since these experiments were conducted *in vivo,* it is possible that β-ecdysone activated the corpora allata indirectly, perhaps via the secretion of some other product from the prothoracic glands or from some other tissue. With the injection of JH into Cynthia pupae, Siew and Gilbert (1971) found that the corpora allata are activated after 12 hours and that the prothoracic glands reach maximum activity after 24 hours (Fig. 3). Thus, as in the case of β-ecdysone, injection of JH stimulates both corpora allata and prothoracic glands, but in reverse chronology.

JH cannot be acting on the corpora allata indirectly via the prothoracic glands since the corpora allata are activated prior to the prothoracic glands, but they may be activated indirectly through another organ system. Support for positive feedback between corpora allata and JH comes from the previously discussed work of Joly *et al.* (1969) who showed that inactive corpora allata of the locust appear to be activated when

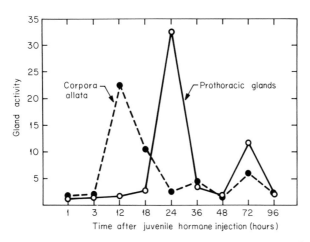

Fig. 3. Juvenile hormone stimulation of the corpora allata and prothoracic glands of *P. cynthia* pupae. Gland activity is a measure of [^{3}H]uridine incorporation into nuclear RNA. From Siew and Gilbert (1971).

transplanted into a locust having active glands. It is of interest to note that the activity of the corpora allata and prothoracic glands elicited by JH injection is more than double that brought about by β-ecdysone injection. The data from these experiments corroborate previous reports that MH can activate prothoracic glands and that JH has prothoraco-tropic activity.

Although the experiments described above demonstrated stimulation of corpora allata and prothoracic glands by the hormones, the question remains as to how the glands are turned off. Female *H. cecropia* pupae on the verge of initiating adult development were injected with β-ecdysone, and the incorporation of [^{3}H]uridine into the nuclear RNA of the prothoracic glands was analyzed. The results of this study showed that although the glands were only moderately active at this initial stage of adult development, this activity began to decrease within 6–12 hours after β-ecdysone injection and the glands were essentially inactive in respect to nuclear RNA synthesis at 18 hours. This experiment suggests that the prothoracic glands activated by normal means (brain hormone) may be turned off by exogenous hormone (i.e., negative feedback).

What then causes the corpora allata and prothoracic glands to become inactive? The above results do not answer this question, although they indicate that the titer of hormone in the hemolymph may be important. On the other hand, it is possible that the glands become exhausted of substrate for hormone (or prohormone) synthesis or that the nervous system "measures" the titer of hormone and inhibits secretion via nerves to the corpora allata and prothoracic glands as discussed previously, or itself triggers the release of chemicals that inhibit endocrine gland activity.

It should be noted that the experiments conducted by Siew and Gilbert were on intact pupae. Since JH is capable of turning on brain neurosecretory cells, the possibility exists that JH and/or MH stimulates the corpora allata and prothoracic glands indirectly via the brain. It has been suggested that MH stimulation of the prothoracic glands ensures that both glands secrete at the same time during the life of the insect and this may be true of JH stimulation of the paired corpora allata as well. JH activation of the prothoracic glands may be the normal means by which insect larvae maintain a critical titer of MH so that tissue growth can occur during all of larval life (Schneiderman and Gilbert, 1964).

2. Prothoracic Gland Maintenance and Degeneration

One reason that adult insects do not molt is that their prothoracic glands degenerate early in adult life. Although it was first believed that they degenerated much earlier in saturniid pharate adults (during the first week of pupal–adult development), we now know that they are in fact present until adult ecdysis (Herman and Gilbert, 1966; Oberlander *et al.*, 1965). Several series of experiments have revealed that the absence of JH is a contributing factor to the breakdown of the prothoracic glands and that they can be maintained in good condition if exogenous JH is applied (Gilbert, 1964). According to Wigglesworth (1955), another humoral factor is released at the adult molt which actively elicits the degeneration process, but this only takes place if the molt has occurred in the absence of JH. It is unlikely that degeneration is a result of signals from the nervous system, since new transplanted prothoracic glands degenerate on schedule (Oberlander *et al.*, 1965; Ozeki, 1968). There have been no reports on the nature of the humoral substance that stimulates prothoracic gland degeneration. Since JH prevents prothoracic gland degeneration as it does the breakdown of other organs and tissues in young insects, the prothoracic glands can be considered to be another larval structure programmed for destruction at the final metamorphic molt in most insects.

IV. The Molting Hormone—Chemistry and Metabolism

A. OCCURRENCE

Since Butenandt and Karlson's initial isolation of the molting hormones α- and β-ecdysone from an insect in 1954 and accomplishment of the complete structure elucidation in 1965 (Huber and Hoppe, 1965), progress in the field of ecdysone chemistry has been extremely rapid. This progress has been made possible through the development of advanced spectroscopic and chromatographic methods, and by the discovery of relatively large amounts of ecdysones in certain plants. Since ecdysone chemistry has been the subject of several recent and very comprehensive reviews (Horn, 1971; Hikino and Hikino, 1970), we will present only a brief account of developments in ecdysone chemistry since 1964, stressing those aspects most pertinent for insect physiologists. The word "ecdysone," although often used to refer specifically to α-ecdysone, will be used generically to refer to steroidal compounds which generally show activity in insect-molting hormone bioassay systems; specific ecdysones will be so designated.

Although ecdysone activity has been demonstrated in extracts of a number of insects and crustaceans, specific ecdysones have been extracted and unequivocally identified in only a few species of higher insects (Table I) and decapod crustaceans [*Jasus* (Horn *et al.*, 1966); *Callinectes* (Faux *et al.*, 1969); *Cancer* (D. King, unpublished information)].

TABLE I

OCCURRENCE OF ECDYSONES IN INSECTS

Species	Stage	Ecdysones	Yield (μg/kg)	References
Bombyx mori	Pupa	α	10–50	Butenandt and Karlson (1954) Karlson *et al.* (1963) Hocks and Wiechert (1966)
		β^a	2–10	Karlson (1956a,b) Hocks and Wiechert (1966) Hoffmeister and Grützmacher (1966)
Dociostaurus maroccanus	Adult female	α, β	—	Karlson and Stamm-Menéndez (1956)
	Adult	α	1100	Stamm (1959)
		β	1300	
Manduca sexta	Pupa, prepupa^b	α	400	Kaplanis *et al.* (1966)
		β	500	
		26-Hydroxy-β^c	75	Thompson *et al.* (1967)
Antheraea pernyi	Pupa	α	$<<6$	Horn *et al.* (1966)
		β	6	
Calliphora vicina (= *erythrocephala*)	Pupa	2-Deoxy-β	—	Chong *et al.* (1970)
		α, β^d	—	Karlson (1956a,b)
Calliphora stygia	Pupa, prepupa	β^e	100	Galbraith *et al.* (1969b)
Schistocerca gregaria	Nymph feces	α	200	Hoffmeister *et al.* (1965)
	Fifth instar nymph	β^f	12–240 ng/nymph	Morgan and Woodbridge (1971)

^{a} Existence of 3 additional ecdysones in this species indicated by CCD studies (Burdette and Bullock, 1963).

^{b} D. King (unpublished information); quantities not determined.

^{c} An additional, slightly less polar ecdysone was also isolated, but has not yet been identified.

^{d} α-Ecdysone not detected in this species by Galbraith *et al.* (1969b).

^{e} No α, 2-deoxy-β, or more polar ecdysones detected.

^{f} No α-ecdysone detected.

The existence in a single species of several closely related hormone molecules, ostensibly serving the same function, is a complex problem (see Section VI). It is of interest to note that α-ecdysone, the first ecdysone to be isolated and identified, and still widely referred to as the molting hormone of insects, does not appear to be as widely distributed in arthropods as β-ecdysone ($20\alpha_F$-hydroxy-α-ecdysone, crustecdysone, ecdysterone). Indeed, in view of the occurrence and action of β-ecdysone in every arthropod species examined (e.g., Krishnakumaran and Schneiderman, 1970), it is tempting to speculate that β-ecdysone is *the* molting hormone of arthropods. The possibility exists that ecdysone may also function in other protostome invertebrates, as ecdysone activity has been detected in extracts of nematodes (*Phocanema,* Rajulu et al., 1972), molluscs (*Australorbis,* Muftic, 1969; *Mytilus,* Takemoto et al., 1967), and polychaete annelids (*Nereis,* D. King and P. Schroeder, unpublished information).

Study of ecdysone biology and chemistry, obviously hampered by the fact that these compounds are present in only microscopic amounts in arthropods, has been facilitated by the fortuitous discovery that ecdysones (particularly β-ecdysone) are often produced in enormous amounts by a number of higher plants. This discovery was made during the course of an investigation of the constituents of a Chinese folk medicine, *paijuchin,* which was prepared from the leaves of a yew (*Podocarpus nakaii*) and reputedly possessed antitumor activity. The structure of the principal constituent (1.6 gm/kg crude drug) was found to be 25-deoxy-β-ecdysone (ponasterone A, Nakanishi *et al.,* 1966). Following this discovery, and the independent finding by Takemoto *et al.,* (1966) of β-ecdysone together with a positional isomer, inokosterone, in another oriental (diuretic) folk drug (derived from the roots of *Achyranthes fauriei),* a large number of plants have been investigated by laboratories all over the world, and many were found to contain ecdysones. The structures of over 40 related phytoecdysones have been elucidated (Horn, 1971) and almost all are biologically active in insects. It is of interest that several (3–6) phytoecdysones generally exist together in the same plant, often in high concentrations (up to 1% of the dry weight), and most often appear to be distributed throughout the entire plant. Notable among the surveys for ecdysone activity in plants is the screening study of Imai *et al.* (1969) of 1056 Japanese plant species belonging to over 180 families, and 350 crude drugs. Activity was found in 54 species, mainly pteridophytes, gymnosperms, and perennial angiosperms, but there appeared to be no correlation of phytoecdysone distribution with any phylogenetic or taxonomic scheme. This study utilized a new ecdysone bioassay involving dipping ligated last-instar larvae of the rice-stem borer (*Chilo suppressalis*) into crude methanol extracts of the plants (Sato *et al.*, 1968). The presence of substances in the crude extracts which mask the effect of ecdysone in bioassays (so-called "anti-ecdysones"), such as ajugalactone (Koreeda *et al.*, 1970), has been postulated (Nakanishi, 1971). The seasonal, geographic, and intraspecific variability of phytoecdysone occurrence has not yet been investigated. In fact, why ecdysones exist at all in plants is a perplexing problem which has yet to be answered. It is of historical interest to note that β-ecdysone was first isolated in 1933 from licorice fern rhizomes, and named polydin (Fischer and Lynn, 1933). The compound was considered to be a glucoside, as was insect-derived ecdysone when first investigated by Becker (1941), but structure elucidation was abandoned after discovering that the compound had no effect when fed to white rats.

B. CHEMISTRY

Now that the full chemical structure of α-ecdysone is known, structure elucidation of new ecdysones, such as the phytoecdysones, can usually be achieved largely through spectroscopic means with a few milligrams of pure compound. It is noteworthy that the entire original structure determination was accomplished with only 275 mg of α-ecdysone isolated from about 5 tons (fresh weight) of *Bombyx* pupae. After the elemental composition of α-ecdysone was determined, and the molecular weight, first approximated by X-ray techniques and later confirmed by mass spectrometry as well as by elemental analysis of the 5-iodo-2,4-dinitrophenylhydrazone derivative, was found to be 464, the molecular formula $C_{27}H_{44}O_6$ could be calculated. That ecdysone was a steroid was consistent with the X-ray data, the NMR spectrum, and the empirical formula. Further proof was obtained by showing that (1) Diels hydrocarbon could be generated on vigorous dehydrogenation of ecdysone [see structure (I)], and (2) α-ecdysone could be biosynthesized from choles-

(I)

terol (Karlson and Hoffmeister, 1963). The α,β-unsaturated ketone (infrared 1657 cm^{-1}; UV λ_{max} (EtOH) 242 nm; ϵ = 12,500), refractory to catalytic reduction, was found by NMR to have a single olefinic proton and was assigned a 6-oxo-7-ene position in the B ring by comparison of the spectral and chemical properties as well as color reactions with those of a number of model compounds. One of the five hydroxyl groups was assigned to C-14 on the basis of the characteristic facile dehydration of ecdysone in dilute ethanolic HCl, leading first to a 7,14-diene (A) (UV λ_{max} 293 nm; infrared 1666 cm^{-1}) and then to the more stable 8,14-diene (B) (UV λ_{max} 244 nm; infrared 1710 cm^{-1}), in which the double bond is no longer conjugated with the carbonyl group [see (II)].

α-Ecdysone   A   B

The presence of a hydroxyl at C-22 would explain the peaks at m/e 99 and 81 (99 − 18) in the mass spectrum as sidechain cleavage fragments, accompanied by the corresponding tetracycle peaks at m/e 348 (464 − 116) and 330 (348 − 18) [see (III) below].

m/e 464 m/e 99 m/e 81

A third hydroxyl was unambiguously assigned to C-25 on the basis of the NMR spectrum [signal for six protons at δ1.38 ppm (pyridine)], and a fourth to C-3 (β) by analogy with other steroids and by the apparent biosynthesis of ecdysone from cholesterol. The position of the remaining hydroxyl was not established, but since the presence of a single vicinal diol (α-glycol) was indicated by periodate oxidation studies, and since the remaining hydroxyl could not be in the sidechain or near C-14, it had to be vicinal to the 3-β-ol, and therefore either at C-2 or C-4. Thus the partial structure (IV) indicated below was proposed.

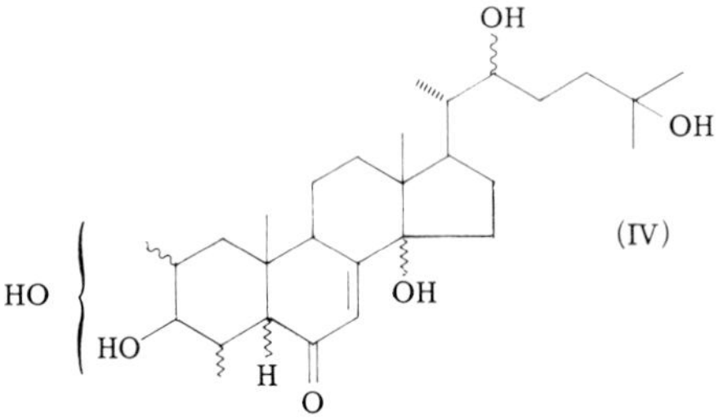

(IV)

The full structure of α-ecdysone, including the stereochemistry at all ten asymmetric centers, was finally elucidated by X-ray crystallography (Huber and Hoppe, 1965). [See (V) and (VI).]

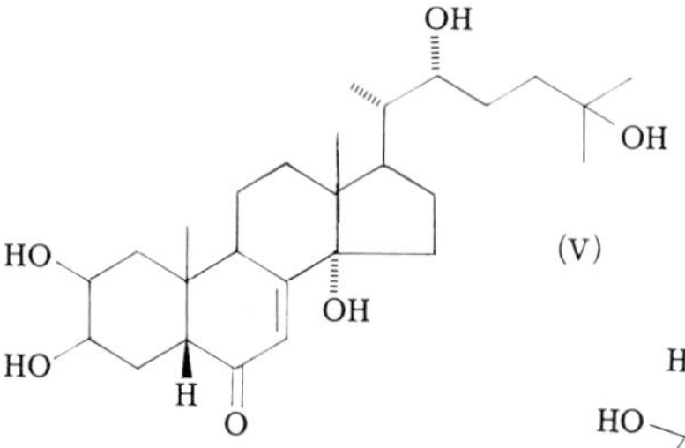

(V)

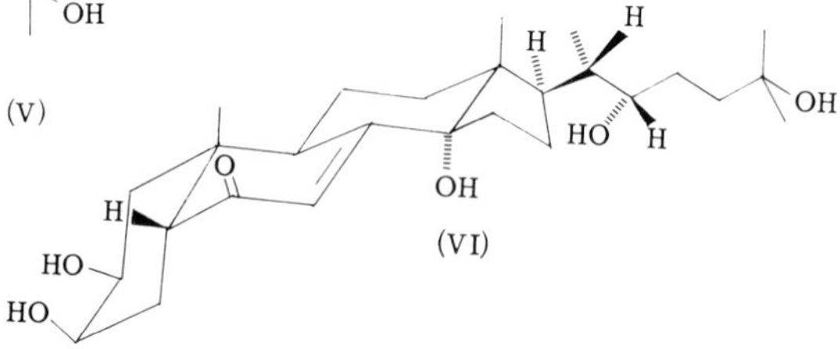

(VI)

Thus α-ecdysone is (20S)-2β,3β,14α,22R,25-pentahydroxy-5β-cholest-7-en-6-one. This structure was confirmed by two independent syntheses, published nearly simultaneously by groups at Syntex (Siddall et al., 1966) and Schering-Hoffman-LaRoche (Kerb et al., 1966). The two syntheses are rather similar, both starting with 23,24-bisnorcholenic acid derivatives readily available from stigmasterol, and proceding by attaching the sidechain after elaboration of the tetracyclic nucleus. Subsequently, both syntheses were modified (Harrison et al., 1966; Furlenmeier et al., 1967), and other syntheses were devised by Mori et al. (1968) and Barton et al. (1970). In comparison with the well-known steroid hormones of the vertebrates, the ecdysone molecule is unusual in a number of respects. Not only does it retain the complete C_{27} (cholestane) steroid carbon skeleton, but it also possesses functional groups in the B ring. The A-B ring junction is fused in the cis-(5β-H) (VII) rather than the usual trans-(5α) configuration (VIII); the cis configuration is more stable in steroids with a 2β (axial) hydroxyl because there is less steric interaction with the 19-methyl group (indicated by arrow below).

5β (A/B *cis*) (VII)   5α (A/B *trans*) (VIII)

Lastly, ecdysone has a sufficiently large number of hydroxyl groups distributed on the molecule to render it appreciably water soluble, perhaps
obviating the necessity of a carrier protein responsible for solubilizing ecdysone to enable transport in the hemolymph (see Section VI, A).

β-Ecdysone was first isolated from an insect source *(Bombyx* pupae)
by Karlson's group (Karlson, 1956a), and later from another insect (a
Moroccan locust, *Dociostaurus)* by Stamm (1959). Compared to α-ecdysone, β-ecdysone was relatively difficult to isolate and crystallize, and
was characterized solely on the bases of its melting point, UV spectrum,
and polarity in several countercurrent distribution and paper chromatographic systems as being closely related to α-ecdysone. Its chemical structure remained unknown until 1966, when it was isolated from various
sources independently in four laboratories, and determined to be identical
to α-ecdysone except possessing an extra hydroxyl group at C-20. Thus
the same compound is known by several synonyms: crustecdysone
[isolated from the Australian spiny lobster *Jasus lalandei* (Hampshire
and Horn, 1966)], 20-hydroxyecdysone [from *Bombyx mori* pupae
(Hocks and Wiechert, 1966) and *Manduca sexta* pupae (Kaplanis
et al., 1966)] and ecdysterone [also from *Bombyx* (Hoffmeister and
Grützmacher, 1966], as well as isoinokosterone [from the herb,
Achyranthes fauriei (Takemoto *et al.,* 1967)] and polypodine B [from
the fern *Polypodium vulgare* (Jizba *et al.,* 1967)]. It seems appropriate
to retain Karlson's original term, β-ecdysone, for this compound.

The structure of β-ecdysone, which is somewhat more polar than α-
ecdysone (and shows very similar UV and infrared spectra), was deduced mainly through careful interpretation of its ^1H NMR and mass
spectra (Hampshire and Horn, 1966). The mass spectrum (molecular
ion at m/e 480) indicated that β-ecdysone possessed one more hydroxyl
group than α-ecdysone. The NMR spectrum was nearly identical to that of
α-ecdysone, except that the C-21 and C-18 proton signals [δ1.25 and 0.70
ppm, respectively, in α-ecdysone (deuteropyridine)] appear shifted down

field ($\delta 1.56$ and 1.20), indicating that the additional hydroxyl is located on C-20. This assignment was supported by the mass spectrum [see (IX)], in which prominent peaks are present at m/e 99, 81 (99 − 18), and 363 (480 − 117) and 345 (363 − 18), indicating facile cleavage of the sidechain (and subsequent dehydration) without rearrangement.

The structure has been confirmed by two syntheses (Hüppi and Siddall, 1967; Kerb *et al.,* 1968).

The identity of β-ecdysone from various animal and plant sources was demonstrated by Galbraith *et al.* (1967) while the stereochemical identity of the nuclear tetracycles of α-ecdysone (synthetic) and β-ecdysone (from *Podocarpus*) was established by Siddall *et al.* (1967). The exact sterochemistry of the β-ecdysone sidechain remained unconfirmed for some time, although it seemed reasonable to assume that the configuration was 20R (20β_F-methyl, 20α_F-hydroxyl), 22R (20β_F-hydroxyl) on the basis that α-ecdysone (20β_F-methyl) is rapidly metabolized to β-ecdysone in a single step (King and Siddall, 1969), and biological hydroxylations occur with retention of configuration. Also, the synthetic 22-epimer of α-ecdysone (22-iso-α-ecdysone; 22α_F hydroxyl) is nearly devoid of biological activity (Siddall, 1970). The 20R,22R configuration of the β-ecdysone (from *Podocarpus*) sidechain has recently been confirmed by X-ray crystallography (Dammeier and Hoppe, 1971) as well as by ORD and NMR studies of ponasterone A (Koreeda *et al.*, 1971). Ponasterone A was shown to have the same configuration as β-ecdysone at C-20 and C-22 [see (X)] by finding that both compounds were produced on catalytic hydrogenation of the same synthetic acetylenic intermediate (Hüppi and Siddall, 1968).

(X)   β-Ecdysone   Ponasterone-A

Since the chemical shifts of the C-21 and C-18 proton resonances of naturally occurring ecdysones (except α-ecdysone and shidasterone) are the same, it is likely that the C-20 and C-22 configurations of all ecdysones are identical.

A third ecdysone, more polar than β-ecdysone, has been identified in extracts of *Manduca* pupae as 26-hydroxy-β-ecdysone (absolute configuration at C-25 unknown) (Thompson *et al.*, 1967). The structure was assigned mainly on the bases of NMR and mass spectral data. The NMR spectrum indicated four instead of the usual five methyl peaks, the C-27 proton peak (δ1.48) occurring at the same frequency as that of a model compound, 25,26-dihydroxycholesterol. The mass spectrum indicated the expected fragments at m/e 133, 115, and 31 (CH_2OH^{+}) resulting from cleavage of the two side chain α-glycol groups as shown in (XI) as well as fragments at m/e 427 $(M - 3 \times 18 - 15)$, 409 $(M - 4 \times 18 - 15)$, and 391

m/e 363 m/e 133

(XI)

m/e 115

$(M - 5 \times 18 - 15)$ resulting from loss of the terminal methyl group (C-27).
The production of this ecdysone metabolite has since been demonstrated in
Manduca larvae and prepupae as well as pupae, and the structure confirmed
by microchemical techniques (King, 1972a,b).

C. Extraction, Isolation and Analysis

Procedures for the large-scale extraction and isolation of ecdysones
from arthropods are all basically modified versions of the original technique devised by Butenandt and Karlson (1954) for the extraction of
α-ecdysone from *Bombyx*. In essence, this procedure involves extraction
with aqueous methanol or ethanol, then with *n*-butanol, rinsing the butanol extract with dilute H_2SO_4, Na_2CO_3, HOAc, and water, defatting
with petroleum ether, chromatography on alumina, and countercurrent
distribution (Karlson, 1956a). As β-ecdysone is more sensitive to acid,
more soluble in water [partition coefficient (K) (*n*-butanol/water) of
β-ecdysone is 5.3; K (α-ecdysone) ~ 10], and more sensitive to alumina
chromatography, several milder and more efficient extraction schemes
have been employed for the isolation of β-ecdysone (Kaplanis *et al.*,
1966; Horn *et al.*, 1968; Horn, 1971). Also, in view of the fact that base
catalyses inversion at C-5 to the inactive 5α-epimers, it seems advisable
to avoid exposure of ecdysone extracts to base altogether.

A small- to moderate-scale extraction procedure, which has been
found to give near quantitative recovery of radiolabelled ecdysones, involves homogenizing the tissue in 65% methanol in water, filtering or
centrifuging the homogenate, and reextracting the residue 2–3 additional
times with aqueous methanol (D. King, unpublished information). After
the methanol extract is concentrated *in vacuo*, the apolar lipids can be removed by rinsing the extract with hexane. Then the methanolic extract is
evaporated to near dryness, dissolved in water, and extracted four times
with water-saturated *n*-butanol; the addition of salt (NaCl) to the
aqueous phase aids the partitioning of ecdysones into the butanol. The
organic extract is then further purified by column chromatography on
silicic acid (elution with benzene containing increasing amounts of
methanol). Final purification can usually be accomplished by preparative
thin-layer chromatography (TLC) on silica gel impregnated with a fluorescent indicator. Double development with the solvent system 96% ethanol
(in water) : chloroform, 1:4, gives a good separation of α-, β-, and 26-
hydroxy-β-ecdysone, which are best eluted with tetrahydrofuran, which
must be distilled over KOH pellets immediately before use to remove pe-
roxides and phenolic stabilizers. As little as 1–5 μg of ecdysones can be

easily visualized on the chromatoplates under UV light, or by spraying the plate with an ethanolic solution of vanillin containing either phosphoric or sulfuric acid, followed by heating to 110°C for several minutes. Different ecdysones produce different and very characteristic colors with this spray reagent (see Horn, 1971).

Other adsorbents have been successfully employed for the purification and separation of ecdysones by column chromatography including CM-Sephadex (Horn *et al.,* 1968), Sephadex G-10 (Hoffmeister *et al.,* 1967), polyamide (Hänsel *et al.,* 1965; Rimpler and Schulz, 1967; Jizba and Herout, 1967), silicic acid containing boric acid (Horn, 1971), and reversed phase chromatography on Celite (Horn *et al.,* 1968; Galbraith *et al.,* 1969a). An excellent method for efficient separation of ecdysones on an analytical (μg) as well as preparative (0.1 gm) scale is high-pressure liquid chromatography. This technique, originally used by Hori (1969) and later extended by Schooley and Nakanishi (1972), involves reversed phase adsorption chromatography on a hydrophobic gel [such as Amberlite XAD-2, Rohm and Haas Co. (polystyrene-divinylbenzene copolymer) or Poragel-PN (cross-linked divinylbenzene-ethyleneglycol dimethacrylate copolymer)] eluted with an aqueous methanol or ethanol gradient (20–80%). The procedure is quantitative and relatively rapid (3 hours); recovery of the sample is simple and the column can be used repeatedly without repacking.

Rapid, efficient analysis of ecdysones (especially α) by gas–liquid partition chromatography (GLPC) is rendered difficult by the fact that ecdysones are large, polar molecules which are heat-sensitive and nonvolatile. Derivatization is essential for GLPC analysis, but the sensitivity of ecdysones to heat, acid, and base limits the type of derivatives that can be formed. Also, since ecdysones are polyfunctional, derivatization often results in the formation of mixtures of derivatives. The GLPC separations which have been accomplished to date involve the formation of trimethylsilyl ether, *O*-methyloxime, and heptafluorobutyrate ester derivatives which are chromatographed on the silicones SE-30 or QF-1 at 230°–250°C (Katz and Lensky, 1970; Morgan and Woodbridge, 1971; Ikekawa *et al.,* 1972).

Other techniques which have been used in the purification of ecdysones are low temperature precipitation of impurities from methanol (-10°C) (Kaplanis *et al.,* 1966), and countercurrent distribution in cyclohexane : *n*-butanol : water (Karlson, 1956a; Kaplanis *et al.,* 1966; Horn, 1971). Another technique which has been applied to the isolation of phytoecdysones, and which may turn out to be very useful in the isolation of zooecdysones, involves the adsorption of ecdysones from a defatted extract onto 20–50 mesh Amberlite XAD-2 beads in a 20% methanol (in water) slurry. Over 99% of the phytoecdysones were adsorbed, and could be eluted with 70% methanol (Schooley et al., 1972). Ecdysones have been crystallized from ethyl acetate: methanol, water, tetrahydrofuran:water, and ethyl acetate:tetrahydrofuran. The approximate solubility of α-ecdysone in water at 20°C is 1 mg/ml; β-ecdysone ∼5 mg/ml. Dry, crystalline ecdysones are quite stable at 0°C, and solutions in ethanol, methanol, aqueous methanol (5°C), or water (frozen) are stable provided the solvents are very pure and neutral.

D. STRUCTURE-ACTIVITY CORRELATIONS

Over the last several years, the relative biological activity of a large number of synthetic ecdysones and phytoecdysones in various bioassays has been measured in an effort to determine which portions of the ecdysone molecule are responsible for its biological activity (Ashburner, 1971; see reviews by Horn, 1971; Wyatt, 1972). The assay systems most commonly employed involve assessing puparium formation in ligated last instar dipteran *(Calliphora, Musca, Sarcophaga)* abdomens injected with aqueous or alcoholic solutions of the compound to be tested. Although results obtained do not always agree in detail (for instance, β-ecdysone has been reported to have more, less, and the same activity as α-ecdysone), certain generalizations have emerged. Regarding the tetracyclic nucleus, the cis A-B ring junction is essential, regardless of whether the 5β substituent is a hydrogen atom or a hydroxyl group; 5α ecdysone epimers have drastically reduced biological activity. In addition, the 6-oxo-7-ene system in the B ring is essential; 6-hydroxy analogues are inactive, as are 7,8-dihydro analogues (Faux et al., 1970). The 3β- and 14α-hydroxyls are necessary for high activity. The presence or absence of hydroxyls at C-2, -5, or -11 seems to make little difference. Regarding the ecdysone sidechain, the only essential feature is the presence of a $22\beta_F$-hydroxyl which is present in all naturally occurring ecdysones. The $22\alpha_F$-epimers of α- or β-ecdysone are inactive, and it is likely that the occasional slight activity shown by 22-iso-α-ecdysone is due to contamination with the 22-epimer. 22-Iso-α-ecdysone serves as an excellent control in experiments to confirm that the observed action of a particular ecdysone is not due to the nonspecific action of any polyhydroxylated steroid. The presence or absence of hydroxyl groups or other functionalities on the sidechain (acetoxyl groups, $24\alpha_F$-ethyl or -methyl groups, lactones, cyclic ethers, or double bonds) generally has little effect on the biological activity of the molecule. The presence of the sidechain is essential for activity, as rubrosterone and poststerone are inactive. Of course, the expected species differences and other unexplainable exceptions to these generalizations have been reported. For instance, poststerone seems to possess biological activity in brainless *Samia* pupae (Siddall *et al.*, 1967), and the β-sitosterol ($24\alpha_F$-ethyl) analogue of β-ecdysone (makisterone C) is as active as β-ecdysone in *Calliphora* but is completely inactive in *Musca* (Kaplanis, 1968, cited in Horn, 1971).

However, information derived from systemic assays such as the *Calliphora* or *Musca* test does not easily lend itself to meaningful interpretation because such assays are greatly complicated by the *in vivo* metabolism of the administered compounds to more active, less active, or inactive metabolites. In these assays, what is measured is the summation of the biological effects produced by the administered compound and its metabolites over a given time period, rather than the intrinsic hormonal properties of the administered compound itself. Thus, the activity of α-ecdysone and various side chain deoxyecdysones is due in part to their metabolism to β-ecdysone (Moriyama *et al.*, 1970), and the enhanced activity of cyasterone is ascribed to its resistance to inactivation (Ohtaki and Williams, 1970). Topical assay systems suffer from additional complications arising from the fact that different compounds penetrate the cuticle at different rates. Thus, apolar ecdysones such as ponasterone A and 22,25-dideoxy-α-ecdysone are far more active than β-ecdysone itself in the *Dermestes* dipping test. The converse is true when the ecdysone analogues are injected rather than applied topically (A. Schrikker, personal communication).

Although the activities of α- and β-ecdysone in most systemic bioassay systems are about the same, β-ecdysone is approximately 100–200 times more active than α-ecdysone *in vitro* in inducing (1) puff formation in *Drosophila* salivary gland chromosomes (Ashburner, 1971), (2) metamorphosis (evagination) of isolated *Drosophila* imaginal discs (Chihara *et al.*, 1972), and (3) ventral nerve cord shortening in *Galleria* (J. Robertson and R. Pipa, personal communication). Neither salivary glands nor imaginal discs are able to convert α-ecdysone to β-ecdysone (D. King, unpublished information; Chihara *et al.*, 1972). Thus, evidence is accumulating suggesting that β-ecdysone functions as the active molting hormone and that α-ecdysone serves as a "prohormone" rather than as a hormone (King, 1972b). α-Ecdysone does not appear to have any biological activity at physiological concentrations (estimated from ecdysone titer determinations; Section VI, C) *in vitro* tissue systems which cannot convert it to β-ecdysone. This situation parallels a number of recently investigated vertebrate systems in which the apparent activity of various biologically active molecules (vitamins, hormones, drugs, toxins) has been shown in fact to be due to a metabolite of the molecule rather than to the molecule itself [for example, vitamin D_3 (Lawson *et al.*, 1971; Holick *et al.*, 1971; Norman *et al.*, 1971) ; testosterone (Bruchovsky and Wilson, 1968)].

E. Biosynthesis

Ecdysone, like the vertebrate steroid hormones, is synthesized from cholesterol. This was first demonstrated by Karlson and Hoffmeister (1963) who showed conversion of [^{3}H]cholesterol into α-ecdysone in very low yield in *Calliphora vicina* (= *erythrocephala*) prepupae. The formation of polar metabolites of α-ecdysone (such as β-ecdysone) was not noted in this investigation. Galbraith *et al.* (1970) have demonstrated incorporation (0.015%) of [^{3}H]cholesterol into β-ecdysone in *C. stygia* [β-ecdysone is the principal ecdysone in both *C. vicina* and *C. stygia* (Galbraith *et al.*, 1969b)]. Willig *et al.* (1971) have shown that both α- (0.018% incorporation) and β-ecdysone (0.034%) are formed from [^{14}C]cholesterol in *C. vicina*. The terminal step in ecdysone biosynthesis, the conversion of α-ecdysone to β-ecdysone, was determined by King and Siddall (1969) in *Calliphora* and several crustaceans and has since been demonstrated in several other insect species. Moriyama *et al.* (1970) have studied the dynamics of α-ecdysone metabolism during the last larval instar of *Bombyx,* and found that the rate of conversion of α- to β-ecdysone increases and the rate of further metabolism of β-ecdysone decreases markedly toward the time of pupation. β-Ecdysone is further metabolized to 26-hydroxy-β-ecdysone in *Manduca* (King, 1972a) . Thus, the biosynthesis of ecdysones from cholesterol has been confirmed and the terminal steps of ecdysone biosynthesis have been defined. However, the steps leading from cholesterol to α-ecdysone have as yet defied elucidation. Because of the large cholesterol pool in arthropod tissues, radiolabeled cholesterol becomes diluted to such an extent that it is impossible to detect the minute amounts of transient intermediates. Also, it is difficult to distinguish between genuine metabolites and polar steroids which are easily generated by autoxidation of cholesterol. Hence, several studies of the metabolism of synthetic side chain deoxyecdysone analogues have been undertaken in an effort to gain insight into the ecdysone biosynthetic pathway. Since sidechain deoxyecdysones possess significant biological activity, it was considered that this activity might be due in part to their metabolism to β-ecdysone, and that some of these deoxy analogues might in fact be natural intermediates in the pathway of β-ecdysone biosynthesis.

25-Deoxy-α-ecdysone is not considered a natural precursor because it is metabolized by *Calliphora* (Thomson *et al.*, 1969) and Manduca (King, 1972a,b) to ponasterone A as well as to other compounds which do not occur normally in insects. 22,25-Dideoxy-α-ecdysone is converted efficiently into α- and β-ecdysones in *Manduca* pupae (Kaplanis *et al.*, 1969). King (1972a,b) has shown that sidechain hydroxylation of this dideoxy analogue takes place in a definite sequence, occurring first at C-25, then C-22β_F, C-20α_F, and C-26 [stereochemistry unknown; see (XII)]. Although this compound is metabolized efficiently to ecdysones

(XII)

22-Deoxy-α-ecdysone α-Ecdysone

22, 25-Dideoxy-α-ecdysone

26-Hydroxy-β-ecdysone β-Ecdysone

in *Manduca* pupae and fifth instar larvae as well as *C. stygia* pupae (Thomson *et al.*, 1971), such is not the case in *Sarcophaga, Gastrimargus, Dermestes* (King, 1972a), *Musca* adults (Thompson *et al.*, 1972), or *Manduca* fourth instar larvae (J. Kaplanis, personal communication) where little if any α- or β-ecdysone is formed. It thus appears unlikely that 22,25-dideoxy- and 22-deoxy-α-ecdysone can be natural ecdysone precursors, although the possibility still remains that they might serve as natural intermediates in some insects. Indeed, the investigations of sidechain deoxyecdysone metabolism mentioned above suggest that sidechain hydroxylation at C-22 and C-25 occurs before elaboration of the complete ecdysone tetracycle.

The finding of 2-deoxy-β-ecdysone (which possesses the same activity as β-ecdysone in the *Calliphora* test) in a crustacean (*Jasus*, Galbraith *et al.*, 1968) and in *Antheraea* (Chong *et al.*, 1970) raises the possibility that ecdysone biosynthesis proceeds through 2-deoxy intermediates. This theory is supported by the recent finding (D. Horn, personal communication) that 2,22,25-trideoxy-α-ecdysone (synthetic) possesses surprisingly high biological activity ($\sim \frac{1}{3}$ the activity of β) in the *Calliphora* test, far more than that shown by 22,25-dideoxy-α-ecdysone ($\sim$ $\frac{1}{50}$–$\frac{1}{10}$ the activity of β).

Elucidation of the first step of cholesterol metabolism to ecdysone would greatly facilitate the study of ecdysone biosynthesis, but has so far eluded discovery. Galbraith *et al.* (1970) have shown that 7-dehydrocholesterol, which is found in relatively high concentrations in *Periplaneta* and *Manduca* prothoracic glands (D. Chen and J. Kaplanis, personal communication; Thompson *et al.*, 1972) and which has been suggested to be a precursor of ecdysone (Robbins *et al.*, 1964), is incorporated into ecdysones in *C. stygia* pupae with only twice the efficiency of cholesterol. It has been shown that 25-hydroxycholesterol, $22\beta_F$-hydroxycholesterol, and cholesteryl sulfate (D. Horn, personal communication; Galbraith *et al.*, 1972) are not ecdysone precursors in this insect. However, in these studies it was not possible to determine whether the administered precursor actually reached the site of ecdysone biosynthesis. The radiolabeled α-ecdysone and deoxyecdysones used in these studies were synthesized (Hafferl *et al.*, 1972; Thomson *et al.*, 1971) by catalytic tritiation of synthetic sidechain unsaturated derivatives. Radiolabeled ecdysones of high specific activity are best stored under N_2 at 5°C in pure benzene containing sufficient methanol to effect solution.

The site of production of ecdysone in insects has long been assumed to be the prothoracic gland despite the lack of direct chemical evidence in support of this theory (see Moriyama *et al.*, 1970; King, 1972a,b) and despite the presence of various reports in the literature describing such phenomena as unimpeded metamorphosis in isolated larval *Tenebrio* abdomens (Stellwaag-Kittler, 1954), continued growth, development, and reproduction in three species of cockroaches deprived of their prothoracic glands (Nutting, 1955; Chadwick, 1955, 1956), and the inability of the lepidopteran, *Calpodes,* to pupate anterior to a ligature placed between the thorax and the abdomen (Weir, 1970). Efficient conversion of α- to β-ecdysone takes place in isolated last larval instar abdomens of *Calliphora* (King, 1969) and *Bombyx* (Moriyama *et al.*, 1970). It has been found that a number of *Manduca* prepupal tissues (fat body, Malpighian tubules, gut, body wall) are able to convert α- to β-ecdysone very efficiently *in vitro* whereas other tissues (blood, oenocytes, muscle, salivary gland, and the prothoracic gland itself) did not effect this conversion (King, 1972a). This study also showed that isolated fat body and Malpighian tubule are able to metabolize 22,25-dideoxy-α-ecdysone to 22-deoxy-α, β,26 hydroxy-β, and a mixture of conjugates. The prothoracic gland is able to metabolize the dideoxy analogue to α-ecdysone, but no further. Experiments attempting to demonstrate the conversion of radiolabeled cholesterol into ecdysones by isolated "active" prothoracic glands have been unsuccessful (King, 1972a; H. Chino, personal communication; J. Thomson, personal communication; J. Kaplanis, personal communication). Conversion ($\sim 0.002\%$) of cholesterol to α- and β-ecdysones has been demonstrated to occur in late (day 6; past the critical period) but not in early (day 2) isolated fifth (last) instar *Bombyx* abdomens (Nakanishi *et al.*, 1972). Gersch and Stürzebecher (1971) have confirmed these results in *Mamaestra,* although the ecdysones were identified only by chromatography.

Thus, it appears that the insect molting hormone, β-ecdysone, is not produced by the prothoracic gland, but rather is manufactured *in situ* by a number of insect tissues from α-ecdysone which occurs together with β-ecdysone in the hemolymph. The role of the glands in the production of α-ecdysone remains conjectural. It seems possible that the prothoracic glands secrete a tropic hormone which stimulates ecdysone production in some abdominal tissue such as the fat body, or secretes a prohormone. It has been shown (D. King, K. Judy, G. Weirich, and J. Fristrom, unpublished information; see, also, Willig *et al.*, 1971) that *Manduca* prothoracic glands cultured *in vitro* produce a butanol-soluble substance with demonstrable biological activity in ligated *Musca,* but not on *Drosophila* imaginal discs. The glands *in vitro* are able to convert cholesterol into a metabolite somewhat more polar then β-ecdysone. The identity of these two principles is presently under investigation.

F. INACTIVATION

Rapid inactivation of exogenous ecdysone as determined by bioassay has been reported by Adelung (1966) in *Carcinus,* by Shaaya (1969) in *Calliphora,* and by Ohtaki *et al.* (1969) and Ohtaki and Williams (1970) in *Sarcophaga* and *Samia.* Indeed, one would expect insects to possess an efficient mechanism of ecdysone inactivation to bring about the dramatic decreases in ecdysone titer which occur at various points during the life cycle of insects. Karlson and Bode (1969) have demonstrated ecdysone inactivation in the 100,000 g supernatant of homogenized *Calliphora* fat body and have achieved a partial purification of the inactivating enzyme. They state that the activity of this enzyme system during the life cycle is a mirror image of the ecdysone titer curve, and Karlson (1970) believes that the inactivation process involves metabolism of α-ecdysone to two unidentified compounds less polar than α-ecdysone. Since apolar ecdysone metabolites have not been encountered in *Calliphora* or other insects *in vivo* or *in vitro,* except in homogenized tissue preparations (King, 1972a), the significance of these apolar metabolites remains unknown. Heinrich and Hoffmeister (1970) present evidence that ecdysone inactivation by *Calliphora* fat body *in vitro* involves formation of α-glucoside conjugates. Moriyama *et al.* (1970) and Cherbas and Cherbas (1970) note the formation of a highly polar, anionic metabolite ("compound A") in *Bombyx* and *Antheraea* which lies at the end of the pathway of ecdysone metabolism. *Bombyx* "compound A" has subsequently been shown to be a steroid sulfate rather than a side chain cleavage fragment (H. Hikino, Y. Ohizumi, and D. King, unpublished information).

α-Ecdysone and its metabolites (β- and 26-hydroxy-β-ecdysone) in *Manduca* are excreted into the gut both as unchanged steroids and as monosulfate ester conjugates (King, 1972a). The conjugate fraction was found to vary considerably in composition depending on the stage of the life cycle and even upon the individual insect, often consisting nearly entirely of conjugates of unidentified polar steroids. Ecdysone glucosides were formed by fat body incubated *in vitro*, but significant amounts were not encountered *in vivo*. In *Sarcophaga* late third instar larvae, both ecdysone sulfate and glucoside conjugates were formed in *in vivo* experiments. It therefore appears that the mechanism of inactivation of exogenous ecdysone may vary with the species of insect, but does not involve side chain scission as was previously suspected (Galbraith *et al.*, 1968; Moriyama *et al.*, 1970; Hikino *et al.*, 1971).

Thompson *et al.* (1972) have obtained nearly identical results in studies of 22,25-dideoxy-α-ecdysone metabolism, namely, that inactivation of both ecdysones and deoxyecdysones involves the formation primarily of sulfate conjugates in *Manduca* pupae, and a mixture of glucosides and sulfates in *Musca* adults. Whether ecdysone glucosides are obligatory intermediates in sulfate formation, which hydroxyl group is sulfated, and where the sulfotransferase is located in the insect are important questions which remain unanswered.

V. The Juvenile Hormone—Chemistry and Metabolism

A. Occurrence

Following Wigglesworth's demonstration in the mid-1930's of the existence of juvenile hormone (JH) in insects, no successful attempts were made to isolate the hormone until 1956 when Williams made the curious but very fortuitous discovery that the abdominal tissues of adult male Cecropia moths contained relatively enormous amounts of JH. The amber oil obtained by extracting the abdomens with ether was found to duplicate all the morphogenetic and gonadotropic effects which could be elicited by implantation of corpora allata. The activity was not present in extracts of insects which had been allatectomized prior to adult development, thus indicating that the active principle was indeed the corpus allatum hormone. Williams and many subsequent workers have found that the Cecrophia hormone is active on insects of several different orders and at various developmental stages, suggesting that the juvenile hormones of many insects may be similar if not identical molecules.

Eleven years after the discovery of a rich source of JH, Röller's group (1967) succeeded in isolating, identifying, and synthesizing the principal (C_{18} JH-I) Cecropia juvenile hormone (Fig. 4). The molecule has a novel carbon skeleton and is also unusual in that it is the only animal hormone known to contain an epoxide function. The following year, Meyer's group (1968) showed that the C_{18} Cecropia hormone was accompanied by smaller amounts ($\sim$ 13–20%) of a more polar, lower (C_{17} JH-II) homologue (Fig. 4) which had escaped Röller's attention

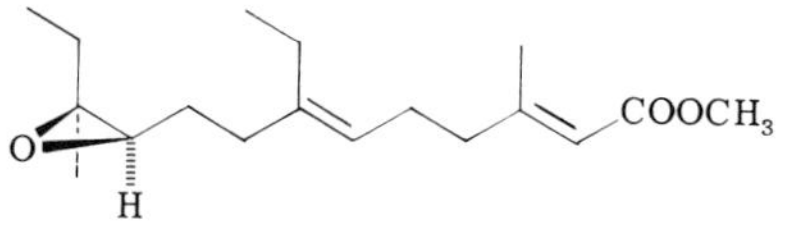

Cecropia C_{18} JH or JH I

Methyl-10, 11-*cis*-epoxy-
7-ethyl-3, 11-dimethyl-
2-*trans*-6-*trans*-tri-
decadienoate

Methyl-12, 14-dihomo-
10-*cis*-juvenate

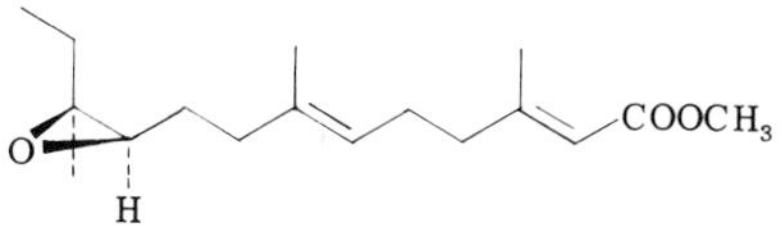

Cecropia C_{17} JH or JH II
Manduca C_{17} JH or JH II

Methyl-10, 11-*cis*-epoxy-
3, 7, 11-trimethyl-2-*trans*-
6-*trans*-tridecadienoate

Methyl-12-homo-10-*cis*-
juvenate

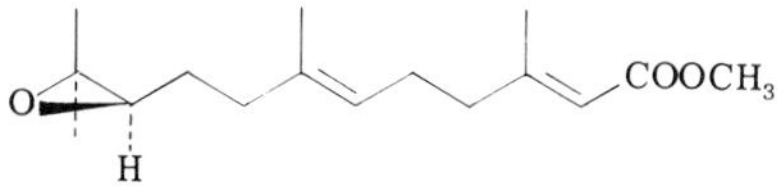

Manduca C_{16} JH or JH I

Methyl-10, 11-epoxy-3, 7,
11-trimethyl-2-*trans*-6-
trans-dodecadienoate

Methyl juvenate

Methyl-10, 11-epoxy-
trans, *trans*-farnesoate
(or farnesenate)

Fig. 4. The juvenile hormones.

TABLE II

OCCURRENCE OF JUVENILE HORMONES IN INSECTS

Species	Stage	Juvenile Hormone	Yield (μg/Animal)	References
Hyalophora cecropia	Adult male abdomens	C_{17}	1	Metzler *et al.* (1971)
		C_{18}	4	Röller *et al.* (1967)
		C_{17}	~0.1	Meyer *et al.* (1968)[a]
		C_{18}	~0.5	
Hyalophora gloveri	Adult male abdomens	C_{17}	0.02–0.12	Dahm and Röller (1970)
		C_{18}	0.2–0.5	
Philosamia cynthia	Adult male abdomens	C_{17}	0.002–0.006	H. Röller (personal communication)
		C_{18}	0.2	
Manduca sexta	Early IV instar larval blood	C_{16}[b]	—	K. Judy, D. Schooley, J. Bergot, L. Dunham and J. Siddall (personal communication)

[a] No C_{18} JH detected.
[b] No C_{18} JH detected; C_{17} JH produced by adult female corpora alla ta *in vitro*, but presence in larva not unambiguously established.

during purification because of its relatively low activity in the *Tenebrio* assay. The structure and nomenclature of the two Cecropia hormones and of a third JH which has recently been found in *Manduca* are shown in Fig. 4. As in the case with ecdysone, JH activity has been demonstrated in extracts of a larger number of insects and crustaceans (Gilbert, 1964). However, the actual hormones have been isolated and identified in only four species of lepidopterans belonging to two closely related families (Table II). Again, parallel to the situation with ecdysones, the existence in each insect species of two very similar juvenile hormones, each ostensibly serving the same function, is somewhat enigmatic. The two molecules are undoubtedly metabolically related, and there is no change in the ratio of JH-I to JH-II during the adult life (Metzler *et al.*, 1971). It is conceivable that they serve qualitatively different functions, although this has not been demonstrated and seems a remote possibility.

After Schmialek's discovery that farnesol and several of its derivatives possessed JH activity (Schmialek, 1961; Gilbert, 1964), the synthesis and investigation of other JH mimetics has continued, largely stimulated by the hope that these compounds may eventually prove useful as insect control agents. It is remarkable that one of these synthetic JH mimetics, methyl-10,11-epoxy-*trans,trans*-farnesoate, first synthesized by Van Tamelen's group (Van Tamelen *et al.*, 1963) and later shown by Bowers *et al.* (1965) to possess high JH activity, has turned out to be one of the natural JH's of *Manduca* (K. Judy, D. Schooley, L. Dunham, M. Hall, J. Bergot, and J. Siddall, personal communication). Law *et al.*, (1966) showed that the crude reaction mixture (hydrochlorination product), produced on treating farnesoic acid with ethanolic HCl, is a potent JH mimetic. This material is a complex mixture containing at least 25 aliphatic and cyclic neutral components (J. Bergot, personal communication); the major component was identified by Romaňuk *et al.* (1967). Several nonsesquiterpenoid 3,4-methylenedioxyphenol (sesamol) derivatives [such as piperonyl butoxide and sesoxane; see (XIII) and (XIV)], which are microsomal oxidase inhibitors used as carbamate and pyrethrin insecticide synergists, interestingly possess JH activity (Bowers, 1968). To date, over 2500 JH analogues (JHA) have been

Sesoxane (XIII)   Piperonyl butoxide (XIV)

synthesized and tested in a number of bioassay systems (see Sláma, 1971; Sláma *et al.*, 1972).

In 1965 Slăma and Williams (1965; Williams and Slăma, 1966) made the interesting discovery that certain American paper products contained a principle which had considerable JH activity on the European bug, *Pyrrhocoris apterus,* but not on other insects. This compound, called "paper factor," originated in the wood of the balsam fir. It was subsequently isolated from ether extracts of the wood pulp, and identified as methyl todomatuate (Bowers *et al.,* 1966). In addition, a side-chain dehydro analogue was identified in a European balsam fir (Cerny *et al.,* 1967) [see structures (XV) and (XVI)].

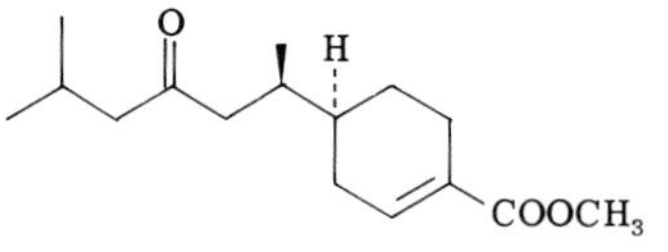

"Paper factor"
methyl todomatuate
or (+)-juvabione   (XV)

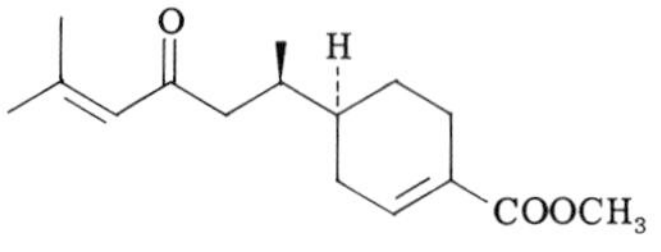

(+)-Dehydrojuvabione   (XVI)

B. CHEMISTRY

Structure elucidation of the principal Cecropia JH (C_{18} JH-I) was accomplished by Röller and his associates (1967; Röller and Dahm, 1968; Trost, 1970) mainly by judicious interpretation of mass and NMR spectral data obtained from less than 300 μg of pure compound. The low resolution mass spectrum showed that the molecular weight was 294, and the provisional empirical formula $C_{18}H_{30}O_3$ was calculated. Appearance of ions at m/e 73, 59, and 263 ($M-31$) indicated that JH was a methyl ester while the presence of a peak at 276 ($M-18$) indicated the presence of a labile oxygen. Catalytic hydrogenation (Pd/EtOH) led to the production of a single compound, a saturated, acyclic, methyl ester with a molecular ion at m/e 284 ($C_{18}H_{36}O_2$), indicating uptake of 3 moles of hydrogen (and hence 3 double bonds or rings in JH which are saturated or cleaved on hydrogenation) and loss of one oxygen. An intense peak at m/e 101 showed the presence of a methyl group at C-3, and the peaks at m/e 143, 185, and 153 ($185 - 32$) indicated an ethyl group at C-7, leading to the partial structure of the deoxyhexahydro JH derivative [see structure (XVII)].

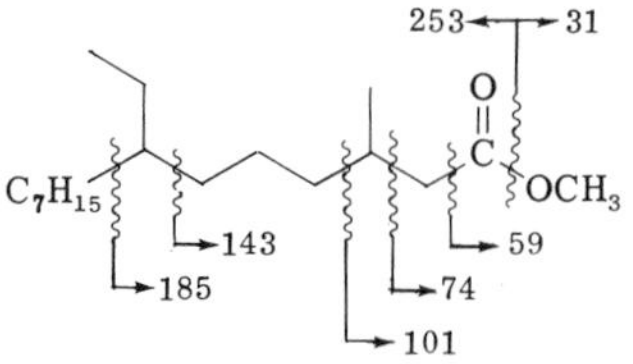

From the NMR spectrum, the partial structures (XVIII) were deduced.

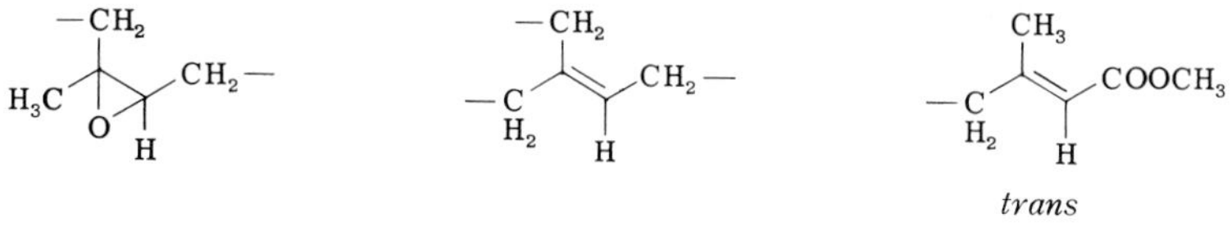

$$2 [-CH_2CH_3] \qquad (XVIII) \qquad 6 [-CH_2-]$$

(total)

The positions of the epoxide group and of the second double bond with respect to the α,β-unsaturated ester were established by isolation of levulinaldehyde and a homolevulinaldehyde on oxidative cleavage of the JH with OsO_4 and $NaIO_4$ [see (XIX)] as well as by mass spectral

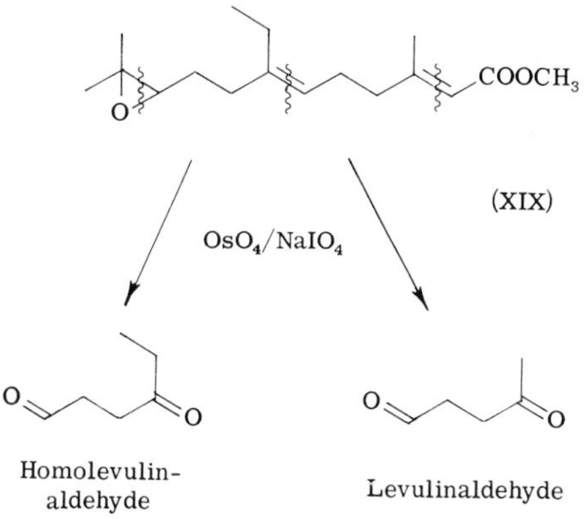

Homolevulin-
aldehyde

Levulinaldehyde

analysis of the model compound, methyl-10,11-epoxyfarnesoate.

Thus, JH-I was established to be a methyl 10-epoxy-7-ethyl-3,11-dimethyl-2-*trans*-6-tridecadienoate. The stereochemistry of the oxirane ring and of the double bond at C-6 was unambiguously established to be *cis* and *trans*, respectively, only after synthesis of the *dl*-pairs of the eight possible geometric isomers and careful comparison of the spectral, chromatographic, and biological properties of the synthetic materials with those of the natural hormone (Dahm *et al.*, 1967). Several very elegant sterospecific syntheses of the C_{18} JH have been achieved (Zurflüh *et al.*, 1968; Corey *et al.*, 1968; Johnson *et al.*, 1968). These have been reviewed by Berkoff (1969), and for a complete listing of the numerous JH syntheses accomplished to date, see Henrick *et al.* (1972).

Complete structure elucidation of the C_{17} JH (JH-II), which accounts for about 10–30% (Metzler et al., 1971) of the JH activity in Cecropia oil, was accomplished by Meyer et al. (1968, 1970, 1971) primarily through careful interpretation of spectral data. The structure has been confirmed by synthesis (Johnson et al., 1969; Anderson et al., 1972). The structure of the C_{16} JH from *Manduca* was deduced (D. Schooley, J. Bergot, L. Dunham, and J. Siddall, personal communication) utilizing only ~7 μg of radiolabeled material which was obtained from the medium in which larval or adult female corpora allata had been cultured *in vitro* with [^{14}C]methyl methionine (K. Judy and S. Hall, personal communication). Approximately equal amounts of C_{16} and C_{17} JH were produced *in vitro*, and structure eludication was accomplished by liquid and gas–liquid chromatography, mass spectrometry, and extensive microchemical derivative formation. Esterification with (+)-α-methoxy-α-trifluoromethylphenylacetyl chloride of the C_{16} diol and C_{17} *threo*-diol, produced on acid-catalyzed hydrolysis of *Manduca* JH-I and -II, respectively, produced single diastereomers, thus indicating that each *Manduca* JH is optically active. Preliminary bioassays indicate that the C_{16} hormone is about ten times more active in *Manduca* than it is in *Galleria* (J. Martin and K. Judy, personal communication).

Meyer et al. (1970) have reported that a 9:1 mixture of Cecropia JH-I and -II exhibits a plain positive optical dispersion curve $[(\alpha)_D \sim +7°]$, and that JH is therefore not racemic. Synthesis of the two enantiomers of JH-I has been accomplished by Loew and Johnson (1971). The absolute configuration at the vicinal chiral centers (C-10 and C-11), the last remaining structural feature of JH to be solved, has recently been determined nearly simultaneously by three groups, both by synthesis of the two enantiomers from starting material of known absolute configuration (Faulkner and Petersen, 1971), and by clarification of the mode of acid hydrolysis of the epoxide followed by determination of the chirality of the resulting α-glycol (Nakanishi et al., 1971; Meyer et al., 1971). The relatively rapid and simple spectral methods utilized by Nakanishi's group are summarized in (XX). The absolute configuration of C_{17} and C_{16} JH is assumed to be the same as that of the C_{18} hormone.

(XX)

(−)-C_{18} JH
(synthetic

threo Isomer

Clockwise glycol
chirality (⊕
Cotton effect)

C. Extraction, Isolation, and Analysis

A number of different methods have been successfully employed in the purification and isolation of JH from the oil obtained by ether extraction of saturniids (Meyer *et al.*, 1970; Röller and Dahm, 1968; Dahm and Röller, 1970). In the scheme utilized by Meyer's group, low and high molecular weight impurities were removed from the oil by molecular distillation ($100°C/10^{-3}$ mm Hg). Acidic impurities were then removed by extracting with base, or by percolating the extract through a basic exchange resin. Purification was continued by leeching with aqueous methanol at −20°C, followed by chromatography on alumina and silicic acid. Pure JH was then obtained by preparative gas chromatography (GLPC) on Carbowax 4000. Meyer and his colleagues stress the importance of utilizing ultrapure solvents during the purification process and of utilizing an all-glass GLPC apparatus to avoid thermal metal-catalyzed rearrangements and pyrolysis. Röller's group employed a similar procedure, involving low temperature (−78°C) precipitation from ether or ether-methanol, molecular distillation (60°–90°C/2 × 10^{-5} mm) and two silica thin-layer chromatography (TLC) separations followed by GLPC on XE-60. Chromatography on Sephadex LH-20 has also been used successfully in a revised scheme for JH isolation (Dahm and Röller, 1970). Schooley and Nakanishi (1972) have obtained excellent separation of JH's, JH isomers, *erythro*- and *threo*-glycols derived from epoxide cleavage, and of diastereomeric glycol derivatives by high pressure liquid–solid chromatography. This technique is complementary to GLPC analysis and offers obvious advantages in preparative separations.

Bieber *et al.* (1972) have devised a novel method for the quantitative determination of C_{18} JH in partially purified insect extracts by adding methyl deuterium labeled JH as carrier and internal standard, and measuring the ratio of protium to deuterium form (of two ions which include the ester group) by combined GLPC–mass spectrometry. Pure JH is quite stable if kept cold and away from light and is stable in solution in pure benzene or hexane. It should be emphasized that JH is extremely sensitive to acids, and is unstable at pH < 5.5. TLC is easily accomplished on silica chromatoplates developed with solvents such as 35% ethyl acetate in n-hexane, and JH can be eluted with pure ether or tetrahydrofuran. For separation of different JH's and their isomers, GLPC utilizing phenyldiethanolamine succinate (PDEAS) as the liquid phase gives excellent results (L. Dunham, personal communication).

D. STRUCTURE-ACTIVITY CORRELATIONS

Although more than 2500 JH analogues have been synthesized and tested by various groups in a number of bioassays, essentially no clear rules or trends correlating structure with activity have emerged from these studies (cf. Röller and Dahm, 1968; Wigglesworth, 1969; Sláma, 1971). As stressed in Section IV, D, interpretation of data derived from topical or systemic bioassays is complicated by a myriad of factors. Very striking species differences in response to a single JH analogue have often been encountered; for example, juvabione is an extremely potent JH mimic in *Pyrrhocoris,* but possesses negligible activity when tested on other insects including hemipterans closely related to *Pyrrhocoris* (Bowers *et al.,* 1966). In fact, even the relative activities of C_{16}, C_{17}, and C_{18} JH vary greatly from insect to insect. Formulation of the hormone or analogue has long been known to be an extremely important factor in bioassays. For instance, Wigglesworth (1963) found that farnesyl methyl ether is very active in *Rhodnius* if dissolved in linseed oil whereas it is completely inactive if administered in emulsified form. Differences in metabolism or excretion rate also influence the apparent activity of JH analogues. Reddy and Krishnakumaran (1972) have shown in parabiosis experiments that two JH analogues which show higher activity than C_{18} Cecropia JH in *Tenebrio* and *Galleria* also have much longer half-lives in these animals. Other factors which probably influence the activity of JH analogues include the conformation of the molecule in solution, the ability of the analogue to bind to hemolymph carrier proteins and to receptor sites, and the polarity of the analogue which would influence the rate of partitioning of the compound from an apolar phase (cuticle wax or oil droplet) into the hemolymph as well as the rate of penetration through the cuticle in topical assays. Consideration of these factors helps to explain phenomena such a Röller and Dahm's finding (1968) that C_{16} JH is as active as farnesol when injected into *Tenebrio,* but is 1600 times more active than farnesol when applied topically.

The sterochemical features of the racemic C_{18} Cecropia JH which seem to determine its activity in *Tenebrio* are as follows (Röller and Dahm, 1968). The *trans* double bond at C-2 is essential for activity; conversion of the double bond at C-6 from trans to cis lowers the activity by a factor of 10; conversion of the epoxide from cis to trans lowers the activity by a factor of 2; and the ethyl ester homologue is eight times more active than the natural hormone.

Preliminary bioassays have shown that a preparation of synthetic $(+)$-C_{18} JH (10 R, 11 S) is at least six-ten times more active than the $(-)$-JH (10S,11R) in *Galleria* and *Tenebrio* (G. Staal and H. Röller, in Loew and Johnson, 1971). However, the $(-)$-JH was contaminated with $\sim 10\%$ of its enantiomer, which could account for most or even all of the observed biological activity. Also, the $(-)$-enantiomer (10S,11S) of the *trans*-epoxide showed ~ 7 times more activity than the $(+)$ isomer (10R,11R) in *Tenebrio* (H. Röller, personal communication) suggesting that activity is governed by the configuration at C-11 more than at C-10. Further work with absolutely pure enantiomers is necessary before quantitative conclusions can be drawn.

E. BIOSYNTHESIS

Investigations on the biosynthesis of C_{17} and C_{18} JH have been undertaken by Metzler *et al.* (1971, 1972) utilizing intact young (day 1–4) adult male Cecropia as the experimental animal. The results of these studies have turned out to be quite surprising: Metzler *et al.* (1971) were unable to demonstrate the incorporation of radiolabeled mevalonate, propionate (a postulated precursor of homomevalonate), farnesol, or farnesyl pyrophosphate into JH, although significant (up to 1%) amounts of mevalonate were incorporated into all *trans*-farnesol. Acetate is incorporated ($\sim 0.003\%$ after 16 hours) into the carbon skeleton of both JH and farnesol. Methyl-labeled L-methionine is also utilized ($\sim 0.1\%$ after 16 hours) in the biosynthesis of JH. Degradation experiments demonstrated that the label was present only in the ester methyl group and not in the carbon skeleton. This finding has been confirmed by K. Judy (personal communication) with *Manduca* corpora allata *in vitro*. Thus, although JH appears to be closely related to the acyclic sesquiterpenes such as farnesol, it may not be synthesized by the classical isoprenoid pathway. However, the possibility still remains that the carbon skeleton is already synthesized prior to adult emergence and that only the finishing touches to its biosynthesis, such as esterification and/or epoxidation, need take place during adult life. The possibility that JH is synthesized from fatty acids or amino acids remains to be explored and it is suggested that studies utilizing corpora allata *in vitro* could well complement *in vivo* studies and offer some distinct advantages. Metzler *et al.* (1972) have also shown that the racemic epoxy acid derived from JH-I by enzymatic hydrolysis is rapidly ($\sim 10\%$ in 15 hours) methylated *in vivo* in adult male Cecropia to form JH-I, although it is not yet shown whether this compound is a natural precursor in JH biosynthesis. Röller and Dahm (1970) have demonstrated the production of C_{18} JH (2–6 μg) by adult Cecropia brain–corpus cardiacum–corpus allatum complexes (50) maintained *in vitro* for 7 days. The hormone was extracted from the culture medium; fresh or cultured glands contained no detectable JH, thus demonstrating that the hormone is not stored in the gland. These experiments, and those of K. J. Judy *et al.* (personal communication) utilizing *Manduca* corpora allata cultured alone in a defined, unsupplemented medium, indicate that JH is indeed produced by the corpus allatum.

F. INACTIVATION

The mechanism of inactivation of exogenous radiolabeled C_{18} and C_{16} JH has now been studied in a number of insect species. The meta-

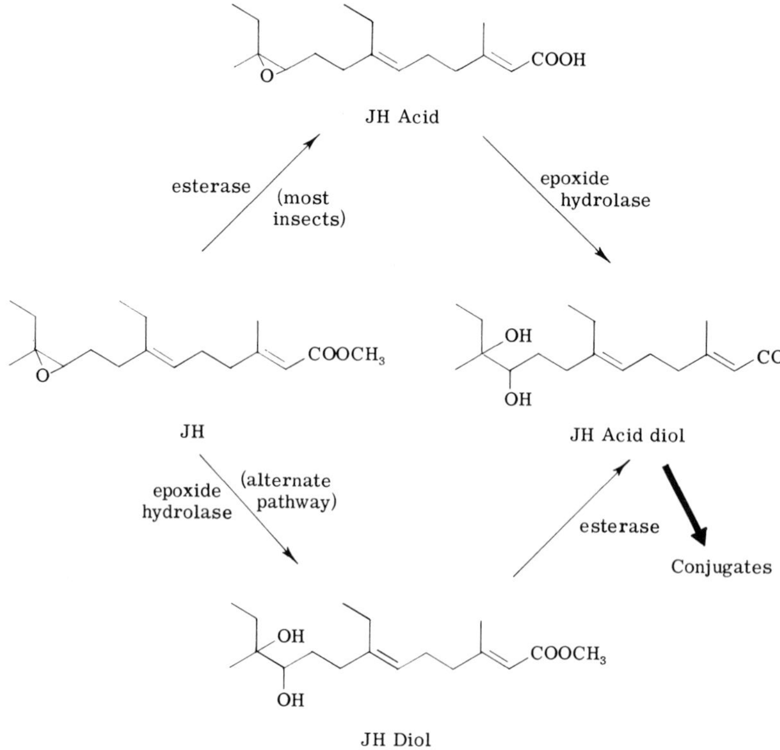

Fig. 5. Routes of juvenile hormone inactivation.

bolic pathway common to most insect species was first defined by Slade and Zibitt (1971), and involves hydrolysis of the methyl ester followed by epoxide hydration, and finally production of a mixture of highly polar metabolites which were determined by preliminary enzymatic hydrolysis studies to be conjugates (M. Slade, personal communication; White, 1972). In this study, conducted on *Manduca* prepupae, it was found that racemic $[2\text{-}^{14}C]_{18}$ JH (synthesis: Hafferl *et al.* 1971) administered in aqueous acetone was rapidly ($t_{1/2} < 1$ hour) metabolized to the carboxylic acid of JH and thence to the acid diol (Fig. 5) which were both found to be essentially devoid of biological activity in the *Galleria* wax test. No cyclization of the C_{18} JH (analogous to the cyclization of 2,3-epoxysqualene to lanosterol) was observed (see, also, Siddall *et al.*, 1971), thus supporting the notion that the JH's which have been isolated so far are hormones per se and not hormone precursors (prohormones). Carboxyl esterase activity occurs in the hemolymph as well as in several other tissues and epoxide hydrolase activity is found in the fat body. Since racemic JH is metabolized nearly quantitatively, neither enzyme system is enantiomer-specific.

The existence of this metabolic pathway has been confirmed in the majority of 32 insect species studied (A. Ajami, personal communication; Ajami and Riddiford, 1971). However, the formation of JH diol from epoxide hydration has been noted in Cecropia (Slade and Zibitt, 1971), *Rhodnius* (White, 1972), and *Tenebrio* and several other lepidopterans (A. Ajami, personal communication), indicating the presence of an alternative pathway as shown in Fig. 5. Rapid metabolism of C_{18} JH has also been found in *Drosophila* imaginal discs *in vitro* (Chihara *et al.*, 1972). Metzler *et al.* (1972) have noted that 90% of the $[^{14}C]C_{18}$ JH administered to adult male Cecropia in either olive or Cecropia oil is metabolized within 24 hours. It should be emphasized that the rate and perhaps even the pathway of inactivation of exogenous JH may differ from that of endogenous (bound) JH.

VI. The Action of Insect Hormones

Prior to discussing the possible mechanisms by which the insect growth hormones interact with target tissues to elicit specific responses that result in the "hormone effect," it is reasonable to probe the means by which the hormones reach the target tissues from the endocrine glands. It is possible that the hormones are in fact modified for transport and may be effective only in this modified form.

A. Hormone Transport

1. Brain Hormone

An obvious obstacle to the study of brain hormone transport is the fact that we are still unsure of the chemical identity of this molecule and in the subsequent discussion it will become clear that the availability of pure labeled hormones is what has allowed some progress in the field of hormone transport. As discussed previously, isolated brains appear to activate the prothoracic glands and it is therefore reasonable to assume that neurosecretory material is released from the brain (via the corpora cardiaca) into the hemolymph and it is possible that the hemolymph-borne material can then enter the prothoracic glands. On the other hand, this may occur under experimental situations, but may not be indicative of the normal situation. For example, we know that neurosecretory material can be carried in a closed system to target tissues and in several cases the prothoracic glands appear to be innervated by neurosecretory fibers from the central nervous system (Section III, B). Finally, it should be mentioned that there have been several suggestions that the hemocytes are involved in the interaction between brain and prothoracic glands since interference with the function of hemocytes invariably inhibits the secretion of MH (Gilbert, 1964). Whether the hemocytes carry the brain hormone or modify it has not been definitively proven, but it is well-known from cytological studies that hemocytes are noted *within* prothoracic glands at those times when the glands are presumably being activated (e.g., Hintze-Podufal, 1970).

2. Molting Hormone

The synthesis of high specific activity [^{3}H]α-ecdysone has permitted several experiments dealing with the transport of MH. The question to be investigated is whether ecdysone is carried as a soluble component of the aqueous portion of the hemolymph, or is bound to particular hemolymph proteins. From the subsequent discussion it will be clear that at least in one insect it appears to be bound while in others it is probably not.

Emmerich (1970a) showed that injection of [^{3}H]ecdysone into the bug *Pyrrhocoris apterus* allowed the recovery of labeled hemolymph proteins from one fraction, and subsequent thin-layer chromatography of the radioactive material suggested that it was indeed ecdysone. Preliminary examination indicated that the ecdysone is reversibly bound, that there is more than one type of binding site, and that several association constants exist for the protein–ecdysone complexes. Further studies with *Drosophila hydei* revealed that what appears to be ecdysone is reversibly bound to three hemolymph proteins (Emmerich, 1970b). If indeed MH is bound to specific hemolymph proteins, these proteins may protect the hormone from degradative hemolymph enzymes or help in the entry of the steroid into target cells. It should be mentioned in this context that other studies suggest that ecdysone freely enters the tissues of saturniids in the absence of hemolymph protein binding (Gorell et al., 1972a). Furthermore, if there are hemolymph protein–ecdysone complexes, there is the possibility that hemolymph proteins actively elicit the entrance of MH into the hemolymph from the gland of synthesis as do hemolymph proteins in the case of cholesterol transit from the gut to the hemolymph (Chino and Gilbert, 1971) and in the case of diglyceride release from the fat body into the hemolymph (Chino and Gilbert, 1965). Finally, the hormone may be released from the endocrine gland as a protein–hormone conjugate. Further studies are necessary to corroborate the above suggestions and to answer the question of specificity of binding.

In a second investigation, *Philosamia* larvae and pupae were exposed to [^{3}H]α-ecdysone either by ingestion or injection and the two major lipoproteins of the hemolymph were then isolated and analyzed (Chino et al., 1970). The data revealed that ingested ecdysone rapidly found its way into the hemolymph, but in no case was the hormone strongly bound to either lipoprotein. Further, gel filtration analysis suggested that ecdysone is not bound to other hemolymph proteins and the results are quite different from those of Emmerich (1970a,b) with *P. apterus* and *D. hydei*. However, it should be noted that during the fractionation of the lipoproteins, most of the fed or injected [^{3}H]ecdysone was found associated with the protein fraction that precipitated with 70% ammonium sulfate and it is possible that the subsequent fractionation procedures utilizing high salt concentration may have cleaved the ecdysone from the protein. Thus, these data support the concept that ecdysone is transported as free hormone, but do not unequivocally rule out the possibility of binding.

3. Juvenile Hormone

In preparation for studies on the transport and action of the lipoidal JH (Section V, B), a series of studies was conducted to characterize the lipoproteins of saturniid hemolymph (Chino et al., 1969; Thomas and Gilbert, 1968, 1969; Thomas, 1972). The ultracentrifugal fractionation data demonstrate the existence of three classes of lipoproteins in the hemolymph of Cecropia pupae. They are low density lipoproteins (LDL; d = 1.046–1.063), high density lipoproteins (HDL; d = 1.156–1.170), and very high density lipoproteins (VHDL; d = 1.26). Electrophoresis demonstrated that each class was composed of several lipoprotein species.

About 75% of the lipid in the total hemolymph lipoproteins is associated with the HDL class and diglyceride is the major neutral lipid component in all three classes. The predominant phospholipid in all classes is phosphatidylcholine, but a substantial amount of phosphatidylethanolamine is also present. It is believed that these lipoproteins are the primary vehicle by which phospholipids, glycerides, and sterols are transported in this insect.

Just recently, Whitmore and Gilbert (1972) have presented cogent evidence for lipoprotein transport of JH. Utilizing $[2\text{-}^{14}C]C_{18}$ JH and a variety of techniques, including column chromatography, thin-layer chromatography, slab-gel electrophoresis, ultrafiltration, and bioassay, they demonstrated the presence of JH in the HDL. Not only is labeled JH associated with the HDL after injection into *Hyalophora* pupae (or when incubated with hemolymph *in vitro*), but the HDL also yields positive bioassays when extracted from male adult hemolymph (Table III), a developmental stage known to yield huge quantities of JH (Gilbert and Schneiderman, 1961). In contrast, pupae do not normally have JH and pupal hemolymph HDL is inactive in bioassay.

We have no knowledge of the specificity of binding of JH to HDL and it is possible that the HDL transports many lipids for various purposes

TABLE III

JUVENILE HORMONE BIOASSAY OF HIGH-DENSITY LIPOPROTEINS[a]

Assay[b]	Sample[b]	Positive	Negative	Percentage positive	Dead
I	Adult male HDL	8	32	25	10
II		20	1	95	3
III		9	29	31	8
I	Pupal male HDL	0	42	0	8
II		0	18	0	5
III		0	40	0	10
I	Adult male hemolymph protein minus HDL	0	41	0	9
II		0	20	0	5
III		0	22	0	5
I	Acrylamide (5%)	0	35	0	5
II		0	18	0	2
III		0	19	0	5

[a] From Whitmore and Gilbert (1972).

[b] I, *Galleria* wax test; II, *Tenebrio* wax test; III, *Galleria* injection test. HDL, high-density lipoprotein.

(e.g., diglycerides which will be metabolized at other sites, cholesterol for use in membrane synthesis) and that the lipoidal nature of the JH molecule simply allows it to be partitioned out of the aqueous hemolymph into the more receptive lipids of the HDL. The HDL–JH complex may have functions in addition to hormone transport in the hemolymph. For example, the HDL may act at the surface of the corpora allata to stimulate the entrance of JH into the hemolymph analogous to its stimulation of cholesterol release from the gut into the hemolymph (Chino and Gilbert, 1971). Alternatively, JH may be released from the corpora allata in the form of the HDL complex since it is known that a lipoprotein resembling the hemolymph HDL is found in other tissues (Thomas and Gilbert, 1969). As mentioned above, sterols such as cholesterol are transported as lipoproteins in saturniid hemolymph (Chino and Gilbert, 1971). Since cytological investigations suggest that sterol precursors of ecdysone may enter the prothoracic glands dissolved in lipid (Romer, 1971a), the possibility exists that the lipoproteins may also be influential in this process.

B. RECOGNITION OF TARGET CELLS

When labeled ecdysone is injected into an insect, it and its metabolites can be recovered from essentially all tissues examined (Moriyama *et al.*, 1970). If indeed insect hormones can freely enter the cells of insect tissues, the question arises as to why some tissues respond (target tissues) while others do not. A great deal of work in mammalian endocrinology has demonstrated the existence of specific proteins in target tissues that possess the capability of binding mammalian hormones or presumed active metabolites of these hormones. Through the now classic experiments of Jensen and Gorski, we know that immature rat and calf uteri which require estradiol for growth, possess a special class of protein molecules that forms complexes with radioactive estradiol. These hormone–protein complexes have been isolated from both the high- and low-speed supernatants derived from uterine homogenates following hormone administration (Toft and Gorski, 1966; Jensen *et al.*, 1966). The possibility therefore exists that specific macromolecules exist in the cells of insect target tissues as well, and the first experiments along this line have shown some promise and in fact have presented a new working hypothesis on MH action. This section will deal exclusively with ecdysone since we know nothing about specific binding proteins in the case of brain hormone and the relationships between JH and a specific hemolymph lipoprotein have been discussed.

In examining the salivary glands of *Drosophila* larvae injected with

[³H]α-ecdysone, Emmerich (1970b) showed that radioactivity was associated with macromolecules in the cytoplasm supernatant and that this complex had a molecular weight of about 65,000. When the salivary glands are incubated in the presence of [³H]α-ecdysone at 0°C, the subsequent homogenate yielded two peaks of radioactivity (3.6 S and 2.0 S) when analyzed by sucrose density gradient centrifugation. It appears that after incubation at 25°C, the 3.6 S complex and the 2.0 S complex are absent from the cytoplasmic fraction but later appear in the soluble nuclear fraction, suggesting a temperature-dependent transport of ecdysone from cytoplasm to nucleus. Once in the nucleus, Emmerich suggests that the hormone becomes bound to the acidic chromatin proteins (to act as a depressor?; see Section VI, D, 3). This most interesting and timely study has major ramifications in the area of ecdysone action, suggesting for one thing that ecdysone is carried into the nucleus where it presumably exerts its effect. Studies on another fly, *Sarcophaga bullata,* using both [³H]α-ecdysone and [³H]β-ecdysone did not reveal the presence of binding proteins (E. Cohen and L. I. Gilbert, unpublished information), but this may be due to species differences or to the fact that they are only discernible at specific developmental stages. It should also be mentioned that Emmerich (1970b) identified the radioactive material bound to the macromolecule on the basis of R_f values alone and did not conduct microchemical analyses. It is well known that many compounds can cochromatograph with ecdysone (Section IV) and the possibility remains that another molecular species is associated with the macromolecules in the *Drosophila* salivary gland studies.

When analogous studies were conducted with saturniid larvae, pupae and pharate adults, there was no evidence of binding of [³H]α-ecdysone to macromolecules in a variety of tissues studied (Cherbas and Cherbas, 1970; Chino *et al.,* 1970; Gorell *et al.,* 1972a). Again, this failure may be due to technical problems and does not rule out the existence of specific binding proteins. Of potential importance are the binding studies utilizing the crustacean hepatopancreas as a model system for ecdysone action and these will be discussed here, since the crustacean and insect MH are probably identical (Gilbert *et al.,* 1971; Gorell *et al.,* 1972b,c). Gorell and his colleagues found that when the crustacean hepatopancreas (analogous to insect fat body) was exposed to very high specific activity [³H]α-ecdysone either *in vivo* or *in vitro* and the supernatant after homogenization and ultracentrifugation was analyzed by gel filtration, there was a protein peak collected that was radioactive suggesting the binding of label to one or more macromolecules. (Control nontarget tissues did not yield elution patterns indicating radioactivity associated with protein fraction in amounts comparable to those obtained with the hepatopancreas.)

When the 105,000 g supernatant was subjected to gel filtration and sucrose density gradient analysis, two discrete peaks of radioactivity were noted which by use of enzyme markers were found to be approximately 11.3 S ($\sim$ 250,000 molecular weight) and 6.35 S ($\sim$ 130,000 molecular weight) (Fig. 6). On standing for several days, the lighter sedimenting radioactive complex appears to aggregate while the heavier material persists indicating a possible subunit relationship between the complexes as is seen in the case of the mammalian estradiol-binding proteins. During the course of these experiments, the question arose as to whether the label associated with the 11.3 S and 6.35 S macromolecules was still attributable to α-ecdysone. On the basis of microchemical analysis, they conclude that the metabolite very probably retains the skeletal carbon atoms and the hydroxylated side chain of α-ecdysone but possesses a quite different pattern of nuclear functionalization. Although the physiological significance of this metabolite–protein complex is not known, it may be important in MH action. Precedence for this point of view comes from studies on the rat prostate demonstrating that testosterone is converted to 5α-dihydrotestosterone and that it is the latter compound which is bound to specific proteins and is in effect responsible for the response of the prostate to exogenous testosterone. It is of extreme interest that in the case of the extradiol-binding protein complex, gene activity is regulated by the complex via control of RNA polymerase activity in the immature

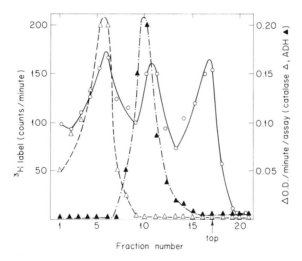

Fig. 6. Sucrose gradient analysis of the two binding proteins for an ecdysone metabolite from the crustacean hepatopancreas. Catalase (Δ) and alcohol dehydrogenase (ADH) ($\blacktriangle$) were used as markers for molecular weight estimation. (o—o) counts per minute for ^{3}H label. From Gorell et al. (1972a).

mammalian uterus (Mohla *et al.,* 1971; see, also, Smuckler and Tata, 1971). It is certainly reasonable to assume that an analogous regulatory system exists in arthropods.

C. Effects at Tissue, Cell, and Biochemical Levels

In this section we will examine the gross effects of the insect hormones. However, these data will not allow a comprehensive hypothesis of the mechanisms of action of hormones at the molecular level. In most of the examples given, the effects studied are far from the site of action of the hormone and may only be the visual culmination of a long series of biochemical reactions and cellular reorganizations.

1. Brain and Corpora Cardiaca

Humoral agents from these two structures will be considered together since in several cases it is not known whether effects attributed to the corpora cardiaca are due to factors stored in the corpora cardiaca but originating in the brain, factors originating in the brain and modified by the corpora cardiaca, or factors synthesized within the corpora cardiaca. Even in the case of the brain itself, some implantation experiments suggest that the corpora cardiaca or structures resembling the corpora cardiaca must be regenerated before the active material from the brain can be released (Gilbert, 1964). Since the possible activation of the prothoracic glands by brain hormone has been discussed, this topic will be omitted from the following discussion as will several other phenomena presumably controlled by the brain–corpora cardiaca system such as "calling" behavior in female saturniid moths (Riddiford and Williams, 1971), oviposition (Truman and Riddiford, 1971), cardioacceleration (Kater, 1968), intestinal contractions (Cazal, 1969), etc.

a. Metabolism. There have been innumerable metabolic effects noted after brain extirpation and/or cardiatectomy and after cauterization of brain neurosecretory cells, some of which may be due to the harsh surgery and inadvertent destruction of other nervous connections. Numerous reports have been published on brain hormone control of various proteins in the hemolymph (Hill, 1962; Laverdure, 1970a) and enzymes in other tissues (Thomsen and Møller, 1963) but these are generally associated with the reproductive process and are discussed in Chapter 3 of this volume. In general, a high concentration of hemolymph protein is associated with an active brain neurosecretory system. It should be pointed out in this regard that quantitative changes in hemolymph proteins are usually analyzed by electrophoresis and as newer techniques become available, more protein bands are discovered. For example, a decade ago, six or seven bands were considered good resolution, but by the use of polyacrylamide gels we now discern about 25 separate hemolymph protein fractions (e.g., Whitmore and Gilbert, 1972). Future techniques may allow the resolution of even more bands and this should be considered when dogmatically postulating a hormonal effect on the protein composition of different tissues and organs.

It appears that the corpora cardiaca do control aspects of fat body respiration (Lüscher and Leuthold, 1965; Wiens and Gilbert, 1965) but not muscle respiration (Keeley and Friedman, 1967). It has been suggested that a factor which inhibits fat body respiration is also released from the corpora cardiaca (Müller and Engelmann, 1968) and these same authors present evidence suggesting that the respiratory control factors are secreted by the corpora cardiaca rather than being transported from the brain to be stored in the corpora cardiaca. Later, Keeley and Friedman (1969) showed that after long-term (30-day) cardiatectomy, cockroach fat body mitochondria had a significantly lower rate of oxygen consumption which could not be reversed by the addition of various metabolic intermediates and cofactors, or induced by corpora cardiaca. This lesion was traced to a decrease in activity of electron transport enzymes analogous to effects of thyroidectomy on the mammal (Keeley, 1971). It is of interest that daily injections of corpora cardiaca extracts reversed the depression of oxygen uptake in the fat body mitochondria of cardiatectomized *Blaberus* suggesting a direct effect in increasing the activity of the electron transport enzymes. Since severing the nervous connections between the brain and corpora cardiaca yields results essentially similar to removal of the corpora cardiaca, Keeley and Waddill (1971) conclude that the active principle is synthesized in the neurosecretory cells of the brain and stored in the corpora cardiaca, although they did not rule out the possibility that the brain stimulates the corpora cardiaca to synthesize and/or release the active material and that nerve severance results in the turning off of the corpora cardiaca. Of interest is that in their reversal studies, boiled corpora cardiaca extracts were ineffective, whereas unboiled extracts did return the mitochondrial oxygen quotient to the normal level. This suggests that the respiratory metabolism factor is a protein and is different from the corpora cardiaca agent responsible for hemolymph hyperglycemia (see below) which retains its activity after boiling.

One of the best studied metabolic phenomena controlled by the brain–corpora cardiaca system is that of carbohydrate metabolism, although as usual it is difficult to determine whether the active substance originates in the corpora cardiaca or whether the corpora cardiaca act as a storage and release center for a brain hormone. There is little doubt that the brain neurosecretory cells do have an effect on carbohydrate metabolism, as for example in the mosquito where a brain hormone presumably inhibits glycogen synthesis in the fat body (Lea and Van Handel, 1970). Let us, however, concentrate on the hyperglycemic factor released from the corpora cardiaca of dictyopterans since most of the work has been conducted on insects of this order.

It was first shown in *Periplaneta* that the concentration of hemolymph trehalose is raised and the glycogen content of the fat body lowered following the injection of corpora cardiaca extracts (Steele, 1961) and it was suggested that this was a result of corpora cardiaca activation of fat body phosphorylase (Steele, 1963; see, also, Ralph and McCarthy, 1964; Bowers and Friedman, 1963). This phenomenon was further investigated by Wiens and Gilbert (1965, 1967a) who found a near maximal stimulation of phosphorylase activity within minutes of corpora cardiaca extract addition suggesting a potent mechanism in *Leucophaea* to control the rate of mobilization of reserve carbohydrate. The rapid response, as well as the relatively large quantity of total carbohydrate mobilized, suggests that this mechanism should be adaptively advantageous to the insect, particularly in situations of environmental stress or other periods of high energy demand. The natural stimulus causing the release of this specific factor(s) from the corpora cardiaca is probably electrical since, at least in the blowfly, electrical stimulation via the brain causes release of this neurohormone within 20 minutes (Normann and Duve, 1969) although some local control via neurosecretory axons cannot be ruled out at this time. Although it was first believed that this hyperglycemic hormone (or hormones; see Natalizi and Frontali, 1966) might be synthesized in the brain and stored in the corpora cardiaca, recent work with *Locusta* suggested that the glandular lobe of the corpora cardiaca had more potent fat body phosphorylase-activating activity than the storage lobe (Goldsworthy, 1970, 1971). However, studies on the regeneration of the corpora cardiaca of the locust revealed that the regenerated "glands" are free of intrinsic neurosecretory cells, glandular lobe tissue, and lateral cerebral neurosecretory cell material, but nevertheless yield extracts that induce hyperglycemia in the cockroach (Highnam and Goldsworthy, 1972). It is concluded by the process of elimination that in the locust at least, the hyperglycemic factor originates in the medial neurosecretory cells of the brain. Since the brain is at least involved in the release of this humoral factor, the regulation of glycogen metabolism in general is likely a joint effort on the part of the brain and corpora cardiaca.

In discussing the possible mechanisms by which the hyperglycemic factor acts, Wiens and Gilbert (1967a) conclude that the corpora cardiaca factor of *L. maderae* appears to affect fat body carbohydrate metabolism in ways that are strikingly similar either to characteristics of the diabetic state or to the metabolic effects of glucagon on mammalian liver. These include (1) activation of phosphorylase through the phosphorylase kinase reaction, (2) increased rate of glycogen degradation, (3) increased concentration of hemolymph carbohydrate, (4) lowered respiratory quotient, (5) decreased oxidation of glucose and incorporation into glycogen, and (6) acceleration of mobilization and metabolism of lipid. The molecule responsible for stimulating trehalose release in *P. americana* appears to be a low molecular weight polypeptide (Brown, 1965) as is glucagon.

As noted above, Wiens and Gilbert (1967a) demonstrated that corpora cardiaca extracts accelerated the mobilization and catabolism of lipids as part of the hyperglycemic effect. Since there is circumstantial evidence that the cockroach corpora cardiaca contains epinephrine (Barton-Browne *et al.*, 1961; see, also, Klemm, 1971), it was possible that epinephrine or an epinephrinelike molecule may have been responsible for the adipokinetic effects. Indeed, when cockroach fat body is incubated in the presence of epinephrine there is a stimulation of release of free fatty acids into the hemolymph with a concomitant depletion of lipid in the fat body presumably due to lipase activation (Bhakthan and Gilbert, 1968, 1971). Since cyclic AMP was also active, and since corpora cardiaca extracts activate fat body phosphorylase via phosphorylase kinase as does cyclic AMP in mammals, it was suggested that epinephrine may act via cyclic AMP in the cockroach fat body and that the corpora cardiaca may secrete an epinephrinelike molecule (Bhakthan and Gilbert, 1968). Mayer and Candy (1969) then found that corpora cardiaca extracts stimulate the release of lipid from the locust fat body into the hemolymph and suggest that the active compound is a peptide since the active fraction is stable to boiling but is inactivated by proteolytic enzymes. It is possible, however, that the active principle is an amine and that it is transported by a carrier protein or peptide prone to digestion by proteolytic enzymes. Of course, we do not know whether the hyperglycemic hormone is identical to the adipokinetic hormone or indeed whether results in one species can be extrapolated to another. In the cockroach, for example, the corpora cardiaca appear to be responsible for determining the hemolymph lipid concentration (hypolipemic factor?) in direct contradistinction to results with the locust (Downer and Steele, 1969). Past studies certainly are strongly suggestive of a peptide nature for the corpora cardiaca hormones

(Natalizi and Frontali, 1966; Kater, 1968; Gersch *et al.*, 1970), but the structures of none have as yet been chemically elucidated.

b. Water Regulation. The question of water balance has been studied in a variety of insects, sometimes with contradictory results, but it is now generally accepted that in some insects excretion is regulated by both diuretic and antidiuretic hormones originating from central nervous system neurosecretory cells (e.g., Maddrell, 1963, 1964; Wall and Ralph, 1962; Wall, 1965; Berridge, 1966; Highnam *et al.*, 1965; Mordue, 1969; Jarial and Scudder, 1971). We will discuss here the diuretic hormone that can be extracted from the brain, corpora cardiaca, and subesophageal ganglion of *Carausius morosus* (Pilcher, 1970) and the mesothoracic ganglion of *Rhodnius* (Maddrell, 1964) because of the elegant *in vitro* studies that have been recently conducted and because we may very well now know more about hormonal mechanisms in this system than any other in insect endocrinology.

Studies utilizing single Malpighian tubules *in vitro* revealed that 5-hydroxytryptamine (5-HT) at concentrations as low as 10^{-8} M stimulates fluid secretion by the Malpighian tubule (Maddrell *et al.*, 1969). Recent studies suggest that 5-HT (and perhaps the diuretic hormone) interact with specific sites on the cell membrane at the basal surface of the cell where the adenyl cyclase system is stimulated and the resulting increase in cyclic AMP then elicits fluid secretion (Maddrell *et al.*, 1971). Experiments with a variety of pharmacological agents have led these authors to suggest that the receptor site has a negative charge to which the terminal nitrogen in the side chain of 5-HT is electrostatically attracted and a positive charge that holds the negatively charged oxygen of 5-HT. Unfortunately, it appears that 5-HT is not the diuretic hormone although they may both utilize the same receptors and in fact have identical mechanisms of action. It is of course possible that 5-HT (and the diuretic hormone) have effects in addition to stimulation of the membrane-bound adenyl cyclase.

Further information on the 5-HT–cyclic AMP system in fluid secretion comes from the elegant work of Berridge and his colleagues (Berridge and Patel, 1968; Berridge, 1970; Oschman and Berridge, 1970; Berridge and Prince, 1971; Prince *et al.*, 1972) using the adult blowfly salivary gland *in vitro* as a model system. In this system, cyclic AMP reproduces many of the effects of 5-HT on fluid secretion, ionic composition of saliva, etc. Fluid secretion is therefore increased by any measures utilized to raise the intracellular level of cyclic AMP including inhibition of the degradation enzyme (phosphodiesterase) and bathing the glands in exogenous cyclic AMP. The proposed model is similar to that for the diuretic

hormone and the Malpighian tubule involving a specific receptor for
5-HT at the cell surface and indicates that 5-HT has one or more roles
in addition to stimulating adenyl cyclase. What does cyclic AMP do once
it has reached a critical titer within the cells of the salivary glands? Studies on the electrical response of isolated salivary glands suggest that while
5-HT affects anion transport in addition to stimulating adenyl cyclase,
the cyclic AMP increases cation transport; the result being increased fluid
secretion. These experiments not only have importance in understanding
the control of fluid secretion, but suggest that this may be an ideal system
to analyze the role of cyclic AMP in regulatory processes in general. The
importance of intracellular and intranuclear ionic alterations on enzyme
activity and even gene activation cannot be overstated at this time (see
Section VI, D, 3).

c. Sexual Differentiation. The classical work on sexual differentiation
in *Lampyris noctiluca* by Naisse (1966a,b,c, 1969) has implicated the
brain neurosecretory cells as a control agent. These coleopterans display
a profound sexual dimorphism as adults (winged males, wingless females) and the gonads do not show differentiation until the third molt. The
testicular follicles have a mesodermal apical tissue lacking in the ovary of
the female and the apical tissue disappears at the onset of spermatogenesis. When testes containing apical tissue are implanted into female
larvae, the result is masculinization of the original female. These and other experiments suggest the secretion of an androgenic hormone by the
apical tissue. However, the chemical nature of this substance is still unknown. On the basis of a large series of endocrine gland implantation and
extirpation experiments as well as cytological studies, Naisse concludes
that it is the neurosecretory cells of the brain that control the development of the apical tissue. The physiological and biochemical details of
this control remain to be worked out as well as the factors controlling the
brain. However, as Naisse suggests, control of these "sex" neurosecretory
cells of the brain may be determined genetically, although not proven at
this writing.

d. Eclosion Hormone. Although there have been several reports in the
past revealing a direct relationship between insect endocrine glands and
behavior (Gilbert, 1964), there have been very few as imaginative or as
complete as the series of studies by Truman (1971a,b; Truman and Riddiford, 1970) revealing that eclosion behavior in saturniid pharate adults
is controlled by a neuroendocrine mechanism.

It has long been known that the silkmoths (and many other insects)
undergo adult ecdysis during a specific time of the day and that this can
be controlled by exposing the developing insect to specific photoperiodic

regimens. In his first experiments, Truman found by extirpation that the brain was necessary for eclosion to occur at the period expected and that brainless pupae developed into adults emerging at random. When brains were implanted into the abdomens of brainless animals, this restored the insect's competence to synchronize eclosion with photoperiod, demonstrating that nervous connections between the brain and the rest of the nervous system were unnecessary. Further studies revealed that the brain picked up photoperiodic cues and retained the information since in a series of brain transplantation experiments among several saturniid species, it was demonstrated that the timing of emergence was characteristic of the species donating the brain and not of the brainless recipient. The fact that implanted brains, brain homogenates, and extracts of hemolymph could entrain the brainless insect with the emergence rhythm of the brain donor demonstrated a hormonal basis for the brain's influence on time of ecdysis. It appears that the hormone is synthesized in brain neurosecretory cells, but is released from the corpora cardiaca. When pre-ecdysial behavior of the pharate moth was examined, it was shown to consist of a species-specific series of stereotyped abdominal movements that was also under the control of the eclosion hormone originating in the brain neurosecretory cells. Although the program for pre-ecdysial behavior lies in the abdominal portion of the central nervous system, it is the eclosion hormone from the brain that initiates the series of emergence events.

This section has attempted to point out the diversity of physiological responses controlled by the brain–corpora cardiaca system and that some progress has been made in unravelling a most complex situation. There are surely several brain hormones, and the corpora cardiaca probably synthesize hormones in addition to storing factors originating in the brain. It is quite possible that different insects have different facets of their physiology controlled by secretion from the brain–corpora cardiaca axis [e.g., lack of phosphorylase activation in the fat body of certain Lepidoptera by the corpora cardiaca (Wiens and Gilbert, 1967b)] so that generalizations are difficult to obtain. Future investigations will surely result in the elucidation of many other phenomena controlled by as yet unknown brain hormones.

2. Juvenile Hormone

With the recent availability of natural Cecropia C_{18} JH and the many mimics of JH, the literature on the effects of JH at the organismic and biochemical levels has grown exponentially over the past few years and only selected examples will be presented here. Since many of the effects of JH occur in coincidence with the action of MH, several will be considered here and others in the following sections. Those studies yielding more direct specific information on the action of JH (e.g., on chromosome puffing) will be discussed in the appropriate subsequent section as well. In 1964 (publication of the first edition of this work), there was still some controversy as to whether JH and gonadotropic hormone are identical, and in this review we will consider them identical and refer to both as JH even if their action is different in the larval and female adult systems. Nomenclature will be the "correct" or "recommended" term from Meyer (1971).

Prior to entering the domain of the insects, it should be pointed out that there have been some effects reported of JH on other organisms. In plants it has been demonstrated that several JH mimetic compounds (farnesol, racemic ethyl ester of the Cecropia C_{18} JH, hydrochlorination product) promoted the growth of stem sections from red-light-exposed pea seedlings, with the latter two substances being as active in the assay as any lipids previously studied (Stowe and Hudson, 1969). Although JH does not normally act by inhibiting growth in insects, but does promote the synthesis of larval structures, it may have a growth-inhibiting effect on the trypanosomatic protozoan, *Crithidea fasciculata,* which is a commensal organism found in the mosquito gut (Ilan *et al.,* 1969). The addition of as little as 5 μg/ml of the hydrochlorination product inhibits the growth of these organisms *in vitro* and the effect can be reversed by washing out. Of course this material with JH activity contains many other substances as well that may have caused the effect, but it is of real interest that there is the suggestion that this primitive organism responds to JH as other protozoan parasites of cockroaches appear to be regulated in aspects of their growth by MH (Gilbert, 1964). In another example of effects of JH on noninsectan material, it was found that farnesol and farnesyl methyl ether inhibit the molting of *Trichinella spiralis* larvae raised in culture, but so did linoleic acid at similar concentrations (Shanta and Meerovitch, 1970; see, also, Davey, 1971). On the other hand, relatively low concentrations of farnesyl methyl ether $(10^{-7} M)$ appeared to be specific in inhibiting the development of the male copulatory appendages (as it does in immature insects). The above preliminary studies suggest that JH (or analogous substances) may play a regulatory role in organisms other than insects.

a. Gross Effects. The fact that JH extracts as well as implanted corpora allata can cause supernumerary larval molts or result in larval–pupal and pupal–adult intermediates is well established (Gilbert, 1964), and we will not dwell on this aspect of the subject even though numerous additional papers revealing essentially the same phenomenon with other insects have appeared in recent years (e.g., White, 1968, 1971; Srivastava and Gilbert, 1968; Staal, 1971; Hintze-Podufal, 1971; Ohtaki et al., 1971; Joly and Meyer, 1970).

b. *Behavior and Color Change*. The influence of hormones on insect behavior is well known from the work of Piepho and his colleagues on the wax moth *Galleria mellonella* (1950a, 1960). Prior to a larval molt the animal spins a silken cocoon longer than the larva and open at both ends. Before the pupal molt the last instar larva spins a short, strong, ovoid cocoon which is closed at both ends. Just prior to pupation, the animal tears one end with its mouthparts, creating a flap which acts as the exit for the moth. Piepho has shown that the type of cocoon constructed depends on the concentration of JH in the animal. For example, a last instar larva receiving implants of active corpora allata will spin an intermediate cocoon when it is destined to molt into a larval–pupal intermediate. If a supernumerary larval molt is induced the animal will spin a typical larval cocoon. In this instance, then, the animal's spinning behavior depends on JH titer which presumably influences the nervous system.

In the hawk moth, *Mimas tiliae*, the behavior of the animal is also influenced by the concentration of JH, but in this case the reaction is all or none (Piepho, 1960; Piepho et al., 1960). The larvae feed at the top of linden trees and larval molts take place on twigs at the top of these trees. Prior to the pupal molt the animal crawls down the tree and digs into the ground where it spins a loose cocoon and pupates. By transplanting active wax moth corpora allata into hawk moth last instar larvae, Piepho obtained gradations of larval–pupal intermediates. Those intermediates that were more pupal than larval came to the ground, while those that were more larval stayed in the tree top. In this case, the concentration of JH determined whether the animal was positively or negatively geotactic. In no instance did the animal remain half-way down the tree, a response which would be analogous to the behavior of wax moth larval–pupal intermediates. Other behavioral patterns may be influenced by JH which may potentiate the phototropic response in some insects (Beetsma et al., 1962).

When young male adult *Schistocera gregaria* are allatectomized, the animals subsequently do not display normal sexual behavior and do not attain the coloration typical of sexually mature animals (Loher, 1961; Pener, 1965). According to Pener, the corpora allata are activated to induce color change and sexual maturation by neurosecretion from the brain (see Section II). Studies on *Locusta* (Joly and Meyer, 1970) reveal that both Cecropia C_{18} JH and Cecropia C_{17} JH have chromatotropic activity (in doses from 5 to 20 μg). That is, the color characteristic of the larva could be maintained in the adult when the hormone was injected into larvae at the proper time (shortly after the period when injection would result in a morphogenetic effect). In *Drosophila* it appears that JH induces the onset of precocious sexual receptivity (Manning, 1966) although these studies were based on implantation of corpora allata together with corpora cardiaca and hypocerebral ganglia. However, the latter two structures may have been active rather than the corpora allata. It is surprising that no further studies with JH or its mimics have been reported in the field of *Drosophila* behavior.

In the mosquito, on the other hand, Lea (1968) has convincingly demonstrated that the corpora allata are essential for sexual receptivity and, in fact, that implantation of active corpora allata into allatectomized females restores receptivity. In *A. aegypti*, females are not receptive to copulation until some 2 days after adult ecdysis, but application of the hydrochlorination product to newly emerged females rendered them receptive to copulation in 1 day (Craig, 1970) suggesting an effect of JH on the mosquito id.

In *Locusta*, allatectomy results in less intensive flight activity (Wajc and Pener, 1971) and a reduction in the spontaneous locomotor activity in adult males (Odhiambo, 1966a) perhaps as an indirect result of the noted decrease in sexual behavior (Strong, 1968). JH, on the other hand, appears to aid males as well in matters of sex since it may stimulate production of a sex pheromone in male beetles (Borden et al., 1969).

c. *Effects on Embryonic Development.* There have been a number of reports that JH and various mimics are effective in blocking embryogenesis (ovicidal) when given to adult females or applied externally in solvent to eggs prior to a critical period of embryogenesis (Sláma and Williams, 1966; Riddiford and Williams, 1967; Novák, 1969; Matolín, 1970; Riddiford, 1970a,b; Retnakaran, 1970). Application after the critical period, as we shall see subsequently, allows normal embryogenesis, but elicits juvenilizing effects later in the life cycle. It should be noted that larger quantities of JH mimics can bring about sterilization of the female. In *Pyrrhocoris*, for example, 1–10 μg of the hydrochlorination product renders the adult female sterile while lesser amounts bring about the aberrations of embryonic development seen for Cecropia (Masner et al., 1968a; see, also, Patterson, 1971). In fact, if a male received the hydrochlorination product, he is able to induce sterility in the female with whom he copulates, presumably by transfer of the mimic (Masner et al., 1968b). Another method of reaching the insect with these JH mimics is through application to the food and it has been recently shown that at least one peptidic analogue for a phytophagous insect can be translocated

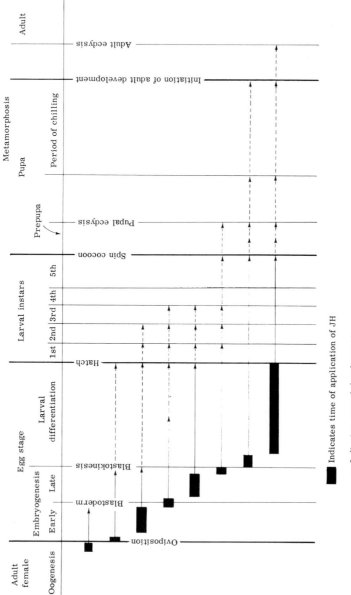

Fig. 7. A diagrammatic summary of the effects on the embryonic and postembryonic development of *H. cecropia* when juvenile hormone is applied to the egg. From Riddiford (1970b).

by the plant and affect insects feeding on the various plant parts (Babu and Slăma, 1972).

In the case of Cecropia (Riddiford, 1971), the Cecropia C_{18} JH and hydrochlorination product were effective in blocking embryogenesis when injected into female pharate adults, a stage at which vitellogenesis is almost completed and prior to chorion formation. After the adult emerged, mated, and eggs were laid, it was determined that embryogenesis was halted in the blastoderm stage just prior to formation of the germ band (Fig. 7). Since analogous effects on other organisms can be obtained by administration of actinomycin D, Riddiford infers that JH may be interfering with mRNA synthesis and that the information needed to form the blastoderm was provided by the maternal genome (long-lived mRNA?). If JH is applied to the egg after fertilization and oviposition, embryonic development is blocked at blastokinesis rather than the earlier blastoderm stage and this is about 1 day prior to the embryonic molt that results in the formation of the cuticle of the first instar larva.

Although the embryo appears to become less sensitive to JH as embryogenesis proceeds, some of the eggs that hatched after JH treatment prior to blastokinesis gave rise to normal-looking first instar larvae, but later in the life cycle certain abnormalities were noted that suggested a delayed JH effect (Fig. 7). For example, intermediates between larvae of several instars were obtained. If JH was applied after blastokinesis, most animals that survived developed into the large last instar larvae but were unable to pupate normally, either remaining as larvae or becoming larval–pupal intermediates. Since these animals have effective means for rapidly breaking down JH (see Section V, F), it is concluded that the JH had a direct effect on the embryos that was subsequently expressed or, as Willis (1969) hypothesized, there may have been a permanent alteration in the corpora allata which caused them to secrete abnormal quantities of JH at the larval–pupal molt (see Section III on positive feedback relations between corpora allata and JH). To investigate the latter possibility, Willis and Lawrence (1970) conducted a series of reciprocal staged integument grafting experiments between *Oncopeltus* larvae treated with the hydrochlorination product late in embryonic development and normal larvae. When a normal graft was applied to the treated larva, the graft developed into an abnormal larval–adult type with the host. In the reciprocal experiment, the graft from a treated animal molted and differentiated normally with the normal larva. Further, morphological considerations suggested that the hormone entered the cell from the cuticle rather than from the hemolymph, and Willis and Lawrence conclude that the postembryonic effects elicited by the JH mimic treatment of embryos are due to persistence of the hormone (in the cuticle?). It is possible that this synthetic JH mimic persists throughout larval development, but it is doubtful that the natural JH would be able to resist the degradative enzymes that must normally be present.

Finally, it was shown by implantation experiments that *Pyrrhocoris* embryos treated with JH gave rise to last instar larvae having very active corpora allata when compared to normal larvae (Riddiford and Truman, 1972). Also, allatectomy of the last instar larvae that had been exposed to JH during embryogenesis resulted in a normal imaginal molt. These data demonstrate that JH is not carried over from the treated embryo to the last instar larva and suggest that a lesion is formed in the treated embryo which manifests itself in the inability of the corpora allata to be turned off at the metamorphic molt.

These experiments do not explain, however, how normal embryogenesis proceeds in the presence of an endogenous bioassayable quantity of JH (Gilbert and Schneiderman, 1961) or whether JH may have some role during normal embryogenesis (see Dorn, 1972). In this regard, it should be mentioned that female Cecropia moths, and in particular female Cecropia moths, have active corpora allata secreting JH (Gilbert and Schneiderman, 1961). Why are the eggs of these animals not affected whereas the addition of exogenous JH has obvious ovicidal effects? Studies on insect polymorphism have suggested a role for JH in embryogenesis. In a series of studies on the cabbage aphid, White (1968, 1971) showed that larvae could be influenced by JH mimics. Of greater significance were her studies on the hormonal control of alate-apterus polymorphism in these insects, phenomena which had previously been shown to be dependent on the environmental stimuli acting on the female adult which were possibly transduced into a humoral stimulus that influenced the embryo in such a way that it became either an alate or apterus aphid. Lees (1967) had expressed the view that it was the embryo's corpora allata that determined the polymorphic state attained subsequently. White's results suggest that most aphid embryos have wing rudiments, but that there is a prenatal loss of the wing buds when the maternal environment contains a relatively high titer of JH. Under this view, the JH of the mother inhibits the differentiation of structures such as wing buds that are to be functional in the adult stage. Theoretically, the application of JH to an aphid population should result in an apterus population and may therefore be a means for control. Although White's theory is consistent with the data, it is not yet a proven fact but is a possible example of the corpora allata of one individual controlling aspects of development in another insect.

d. Tumor Induction. In their investigation demonstrating that the JH mimic farnesyl methyl ether applied to final instar nymphs of *Blatella germanica* results in the persistence of their ability to regenerate limbs, O'Farrell and Stock (1964) noted large genital tumors in the treated cockroaches. In this instance the JH mimic acted as a chemical carcinogen. When a variety of chemicals with JH activity were fed to a strain of *Drosophila* disposed to the development of melanotic tumors, it was shown that they were extremely tumorigenic (Bryant and Sang, 1969). Since substances such as farnesyl methyl ether do not induce tumor formation in strains in which melanotic tumor genes are absent, it is unlikely that tumor induction can be generally considered a direct result of increases in JH titer and the authors conclude that these chemicals operate by exaggerating a preexisting endocrine defect in a system regulated by JH in these susceptible flies. Whether these melanotic tumors are tumors in the strict definition of the word continues to be a matter of conjecture.

e. Postembryonic Development—Internal Morphology. As has been stated several times in this review as well as in the earlier review, JH and its analogues applied to larval or pupal insects yields the same results as implantation of active corpora allata. That is, there is a retention of larval characteristics or pupal characteristics depending on the stage tested and, in a few cases, a reversal of metamorphosis for implants or grafts (Gilbert, 1964). In general, the above observations were conducted on the external morphology of the organism and consisted in most cases of distinguishing between larval, pupal, and adult cuticles, and therefore was an analysis of the products of the epidermal cells which are of course a prime target of JH.

A classic set of experiments, which have greatly enhanced our knowledge of the hormonal control of metamorphosis, were conducted on the wax moth, *Galleria mellonella,* by Piepho and his associates (Piepho, 1942, 1946, 1950a,b,c, 1951, 1952; Piepho and Meyer, 1951; Wiedbrauck, 1953). When a fragment of integument from one larva is implanted into the abdominal cavity of another, the epidermis of the fragment regenerates and grows around the cuticle of the implant to form an epidermal vesicle with cuticle at its interior. When the host molts, the vesicle molts with it and the type of cuticle secreted by the epidermal cells of the vesicle can be determined. Piepho and his colleagues found that a fragment of integument, excised from a first instar larva (even one newly hatched from the egg) and implanted into the hemocoel of a last instar larva, formed a vesicle which molted with the host and formed pupal cuticle, omitting four larval molts. At the adult molt of the host, this vesicle again molted and formed adult cuticle with scales. When they implanted larval integument into a pupal host, it molted directly to the adult state, omitting the pupal stage. Pupal integument implanted in last instar larvae underwent a second pupal molt. By implanting adult integument into last instar larvae, they obtained several supernumerary molts of the adult cuticle. These simple experiments conclusively demonstrated that molting was under hormonal control and that the epidermis reacts to JH by laying down larval structures. There is less JH present in a pupal molt than in a larval molt and very little or none at the final molt to the adult. By implanting pieces of young pupal integument into very young larvae, Piepho found that the implant finally produced a complete larval cuticle after several molts. The epidermis then produced another larval cuticle with the host and then pupal and adult cuticle. In many cases, the midpart of the implanted vesicle molted to pupal cuticle while the portion that had regenerated to close the vesicle gave rise to larval cuticle after one molt (indicating the extreme sensitivity of regenerating epidermis to JH). At each succeeding larval molt, the midpart of pupal cuticle diminished in size, and more larval cuticle formed. This, then, was a reversal of metamorphosis under the control of JH. Reversion of integument from adult to larval has also been demonstrated by Wigglesworth (1940) in *Rhodnius*. Piepho and Meyer (1951) and Wiedbrauck (1953) demonstrated that they could take metamorphosis forward, reverse it, and take it forward again. They implanted integument of a last-stage *Galleria* larva into another last-stage larva where the implant formed a vesicle and molted with the host through the pupal and adult stages, at which time it formed scales. They reimplanted vesicles of this kind into young larvae, older larvae, or pupae, and in most instances found that, when the adult integument molted, it produced a second set of almost normal scales. In several experiments this adult epidermis gave rise to pupal cuticle which then molted with the host to form adult structures. More amazing were the results attained in a few cases where the adult integument implanted into a young larva produced abnormal, but definite, larval cuticle, which was followed by pupal cuticle when the host molted to a pupa, and, finally, by adult cuticle. This emphasizes the remarkable plasticity of the insect's epidermal cells. The work has many ramifications but can be understood most simply in terms of a hormone secreted by the corpora allata which influences metamorphosis by promoting the synthesis of larval structures.

On the basis of morphological data, various workers have argued pro and con as to whether JH prevents adult development (keeps the organism in a *status quo* condition) by inhibiting the cell in its inherent drive toward the adult state, or whether the JH actively causes the cell to indulge in more "juvenile" synthesis and that cells have an inherent resistance to reversion. The many cases of reversion of transplanted epidermal cells (Gilbert, 1964) and tissues (Piepho and Holz, 1959) argues for the latter theory, although the counter-argument is that the transplants have undergone mitosis (DNA replication) and therefore the more juvenile cuticle secreted is from the descendants of the original cell rather than from the original transplanted cells. If the very same cell can secrete larval or adult cuticle, then we must consider JH as an activator rather than a *status quo* hormone. The problem is most complex and the possibility exists that both theories are correct in principle and that each in turn applies to a specific temporal and tissue-specific sequence of events.

Let us now consider some recent studies dealing with the effects of JH at the organ and tissue levels. In all studies on the effects of JH on post-embryonic development, it should be remembered that JH is acting as a modulator of MH action and in almost all cases studied, JH is ineffective in the absence of MH. As one example of JH effects at the organismic level, we will consider the studies of Sehnal and Meyer (1968) on the larval–pupal transformation of *Galleria mellonella*. Last instar larvae (and allatectomized larvae) were injected with a highly purified extract of Cecropia JH at various days during the instar. The data revealed that animals injected 3 days after larval ecdysis molted into supernumerary larvae, while those injected some 5 days later (1 day prior to pupation) were unaffected. Gradation of response was noted from day 3 to day 6 larvae with injection into younger larvae eliciting a greater JH response. Of interest is that animals injected prior to day 3 of the last larval instar appeared refractory to the JH, although sensitive, since multiple injections of JH at several times (2 and 4 days) revealed that a lower quantity of JH was required at day 4 to produce a maximum effect if the larva was pretreated with JH at day 2. The experiment reveals that epidermal cells are sensitive to JH during the middle of the larval instar rather than the beginning of the developmental stage as has been documented by many studies on pupal–adult development in Lepidoptera (e.g., Gilbert and Schneiderman, 1960). If injected too early (prior to the critical period), JH is efficiently catabolized (see Sections V, F and VI, D). This simple series of experiments reveals the importance of timing both in studies utilizing exogenous application of JH and secretion by the animal's own corpora allata. On the other hand, JH analogues which cannot be metabolized by the insect should be effective any time prior to, and at, the critical period. The critical period is presumably the time at which the cells are also exposed to MH and prior to the occurrence of mitosis in the epidermal cells (Sehnal and Novák, 1969). This latter point is important because it implies that once mitosis (DNA replication) takes place, the cell is no longer responsive to JH at that instar and perhaps contradicts what was once believed: that the same epidermal cell is capable of secreting larval, pupal, and adult cuticle (see, however, Hinton, 1963).

A number of studies have appeared suggesting that DNA replication must precede metamorphosis (e.g., Lawrence, 1966; Krishnakumaran *et al.*, 1967). Thus, once DNA replication has occurred in the epidermal cells of the last instar larvae, the resulting cells will produce pupal cuticle no matter what concentration of JH they are subsequently exposed to. That is, the genetic memory of the cell to produce larval cuticle is erased and under this view the few cases of reversion (e.g., implants of adult epidermal cells ultimately producing larval cuticle) are contingent upon DNA replication and the proper hormonal environment. However, this view is not unanimously accepted. For example, according to Whitten, who studied the ultrastructure of tracheal cuticle and the epidermal cells secreting the cuticle during the development of the cyclorrhaphan fly, *S. bullata*, "the same epidermal cell would seem to be capable of forming the larval and pupal cuticles and, in some areas, also the highly specific adult cuticle" (Whitten, 1972, p. 390). Results more than three decades ago suggested that bristles and cuticle intermediate between larva and adult could be formed (Wigglesworth, 1936) and this has recently been confirmed on another insect (Lawrence, 1966). In an analysis utilizing the polarizing microscope and electron microscope, Caveney (1970) showed that under certain regimens of JH analogue application, *Tenebrio* epidermis is capable of secreting larval endocuticle and then adult endocuticle without an intervening molt. This implies that the *same* epidermal cell can indeed secrete larval or adult cuticle and need not be reprogrammed by DNA replication before metamorphosis. Our view is that the question has still not been answered unequivocally.

There have been a number of cytophysiological studies suggesting that JH influences the protein bodies in the fat body. Most of this work reveals correlations and not direct effects. For example, in the Colorado beetle, the maximum amount of protein bodies is associated with adults having inactive corpora allata and it is postulated that a lack of JH induces the formation of these organelles (de Loof and Lagasse, 1970), and similar correlations are found during the metamorphosis of the American silkmoth (Bhakthan and Gilbert, 1972). Ultrastructural studies suggest that JH controls depletion of protein bodies from the fat body during vitellogenesis in the viviparous cockroach, *Diploptera punctata* (Stay and Clark, 1971).

In a study of the effect of the hydrochlorination product on ovarian development in *Pyrrhocoris,* Masner (1969) showed that gradual differentiation of the ovarian rudiments during larval life occurs despite the presence of the JH mimic even when the epidermal cells are affected. However, in order to obtain normal ovaries in the adult, there must be an absence of JH in the environment of the prefollicular tissue for 2 days at the beginning of the last larval instar. [Recent *in vitro* studies suggest that excess JH can inhibit aspects of oogenesis (Adams and Eide, 1972) .] Subsequent vitellogenesis required JH. This suggests that different tissues (and different cells within a tissue) may respond uniquely to JH and emphasizes our lack of knowledge of tissues other than epidermis undergoing morphogenesis in the presence of varying concentrations of JH. The complexity of the effects of JH on the larval development of internal organs is exemplified by Sehnal's (1968) studies on *Galleria.* During larval life, some of the internal organs develop continuously (e.g., wing discs, gonads, fat body, etc.) but some of ectodermal origin develop only during the molting period. If corpora allata are implanted early enough in the last instar, several internal organs continue to grow rather than undergo metamorphosis, suggesting that JH promotes the growth of larval structures and that it prevents the metamorphosis of internal organs just as it does with the cuticle. Of particular interest is that a number of naturally occurring histolytic processes that occur at metamorphosis are inhibited by JH. This is consistent with a recent hypothesis that MH may act to stimulate the release of hydrolytic enzymes from lysosomes while JH stabilizes the lysosomal membrane (W. Vedeckis, personal communication) .

The alimentary canal of the larval saturniid consists of an essentially straight tube which undergoes a precise regimen of differentiative steps during metamorphosis from the larva to pupa and from the pupa to the adult (Judy and Gilbert, 1969, 1970a) . One of the most complex structures seen in this differentiation process is the rectal pad (functioning in water reabsorption) during adult development. To test whether the presence of JH in the larva is responsible for maintaining the larval nature of the gut, a series of experiments were conducted in which Cecropia JH extract or the hydrocholorination product were injected into the animals and the effects on the gut analyzed cytologically (Judy and Gilbert, 1970b) . The results demonstrate that the small pupal hindgut cells that normally divide to form the general rectal wall of the adult appear to be sensitive to JH since doses above a certain minimum effectively inhibit mitosis and the histological changes that normally follow division. Indeed, some believe that JH acts as an antimitotic agent and that, when applied to a pupa, the affected epidermal cells are prevented from dividing and therefore secrete the pupal cuticle they are programmed for rather than being reprogrammed to secrete adult cuticle (e.g., Zlotkin and Levinson, 1968a). This view is supported by recent work revealing that both RNA and protein synthesis are inhibited in cell cultures when JH is added (Cohen and Gilbert, 1972). On the other hand, some postmitotic cells in the insect epidermis respond to JH treatment (Willis, 1969) and certain regions of *Rhodnius* respond to JH by increased mitotic activity (Wigglesworth, 1959).

One developing structure that holds great promise for analyzing the effects of JH is the flight muscles since they are relatively easy to study both at the ultrastructural and biochemical levels. As discussed in Chapter 2, de Wilde's group has clearly demonstrated that adult diapause in the Colorado beetle is due to the inactivity of the corpora allata. Among the characteristics of this "pseudo-allatectomy" syndrome is the degeneration of the flight muscles (Stegwee *et al.*, 1963) consisting of a greatly reduced diameter of the muscle fibrils and the virtual absence of sarcosomes. When the corpora allata are removed from animals destined not to enter diapause, the above syndrome ensues. However, muscle regeneration will take place if active corpora allata are implanted. This elegant study demonstrated a regulatory role for JH in muscle development although the effect of JH could have been indirect as is possible in all *in vivo* situations studied. Recent results suggest that in diapause beetles the muscles have not degenerated but have simply not developed (de Kort and Raak, 1971). Under this view, active corpora allata induce muscle development. On the other hand, in some insects, such as *Dysdercus intermedius,* flight muscle histolysis accompanies oogenesis and both processes can be stimulated by implantation of the corpora cardiaca–corpora allata complex (Edwards, 1970). Edwards suggests that JH does indeed induce yolk deposition, but that some other hormone elicits flight muscle histolysis. The possibility remains, however, that it is JH that stimulates the histolytic process since it certainly appears to do so in *Ips confusus* (Borden and Slater, 1968; see, also, Poels and Beenakkers, 1969). In these latter instances, substrates resulting from flight muscle degeneration are presumably utilized by the developing oocyte (Bhakthan *et al.*, 1970) and it is not surprising that both processes could be JH mediated. Although the metabolic mechanisms for the relationship between JH and flight muscle development are not understood, de Kort (1969) postulates that a low level of JH prevents flight muscle development in the Colorado beetle indirectly by lowering the overall capacity of the insect to synthesize proteins (perhaps via the brain neurosecretory cells). Recent studies suggest that the metamorphosis of the nerve cord may also be a promising system for styding the effects of JH (Schwartz, 1971).

f. Juvenile Hormone Effects on Metabolism. There have been a large number of *in vivo* metabolic effects reported after allatectomy, corpora allata implantation, and JH administration (see Gilbert, 1964). Since there is a complex interaction between the corpora allata and other endocrine glands (Section II), it is very difficult to distinguish between direct and indirect effects. Except for those studies dealing with the adult insect (e.g., control of oogenesis) and the interaction between JH and endocrine glands (Section II), JH is an ineffective metabolic control agent except where it is acting as a modulator of MH action (e.g., Oberlander and Schneiderman, 1966; Sehnal and Sláma, 1966), particularly in cells actively engaged in DNA synthesis (Krishnakumaran *et al.,* 1967). Many of the metabolic phenomena previously attributed to JH are in fact an indirect result of the morphogenetic effects of the hormone. For example, as we have just discussed, application of JH to some insects results in muscle degeneration. Thus, all the hydrolytic reactions involved in muscle breakdown could be attributed to JH, but these data give us no solid information on the mechanism of action of the hormone. The same can be said of phenomena wherein the corpora allata may have a direct effect on the nervous system, resulting in increased locomotory activity with decreases in the substrates utilized for locomotory energy (e.g., Odhiambo, 1966a).

Since de Wilde (Chapter 3) has discussed in detail the hormonal control of gametogenesis and associated events, we will only briefly mention some aspects of JH effects on metabolism related to these phenomena. It is now an established fact that specific hemolymph proteins are incorporated into the developing oocyte of almost all insects studied and that in many the synthesis, uptake by the oocyte, and perhaps release from the fat body of this protein are under the control of JH (e.g., Engelmann, 1969; Brookes, 1969; Lüscher, 1968; Thomas and Nation, 1966; Bell and Barth, 1971) and the dependence of egg maturation on JH has even been extended to those lepidopterans feeding as adults (Sroka and Gilbert, 1971; Pan and Wyatt, 1971). [On the other hand, in moths not feeding as adults, JH can block the accumulation of a specific blood protein, likely as a result of preventing adult differentiation of which oogenesis is one facet (Blumenfeld and Schneiderman, 1968).] Studies by Engelmann (1971) on *Leucophaea* reveal that both the Cecropia C_{18} JH and C_{17} JH are effective in stimulating the synthesis of the female-specific protein in the fat body and his actinomycin D experiments suggest that JH is acting at the transcriptional level in this case. In this regard, the synthesis of products of the colleterial glands of cockroaches that are responsible for formation of the ootheca subsequent to oogenesis and fertilization also appear to be under the control of JH. In the presence of JH, the colleterial glands increase their rates of RNA and protein synthesis (Zalokar, 1968) which probably reflects the synthesis of proto-catechuic acid glucoside needed for tanning of the ootheca (Willis and Brunet, 1966; Shaaya and Bodenstein, 1969).

There is increasing evidence that JH is involved with aspects of lipid metabolism in some adult insects, presumably acting in a manner such that lipid stored in the fat body can be shunted to the developing oocytes where it can ultimately act as substrate for embryogenesis. The original observation was made almost 30 years ago that allatectomy of adult female *Melanopus* results in hypertrophy of fat body with greater than normal quantities of lipid (Pfeiffer, 1945), and it has been corroborated by several recent studies in other insects (e.g., El-Ibrashy and Boctor, 1970; Odhiambo, 1966c; Orr, 1964; see, however, Butterworth and Bodenstein, 1969). Gilbert (1967a) examined the question of how the loss of the corpora allata may result in lipid accumulation in the fat body of the adult female ovoviviparous cockroach, *Leucophaea maderae*. The data reveal that lipid serves as an important substrate for embryogenesis in this insect and that there is a rapid rise in the lipid content of eggs undergoing maturation. This finding that the decrease in fat body lipid during the latter stages of oogenesis precedes the peak of oocyte lipid content indirectly suggests some transfer of metabolites from the fat body to the ovary. That this transfer from fat body to ovary is physiologically possible was revealed by *in vitro* studies demonstrating the capacity of the ovary to accept lipid from the fat body. The fact that castration prevents the decrease in fat body lipid is further evidence for this supposition.

The results indicate that egg maturation (yolk deposition) and accumulation of fat body lipid by the ovary occur at a time when the corpus allatum is maximally active. *In vitro* studies revealed that in the presence of JH, isolated ovaries (with maturing oocytes) incorporate palmitate into glycerides and phospholipid at a rate far exceeding that of the controls. This may be due to a general metabolic enhancement of the ovary, a specific effect on the permeability properties of the structure allowing a greater influx of substrate, or a specific effect on one or more aspects of lipid synthesis. It is, however, a direct effect on the ovary or oocytes.

The data also suggest that JH may act to depress the synthesis of neutral lipids in the fat body (see, also, Stephen and Gilbert, 1970). This would, of course, make more substrate available for yolk deposition in the developing oocyte, and perhaps at this stage the metabolic machinery of the fat body is primed for shunting stored metabolites to the ovary rather than synthesizing more lipid. Lipid is stored by the fat body during the first 10 days of oogenesis but decreases in amount as the lipid content of the developing oocytes continues to rise. The data of Lüscher and Wyss-Huber (1964) suggest that the activity of the corpus allatum during the reproductive cycle of *L. maderae* reaches a maximum at about 15 days and remains near this point during the remaining 5 days of oogenesis. Perhaps a low titer of JH enhances the capacity of the fat body to synthesize lipid, but at higher concentrations it opposes lipid synthesis and has an adipokinetic effect.

3. Molting Hormone

In this section we will use the terms MH and ecdysone interchangeably (see, however, Section IV, E) .

a. Effects on Mammals. Both because of the unique structure of the polyhydroxy steroid ecdysone and its possible (but probably impractical) use as an agent for insect control, a series of studies has been conducted on mammalian cell cultures, rats, and mice to determine whether ecdysone and several phytoecdysones may have any adverse or beneficial effects. The results of the several published reports are in general contradictory. For example, it was first reported that ecdysone extracts (not crystalline) suppressed the growth of sarcoma cultures within 24 hours in a dose-dependent manner (Burdette and Richards, 1961) but this was not true in the case of HeLa cells or the development of the chick embryo when pure ecdysone was used (Hoffmeister and Lang, 1964) . The reader is referred to the following references for further studies utilizing mammals *in vivo:* Hirono *et al.* (1969) , Lupien *et al.* (1969) , Masuoka *et al.* (1970) , Otaka *et al.* (1968, 1969) , Hikino *et al.* (1969) , and Chaudary *et al.* (1969) .

b. Effects at Tissue and Organ Levels in Vivo. As a point of reference let us consider the MH content in *Bombyx mori* during development (Shaaya and Karlson, 1965) . The content increases during the larval instar and peaks just prior to ecdysis, while in the last instar it peaks just prior to the time of spinning the pupal cocoon. The hormone is, in fact, measurable during the entire instar and the peaks, when they do occur, are not sharp. The amounts present are considerably less than those needed to obtain effects by exogenous application and suggest that subliminal effects may be exerted by the hormone prior to the manifestations of the studied morphological and biochemical effects noted immediately after injection of large quantities. This suggests that ecdysone must act for a prolonged time rather than exciting a "triggering" effect on target cells (see, for example, Berreur and Fraenkel, 1969; Zdarek and Fraenkel, 1970) . The highest content is found at the initiation of pharate adult development (see, also, Kaplanis *et al.,* 1966) and, interestingly enough, peaks again midway through pharate adult development. This latter observation explains the ability of some workers to extract ecdysone from adult insects (e.g., Karlson and Stamm-Menéndez, 1956) and implies a role for MH in adult life, e.g., egg development (Laverdure, 1970b; see, however, Robbins et al., 1968; Wright et al., 1971). It appears that ecdysone may have a role in embryonic development as well (Ohnishi et al., 1971), but further study is needed on this point.

In addition to initiating the molting process in insects, the ecdysones are effective in other arthropods as well (e.g., Krishnakumaran and Schneiderman, 1970). It is well known that MH secretion or exogenous application breaks insect diapause in some species (Gilbert, 1964) and the availability of pure ecdysones has resulted in similar reports in more insects including the alkali bee which enters diapause as a prepupa (Hsiao and Hsiao, 1969) and also in noninsectan arthropods (e.g., tick, Wright, 1969).

The most common bioassay for MH is the isolated larval abdomen of flies which undergoes tanning to produce the puparium when injected with an active preparation. Prior to forming the puparium, however, the larva typically shortens and thickens to a barrel shape and, although this shortening process is coordinated by the brain, it is elicited by MH (Berreur and Fraenkel, 1969). When exogenous ecdysone is applied at a critical time, one can achieve tanning without shortening (Thomson and Horn, 1969), suggesting interference with the coordinative activities of the brain. The dosages needed to obtain *normal* development when applied to diapausing animals, debrained pupae, or isolated abdomens are therefore critical. For example, the injection of too much ecdysone into lepidopteran pupae resulted in an external morphology reminiscent of animals receiving JH injections, i.e., interference with scale formation, eye development, internal differentiation, etc. (Kobayashi et al., 1967; Beck and Shane, 1969; Sakurai and Hasegawa, 1969; Judy and Gilbert, 1970b), although in the latter study no true second pupal cuticle was seen. Many of these external morphological effects are likely due to the acceleration of development (Ito et al., 1970) with premature cuticle deposition. Perhaps the study of the internal morphology of some developing organ systems would provide more basic information on ecdysone action.

Judy and Gilbert (1970b) showed that when pupae are injected with varying doses of β-ecdysone, the resulting abnormal development of the rectal epithelium is qualitatively different from that following injection of JH. The total number of cells comprising the general epithelium in β-ecdysone treated insects suggests the occurrence of many cell divisions. The full extent of the abnormalities induced in the general epithelium is difficult to interpret. However, the regular cuboidal appearance of the cells, their arrangement into a uniform simple layer, and the secretion of a normal adult intima indicates that the excess of β-ecdysone had only a limited influence on differentiation. That is, it inhibited the final transformation to a squamous cell sheet.

The cortex cells invariably develop whenever adult development has been initiated. Although a few of the JH-treated pupae formed small cortex cell clusters, all the high dose and most of the intermediate dose MH-treated insects formed large, elongate complexes. These typically occur in six areas within the rectum, a condition most likely related to the six longitudinal folds in the pupal rectal pouch. Rectal pads formed as six raised ridges of modified epithelial cells are common in most insect orders (Reichenbach-Klinke, 1952) and this is generally considered to be the most primitive condition in terms of the evolution of rectal pads. Lepidoptera are somewhat unique in forming several hundred small rectal pads. From Judy and Gilbert's observations on normal rectal-pad development, it is concluded that the normal condition in Lepidoptera is derived from a basic plan in which six presumptive cortex areas exist in the pupa. These become segregated by mitotically active epithelial cells and it is this segregation process that is being inhibited by the higher dose of β-ecdysone.

Histolytic changes also occur during metamorphosis as larval tissues degenerate and are replaced by adult tissue. In *Sarcophaga bullata* larvae about to undergo metamorphosis, the midgut epithelial cells shrink and become filled with lysosomes as a prelude to degeneration and replacement by adult cells. On the assumption that this proliferation of lysosomes may be due to an increased titer of MH at a time when the JH titer was relatively low, Radford and Misch (1971) studied the micromorphology of these cells after injection of β-ecdysone. When larvae are injected with a large dose (6 μg) of β-ecdysone, the midgut epithelial cells prematurely accumulated increased numbers of lysosomes displaying acid phosphatase activity with mitochondria and endoplasmic reticulum within them (Fig. 8). Lysosome proliferation and cell death continued for almost a day after hormone injection, suggesting sequential events finally leading to lysosome appearance. It can therefore be concluded that lysosome induction along with the synthesis or sequestering of hydrolytic enzymes are a result of MH action and that the MH must be considered a "cell death hormone" as well as a "growth hormone."

The above effects of ecdysone on the external and internal morphology of the insect leave open the possibility that ecdysone is acting indirect-

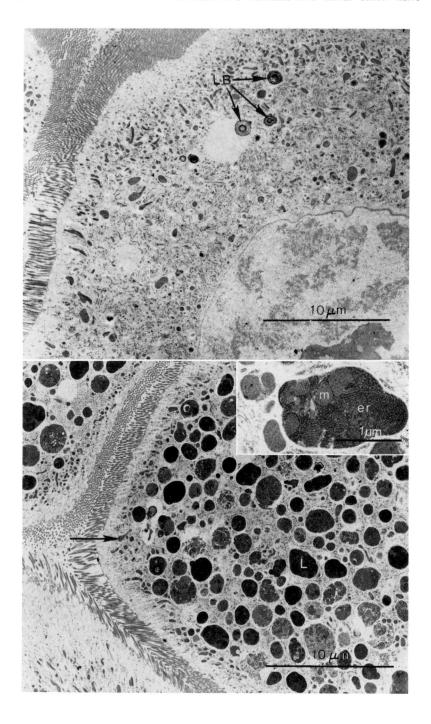

ly on the tissues and organs observed and that MH stimulated another endocrine gland or tissue to secrete the substance causing the effects. Perhaps the study of ecdysone action *in vitro* would help answer this question.

c. Effects at Tissue and Organ Levels in Vitro. Some examples of ecdysone action *in vitro* will be illustrated below but others will be reserved for the next section which considers responses close to the site of hormone action. For a comprehensive survey of the literature prior to 1970, the reader is referred to Marks (1970).

Since several points on the effects of JH and MH have been exemplified in this review by the metamorphosing lepidopteran gut, let us first consider the elegant studies of Judy and Marks (1971; Judy, 1969) on the behavior of the tobacco hornworm gut *in vitro*. Utilizing doses of 5–50 μg of β-ecdysone in organ culture, they showed that larval tissues underwent changes typical of those normally seen during the larval–pupal metamorphosis while the use of diapausing pupal tissues resulted in changes normally seen during pupal–adult metamorphosis. The fact that these tissues were maintained *in vitro* for up to ten months allowed exhaustive observations. It should be noted that none of the changes were elicited in the presence of the inactive isomer, 22-isoecdysone. The tissue culture medium utilized was a complex mixture including bovine serum and several unknown protein components. During the *in vitro* ecdysone-stimulated development, the pupal hindgut expanded as it does during normal adult development and a thin, adult rectal epithelium was formed. No changes were noted in gut differentiation during the first 10–24 hours after application of β-ecdysone, again suggesting that a series of biochemical events preceded the morphological changes.

The testes of diapausing insects are normally quiescent but are induced to undergo spermatogenesis when development ensues due to the presence of a critical titer of MH, and this organ has been a favorite for insect physiologists wishing to study differentiation *in vitro* (Marks, 1970). In an important study, Yagi *et al.* (1969) were able to demonstrate that spermatogenesis in diapausing larval rice borer testes was indeed stimulated by β-ecdysone (200 μg/ml) *in vitro*. While cysts cultured in the CSM–2F medium (no hemolymph but contains yeast hydrolysate, etc.) underwent some differentiation in the absence of β-ecdy-

---

Fig. 8. β-Ecdysone induction of lysosomes in the midgut cells of *S. bullata*. Top: apical portion of cytoplasm 9 hours after control injection. LB, lamellated bodies. Bottom: apical portion of epithelial cell 9 hours after β-ecdysone injection. L, lysosomes fill the cytoplasm. Inset: appearance of secondary lysosomes containing fragments of mitochondria (m) and endoplasmic reticulum (er). From Radford and Misch (1971).

sone, the intact testis with its protective surrounding sheath only developed and differentiated in the presence of β-ecdysone. It therefore appeared that β-ecdysone affected the permeability of the sheath and that something in the medium stimulated spermatogenesis as had been indirectly suggested by Mitsuhashi (1965).

At about the same time, it was shown that a similar phenomenon existed when diapausing saturniid pupal testes were incubated *in vitro* (Kambysellis and Williams, 1971a,b). In this case a "macromolecular factor" extracted from insect blood is requisite for spermatogenesis to occur in isolated cysts, while both this factor and ecdysone were needed for *in vitro* spermatogenesis to occur in intact testes (see, also, Nowock, 1971; Economopoulos and Gordon, 1971). Although the action of the macromolecular factor is spectacular, the response is not specific. That is, one or more of the large proteins (or some other substance) in the medium utilized by Yagi and his colleagues can obviously substitute for the "natural" factor found in insect hemolymph. Whether this phenomenon is restricted to spermatogenesis or gametogenesis in general (JH plus macromolecular factor?) or is important in the general action of ecdysone on other insect tissues remains to be seen. However, the recent finding that the inactive ecdysone analogue, rubrosterone, has even greater activity in stimulating spermatogenesis than ecdysone (Takeda, 1972) suggests that this system is not a good model for MH action.

The obvious system for visualizing ecdysone action is cuticle synthesis by epidermal cells. This has been shown by *in vivo* transplants (Gilbert, 1964) and there is now evidence that epidermis can retract from the old cuticle (apolysis) and synthesize new cuticle *in vitro* under the influence of β-ecdysone (e.g., Agui *et al.*, 1969a; Marks and Leopold, 1971). Some of the *in vitro* responses of explanted tissues may be due to the exquisite sensitivity of regenerating epidermal cells to both MH and JH. In fact, regenerating epidermal cells in locusts from which the prothoracic glands have been extirpated are capable of both cell division (DNA synthesis) and cuticle deposition (Rinterknecht, 1966) despite the fact that the animal does not molt. The presence of ecdysone does not appear to be requisite for DNA synthesis in several other larval insects either (Krishnakumaran, 1972). On the other hand, cockroach leg regenerates only secrete cuticle *in vitro* in the presence of MH (Marks and Leopold, 1970) and several other characteristics of regeneration may also be dependent on ecdysone (e.g., Madhaven and Schneiderman, 1969). If, indeed, epidermal cells respond to ecdysone *in vitro* by depositing a new cuticle, it would be an ideal system to study the interaction of MH and JH. For example, can pupal or adult epidermal cells be induced to lay down larval cuticle by prolonged exposure to JH? Is it the ratio of MH to JH that determines the nature of the cuticle layed down or is it the absolute quantity of JH?

Studies on the control of imaginal disc differentiation deserve a chapter in this treatise and only a few examples can be considered here. For further information the reader should consult the many fine publications of Hadorn and his disciples as well as those of Schneiderman and his colleagues. That β-ecdysone and cyasterone are effective in eliciting the complete metamorphosis of larval *Drosophila* leg discs incubated in adult female abdomens was demonstrated by Postlethwait and Schneiderman (1970). Their data reveal that the discs everted, formed pupal cuticle followed by the formation of adult cuticle complete with bristles, hairs, and sensilae when exposed to a high and sustained titer of ecdysone. Since these experiments were carried out in a "living tissue culture vessel," there is of course the persisting possibility that the effects on the discs were indirectly exerted. However, past studies in which dipteran discs underwent metamorphosis when incubated *in vitro* with ring glands support the postulate that the effect is direct (e.g., Kuroda and Yamaguchi, 1956; Schneider, 1966). Just recently, thoracic imaginal discs from *Drosophila* were studied *in vitro* in a special medium by Mandaron (1971) and he was able to demonstrate that ecdysone is the sole factor, of the many tested, that is requisite for the initiation of disc evagination. Since ring glands and ecdysone give the same results *in vitro,* one can only conclude that the ring glands secrete ecdysone or a precursor of ecdysone that is converted to ecdysone by the target tissue.

In the lepidopteran, it was shown that ecdysone could elicit the growth and partial metamorphosis of wing discs *in vitro* (Oberlander and Fulco, 1967), but only after they are extirpated from insects at a stage when the discs are responsive (not refractory) to MH (Agui *et al.,* 1969b). Of interest are the recent *in vitro* studies of Oberlander with the wing discs from *Galleria* larvae. Although α-ecdysone, β-ecdysone, and inkosterone could initiate metamorphosis of the discs, only α-ecdysone enabled the discs to continue prolonged DNA synthesis (Oberlander, 1969a) and, in fact, was most efficient in turning on DNA synthesis in quiescent discs (Oberlander, 1969b). Though morphological effects (tracheal migration) were stimulated with a 2-hour exposure to α-ecdysone, promotion of DNA synthesis required 24 hours of exposure. These data suggest that different hormonal requirements are needed for the various components of metamorphosis and are in obvious conflict with the supposition that DNA synthesis must precede metamorphic events (see, also, Madhaven and Schneiderman, 1968). In a recent study of this system, Oberlander

(1972a) found that β-ecdysone inhibits the α-ecdysone-induced stimulation of DNA synthesis. He suggests that α-ecdysone initiates metamorphosis and DNA synthesis, but that when the original α-ecdysone is converted to β-ecdysone, DNA synthesis stops although morphogenesis proceeds. One question that can be raised, however, is whether tracheal migration is a credible indicator of metamorphosis. However, this objection appears to have been alleviated by Oberlander's (1972b) use of cuticle deposition as an end point in studies demonstrating β-ecdysone-induced secretion of cuticle *in vitro*. Of further interest was the observation that the response was inhibited by JH. The reason for the reported synergistic effects of the fat body and α-ecdysone on the development of these wing discs is probably a result of the conversion of α- to β-ecdysone by the fat body (Richman and Oberlander, 1971; Oberlander, 1972b). The fact that the age of the larva donating the discs is important in the ultimate effect of α-ecdysone *in vitro* suggests the possibility that the discs differ in their permeability to α-ecdysone during the instar.

All the above studies on organ culture, tissue culture, and imaginal discs *in vitro* involve more than one cell type (perhaps with the exception of studies on the epidermis). To study the mechanism of action of hormones at the molecular level, it would be useful to investigate the responses of homogeneous populations of cells to minimize inductive or inhibitory influences of one cell type on another. Several studies on ecdysone and insect cell cultures have indeed been carried out, but with questionable results.

When cultures of cells originally derived from the pupal ovaries of *Antheraea eucalypti* were tested in several variations of Grace's tissue culture medium with β-ecdysone or ponasterone A, it was found that there was a slight stimulation of growth of the cells by β-ecdysone on the second day in the media containing hemolymph and bovine plasma albumin (Mitsuhashi and Grace, 1970). It is of interest that the higher concentration of β-ecdysone (10 μg/ml) was slightly inhibitory. Further studies utilized the same cell line as well as one from *T. ni*, both adapted to a hemolymph-free medium (but containing numerous macromolecules). Since, as we shall see subsequently, the initial metabolic effects of ecdysone are noted in hours (and perhaps in minutes) and not in days, the experiments were conducted for up to 5 hours. No effects on RNA or protein synthesis were noted with from 1 to 50 μg/ml of α- or β-ecdysone (Cohen and Gilbert, 1972). The question arose as to whether the MH passes through the plasmalemma of the cells, so they were incubated with either [^{3}H]α-ecdysone or [^{3}H]β-ecdysone. After a 4-hour incubation, essentially no α-ecdysone could be extracted from the *A. eucalypti* and *T.*

ni cells and less than 0.1% of the labeled β-ecdysone in the incubation medium was in the cells. Furthermore, no labeled metabolites of the ecdysone were found in the cells or the medium. Although some stimulation of uptake of β-ecdysone was found when the incubation medium was supplemented with either pupal hemolymph or fetal bovine serum albumin, there was no increase in the rates of macromolecular synthesis. The above is not too surprising if we consider that these cells have been subcultured for several years, are polyploid, do not normally require MH for growth, and are certainly not typical insect cells (Cohen and Gilbert, 1972). To add to the complexity of the situation, other studies using the same adapted strain of *A. eucalypti* cells revealed long-term effects of β-ecdysone on cell motion (see, also, Judy, 1969), and on the uptake and breakdown of uridine, but also a *decreased* rate of growth of the cell population (Reinecke and Robbins, 1971). Similar experiments should be conducted on primary cultures which have not yet had the time to escape MH regulation.

For general biochemical effects of MH (e.g., enzyme and substrate changes during development), the reader is referred to Chapter 4 of this volume and the reviews of Gilbert (1967b) and Wyatt (1968). Biochemical events close to the site of action of insect hormones will be considered in Section VI, D.

D. EFFECTS CLOSE TO SITE OF ACTION

The *exact* manner in which JH and MH elicit the many effects previously described is still not known with certainty and in fact the question of the mechanism of hormone action remains an enigma. In this section we will consider the possible effects of the insect growth hormones on membrane permeability, macromolecular synthesis, and the membrane-bound enzyme adenyl cyclase. We will present available evidence, but will not repeat the often cited variations of the Jacob–Monod model since the evidence for such a system in insect development is circumstantial at best. Indeed, we do not yet know whether the hormones act primarily at the transcriptional or translational levels.

1. Macromolecular Synthesis

The fact that protein, RNA, and DNA are synthesized during development is a basic fact, and there is no question but that the synthesis of these macromolecules is initiated or stimulated in arthropods after injection of α- or β-ecdysone (e.g., Arking and Shaaya, 1969; Sahota and Mansingh, 1970; Neufeld and Thomson, 1968; Gorell and Gilbert, 1969;

Wyatt and Wyatt, 1971; Reddy and Wyatt, 1967). A qualitative but very comprehensive study has been made on saturniid silkworms by Schneiderman and his colleagues (Berry *et al.,* 1967; Krishnakumaran *et al.,* 1967) which allows us to assume certain important temporal relationships between growth, differentiation, RNA synthesis, and DNA synthesis. In some tissues that must synthesize and secrete new cuticle at the molt (e.g., epidermis and trachea), the patterns of RNA and DNA synthesis were well correlated with the molting process (controlled by MH) while in others there was no correlation. As one might expect, RNA synthesis, in general, paralleled the metabolic state of the animal. That is, it is highest in larvae, lowest during pupal diapause, with an increasing rate during pharate adult development. If the metabolism of the diapausing pupa was stimulated by injury, RNA synthesis was also stimulated. Almost every epidermal cell participated in DNA synthesis during each molting cycle, although some tissues did not synthesize DNA if they had undergone one molt in the absence of JH (e.g., Malpighian tubules and prothoracic glands). In contradistinction to RNA synthesis, DNA synthesis was not stimulated by integumentary injury to diapausing pupae even when the general metabolic rate was increased many times (although there was local DNA synthesis at the wound site). Only the injection of ecdysone could stimulate DNA synthesis in diapausing pupae. However, by a series of interesting maneuvers, they were able to demonstrate that cuticle formation and molting could take place in the absence of DNA synthesis and conclude that DNA synthesis is not the primary target of MH. According to these studies, ecdysone is a molting hormone in the true sense of the word and "stimulates the synthesis or translation of certain messenger RNA's which were previously nonexistent or nonfunctional and which are necessary for molting" (Krishnakumaran *et al.,* 1967, p. 3).

With these studies in mind, we can now explore some recent work on ecdysone and JH effects on macromolecular synthesis in isolated tissues, cells, and nuclei. When wing epidermal fragments from diapausing Cecropia pupae are incubated *in vitro* one can study the rates of protein and RNA synthesis and, as expected, when pupae were injected with ecdysone 10 hours previously, the rates of synthesis *in vitro* were significantly greater than the noninjected controls (Reddy and Wyatt, 1967). This of course agrees with the premise derived from *in vivo* experiments that ecdysone is a stimulator of RNA synthesis. In a significant series of experiments, Wyatt and Wyatt (1971) demonstrated that minced wing tissue from diapausing Cecropia pupae responded to β-ecdysone *in vitro*. That is, when wing mince was incubated with from 1 to 20 μg/ml β-ecdysone, it had the capacity to synthesize RNA at a much greater rate than controls or mince incubated in the presence of the inactive isomer, 22-iso-ecdysone. It is of interest that α-ecdysone was less effective than β-ecdysone. This demonstration of a true *in vitro* effect of ecdysone on tissue from a diapausing insect suggests that if binding proteins are necessary for ecdysone action (Section VI, B), they must be present in the wing epidermis.

The studies from Wyatt's laboratory have yielded some very useful and intriguing information, but it is important in our attempt to understand the mechanism of MH action that we know the nature of the newly synthesized RNA. This is also true of studies involving the effects of ecdysone and JH on nuclei isolated from the fat body of fly larvae (Congote *et al.*, 1969). The latter experiments revealed a stimulation of RNA synthesis by ecdysone *in vitro* and the authors suggest that this excludes the possibility that ecdysone acts via the cytoplasm. Although this point will be considered in the next section, it should be pointed out that their conclusion is based on the premise that the fat body nuclei were completely clean and physiologically normal. Their studies with Cecropia C_{18} JH lead them to conclude that JH stimulates RNA polymerase activity in fat body nuclei from young larvae, but one must be wary of results using

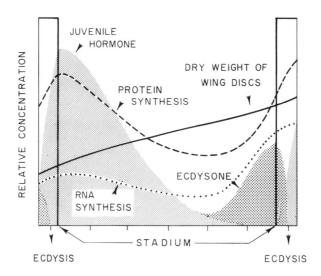

Fig. 9. Diagrammatic summary of the relationship of juvenile hormone and ecdysone concentrations, their influence on the capacity of wing discs to synthesize RNA and protein, and their relationship to the rate of growth of the disc. From Patel and Madhaven (1969).

this water-insoluble material *in vitro* (see Section VI, A, and subsequent discussion). If their data are correct, however, there appears to be an antagonistic action between JH and ecdysone since there was no stimulation of RNA synthesis when both hormones were present in the incubation medium. This is another example of the antagonistic effects of the two hormones (see, also, Section VI, D, 2). The above data are in fact similar to the results derived from studies of the effects of α- and β-ecdysone and the hydrochlorination product on the RNA-synthesizing capacity of wing discs from the Cynthia silkworm (Patel and Madhaven, 1969). α-Ecdysone, β-ecdysone, and the hydrochlorination product stimulated RNA synthesis when administered separately to the larva, but no stimulation was noted when the JH mimic and ecdysone were injected simultaneously. It is of some interest that JH appeared to be most effective in enhancing RNA synthesis just prior to ecdysis, while ecdysone was most effective just after ecdysis. JH was effective when the endogenous ecdysone titer was at its peak (Fig. 9) and the JH concentration at its nadir, while ecdysone was most effective when JH concentration was at its peak and the endogenous MH concentration at its low point. Whether the peak stimulation is related to the low endogenous titer of the same hormone or to the high titer of the other hormone is not known, but is certainly worthy of further experimentation. It should be remembered that with *in vivo* studies one must consider the possibility of ecdysone and JH stimulating the corpora allata, prothoracic glands, and the brain (see Section III).

Studies in the laboratories of Karlson, Ilan, and Fristrom have provided us with some insights regarding the nature of the RNA synthesized under the control of the growth hormones and have led to some interesting working hypotheses on their mode of action. Utilizing the techniques of sucrose density centrifugation and RNA–DNA hybridization, Congote *et al.* (1970) demonstrated that dipteran fat body nuclei synthesize different RNA depending on the hormone regimen to which the nuclei are subjected. The newly synthesized RNA was polydisperse with a maximum at about 14 S and in general had a lower molecular weight than the rapidly labeled RNA synthesized *in vivo*, as is true in many other organisms. The fact that both JH and ecdysone elicited the synthesis of RNA qualitatively different from controls (possibly with higher messenger capability) suggests that both hormones act at the transcriptional level. It is of real interest that the isolated nuclei are competent to respond to JH or are refractory, depending on the age of the donor (Karlson *et al.*, 1971), which is consistent with many *in vivo* observations and the above-mentioned data of Patel and Madhaven. Karlson's group suggests that some genes are regulated by both hormones simultaneously; for example, ecdysone could turn on both ecdysone- and JH-dependent genes while the presence of critical titers of both hormones would prevent this gene activation. They leave open the possibility that genes specific for each of the hormones may also exist. This is a good working hypothesis and although their data are suggestive of such a phenomenon, it is far from a proven fact and alternative explanations are as valid. There are many dangers inherent in working with isolated nuclei including the possibility that part of the total MH response consists of specialized particles carrying rapidly labeled RNA into the cytoplasm of insect cells (Kafatos, 1968), not to mention the distinct chance of nuclear damage during the isolation procedure.

Further information has been derived from the elegant studies of Fristrom and his colleagues on RNA synthesis in the imaginal discs of *Drosophila* larvae (Fristrom *et al.,* 1970; Raikow and Fristrom, 1971; Petri *et al.,* 1971). When these discs are cultured *in vitro,* they synthesize 38 S, 28 S, and 18 S ribosomal RNA's (rRNA's) which are indistinguishable from their counterparts synthesized *in vivo.* The 38 S RNA is probably a precursor for the 28 S and 18 S rRNA's. When β-ecdysone is added to the culture medium, there is a stimulation within minutes of new rRNA synthesis as well as increases in the rate of formation of 28 S and 18 S rRNA from the 38 S molecule. This stimulation of rRNA synthesis may be important in the transport of new messenger RNA (mRNA) to the cytoplasm. It should be mentioned here that when ecdysone is influential in triggering cell death (see previous section), it appears to inhibit the synthesis of rRNA in those tissues destined to degenerate (Hughes and Kambysellis, 1970). On the other hand, since the discs used in the above experiments may have been exposed to ecdysone *in vivo,* and since without ecdysone in the medium the 38 S precursor is processed abnormally, the observed stimulation of rRNA synthesis may actually be the normal rate of synthesis and ecdysone could then be considered to be an important growth factor in the organ culture medium. Of course, ecdysone had an effect in producing disc evagination as it had in other imaginal discs studies (see previous section). In these studies as well there appears to be an antagonism between JH and ecdysone action since a large dose of 1 mg/ml of the hydrochlorination product inhibits evagination as well as RNA synthesis. Most important is the observation that the JH mimic can be washed out and the discs recover and proceed to synthesize RNA and evaginate. Presumably the same effect is obtained with the Cecropia C_{18} JH (Chihara *et al.,* 1972), except that the hormone cannot be washed out. These studies suggest that the hormones act at the transcriptional level, but also suggest that ecdysone may have multiple points of regulation since some artificial reagents can cause similar increases in the synthesis of rRNA but do not elicit evagination.

On the other hand, there is equally cogent evidence from studies in molecular biology that JH at least acts to control translational events (Ilan, 1969a,b; Ilan et al., 1970). Using nuclei isolated from Tenebrio pupae, Ilan was able to identify mRNA on the basis of template activity and base composition. [It is of real interest in this regard that the Bombyx mori mRNA for silk fibroin synthesis has just been isolated (Suzuki and Brown, 1972).] This is important since previous studies on insects had only indirectly and circumstantially identified mRNA. With data from inhibitor studies indicating the presence of stable mRNA for adult cuticular protein on the first day of pupation but translated 1 week later, and the belief that cuticular protein is tyrosine rich, Ilan and his colleagues were able to demonstrate an increase in tyrosine-rich (cuticular) protein in a cell-free system. This specific mRNA has a vital role in the translational process. If adult cuticular protein is to be synthesized, the transfer RNA (tRNA) and an activating system from 7 pharate adults are required. Using the JH mimic dodecylmethyl ether (DME) which is very potent in Tenebrio, they were able to produce second pupae, the cuticular protein of which is relatively low in tyrosine, and allowed them to distinguish pupal cuticular protein from adult. When tRNA from DME treated animals was added to normal ribosomes containing mRNA for adult cuticular protein, the system was inhibited from synthesizing the adult protein and suggested that tRNA from a more differentiated state is necessary for the translation of specific mRNA. Reciprocal experiments were consistent with this idea. Their results further suggest that translation is controlled by specific tRNA synthetases as well as specific tRNA and that JH affects development by its action on tRNA and its activation enzyme. Further studies from this laboratory revealed the presence of stage-specific initiating factors (part of ribosomal proteins) in Tenebrio that can discriminate between mRNA's extracted from insects at different developmental stages (Ilan and Ilan, 1971). The stage-specific mRNA may have a specific sequence of nucleotides or may have a specific secondary structure allowing it to be recognized by a unique initiation factor. Insect hormones may act to induce the formation of these stage-specific initiating factors. If the above hypothesis is true, then the hormones elicit the formation of specific mRNA as well as initiating factors. The studies of the Ilans again suggest the presence of a multitude of control points at which insect hormones can exert their effects.

The various means by which RNA synthesis may be controlled in eukaryotic cells has been the subject of books and numerous reviews and cannot be treated here. It is a very complex subject and several aspects will be discussed along with chromosome puffing. Suffice it to say that there is evidence for both transcriptional and translational control by hormones.

2. Enzyme Induction

There are a number of examples of the induction by ecdysone and JH of proteins including enzymes. One is the JH stimulation of synthesis of the female protein involved in oogenesis by the fat body of several adult insects. Whether this is induction (*de novo* synthesis) or acceleration of the rate of synthesis is open for discussion and depends on the techniques used. That is, the less sensitive the detection technique, the more it will appear to be *de novo* synthesis. Studies on the female protein are considered in Chapter 3 of this volume. Many studies have dealt with changes in the patterns of proteins in various tissues (mainly hemolymph) during development (e.g., Patel, 1971) and these probably reflect complicated alterations in the hormonal milieu. Although interesting, they too will not be considered here since they in general add little to our basic knowledge of hormone action.

a. Ecdysone-Dopa Decarboxylase. This system has been the subject of intensive work by Karlson's laboratory (e.g., Sekeris and Karlson, 1962, 1966) as well as others and has been exhaustively reviewed. It is, however, a possible example of enzyme induction by a hormone and will be briefly considered. We have previously discussed the fact that ecdysone is responsible for puparium formation by last instar fly larvae and that the events are coordinated by the brain. Sclerotization of the larval cuticle to form the hard, dark brown puparium is also controlled by ecdysone (Sekeris and Karlson, 1966). Chemical events involved in sclerotization include the conversion of tyrosine $\rightarrow$ Dopa $\rightarrow$ dopamine $\rightarrow$ N-acetyldopamine$\rightarrow$sclerotin. The German workers suggest that the epidermal enzyme, Dopa decarboxylase, is induced by ecdysone. In fact, the titers of endogenous ecdysone and Dopa decarboxylase show similar curves during pupation (Shaaya and Sekeris, 1965). Studies using antibiotic inhibitors suggest that the enzyme is indeed synthesized *de novo* when competent epidermis is exposed to MH (Sekeris and Karlson, 1964). The fact that actinomycin D inhibits the synthesis of this DOPA decarboxylase suggests that ecdysone may in this case be acting at the transcriptional level. It should be mentioned that there may be additional ecdysone control points for the sclerotization process in some flies. In *Sarcophaga bullata* larvae, for example, a large amount of the dipeptide, β-alanyl-L-tyrosine, is present (Levenbook *et al.*, 1969) and dramatical-

ly declines during sclerotization of the puparium. In a careful series of
studies, Bodnaryk (1971) has shown that β-ecdysone stimulates the activity of a dipeptidase causing the release of free tyrosine from the dipeptide which can then act as substrate for the ultimate formation of N-ace-
tyl dopamine. In addition, there also appears to be an induction of a
DOPA decarboxylase as in the studies discussed above. Whether the dipeptidase is really induced or whether enzyme activity is stimulated
awaits further investigation. Finally, there is the possibility that JH may
interfere with the normal sequence of chemical reactions that terminate
in sclerotization although the mechanism is unknown (Zlotkin and Levinson, 1968b).

   b. *Juvenile Hormone—Enzymes.* As pointed out in Section V, F, an
initial step in the breakdown of Cecropia C_{18} JH appears to be the hydrolysis of the ester bond, resulting in the epoxy acid. Whitmore *et al.*
(1972) demonstrated by slab-gel electrophoresis that several esterases
were present in larval and pupal hemolymph, several of which were
shown to be carboxyl esterases on the basis of inhibition (e.g., DFP)
studies. Further investigation revealed that isozymes of these esterases
that migrated the most rapidly were absent from diapausing silkmoth pupae, a stage in the life cycle where no JH is detectable (Gilbert and
Schneiderman, 1961) and suggested that these enzymes were only found
in the hemolymph containing a significant titer of JH. When these particular carboxyl esterases were eluted from the gel, it was pointedly demonstrated with the aid of $[2\text{-}^{14}C]C_{18}$ JH that they quickly and efficiently
broke down JH (perhaps to the free carboxylic acid and may also show
epoxide hydrolase activity) suggesting a physiological role for the enzymes in hormone regulation. Although the present review has not delved
into the question of hormone breakdown as a critical factor in regulation
because of the lack of data in insects, degradation processes are obviously
as important to maintaining a critical hormone titer as are synthetic and
secretory processes. For example, it now appears that the phosphodiesterase activity of cells may be equally important as the adenyl cyclase activity in controlling cyclic AMP levels and may in fact be a control point
(e.g., D'Armiento *et al.*, 1972).

   Since these carboxyl esterases were absent from pupal hemolymph, it
was decided to investigate their possible induction. Indeed, when Cecropia C_{18} JH was injected into these pupae, the esterases were detected in
the hemolymph within a few hours. Ecdysone did not elicit the appearance of these esterases and they appeared when JH was injected into
brainless pupae, suggesting that JH was not acting via stimulation of the
prothoracic glands or brain. Further, the carboxyl esterases did not ap-

pear in the hemolymph when puromycin or actinomycin D were administered prior to JH injection, suggesting that the esterases were synthesized
de novo under the influence of JH, acting at least in part at the level of
transcription. This is the first example in animals of a hormone inducing
the formation of an enzyme for the purposes of self-destruction and is a
particularly simple and indeed excellent means of insuring that the JH titer does not increase above a "physiological" limit, particularly in light of
the finding that excess JH can activate the corpora allata (Section III).
The phenomenon of enzyme induction by hormones in vertebrates has
been demonstrated many times both *in vivo* and *in vitro* and in at least
one case it appears that regulation is at the post-transcriptional level
(e.g., Tomkins, 1970).

3. *Chromosome Puffing and Membranes*

"Polytene chromosome puffs may be defined as structural modifica-
tions of the DNA and its associated substances of single bands which involve an uncoiling of the chromosome fibers allowing the synthesis of
specific RNA species and the accumulation of RNA and other substances
at the site. This accumulation often results in the enlargement of the specific chromosome region" (Ashburner, 1970, p. 11). Several excellent
and comprehensive reviews of this subject have recently appeared (Lezzi,
1970; Ashburner, 1970; Berendes, 1971) and the question of how genes
are activated by MH was covered in the previous review (Gilbert, 1964).
In the last 8 years, a literal barrage of publications has appeared on puffing in the dipteran polytene chromosomes, many concerned with possible
hormonal control and several on the biochemical characterization of the
RNA species in nuclei, chromosomes, and indeed in Balbiani rings of
these chromosomes (e.g., Egyházi *et al.,* 1969; Daneholt *et al.,*
1969a,b,c; Ringborg *et al.,* 1970a,b). With this deluge of data, however,
we are really no closer to understanding how ecdysone exerts its effects
at specific gene loci along these polytene chromosomes than we were
eight years ago.

We will consider the puff in this discussion as a visual manifestation of
mRNA synthesis, although this has not been proven, and accept the
working hypothesis that puff induction requires prior RNA synthesis
(however, see Berendes, 1968) but does not require prior protein synthesis (Clever, 1968). In this section we will consider the theories of how
MH and JH elicit gene activation in these polytene chromosomes and attempt to correlate this activation with selected examples of physiological
function. Basically the question can be resolved into whether the hor-
mone(s) act directly within the nucleus or indirectly via changes in the

permeability of the nuclear envelope or plasmolemma so as to alter the ionic environment of the chromosomes. We can immediately state with some assurance that the question has not been resolved and it is probable that the hormones have multivalent effects at several levels of organization.

a. Direct Effects. If DNA is repressed by proteins such as histones, it is not unreasonable to assume that derepression could be induced by ecdysone through histone acetylation (Allfrey, 1966), phosphorylation (Langan, 1968; Benjamin and Goodman, 1969) or DNA methylation (Turkington and Spielvogel, 1971), although one wonders whether there is enough information in this rather simple steroid to selectively derepress. If, however, MH is bound to a protein (Section VI, B; see, also, Helmsing and Berendes, 1971), conformational changes in the protein may result and this more sophisticated molecule may indeed have sufficient information for selective gene activation. The fact that ecdysone administration *in vivo* leads to prompt (within minutes), specific, and dose-dependent changes in puffing activity (Clever and Karlson, 1960; Berendes, 1967; Clever, 1968) is somewhat supportive of a direct effect. Further support comes from studies on the induction of puffs in isolated glands in *Drosophila* by ecdysone and several analogues (Ashburner, 1971). When $[^3H]\beta$-ecdysone is injected into *Calliphora,* the fat body cells show differential uptake of label into the nucleus prior to puparium formation, although not in the cells comprising the salivary glands (Thomson *et al.,* 1970a). In fact, several autoradiographic studies utilizing $[^3H]$ecdysone and dipteran salivary glands yielded inconclusive results in our opinion (Emmerich, 1969; Weirich and Karlson, 1969; Claycomb *et al.,* 1971). It is of some interest, however, that changes in the nuclear envelope have been detected at the ultrastructural level after ecdysone administration. For example, there appears to be a change in regions of the nuclear envelope so that the envelope appears nonmembranous and fibrillar (Thomson *et al.,* 1970b; See, also, Ishizaki, 1963). As we shall see subsequently, this change may also be supportive of membrane effects.

As previously discussed, ecdysone and JH can stimulate RNA synthesis in isolated nuclei of *Calliphora* larvae. Congote *et al.* (1969) also found that Na^+ stimulated RNA synthesis while K^+ was without effect. Since the effects of ecdysone and Na^+ are additive, they conclude that Na^+ and ecdysone act via two different systems and that it is the ionic strength of the medium rather than specific ions that is effective. Since isolated nuclei can regulate their ionic environment and since there may be some question as to the purity and physiological integrity of these nuclei, the results can only be taken as suggestive at this time. It is of interest in this regard that when JH and ecdysone are administered simultaneously, RNA synthesis is not stimulated (Section VI, D, 1), and indeed Lezzi and Gilbert (1969) have shown that ecdysone-specific puffs are inhibited by JH, a further example of antagonistic action between the two hormones.

b. Indirect Effects. Although effects on permeability will be discussed here, the fact that the hormones may act at the membrane level does not automatically prove that the K^+/Na^+ ratio in the nucleus is responsible for selective derepression. We will proceed in this discussion with the acceptance of the facts that administration of ecdysone *in vivo* and to whole salivary glands *in vitro* results in the activation of certain genetic loci; that there are loci specific for JH as well (Lezzi and Gilbert, 1969); and that here is an antagonistic action at this level between the two hormones. Subsequently we will discuss the significance of this hormone-induced puffing; i.e., what do these specific active genes code for?

There is no question but that the nature of the ionic environment is of profound importance for a variety of physiological and biochemical processes and that histones can be stripped from DNA by solutions of high ionic strength. *In vitro* studies on rat liver nuclei and nucleoli reveal that the ionic strength of the system has regulatory effects on RNA polymerase and suggest that precursor rRNA and DNA-like RNA (mRNA?) synthesis can be specifically stimulated by low and high ionic strength solutions respectively (Johnson *et al.*, 1971). In general biochemical mechanisms such as glycolysis, there is no question of the regulatory role of ions (Bygrave, 1967). In the insect as well, glycogenlysis is controlled at least in part by the Na^+ concentration (Steele, 1969). There are a number of examples of the importance of ionic species in differentiation, as for example Na^+ and Ca^{2+} in cell differentiation in *Hydra* (Macklin and Burnett, 1966). Thus it is not surprising that alterations in the ionic environment of the salivary gland (both *in vivo* and *in vitro*) can simulate ecdysone and JH in eliciting specific puffs (Kroeger, 1968). Of course, injection of salt solutions does not result in molting, but nobody has definitely proven that the puffs so far studied in relation to ecdysone action are responsible for molting, and certainly the insect can regulate its ionic environment. Basically, Kroeger's argument depends on the observations that an environment with a relatively high K^+ concentration can simulate ecdysone in inducing puffing while a high Na^+ concentration causes puffing presumably similar to the effects of JH.

To determine directly the effects of these ions on the chromosomes, a series of experiments was performed on isolated *naked* salivary gland chromosomes from *Chironomus tentans* (Lezzi and Gilbert, 1970). It was shown that K^+-containing salt solutions and Na^+-containing salt solutions differ in their effects on the structure of specific bands in these isolated chromosomes. The band at I-18-C that is specifically affected by K^+ is a band that forms a puff if larvae are treated with ecdysone (Clever and Karlson, 1960; Lezzi and Gilbert, 1969). Ecdysone in turn appears to increase the nuclear K^+/Na^+ ratio in the salivary glands of *Chironomus thummi* (Kroeger, 1966). The bands at I-19-A which specifically fade in a Na^+-containing salt mixture form puffs both in isolated salivary gland nuclei that are incubated in a Na^+-rich medium (Lezzi, 1966) and when prepupae are treated with JH (Lezzi and Gilbert, 1969). In contradistinction to ecdysone, JH appears to decrease the nuclear K^+/Na^+ ratio in salivary glands (*Galleria mellonella;* Baumann, 1968) and may be a result of JH interacting directly with the lipids of the membrane (Baumann, 1969). In this regard, it should be noted that oubain injected into *Tenebrio* pupae results in the formation of pupal–adult intermediates similar to those produced by JH application (Chase, 1970). Since oubain is thought to act by "sealing" the membrane (inactivating the mechanism for actively extruding Na^+ from the cell), it would lead to a decrease in the K^+/Na^+ ratio within the cell which is consistent with the idea of a relationship between JH and high Na^+ concentration. The question of how changes in the monovalent cation concentration of the immediate environment elicit puffing is not known, but the results of Lezzi and Gilbert (1970) have been confirmed and extended very recently (Robert, 1971). Theoretical considerations have led to the conclusion that even minute variations in the relative concentrations of K^+, Na^+, Mg^{2+} and Ca^{2+} can suffice in eliciting highly specific alterations in the gene activity pattern (Robert, 1971). It would be of real interest to determine the concentration of these various ions in the nuclei of the salivary gland cells at several developmental stages as has been done with nuclei from the amphibian oocyte (Century *et al.,* 1970) and to correlate these with the puffing picture. In addition, one would then be able to determine whether the hormones do alter the ionic environment of the chromosomes. It should be mentioned that in the amphibian oocyte there are very significant differences in the concentrations of K^+ and Na^+ between the nucleus and cytoplasm, which suggests the nuclear envelope as a potential site of hormone action. Further, there is recent evidence that the nuclear pores are involved in regulating cellular activity by controlling nuclear envelope permeability (Feldherr, 1971). The fact that there is a rise in the electrical potential difference between the nuclear and cell membrane within a minute of addition of ecdysone to the salivary gland *in vitro* (Kroeger, 1966) is further supportive evidence for changes in cell permeability (see, also, Ito and Loewenstein, 1965) as a result of ec-dysone application. The recent demonstration of electrical uncoupling of the salivary gland cells before pupation in *Drosophila* is supportive of the notion of ionic events being correlated with developmental events (Kislov and Veprintsev, 1971). If indeed the insect hormones act at the mem-brane level and this results in changes in the ionic milieu, it is difficult to understand how these ubiquitous ions can possess the information needed to induce *specific* gene repression, unless we assume an as yet unproven genetic-based differential sensitivity of the repressor–DNA complex to these ions (Kroeger, 1971).

In essence, the experiments by Becker, Clever, Kroeger, Lezzi, Ber-endes, Pelling, Ashburner, etc., on hormonal control of puffing have been elegant and well done. Most of the raw data have been confirmed with minor discrepancies due perhaps to species differences among the experi-mental insects. The conflict is in the interpretation of the results and it is our opinion that neither side has conclusively proven its point. It is ob-viously a complicated and involved phenomenon and it would be too sim-plistic an explanation to attribute the turning on of specific genes entirely to ecdysone or to the K^+/Na^+ ratio. [The recent demonstration that certain puffs are specific for either α-ecdysone or β-ecdysone (U. Clev-er, personal communication) supports the contention that we are far from understanding the complete story of hormonally induced puffs and further suggests separate roles for the two ecdysones. To add to the com-plexity, it now appears that the proteinaceous brain hormone (activation factor) may also induce at least one specific puff (M. Gersch, personal communication.)] As we shall explore in the next section, there are membrane-bound enzymes (e.g., adenyl cyclase) which may also be in-volved. At this point, however, let us consider some examples of the sig-nificance of the puffing phenomenon. That is, what are the end products of this gene activation?

c. Puff Function. It is amazing that although so much research has been conducted on salivary gland chromosomal puffs, it is only recently that reasonable functions have been assigned to the dipteran larval gland. In *Drosophila* the glands secrete an adhesive substance for fastening the puparium to its substrate (Fraenkel and Brookes, 1953) and in some flies the function is still in doubt. Whether the puffing pattern seen during late larval life reflects the signal for secretion or for histolysis of the glands is still being debated.

Several studies from the laboratory of Berendes have attempted to cor-relate puffing, ecdysone action and morphological change in *Drosophila hydei*. [It should be mentioned that a unique and possible ideal system for such studies are the footpads of *S. bullata* that have giant cells with polytene chromosomes. These cells are epidermal and secrete the adult cuticle of the foot. Studies have already demonstrated correlations between puffing patterns, cuticular secretion, and protein patterns. Since no hormonal studies have been reported yet, the analysis will not be discussed here. However, see Whitten (1969a,b).] Poels (1970) has shown that ecdysone can initiate changes in gene activity, mucopolysaccharide secretion and pigmentation during the entire last larval instar, events that normally take place at the end of the instar. The MH-induced secretion of the mucopolysaccharide into the lumen of the salivary glands is accompanied by a number of definite changes in the ultrastructure of the cells of the salivary glands that resemble those normally occurring just prior to puparium formation (Poels *et al.*, 1971). It is of interest that analogous changes in structure (e.g., reduction in the basal system of membrane infoldings) as well as puffing pattern were noted in the cells of the Malpighian tubules and add further indirect support for the supposition that changes in cell morphology are a result of alterations in puffing activity (Berendes and Willart, 1971).

Ultimately it would be of great value to determine a specific protein (or mRNA) that could be conclusively demonstrated to be a gene product of a specific puffing region and show that the synthesis of this protein could be manipulated by varying the hormone titer. Although this has not yet been achieved, a beginning has been made. Among the regions of the salivary gland polytene chromosomes that are activated by ecdysone and inactivated by JH is Balbiani ring 1 (BR1; Fig. 10) (see Lezzi and Gilbert, 1969, 1972). This finding is of interest since BR1 can contribute up to 30% of the total nonnucleolar RNA synthesized in the nuclei of the salivary gland. These Balbiani rings appear to be important in the formation of the salivary gland secretory product and Grossbach (1969), using microdisc electrophoresis and cytogenetic analysis, demonstrated that a single component (single protein or polypeptide chain?) was absent from the secretion when BR1 was inactive (see, however, Wobus *et al.*, 1970; 1971). Preliminary work by W. Pankow (discussed in Lezzi and Gilbert, 1972) revealed that the protein seemed to appear when the ecdysone titer was expected to be high, suggesting that BR1 is activated by ecdysone and that a specific protein is the ultimate product. If the thesis is correct, then JH should inhibit synthesis of this protein and ecdysone should stimulate its appearance at a stage when it is normally absent. The final step would be the isolation and characterization of a specific mRNA which will translate information for the synthesis of this protein in a cell-free system. A great deal more work is obviously needed before one can con-

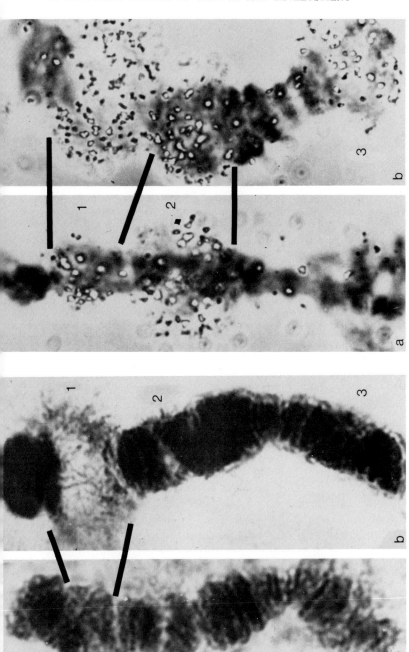

Fig. 10. Effects of β-ecdysone on Balbiani ring activity in young fourth instal larval *C. tentans* salivary gland chromosome IV. Left: (a) control; (b) animal injected with β-ecdysone. 1,2,3 denote Balbiani rings. Right: same experiment as left except showing incorporation of [³H]uridine by autoradiography; phase contrast. From *Lezzi and Gilbert* (1969).

clusively state that the hormone-induced puffs have the physiological significance attributed to them.

d. Cyclic AMP. The central role of cyclic AMP (synthesized from ATP under the control of membrane-bound adenyl cyclase) in control systems from bacteria to mammals is an established fact (Robison *et al.,* 1971) and will not be belabored here. In 1962, adenyl cyclase activity was determined in insects (fly larvae homogenates; Sutherland *et al.,* 1962) and cyclic AMP was identified in 1970 in saturniid pupae (E. Whitmore, L. I. Gilbert, and R. W. Butcher, unpublished information; see also Berridge's studies in Section VI). In general, it was not believed that steroid hormones act via cyclic AMP until the work of Szego and Davis (1967) on estradiol action and some recent corroborative studies (Hechter and Soifer, 1971). Therefore, there was no reason to assume that ecdysone may act via cyclic AMP until very recently.

In a most significant study, Leenders *et al.* (1970) demonstrated that cyclic AMP (10^{-3} M) did not induce ecdysone-specific puffs in *Drosophila* salivary glands *in vitro,* but enhanced the response of those genetic loci stimulated by β-ecdysone. An inhibitor of the phosphodiesterase which hydrolyzes cyclic AMP is also synergistic with the action of cyclic AMP. Isolated nuclei, on the other hand, did not respond to ecdysone, cyclic AMP, or a combination of both (contrast with RNA synthesis stimulation by ecdysone in isolated fat body nuclei discussed in Section VI, C). Using the very sensitive myxamoebae assay, the Dutch workers were also able to determine that salivary glands incubated with β-ecdysone for 20 minutes had four times more cyclic AMP than control glands incubated in the absence of the hormone. It therefore appears that, in addition to enhancing the effect of ecdysone at the chromosomal level, cyclic AMP formation is stimulated by ecdysone which is further evidence for multivalent effects of ecdysone as well as the complexity of control of puffing. In regard to the synergistic effect of cyclic AMP on ecdysone action, analogous results have been obtained in vertebrate systems. For example, hydrocortisone stimulates the tyrosine transaminase activity in fetal rat liver organ cultures as does cyclic AMP and dibutyryl cyclic AMP (Wicks, 1970). When the hormone and cyclic AMP are utilized together, a very pronounced synergistic effect can be obtained (i.e., effect is more than additive) and it is postulated that the two substances act sequentially. It is possible that in the salivary gland chromosome experiments, cyclic AMP is necessary for ecdysone action but cannot substitute for the hormone. As pointed out by Rutter (1970), there are at least a dozen possible regulatory points for specific protein synthesis in eukaryotic cells between transcription and translation (e.g., RNA polymerase, RNA stabilization, RNA transport to cytoplasm and converse, etc.) and the data on insects thus far do not allow us to distinguish between them.

Additional work has been recently published showing that the injection of β-ecdysone into saturniid pupae results in the stimulation of adenyl cyclase in wing epidermis and this also occurs with pupal wings *in vitro* and in wing epidermal homogenates (Applebaum and Gilbert, 1972). The stimulation of adenyl cyclase precedes increases in the rates of RNA and protein synthesis and occurs within minutes after addition of MH. The injection of cyclic AMP (or the dibutyryl derivative) into debrained pupae does not elicit development (E. Whitmore and L. I. Gilbert, unpublished information) and the addition of cyclic AMP does not mimic all the initial effects of β-ecdysone on wing epidermis *in vitro* (e.g., RNA synthesis) (Applebaum and Gilbert, 1972). This suggests again that β-ecdysone exerts effects independent of its activation of adenyl cyclase. In addition, it appears that β-ecdysone can stimulate guanyl cyclase as well, suggesting that cyclic GMP may play a significant role in mediating the influence of β-ecdysone on target cells. In support of this view are the facts that crickets yield two to three times more cyclic GMP than cyclic AMP (Ishikawa *et al.*, 1969) and that insect tissues are very rich in cyclic GMP-dependent protein kinases (Kuo *et al.*, 1971). A recent theory on estrogen action attempts to correlate adenyl cyclase stimulation by estrogen and the phenomenon of hormone-binding protein complexes (Arnaud *et al.*, 1971) and should be tested in the insect system as well. According to the authors, estrogen activates adenyl cyclase resulting in the production of cyclic AMP. Cyclic AMP in turn causes the phosphorylation of a specific binding protein which then specifically activates nucleolar RNA polymerase. Since the cyclases are membrane-situated, it is possible that many of the actions of insect hormones at the membrane level are mediated by cyclic AMP or cyclic GMP.

There are further recent data supporting the view that JH may act at the membrane level. Cohen and Gilbert (1972) studied the effects of Cecropia C_{18} JH on insect cell cultures. Their data are clear but the interpretation of the results is a matter of speculation. There is little question that they demonstrated that JH inhibits RNA synthesis in a dose-related manner, but so did several other lipids not possessing JH activity. The effects can be considered toxic, especially since cytological studies suggest that the hormone causes swelling lesions in the plasma membrane and may explain the results of Mitsuhashi and Grace (1970) who found a marked decrease in cell population when *A. eucalypti* cells in a protein-free medium were incubated in the presence of the weak JH mimic, farnesol, at a concentration of 10 μg/ml. On the other hand, JH inhibited RNA synthesis to a far greater extent than the other lipids tested, suggesting some degree of specificity. The fact that the aqueous lipoprotein–JH complex (see Section VI, A) also inhibits RNA and protein synthesis in the *T. ni* cells (although by a substantially lower percentage than JH) cannot be easily explained by the action of a "toxic" lipid on the plasma membrane. The possibility therefore exists that JH may indeed act at the level of the plasma membrane to perhaps alter the normal ionic environment of the cell or to inhibit a membrane-bound enzyme such as adenyl cyclase which then results in a decreased rate of macromolecular synthesis.

VII. Conclusions

The foregoing is a selected review of studies within the last 8 years in the field of insect endocrinology and, due to some conflicting results and interpretations, it can readily be seen that the overall picture is far from complete. At this time, we are not as confident of the classical scheme for endocrine control as we were in 1964, although important developments have occurred in the field of insect hormone chemistry. The mechanism of action of none of the insect hormones is known with certainty and it is postulated that they may act at several of the many possible control points. Since several orders of insects are separated widely in evolutionary time, it may be that the growth hormones do not act uniformly in all insects.

Prior to any future edition of this treatise, the interrelationships among the several endocrine glands should be definitively proven and the biosynthesis and degradation of the known hormones will be understood in diverse insect species. A vital question is how MH and JH exert their effects and we cannot predict the length of time and amount of effort needed to obtain definitive answers. Certainly more intensive work at the molecular level is requisite. For example, does ecdysone play a role in polysome binding within the cell as vertebrate steroid hormones may (James *et al.*, 1969)? Do JH and ecdysone have multivalent actions because they have a general effect on cellular structures perhaps by alteration of the hydration layer of cell membranes as may be the case with vertebrate steroid hormones (Gershfeld and Muramatsu, 1971)? Is the level of action at the "sigma factor" (RNA polymerase) and is this action due to the presence of an active hormone-binding protein complex as in the estradiol–uterus system (Mohla *et al.*, 1971)? It is of interest in this regard that cholesteryl-14-methylhexadecanoate stimulates RNA polymerase in rat liver nuclei *in vivo* and *in vitro* (Komárková and Hradec, 1971) and both moieties of this ester resemble ecdysone and JH, respectively. Are less obvious subcellular organelles involved in hormone action? For example, steroid sex hormones of mammals provoke labilization of lysosomal membranes in a dose-dependent manner in target organs leading to the liberation of the sequestered enzymes (Szego *et al.*, 1971) and this may be the signal for derepression in the insect system (e.g., puffing). Is cell division in the epidermis a mechanism for making the cells more susceptible to hormones (Stockdale and Topper, 1966); is this why regenerating epidermis is exquisitely sensitive to JH, and what biochemical changes occur within the dividing cells so that hormonal effects are so dramatically elicited?

Is the nuclear envelope a controlling force in the rate of DNA synthesis (Alfert and Das, 1969)? If so, can the hormones exert their effects by acting on the nuclear envelope perhaps via or in conjunction with cyclic AMP or cyclic GMP? Although there have been several recent studies on the effects of JH and ecdysone on protein, RNA and DNA synthesis, cells must also manufacture membranes if they are to grow and divide. Do the growth hormones control membrane phospholipid synthesis (Tata, 1967) and thus membrane biogenesis as well as acting at the membrane? What are the relationships between the insect hormones and ions and how might a change in the ionic milieu affect translation? We now know that when the K^+ concentration of the medium bathing baby hamster kidney cells is raised by equimolar replacement of Na^+, DNA synthesis and cell multiplication are almost completely inhibited (Orr *et al.*, 1972). The effects are reversible and may be due to changes in the membrane potential. Many more questions dealing with gene expression could be asked (Tomkins *et al.*, 1969; Britten and Davidson, 1969). In short there are many problems to be pursued and it is hoped that skillful and imaginative investigators will undertake these projects on the endocrine aspects of the physiology of growth and development.

Acknowledgments

We thank our associates for helpful comments, particularly Dr. E. Cohen, Dr. D. Whitmore, Dr. E. Whitmore, Dr. J. Koeppe, Mrs. L. Kollett, Mr. P. Sroka and Mr. W. Vedeckis. We are also grateful to Pergamon Press, Springer-Verlag, the Rockefeller University Press, and the National Academy of Sciences for allowing us to reproduce the figures used in this article. Special thanks are given to Mrs. Clay Curvey for her excellent secretarial assistance.

References

Adams, T. S., and Eide, P. E. (1972). *Gen. Comp. Endocrinol.* **18**, 12.

Adelung, D. (1966). *Verh. Deut. Zool. Ges. Gottingen* **30**, Suppl., 264.

Agui, N., Yagi, S., and Fukaya, M. (1969a). *Appl. Entomol. Zool.* **4**, 156.

Agui, N., Yagi, S., and Fukaya, M. (1969b). *Appl. Entomol. Zool.* **4**, 158.

Ajami, A., and Riddiford, L. M. (1971). *Amer. Zool.* **11**, 644.

Alfert, M., and Das, N. K. (1969). *Proc. Nat. Acad. Sci. U.S.* **63**, 123.

Allfrey, V. G. (1966). *Cancer Res.* **26**, 2026.

Anderson, R. J., Henrick, C. A., Siddall, J. B., and Zurflüh, R. (1972). *J. Amer. Chem. Soc.* (in press).

Applebaum, S. W., and Gilbert, L. I. (1972) . *Develop. Biol.* **27**, 165.

Arking, R., and Shaaya, E. (1969). *J. Insect Physiol.* **15**, 287.

Arnaud, M., Beziat, Y., Borgna, J. L., Guilleux, J. C., and Mousseron-Canet, M. (1971). *Biochim. Biophys. Acta* **254**, 241.

Ashburner, M. (1970). *Nature (London)* **227**, 187.

Ashburner, M. (1971). *Nature (London), New Biol.* **230**, 222.

Babu, T. H., and Slăma, K. (1972). *Science* **175**, 78.

Barton, D. H. R., Feakins, P. G., Poyser, J. P., and Sammes, P. G. (1970). *J. Chem. Soc., C* p. 1584.

Barton-Browne, L., Dodson, L. F., Hodgson, E. S., and Kiraly, J. K. (1961). *Gen. Comp. Endocrinol.* **1**, 232.

Baumann, G. (1968). *J. Insect Physiol.* **14**, 1459.

Baumann, G. (1969). *Nature (London)* **223**, 316.

Beaulaton, J. (1968). *J. Ultrastruct. Res.* **23**, 499.

Beck, S. D., and Shane, J. L. (1969). *J. Insect Physiol.* **15**, 721.

Becker, E. (1941). *Biol. Zentralbl.* **61**, 360.

Beetsma, J., de Ruiter, L., and de Wilde, J. (1962). *J. Insect Physiol.* **8**, 251.

Bell, W. J., and Barth, R. H., Jr. (1971). *Nature (London), New Biol.* **230**, 220.

Benjamin, W. B., and Goodman, R. M. (1969). *Science* **166**, 629.

Berendes, H. D. (1967). *Chromosoma* **22**, 274.

Berendes, H. D. (1968). *Chromosoma* **24**, 418.

Berendes, H. D. (1971). *In* "Control Mechanisms of Growth and Differentiation" (D. D. Davies and M. Balls, eds.), pp. 145–161. Cambridge Univ. Press, London and New York.

Berendes, H. D., and Willart, E. (1971). *J. Insect Physiol.* **17**, 2337.

Berkoff, C. E. (1969). *Quart. Rev., Chem. Soc.* **23**, 372.

Bern, H. A. (1962). *Gen. Comp. Endocrinol., Suppl.* **1**, 117.

Berreur, P., and Fraenkel, G. (1969). *Science* **164**, 1182.

Berridge, M. J. (1966). *J. Exp. Biol.* **44**, 533.

Berridge, M. J. (1970). *J. Exp. Biol.* **53**, 171.

Berridge, M. J., and Patel, N. G. (1968). *Science* **162**, 462.

Berridge, M. J., and Prince, W. T. (1971). *Phil. Trans. Roy. Soc. London, Ser. B* **262**, 111.

Berry, S. J., Krishnakumaran, A., Oberlander, H., and Schneiderman, H. A. (1967). *J. Insect Physiol.* **13**, 1511.

Bhakthan, N. M. G., and Gilbert, L. I. (1968). *Gen. Comp. Endocrinol.* 11, 186.

Bhakthan, N. M. G., and Gilbert, L. I. (1971). *Ann. Entomol. Soc. Amer.* 64, 68.

Bhakthan, N. M. G., and Gilbert, L. I. (1972). *Z. Zellforsch. Mikrosk. Anat.* 124. 433.

Bhakthan, N. M. G., Borden, J. H., and Nair, K. K. (1970). *J. Cell Sci.* 6, 807.

Bieber, M. A., Sweeley, C. C., Faulkner, D. J, and Petersen, M. R. (1972). *Anal. Biochem.* 47, 264.

Bloch, B., Thomsen, E., and Thomsen, M. (1966). *Z. Zellforsch. Mikrosk. Anat.* 70, 185.

Blumenfeld, M., and Schneiderman, H. A. (1968). *Biol. Bull.* 135, 466.

Bodenstein, D. (1936). *Ergeb. Biol.* 13, 174.

Bodenstein, D. (1938). *Wilhelm Roux' Arch. Entwicklungsmech. Organismen* 133, 156.

Bodenstein, D. (1953). *J. Exp. Zool.* 123, 413.

Bodnaryk, R. P. (1971). *Gen. Comp. Endocrinol.* 16, 363.

Borden, J. H., and Slater, C. E. (1968). *Z. Vergl. Physiol.* 61, 366.

Borden, J. H., Nair, K. K., and Slater, C. E. (1969). *Science* 166, 1626.

Bounhiol, J. J. (1938). *Bull. Biol., Suppl.* 24, 1.

Bowers, W. S. (1968). *Science* 161, 895.

Bowers, W. S., and Blickenstaff, C. C. (1966). *Science* 154, 1673.

Bowers, W. S., and Friedman, S. (1963). *Nature (London)* 198, 685.

Bowers, W. S., Thompson, M. J., and Uebel, E. C. (1965). *Life Sci.* 4, 2323.

Bowers, W. S., Fales, H. M., Thompson, M. J., and Uebel, E. C. (1966). *Science* 154, 1020.

Britten, R. J., and Davidson, E. H. (1969). *Science* 165, 349.

Brookes, V. J. (1969). *Develop. Biol.* 20, 459.

Brousse-Gaury, P. (1970). *Ann. Sci. Nat. Zool. Biol. Anim.* [12] 12, 51.

Brown, B. E. (1965). *Gen. Comp. Endocrinol.* 5, 387.

Bruchovsky, N., and Wilson, J. D. (1968). *J. Biol. Chem.* 243, 2012.

Bryant, P. J., and Sang, J. H. (1969). *Genetics* 62, 321.

Burdette, W. J., and Bullock, M. W. (1963). *Science* 140, 1311.

Burdette, W. J., and Richards, R. C. (1961). *Nature (London)* 189, 666.

Butenandt, A., and Karlson, P. (1954). *Z. Naturforsch.* 9b, 389.

Butterworth, F. M., and Bodenstein, D. (1969). *Gen. Comp. Endocrinol.* 13, 68.

Bygrave, F. L. (1967). *Nature (London)* 214, 667.

Carlisle, D. B., and Ellis, P. E. (1968). *Nature (London)* 220, 706.

Caspari, E., and Plagge, E. (1935). *Naturwissenschaften* 23, 751.

Caveney, S. (1970). *J. Insect Physiol.* 16, 1087.

Cazal, M. (1969). *Arch. Zool. Exp. Gen.* 110, 83.

Cazal, P. (1947). *Bull. Biol. Fr. Belg.* 80, 347.

Cazal, P. (1948). *Bull. Biol. Fr. Belg., Suppl.* 32, 1.

Century, T. J., Fenichel, I. R., and Horowitz, S. B. (1970). *J. Cell Sci.* 7, 5.

Cerny, V., Dolejš, L., Lábler, L., Sorm, F., and Slăma, K. (1967) . *Collect Czech. Chem. Commun.* 32, 3926.

Chadwick, L. E. (1955). *Science* 121, 435.

Chadwick, L. E. (1956). *J. Exp. Zool.* 131, 291.

Chase, A. M. (1970). *J. Insect Physiol.* 16, 865.

Chaudhary, K. D., Lupien, P. J., and Hinse, C. (1969). *Experientia* 25, 250.

Cherbas, L., and Cherbas, P. (1970). *Biol. Bull.* 138, 115.

Chihara, C. J., Petri, W. H., Fristrom, J. W., and King, D. S. (1972). *J. Insect Physiol.* 18, 1115.

Chino, H., and Gilbert, L. I. (1965). *Biochim. Biophys. Acta* **98**, 94.

Chino, H., and Gilbert, L. I. (1971). *Insect Biochem.* **1**, 337.

Chino, H., Murakami, S., and Harashima, K. (1969). *Biochim. Biophys. Acta* **176**, 1.

Chino, H., Gilbert, L. I., Siddall, J. B., and Hafferl, W. (1970). *J. Insect Physiol.* **16**, 2033.

Chong, Y. K., Galbraith, M. N., and Horn, D. H. S. (1970). *Chem. Commun.* p. 1217.

Claycomb, W. C., LaFond, R. E., and Villee, C. A. (1971). *Nature (London)* **234**, 302.

Clever, U. (1968). *Annu. Rev. Genet.* **2**, 11.

Clever, U., and Karlson, P. (1960). *Exp. Cell Res.* **20**, 623.

Cohen, E., and Gilbert, L. I. (1972) . *J. Insect Physiol.* **18**, 1061.

Congote, L. F., Sekeris, C. E., and Karlson, P. (1969). *Exp. Cell Res.* **56**, 338.

Congote, L. F., Sekeris, C. E., and Karlson, P. (1970) *Z. Naturforsch.* **25b**, 279.

Corey, E. J., Katzenellenbogen, J. A., Gilman, N. W., Roman, S. A., and Erickson, B. W. (1968). *J. Amer. Chem. Soc.* **90**, 5618.

Craig, G. B., Jr., (1970). *Misc. Publ. Entomol. Soc. Amer.* **7**, 130.

Dahm, K. H., and Röller, H. (1970). *Life Sci.* **9**, 1397.

Dahm, K. H., Trost, B. M., and Röller, H. (1967). *J. Amer. Chem. Soc.* **89**, 5292.

Dammeier, B., and Hoppe, W. (1971). *Chem. Ber.* **104**, 1660.

Daneholt, B., Edström, J.-E., Egyházi, E., Lambert, B., and Ringborg, U. (1969a). *Chromosoma* **28**, 379.

Daneholt, B., Edström, J.-E., Egyházi, E., Lambert, B., and Ringborg, U. (1969b). *Chromosoma* **28**, 399.

Daneholt, B., Edström, J.-E., Egyházi, E., Lambert, B., and Ringborg, U. (1969c). *Chromosoma* **28**, 418.

D'Armiento, M., Johnson, G. S., and Pastan, I. (1972). *Proc. Nat. Acad. Sci. U.S.* **69**, 459.

Davey, K. G. (1971) . *Int. J. Parasitol.* **1**, 61.

de Kort, C. A. D. (1969). "Hormones and the Structural and Biochemical Properties of the Flight Muscles in the Colorado Beetle." Veenman, Wageningen.

de Kort, C. A. D., and Raak, C. J. (1971). *Endocrinol. Exp.* **5**, 57.

de Loof, A., and Lagasse, A. (1970). *Z. Zellforsch. Mikrosk. Anat.* **106**, 439.

de Wilde, J., and de Boer, J. A. (1961). *J. Insect Physiol.* **6**, 152.

Dogra, G. S. (1967). *J. Insect Physiol.* **13**, 1895.

Dorn, A. (1972). *Z. Morphol. Tiere* **71**, 52.

Downer, R. G. H., and Steele, J. E. (1969). *Proc. Entomol. Soc. Ont.* **100**, 113.

Dutkowski, A. B., Cymborowski, B., and Przelecka, A. (1971). *J. Insect Physiol.* **17**, 1763.

Economopoulos, A. P., and Gordon, H. T. (1971). *J. Exp. Zool.* **177**, 391.

Edwards, F. J. (1970). *J. Insect Physiol.* **16**, 2027.

Edwards, J. S. (1966). *J. Insect Physiol.* **12**, 1423.

Egyházi, E., Daneholt, B., Edström, J.-E., Lambert, B., and Ringborg, U. (1969). *J. Mol. Biol.* **44**, 517.

El-Ibrashy, M. T., and Boctor, I. Z. (1970). *Z. Vergl. Physiol.* **86**, 111.

Emmerich, H. (1969). *Exp. Cell Res.* **58**, 261.

Emmerich, H. (1970a). *J. Insect Physiol.* **16**, 725.

Emmerich, H. (1970b). *Z. Vergl. Physiol.* **68**, 385.

Engelmann, F. (1965). *Arch. Anat. Microsc. Morphol. Exp.* **54**, 387.

Engelmann, F. (1969). *Science* **165**, 407.

Engelmann, F. (1971). *Science* **174**, 1041.

Faulkner, D. J., and Petersen, M. R. (1971). *J. Amer. Chem. Soc.* **93**, 3767.

Faux, A., Horn, D. H. S., Middleton. E. J, Fales, H. M., and Lowe, M. E. (1969). *Chem. Commun.* p. 175.

Faux, A., Galbraith, M. N., Horn, D. H. S., Middleton, E. J., and Thomson, J. A. (1970). *Chem. Commun.* p. 243.

Feldherr, C. M. (1971). *Tissue Cell* 3, 1.

Fischer, L., and Lynn, E. V. (1933). *J. Amer. Pharm. Ass.* 22, 1225.

Fraenkel, G. (1935). *Proc. Roy. Soc., Ser. B* 118, 1.

Fraenkel, G., and Brookes, V. J. (1953). *Biol. Bull.* 105, 442.

Fristrom, J. W., Raikow, R., Petri, W. H., and Stewart, D. (1970). *In* "Problems in Biology: RNA in Development" (E. W. Hanly, ed.), pp. 381–398. Univ. of Utah Press, Salt Lake City.

Fukuda, S. (1940a). *Proc. Imp. Acad. (Tokyo)* 16, 414.

Fukuda, S. (1940b). *Proc. Imp. Acad. (Tokyo)* 16, 417.

Fukuda, S. (1941). *Annot. Zool. Jap.* 20, 9.

Fukuda, S. (1944). *J. Fac. Sci., Univ. Tokyo, Sect. 4* 6, 477.

Furlenmeier, A., Fürst, A., Langemann, A., Waldvogel, G., Hocks, P., Kerb, U., and Wiechert, R. (1967). *Helv. Chim. Acta* 50, 2387.

Gabe, M. (1954). *Annee Biol.* 30, 5.

Galbraith, M. N., Horn, D. H. S., Hocks, P., Schulz, G., and Hoffmeister, H. (1967). *Naturwissenschaften* 54, 471.

Galbraith, M. N., Horn, D. H. S., Middleton, E. J., and Hackney, R. J. (1968). *Chem. Commun.* p. 83.

Galbraith, M. N., Horn, D. H. S., Middleton, E. J., Thomson, J. A., Siddal, J. B., and Hafferl, W. (1969a). *Chem. Commun.* p 1134.

Galbraith, M. N., Horn, D. H. S., Thomson, J. A., Neufeld, G. J., and Hackney, R. J. (1969b). *J. Insect Physiol.* 15, 1225.

Galbraith, M. N., Horn, D. H. S., Middleton, E. J., and Thomson, J. A. (1970). *Chem. Commun.* p. 179.

Galbraith, M. N., Horn, D. H. S., Middleton, E. J., and Thomson, J. A. (1972). *Experientia* 28, 264.

Gersch, M. (1960). *Symp. Biol. Hung.* 1, 153.

Gersch, M. (1961a). *In* "The Ontogeny of Insects" (I. Hrdy, ed.), pp. 127–132. Academic Press, New York.

Gersch, M. (1961b). *Amer. Zool.* 1, 53.

Gersch, M. (1962). *Gen. Comp. Endocrinol., Suppl.* 1, 322.

Gersch, M., and Stürzebecher, J. (1970). *J. Insect Physiol.* 16, 1813.

Gersch, M., and Stürzebecher, J. (1971). *Experientia* 27, 1475.

Gersch, M., Richter, K., Böhm, G.-A., and Stürzebecher, J. (1970). *J. Insect Physiol.* 16, 1991.

Gershfeld, N. L., and Muramatsu, M. (1971). *J. Gen. Physiol.* 58, 650.

Gilbert, L. I. (1964). *In* "The Physiology of Insecta" (M. Rockstein, ed.), Vol. 1, pp. 149–225. Academic Press, New York.

Gilbert, L. I. (1967a). *Comp. Biochem. Physiol.* 21, 237.

Gilbert, L. I. (1967b). *Compr. Biochem.* 28, 199–252.

Gilbert, L. I., and Schneiderman, H. A. (1959). *Nature (London)* 184, 171.

Gilbert, L. I., and Schneiderman, H. A. (1960). *Trans. Amer. Microsc. Soc.* 79, 38.

Gilbert, L. I., and Schneiderman, H. A. (1961). *Gen. Comp. Endocrinol.* 1, 453.

Gilbert, L. I., Applebaum, S. W., Gorell, T. A., Siddall, J. B., and Siew, Y. C. (1971) . *Bull. WHO* 44, 397.

Goldsworthy, G. J. (1970). *Gen. Comp. Endocrinol.* 14, 78.

Goldsworthy, G. J. (1971). *J. Endocrinol.* 50, 237.

Gorell, T. A., and Gilbert, L. I. (1969). *Gen. Comp. Endocrinol.* 13, 308.

Gorell, T. A., Gilbert, L. I., and Tash, J. (1972a). *Insect Biochem.* **2**, 94.

Gorell, T. A., Gilbert, L. I., and Siddall, J. B. (1972b). *Proc. Nat. Acad. Sci. U.S.* **69**, 812.

Gorell, T. A., Gilbert, L. I., and Siddall, J. B. (1972c). *Amer. Zool.* **12**, 347.

Gosbee, J. L., Milligan, J. V., and Smallman, B. N. (1968). *J. Insect Physiol.* **14**, 1785.

Grossbach, U. (1969). *Chromosoma* **28**, 136.

Hachlow, V. (1931). *Wilhelm Roux' Arch. Entwicklungsmech. Organismen* **125**, 46.

Hafferl, W., Zurflüh, R., and Duhman, L. (1971). *J. Label. Compounds* **7**, 331.

Hafferl, W., Wren, D. L., Marshal, J. P., Calzada, M. C., and Siddall, J. B. (1972). *J. Label. Compounds* **8**, 81.

Hampshire, F., and Horn, D. H. S. (1966). *Chem. Commun.* p. 37.

Hänsel, R., Leuckert, C. H., Rimpler, H., and Schaaf, K. D. (1965). *Phytochemistry* **4**, 19.

Hanström, B. (1938). *Acta Univ. Lund., Sect. 2* **39**, 1.

Harmsen, R., and Beckel, W. E. (1960). *Can. J. Zool.* **38**, 1093.

Harrison, I. T., Siddall, J. B., and Fried, J. H. (1966). *Tetrahedron Lett.* p. 3457.

Hechter, O., and Soifer, D. (1971). *In* "Basic Actions of Sex Steroids on Target Organs" (P. O. Hubinot, F. Leroy, and D. Garland, eds.), pp. 93–111. Karger, Basel.

Heinrich, G., and Hoffmeister, H. (1970). *Z. Naturforsch.* **25b**, 358.

Helmsing, P. J., and Berendes, H. D. (1971). *J. Cell Biol.* **50**, 893.

Henrick, C. A., Schaub, F., and Siddall, J. B. (1972). *J. Amer. Chem. Soc.* (in press).

Herman, W. S. (1967). *Int. Rev. Cytol.* **22**, 269–347.

Herman, W. S., and Gilbert, L. I. (1965). *Nature (London)* **205**, 926.

Herman, W. S., and Gilbert, L. I. (1966). *Gen. Comp. Endocrinol.* **7**, 275.

Highnam, K. C., and Goldsworthy, G. J. (1972). *Gen. Comp. Endocrinol.* **18**, 83.

Highnam, K. C., and West, M. W. (1971). *Gen. Comp. Endocrinol.* **16**, 574.

Highnam, K. C., Hill, L., and Gingell, D. J. (1965). *J. Zool.* **147**, 201.

Hikino, H., and Hikino, Y. (1970). *Fortschr. Chem. Org. Naturst.* **28**, 256.

Hikino, H., Nabetani, S., Nomoto, K., Arai, T., Takemoto, T., Otaka, T., and Uchiyama, M. (1969). *Yakugaku Zasshi* **89**, 235.

Hikino, H., Ohizumi, Y., and Takemoto, T. (1971). *Chem. Commun.* p. 1036.

Hill, L. (1962). *J. Insect Physiol.* **8**, 609.

Hinks, C. F. (1971). *J. Entomol. (A)* **46**, 13.

Hinton, H. E. (1963). *Sci. Progr. (London)* **51**, 306.

Hintze, C. (1968). *Wilhelm Roux' Arch. Entwicklungsmech. Organismen* **160**, 313.

Hintze-Podufal, C. (1970). *Experientia* **26**, 1269.

Hintze-Podufal, C. (1971). *Z. Naturforsch.* **26b**, 154.

Hirono, I., Sasaoka, I., and Shimizu, M. (1969). *Gann* **60**, 341.

Hocks, P., and Wiechert, R. (1966). *Tetrahedron Lett.* p. 2989.

Hoffmeister, H., and Grützmacher, H. F. (1966). *Tetrahedron Lett.* p. 4017.

Hoffmeister, H., and Lang, N. (1964). *Naturwissenschaften* **51**, 112.

Hoffmeister, H., Rufer, C., and Ammon, H. (1965). *Z. Naturforsch* **20b**, 130.

Hoffmeister, H., Grützmacher, H. F., and Dünnebeil, K. (1967). *Z. Naturforsch.* **22b**, 66.

Holick, M. F., Schuves, H. K., and DeLuca, H. F. (1971). *Proc. Nat. Acad. Sci. U.S.* **68**, 803.

Hori, M. (1969). *Steroids* **14**, 33.

Horn, D. H. S. (1971). *In* "Naturally Occurring Insecticides" (M. Jacobson and D. G. Crosby, eds.), pp. 333–459. Dekker, New York.

Horn, D. H. S., Middleton, E. J., Wunderlich, J. A., and Hampshire, F. (1966). *Chem. Commun.* p. 339.

Horn, D. H. S., Fabbri, S., Hampshire, F., and Lowe, M. E. (1968). *Biochem. J.* **109,** 399.

Horn, D. H. S., Galbraith, M. N., Middleton, E. J., and Thomson, J. A. (1972). *Proc. Int. Congr. Horm. Steroids, 3rd, 1971* pp. 176–183.

Hsiao, C., and Hsiao, T. H. (1969). *Life Sci.* **8,** 767.

Huber, R., and Hoppe, W. (1965). *Chem. Ber.* **98,** 2403.

Hughes, M., and Kambysellis, M. P. (1970). *Drosophila Inform. Serv.* **45,** 102.

Hüppi, G., and Siddall, J. B. (1967). *J. Amer. Chem. Soc.* **89,** 6790.

Hüppi, G., and Siddall, J. B. (1968). *Tetrahedron Lett.* p. 1113.

Ichikawa, M., and Nitshiitsutsuji-Uwo, J. (1959). *Biol. Bull.* **116,** 88.

Ikekawa, N., Hattori, F., Rubio-Lightbourn, J., Miyazaki, H., Ishibashi, M., and Mori, C. (1972). *J. Chromatogr. Sci.* **10,** 233.

Ilan, J. (1969a). *Biochemistry* **8,** 4825.

Ilan, J. (1969b). *In* "The Mechanism of Protein Synthesis," pp. 787–791. Cold Spring Harbor Lab., Long Island, New York.

Ilan, J., and Ilan, J. (1971). *Develop. Biol.* **25,** 280.

Ilan, J., Ilan, J., and Ricklis, S. (1969). *Nature (London)* **224,** 179.

Ilan, J., Ilan, J., and Patel, N. (1970). *J. Biol. Chem.* **245,** 1275.

Imai, S., Toyosato, T., Sakai, M., Sato, Y., Fujioka, S., Murata, E., and Goto, M. (1969). *Chem. Pharm. Bull.* **17,** 335.

Ishikawa, E., Ishikawa, S., Davis, J. W., and Sutherland, E. W. (1969). *J. Biol. Chem.* **244,** 6371.

Ishizaki, H. (1963). *Exp. Cell Res.* **31,** 606.

Ito, H. (1918). *Bull. Sericult. Exp. Sta. Jap.* **1,** 63.

Ito, S., and Loewenstein, W. R. (1965). *Science* **150,** 909.

Ito, T., Horie, Y., and Watanabe, K. (1970). *Annot. Zool. Jap.* **43,** 175.

James, D. W., Rabin, B. R., and Williams, D. J. (1969). *Nature (London)* **224,** 371.

Jarial, M. S., and Scudder, G. G. E. (1971). *Can. J. Zool.* **49,** 1369.

Jensen, E. V., Jacobson, H. I., Flesher, J. W., Saha, N. N., Gupta, G. N., Smith, S., Colucci, V., Shiplacoff, D., Neumann, H. G., De Sombre, E. R., and Jungblut, P. W. (1966). *In* "Steroid Dynamics" (G. Pincus, J. Tait, and T. Nakao, eds.), pp. 133–156. Academic Press, New York.

Jizba, J., and Herout, V. (1967). *Collect. Czech. Chem. Commun.* **32,** 2867.

Jizba, J., Herout, V., and Sorm, F. (1967). *Tetrahedron Lett.* p. 1689.

Johnson, B., and Bowers, B. (1963). *Science* **141,** 264.

Johnson, J. D., Jant, B. A., Kaufman, S., and Sokoloff, L. (1971). *Arch. Biochem. Biophys.* **142,** 489.

Johnson, W. S., Li, T., Faulkner, D. J., and Campbell, S. F. (1968). *J. Amer. Chem. Soc.* **90,** 6225.

Johnson, W. S., Campbell, S. F., Krishnakumaran, A., and Meyer, A. S. (1969). *Proc. Nat. Acad. Sci. U. S.* **62,** 1005.

Joly, L., Joly, P., Porte, A., and Girardie, A. (1968). *Arch. Zool. Exp. Gen.* **109,** 703.

Joly, L., Joly, P., Porte, A., and Girardie, A. (1969). *Arch. Zool. Exp. Gen.* **110,** 617.

Joly, P. (1967). *Ann. Soc. Entomol. Fr.* [N.S.] **3,** 601.

Joly, P., and Meyer, A. S. (1970). *Arch. Zool. Exp. Gen.* **111,** 51.

Judy, K. J. (1969). *Science* **165,** 1374.

Judy, K. J. (1972). *Life Sci.* **11,** 605.

Judy, K. J., and Gilbert, L. I. (1969). *Ann. Entomol. Soc. Amer.* **62**, 1438.

Judy, K. J., and Gilbert, L. I. (1970a). *J Morphol.* **131**, 277.

Judy, K. J., and Gilbert, L. I. (1970b). *J. Morphol.* **131**, 301.

Judy, K. J., and Marks, E. P. (1971). *Gen. Comp. Endocrinol.* **17**, 351.

Kafatos, F. C. (1968). *Proc. Nat. Acad. Sci. U. S.* **59**, 1251.

Kambysellis, M. P., and Williams, C. M. (1971a). *Biol. Bull.* **141**, 527.

Kambysellis, M. P., and Williams, C. M. (1971b). *Biol. Bull.* **141**, 541.

Kaplanis, J. N., Thompson, M. J., Yamamoto, R. T., Robbins, W. E., and Louloudes, S. J. (1966). *Steroids* **8**, 605.

Kaplanis, J. N., Robbins, W. E., Thompson, M. J., and Baumhover, A. H. (1969). *Science* **166**, 1540.

Karlson, P. (1956a). *Vitam. Horm. (New York)* **14**, 227–266.

Karlson, P. (1956b). *Ann. Sci. Nat. Zool. Biol. Anim.* [12] **18**, 125.

Karlson, P. (1970). *In* "Natural Substances Formed Biologically from Mevalonic Acid" (T. W. Goodwin, ed.), pp. 145–156. Academic Press, New York.

Karlson, P., and Bode, C. (1969). *J. Insect Physiol.* **15**, 111.

Karlson, P., and Hoffmeister, H. (1963). *Hoppe-Seyler's Z. Physiol. Chem.* **331**, 298.

Karlson, P., and Stamm-Menéndez, M. D. (1956). *Hoppe-Seyler's Z. Physiol. Chem.* **306**, 109.

Karlson, P., Hoffmeister, H., Hoppe, W., and Huber, R. (1963). *Justus. Liebig's Ann. Chem.* **662**, 1.

Karlson, P., Congote, L. F., and Sekeris, C. E. (1971). *Bull. Soc. Entomol. Suisse* **44**, 171.

Kater, S. B. (1968). *Science* **160**, 765.

Katz, M., and Lensky, Y. (1970). *Experientia* **26**, 1043.

Ke, O. (1930). *Bull. Sci. Fac. Terkult. Kiusu J. Univ.* **4**, 12.

Keeley, L. L. (1971). *J. Insect Physiol.* **17**, 1501.

Keeley, L. L., and Friedman, S. (1967). *Gen. Comp. Endocrinol.* **8**, 129.

Keeley, L. L., and Friedman, S. (1969). *J. Insect Physiol.* **15**, 509.

Keeley, L. L., and Waddill, V. H. (1971). *Life Sci.* **10**, 737.

Kerb, U., Schulz, G., Hocks, P., Wiechert, R., Furlenmeier, A., Fürst, A., Langemann, A., and Waldvogel, G. (1966). *Helv. Chem. Acta* **49**, 1601 (and references cited therein).

Kerb, U., Wiechert, R., Furlenmeier, A., and Fürst, A. (1968). *Tetrahedron Lett.* p. 4277.

King, D. S. (1969). *Gen. Comp. Endocrinol.* **13**, 512.

King, D. S. (1972a). *Amer. Zool.* **12**, 343.

King, D. S. (1972b). *Gen. Comp. Endocrinol., Suppl.* **3**, 221.

King, D. S., and Siddall, J. B. (1969). *Nature (London)* **221**, 955.

King, R. C., Aggarwal, S. K., and Bodenstein, D. (1966). *J. Exp. Zool.* **161**, 151.

Kislov, A. N., and Veprintsev, B. N. (1971). *Comp. Biochem. Physiol,* **39A**, 521.

Klemm, N. (1971). *Z. Naturforsch.* **26b**, 1085.

Kobayashi, M., Takemoto, T., Ogawa, S., and Nishimoto, N. (1967). *J. Insect Physiol.* **13**, 1395.

Komárková, E., and Hradec, J. (1971). *FEBS Lett.* **18**, 109.

Kopec, S. (1917). *Bull. Int. Acad. Sci. Cracovie* **BB**, 57.

Kopec, S. (1922). *Biol. Bull.* **42**, 323.

Koreeda, M., Nakanishi, K., and Goto, M. (1970). *J. Amer. Chem. Soc.* **92**, 7512.

Koreeda, M., Schooley, D. A., Nakanishi, K., and Hagiwara, H. (1971). *J. Amer. Chem. Soc.* **93**, 4084.

Krishnakumaran, A. (1972). *Biol. Bull.* **142**, 281.

Krishnakumaran, A., and Schneiderman, H. A. (1970). *Biol. Bull.* **139**, 520.

Krishnakumaran, A., Berry, S. J., Oberlander, H., and Schneiderman, H. A. (1967). *J. Insect Physiol.* **13**, 1.

Kroeger, H. (1966). *Exp. Cell Res.* **41**, 64.

Kroeger, H. (1968). *In* "Metamorphosis: A Problem in Developmental Biology" (W. E. Etkin and L. I. Gilbert, eds.), pp. 185–219. Appleton, New York.

Kroeger, H. (1971). *Endocrinol. Exp.* **5**, 108.

Kühn, A., and Piepho, H. (1936). *Ges. Wiss. Gottingen Nachr. Biol.* **2**, 141.

Kuo, J. F., Wyatt, G. R., and Greengard, P. (1971). *J. Biol. Chem.* **246**, 7159.

Kuroda, Y., and Yamaguchi, K. (1956). *Jap. J. Genet.* **31**, 98.

Langan, T. A. (1968). *Science* **162**, 579.

Laverdure, A. M. (1970a). *Ann. Endocrinol.* **31**, 504.

Laverdure, A. M. (1970b). *Ann. Endocrinol.* **31**, 516.

Law, J. H., Yuan, C., and Williams, C. M. (1966). *Proc. Nat. Acad. Sci. U. S.* **55**, 576.

Lawrence, P. A. (1966). *J. Exp. Biol.* **44**, 507.

Lawson, D. E. M., Fraser, D. R., Kodicek, E., Morris, H. R., and Williams, D. H. (1971). *Nature (London)* **230**, 228.

Lea, A. O. (1968). *J. Insect Physiol.* **14**, 305.

Lea, A. O., and Van Handel, E. (1970). *J. Insect Physiol.* **16**, 319.

Lea, A. O., and Thomsen, E. (1969). *J. Insect Physiol.* **15**, 477.

Lee, H. (1948). *Ann. Entomol. Soc. Amer.* **41**, 200.

Leenders, H. J., Wullems, G. J., and Berendes, H. D. (1970). *Exp. Cell Res.* **63**, 159.

Lees, A. D. (1967). *J. Insect Physiol.* **13**, 289.

Levenbook, L., Bodnaryk, R. P., and Spande, T. F. (1969). *Biochem. J.* **113**, 837.

Lezzi, M. (1966). *Exp. Cell Res.* **43**, 571.

Lezzi, M. (1970). *Int. Rev. Cytol.* **29**, 127–168.

Lezzi, M., and Gilbert, L. I. (1969). *Proc. Nat. Acad. Sci. U.S.* **64**, 498.

Lezzi, M., and Gilbert, L. I. (1970). *J. Cell Sci.* **6**, 615.

Lezzi, M., and Gilbert, L. I. (1972). *Gen. Comp. Endocrinol., Suppl.* **3**, 159.

Locke, M. (1969). *Tissue Cell* **1**, 103.

Loew, P., and Johnson, W. S. (1971). *J. Amer. Chem. Soc.* **93**, 3765.

Loher, W. (1961). *Proc. Roy. Soc.* **153**, 380.

Lupien, P. J., Hinse, C., and Chaudhary, K. D. (1969). *Arch. Int. Physiol. Biochim.* **77**, 206.

Lüscher, M. (1968). *J. Insect Physiol.* **14**, 499.

Lüscher, M., and Leuthold, R. (1965). *Rev. Suisse Zool.* **72**, 618.

Lüscher, M., and Wyss-Huber, M. (1964). *Rev. Suisse Zool.* **71**, 183.

Macklin, M., and Burnett, A. L. (1966). *Exp. Cell Res.* **44**, 665.

Maddrell, S. H. P. (1963). *J. Exp. Biol.* **40**, 247.

Maddrell, S. H. P. (1964). *J. Exp. Biol.* **41**, 163.

Maddrell, S. H. P. (1965). *Science* **150**, 1033.

Maddrell, S. H. P. (1970). *In* "Insect Ultrastructure" (A. C. Neville, ed.), pp. 101–116. Blackwell, Oxford.

Maddrell, S. H. P., Pilcher, D. E. M., and Gardiner, B. O. C. (1969). *Nature (London)* **222**, 784.

Maddrell, S. H. P., Pilcher, D. E. M., and Gardiner, B. O. C. (1971). *J. Exp. Biol.* **54**, 779.

Madhaven, K., and Schneiderman, H. A. (1968). *J. Insect Physiol.* **14**, 777.

Madhaven, K., and Schneiderman, H. A. (1969). *Biol. Bull.* **137**, 321.

Mandaron, P. (1971). *Develop. Biol.* **25**, 581.

Manning, A. (1966). *Nature (London)* **211**, 1321.

Mansingh, A., and Smallman, B. N. (1967). *J. Insect Physiol.* **13**, 447.

Marks, E. P. (1970). *Gen. Comp. Endocrinol.* **15**, 289.

Marks, E. P., and Leopold, R. A. (1970). *Science* **167**, 61.

Marks, E. P., and Leopold, R. A. (1971). *Biol. Bull.* **140**, 73.

Masner, P. (1969). *Acta Entomol. Bohemoslov.* **66**, 81.

Masner, P., Släma, K., and Landa, V. (1968a) . *J. Embryol. Exp. Morphol.* **20**, 25.

Masner, P., Släma, K., and Landa, V. (1968b) . *Nature (London)* **219**, 395.

Masuoka, M., Orita, S., Shino, A., Matsuzawa, T., and Nakayama, R. (1970). *Jap. J. Pharmacol.* **20**, 142.

Matolín, S. (1970). *Acta Entomol. Bohemoslov.* **67**, 9.

Mayer, R. J., and Candy, D. J. (1969). *J. Insect Physiol.* **15**, 611.

Metzler, M., Dahm, K. H., Meyer, D., and Röller, H. (1971). *Z. Naturforsch.* **26b**, 1270.

Metzler, M., Meyer, D., Dahm, K., Röller, H., and Siddall, J. B. (1972). *Z. Naturforsch.* **27b**, 321.

Meyer, A. S. (1971). *Bull. Soc. Entomol. Suisse* **44**, 37.

Meyer, A. S., and Hanzmann, E. (1970). *Biochem. Biophys. Res. Commun.* **41**, 891.

Meyer, A. S., Schneiderman, H. A., Hanzmann, E., and Ko, J. H. (1968). *Proc. Nat. Acad. Sci. U. S.* **60**, 853.

Meyer, A. S., Hanzmann, E., Schneiderman, H. A., Gilbert, L. I., and Boyette, M. (1970). *Arch. Biochem. Biophys.* **137**, 190.

Meyer, A. S., Hanzmann, E., and Murphy, R. C. (1971). *Proc. Nat. Acad. Sci. U.S.* **68**, 2312.

Mitsuhashi, J. (1965). *Jap. J. Appl. Entomol. Zool.* **9**, 217.

Mitsuhashi, J., and Grace, T. D. C. (1970). *Appl. Entomol. Zool.* **5**, 182.

Mohla, S., De Sombre, E. R., and Jensen, E. V. (1971). *Fed. Proc., Fed. Amer. Soc. Exp. Biol.* **30**, 1214.

Mordue, W. (1969). *J. Insect Physiol.* **15**, 273.

Morgan, E. D., and Woodbridge, A. P. (1971). *Chem. Commun.* p. 475.

Mori, H., Shibata, K., Tsuneda, K., and Sawai, M. (1968). *Chem. Pharm. Bull.* **16**, 563.

Moriyama, H., Nakanishi, K., King, D. S., Okauchi, T., Siddall, J. B., and Hafferl, W., (1970). *Gen. Comp. Endocrinol.* **15**, 80.

Muftic, M. (1969). *Parasitology* **59**, 365.

Müller, H. P., and Engelmann, F. (1968). *Gen. Comp. Endocrinol.* **11**, 43.

Nabert, A. (1913). *Z. Wiss. Zool.* **104**, 181.

Naisse, J. (1966a). *Arch. Biol.* **77**, 139.

Naisse, J. (1966b). *Gen. Comp. Endocrinol.* **7**, 85.

Naisse, J. (1966c). *Gen. Comp. Endocrinol.* **7**, 105.

Naisse, J. (1969). *J. Insect Physiol.* **15**, 877.

Nakanishi, K. (1971). *Int. Congr. Pure Appl. Chem., 23rd, 19* Vol. 3, p. 27.

Nakanishi, K. (1972). *Pure Appl. Chem.* **25**, 167.

Nakanishi, K., Koreeda, M., Sasaki, S., Chang, M. L., and Hsu, H. Y. (1966). *Chem. Commun.* p. 917.

Nakanishi, K., Schooley, D. A., Koreeda, M., and Dillon, J. (1971). *Chem. Commun.* p. 1235.

Nakanishi, K., Moriyama, H., Okauchi, T., Fujioka, S., and Koreeda, M. (1972). *Science* **176**, 51.

Natalizi, G. M., and Frontali, N. (1966). *J. Insect Physiol.* **12**, 1279.

Neufeld, G. J., and Thomson, J. A. (1968). *J. Insect Physiol.* **14**, 789.

Norman, A. W., Myrtle, O. F., Midgett, R. J., Nowicki, H. G., Williams, V., and Popják, G. (1971). *Science* **173**, 51.

Normann, T. C. (1965). *Z. Zellforsch. Mikrosk. Anat.* **67**, 461.

Normann, T. C. (1969). *Exp. Cell Res.* **55**, 285.

Normann, T. C., and Duve, H. (1969). *Gen. Comp. Endocrinol.* **12**, 449.

Novák, V. J. A. (1969). *J. Embryol. Exp. Morphol.* **21**, 1.

Nowock, J. (1971). *Wilhelm Roux' Arch. Entwicklungsmech. Organismen* **168**, 20.

Nutting, W. L. (1955). *Science* **122**, 30.

Oberlander, H. (1969a). *J. Insect Physiol.* **15**, 297.

Oberlander, H. (1969b). *J. Insect Physiol.* **15**, 1803.

Oberlander, H. (1972a). *J. Insect Physiol.* **18**, 223.

Oberlander, H. (1972b). (personal communication).

Oberlander, H., and Fulco, L. (1967). *Nature (London)* **216**, 1140.

Oberlander, H., and Schneiderman, H. A. (1966). *J. Insect Physiol.* **12**, 37.

Oberlander, H., Berry, S. J., Krishnakumaran, A., and Schneiderman, H. A. (1965). *J. Exp. Zool.* **159**, 15.

Odhiambo, T. R. (1966a). *J. Exp. Biol.* **45**, 45.

Odhiambo, T. R. (1966b). *J. Exp. Biol.* **45**, 51.

Odhiambo, T. R. (1966c). *J. Insect Physiol.* **12**, 995.

O'Farrell, A. F., and Stock, A. (1964). *Life Sci.* **3**, 491.

Ohnishi, E., Ohtaki, T., and Fukuda, S. (1971). *Proc. Jap. Acad.* **47**, 413.

Ohtaki, T., and Williams, C. M. (1970). *Biol. Bull.* **138**, 326.

Ohtaki, T., Milkman, R. D., and Williams, C. M. (1969). *Biol. Bull.* **135**, 322.

Ohtaki, T., Takeuchi, S., and Mori, K. (1971). *Jap. J. Med. Sci. Biol.* **24**, 251.

Orr, C. W. M. (1964). *J. Insect Physiol.* **10**, 103.

Orr, C. W. M., Yoshikawa-Fukada, M., and Ebert, J. D. (1972). *Proc. Nat. Acad. Sci. U.S.* **69**, 243.

Oschman, J. L., and Berridge, M. J. (1970). *Tissue Cell* **2**, 281.

Otaka, T., Uchiyama, M., Okui, S., Takemoto, T., Hikino, H., Ogawa, S., and Nishimoto, N. (1968). *Chem. Pharm. Bull.* **16**, 2426.

Otaka, T., Okui, S., and Uchiyama, M. (1969). *Chem. Pharm. Bull.* **17**, 75.

Ozeki, K. (1968). *Sci. Pap. Coll. Gen. Educ., Univ. Tokyo* **18**, 199.

Pan, M. L., and Wyatt, G. R. (1971). *Science* **174**, 503.

Patel, N. G. (1971). *Insect Biochem.* **1**, 391.

Patel, N. G., and Madhaven, K. (1969). *J. Insect Physiol.* **15**, 2141.

Patel, N. G., and Schneiderman, H. A. (1969). *J. Insect Physiol.* **15**, 643.

Patterson, J. W. (1971). *Nature (London), New Biol.* **233**, 176.

Pener, M. P. (1965). *J. Zool.* **147**, 119.

Petri, W. H., Fristrom, J. W., Stewart, D. J., and Hanly, E. W. (1971). *Mol. Gen. Genet.* **110**, 245.

Pfeiffer, I. W. (1945). *J. Exp. Zool.* **99**, 183.

Pflugfelder, O. (1958). "Entwicklungsphysiologie der Insekten," 2nd ed. Akad. Verlagsges, Leipzig.

Piepho, H. (1942). *Wilhelm Roux' Arch. Entwicklungsmech. Organismen* **141**, 500.

Piepho, H. (1946). *Biol. Zentralbl.* **65**, 141.

Piepho, H. (1950a). *Z. Tierpsychol.* **7**, 424.

Piepho, H. (1950b). *Biol. Zentralbl.* **69**, 261.

Piepho, H. (1950c). *Biol. Zentralbl.* **69**, 1.

Piepho, H. (1951). *Ver. Deut. Zool. Ges.* p. 62.

Piepho, H. (1952). *Z. Lepid.* 2, 105.

Piepho, H. (1960). *Ann. N. Y. Acad. Sci.* 89, 564.

Piepho, H., and Holz, I. (1959). *Biol. Zentralbl.* 78, 417.

Piepho, H., and Meyer, H. (1951). *Biol. Zentralbl.* 70, 252.

Piepho, H., Böden, E., and Holz, I. (1960). *Z. Tierpsychol.* 17, 261.

Pilcher, D. E. M. (1970). *J. Exp. Biol.* 52, 653.

Pipa, R. .L (1971). *J. Insect Physiol.* 17, 2441.

Poels, C. L. M. (1970). *Develop. Biol.* 23, 210.

Poels, C. L. M., and Beenakkers, A. M. T. (1969). *Entomol. Exp. Appl.* 12, 312.

Poels, C. L. M., de Loof, A., and Berendes, H. D. (1971). *J. Insect Physiol.* 17, 1717.

Possompès, B. (1949a). *C. R. Acad. Sci.* 228, 1527.

Possompès, B. (1949b). *C. R. Acad. Sci.* 230, 409.

Possompès, B. (1953). *Arch. Zool. Exp. Gen.* 89, 203.

Postlethwait, J. H., and Schneiderman, H. A. (1970). *Biol. Bull.* 138, 47.

Prince, W. T., Berridge, M. J., and Rasmussen, H. (1972). *Proc. Nat. Acad. Sci. U. S.* 69, 553.

Radford, S. V., and Misch, D. W. (1971). *J. Cell Biol.* 49, 702.

Raikow, R., and Fristrom, J. W. (1971). *J. Insect Physiol.* 17, 1599.

Rajulu, G., Kulasekarapandian, S., and Krishnan, N. (1972). *Curr. Sci.* 41, 67.

Ralph, C. L., and McCarthy, C. (1964). *Nature (London)* 203, 1195.

Reddy, G., and Krishnakumaran, A. (1972). *J. Insect Physiol.* 18, 2019.

Reddy, S. R. R., and Wyatt, G. R. (1967). *J. Insect Physiol.* 13, 981.

Reichenbach-Klinke, H. H. (1952). *Zool. Jahrb., Abt. Anat. Ontog. Tiere* 72, 230.

Reinecke, J. P., and Robbins, J. D. (1971). *Exp. Cell Res.* 64, 335.

Rensing, L., Thach, B., and Bruce, V. (1965). *Experientia* 21, 103.

Retnakaran, A. (1970). *Can. Entomol.* 102, 1592.

Richman, K., and Oberlander, H. (1971). *J. Insect Physiol.* 17, 269.

Riddiford, L. M. (1970a). *Science* 167, 287.

Riddiford, L. M. (1970b). *Develop. Biol.* 22, 249.

Riddiford, L. M. (1971). *Bull. Soc. Entomol. Suisse* 44, 177.

Riddiford, L. M., and Truman, J. W. (1972). *Nature (London)* 237, 458.

Riddiford, L. M., and Williams, C. M. (1967). *Proc. Nat. Acad. Sci. U. S.* 57, 595.

Riddiford, L. M., and Williams, C. M. (1971). *Biol. Bull.* 140, 1.

Rimpler, H., and Schulz, G. (1967) . *Tetrahedron Lett.* p. 2033.

Ringborg, U., Daneholt, B., Edström, J.-E., Egyházi, E., and Lambert, B. (1970a). *J. Mol. Biol.* 51, 327.

Ringborg, U., Daneholt, B., Edström, J.-E., Egyházi, E., and Rydlander, L. (1970b). *J. Mol. Biol.* 51, 679.

Rinterknecht, E. (1966). *Bull. Soc. Zool. Fr.* 90, 645.

Robbins, W. E., Thompson, M. J., Kaplanis, J. N., and Shortino, T. J. (1964). *Steroids* 4, 635.

Robbins, W. E., Kaplanis, J. N., Thompson, M. J., Shortino, T. J., Cohen, C. F., and Joyner, S. C. (1968). *Science* 161, 158.

Robert, M. (1971). *Chromosoma* 36, 1.

Robison, G. A., Sutherland, E. W., and Butcher, E. W. (1971). "Cyclic AMP." Academic Press, New York.

Röller, H., and Dahm, K. H. (1968). *Recent Progr. Horm. Res.* 24, 651.

Röller, H., and Dahm, K. H. (1970). *Naturwissenschaften* 57, 454.

Röller, H., Dahm, K. H., Sweeley, C. C., and Trost, B. M. (1967). *Angew. Chem., Int. Ed. Engl.* **6**, 179.
Romaňuk, M., Sláma, K., and Sorm, F. (1967). *Proc. Nat. Acad. Sci. U. S.* **57**, 349.
Romer, F. (1971a). *Z. Zellforsch. Mikrosk. Anat.* **122**, 425.
Romer, F. (1971b). *Naturwissenschaften* **6**, 324.
Rutter, W. J. (1970). *In* "Problems in Biology: RNA in Development" (E. W. Hanly, ed.), pp. 425–441. Univ. of Utah Press, Salt Lake City.
Sahota, T. S., and Mansingh, A. (1970). *J. Insect Physiol.* **16**, 1649.
Sakurai, H., and Hasegawa, K. (1969). *Appl. Entomol. Zool.* **4**, 59.
Sato, Y., Sakai, M., Imai, S., and Fujioka, S. (1968). *Appl. Entomol. Zool.* **3**, 49.
Scharrer, B. (1948). *Biol. Bull.* **95**, 186.
Scharrer, B. (1963). *Z. Zellforsch. Mikrosk. Anat.* **60**, 761.
Scharrer, B. (1964). *Z. Zellforsch. Mikrosk. Anat.* **62**, 125.
Scharrer, B. (1968). *Z. Zellforsch. Mikrosk. Anat.* **89**, 1.
Scharrer, B. (1971). *Z. Zellforsch. Mikrosk. Anat.* **120**, 1.
Scharrer, B., and Kater, S. B. (1969). *Z. Zellforsch. Mikrosk. Anat.* **95**, 177.
Scharrer, B., and Weitzman, M. (1970). *In* "Aspects of Neuroendocrinology" (W. Bargmann and B. Scharrer, eds.), pp. 1–23. Springer-Verlag, Berlin and New York.
Scharrer, E., and Scharrer, B. (1954). *Recent Progr. Horm. Res.* **10**, 183.
Schmialek, P. (1961). *Z. Naturforsch.* **16b**, 461.
Schmieder, R. G. (1942). *Anat. Rec.* **84**, 514.
Schneider, I. (1966). *J. Embryol. Exp. Morphol.* **15**, 271.
Schneiderman, H. A., and Gilbert, L. I. (1964). *Science* **143**, 325.
Schooley, D. A., and Nakanishi, K. (1972). *In* "Modern Methods of Steroid Analysis" (E. Heftmann, ed.). Academic Press, New York (in press).
Schooley, D. A., Weiss, G., and Nakanishi, K. (1972). *Steroids* **19**, 377.
Schwartz, J. L. (1971). *Gen. Comp. Endocrinol.* **17**, 293.
Sehnal, F. (1968). *J. Insect Physiol.* **14**, 73.
Sehnal, F., and Edwards, J. S. (1969). *Biol. Bull.* **137**, 352.
Sehnal, F., and Meyer, A. S. (1968). *Science* **159**, 981.
Sehnal, F., and Novák, V. J. A. (1969). *Acta Entomol. Bohemoslov.* **66**, 137.
Sehnal, F., and Sláma, K. (1966) . *J. Insect Physiol.* **12**, 1333.
Sekeris, C. E., and Karlson, P. (1962). *Biochim. Biophys. Acta* **62**, 103.
Sekeris, C. E., and Karlson, P. (1964). *Arch. Biochem. Biophys.* **105**, 483.
Sekeris, C. E., and Karlson, P. (1966). *Pharamocol. Rev.* **18**, 89.
Sellier, R. (1951). *Arch. Zool. Exp. Gen.* **88**, 61.
Shaaya, E. (1969). *Naturforsch.* **24b**, 718.
Shaaya, E., and Bodenstein, D. (1969). *J. Exp. Zool.* **170**, 281.
Shaaya, E., and Karlson, P. (1965). *Develop. Biol.* **11**, 424.
Shaaya, E., and Sekeris, C. E. (1965). *Gen. Comp. Endocrinol.* **5**, 35.
Shanta, C. S., and Meerovitch, E. (1970). *Can. J. Zool.* **48**, 617.
Siddall, J. B. (1970). *In* "Chemical Ecology" (E. Sondheimer and J. B. Simeone, eds.), pp. 281–306. Academic Press, New York.
Siddall, J. B., Cross, A. D., and Fried, J. H. (1966). *J. Amer. Chem. Soc.* **88**, 862 (and references cited therein).
Siddall, J. B., Horn, D. H. S., and Middleton, E. J. (1967). *Chem. Commun.* p. 899.
Siddall, J. B., Anderson, R. J., and Henrick, C. A. (1971). *Proc. Int. Congr. Pure Appl. Chem., 23rd, 1900* Vol. 3, p. 17.
Siew, Y. C., and Gilbert, L. I. (1971). *J. Insect Physiol.* **17**, 2095.

Slade, M., and Zibitt, C. H. (1971). *In* "Chemical Releasers in Insects" (A. S. Tahori, ed.), Vol. 3, pp. 45–58.

Slăma, K. (1971). *Annu. Rev. Biochem.* **40**, 1079.

Slăma, K., and Williams, C. M. (1965). *Proc. Nat. Acad. Sci. U.S.* **54**, 411.

Slăma, K., and Williams, C. M. (1966). *Nature (London)* **210**, 329.

Slăma, K., Romaňuk, M., and Sorm, F. (1972). "Chemistry and Physiology of Insect Hormones." Springer-Verlag, Berlin and New York (in press).

Smith, U. (1970). *Tissue Cell* **2**, 427.

Smith, U., and Smith, D. S. (1966). *J. Cell Sci.* **1**, 59.

Smuckler, E. A., and Tata, J. R. (1971). *Nature (London)* **234**, 37.

Srivastava, K. P., and Singh, H. H. (1968). *Experientia* **24**, 838.

Srivastava, U. S., and Gilbert, L. I. (1968). *Science* **161**, 61.

Sroka, P., and Gilbert, L. I. (1971). *J. Insect Physiol.* **17**, 2409.

Staal, G. B. (1971). *Endocrinol. Exp.* **5**, 35.

Stamm, M. D. (1959). *An. Real Soc. Espan. Fis. Quim., Ser. B* **55**, 171.

Stay, B., and Clark, J. K. (1971). *J. Insect Physiol.* **17**, 1747.

Steel, C. G. H., and Harmsen, R. (1971). *Gen. Comp. Endocrinol.* **17**, 125.

Steele, J. E. (1961). *Nature (London)* **192**, 680.

Steele, J. E. (1963). *Gen. Comp. Endocrinol.* **3**, 46.

Steele, J. E. (1969). *J. Insect Physiol.* **15**, 421.

Stegwee, D., Kimmel, E. C., de Boer, J. A., and Henstra, S. (1963). *J. Cell Biol.* **19**, 519.

Stellwag-Kittler, F. (1954). *Biol. Zentralbl.* **73**, 12.

Stephen, W. F., Jr., and Gilbert, L. I. (1970). *J. Insect Physiol.* **16**, 851.

Stockdale, F. E., and Topper, Y. J. (1966). *Proc. Nat. Acad. Sci. U. S.* **56**, 1283.

Stowe, B. B., and Hudson, V. W. (1969). *Plant Physiol.* **44**, 1051.

Strong, L. (1968). *J. Insect Physiol.* **14**, 1685.

Sutherland, E. W., Rall, T. W., and Menon, T. (1962). *J. Biol. Chem.* **237**, 1220.

Suzuki, Y., and Brown, D. D. (1972). *J. Mol. Biol.* **63**, 409.

Szego, C. M., and Davis, J. S. (1967). *Proc. Nat. Acad. Sci. U. S.* **58**, 1711.

Szego, C. M., Seller, B. J., Steadman, R. A,. Hill, D. F., Kimura, A. K., and Roberts, J. A. (1971). *Biochem. J.* **123**, 523.

Takeda, N. (1972). *J. Insect Physiol.* **18**, 571.

Takemoto, T., Ogawa, S., and Nishimoto, N. (1966). *Yakugaku Zasshi* **87**, 325.

Takemoto, T., Ogawa, S., Nishimoto, N., and Hoffmeister, H. (1967). *Z. Naturforsch.* **22b**, 681.

Tata, J. R. (1967). *Nature (London)* **214**, 566.

Thomas, K. K. (1972). *Insect Biochem.* **2**, 107.

Thomas, K. K., and Gilbert, L. I. (1968). *Arch. Biochem. Biophys.* **127**, 512.

Thomas, K. K., and Gilbert, L. I. (1969). *Physiol. Chem. Phys.* **1**, 293.

Thomas, K. K., and Nation, J. L. (1966). *Biol. Bull.* **130**, 254.

Thompson, M. J., Kaplanis, J. N., Robbins, W. E., and Yamamoto, R. T. (1967). *Chem. Commun.* p. 650.

Thompson, M. J., Svoboda, J. A., Kaplanis, J. N., and Robbins, W. E. (1972). *Proc. Roy. Soc. Ser. B* **180**, 203.

Thomsen, E., and Møller, I. (1963). *J. Exp. Biol.* **40**, 301.

Thomsen, E., and Thomsen, M. (1970). *Z. Zellforsch. Mikrosk. Anat.* **110**, 40.

Thomson, J. A., and Horn, D. H. S. (1969). *Aust. J. Biol. Sci.* **22**, 761.

Thomson, J. A., Siddall, J. B., Galbraith, M. N., Horn, D. H. S., and Middleton, E. J. (1969). *Chem. Commun.* p. 669.

Thomson, J. A., Imray, F. P., and Horn, D. H. S. (1970a). *Aust. J. Exp. Biol. Med. Sci.* **48,** 321.

Thomson, J. A., Rogers, D. C., Gunson, M. M., and Horn, D. H. S. (1970b). *Cytobios* **6,** 79.

Thomson, J. A., Hafferl, W., Galbraith, M. N., Horn, D. H. S., and Middleton, E. J. (1971). *Chem. Commun.* p. 1023.

Toft, D., and Gorski, J. (1966). *Proc. Nat. Acad. Sci. U. S.* **55,** 1574.

Tombes, A. S., and Smith, D. S. (1970). *J. Morphol.* **132,** 137.

Tomkins, G. M. (1970). *In* "Problems in Biology: RNA in Development" (E. W. Hanly, ed.), pp. 144–154. Univ. of Utah Press, Salt Lake City.

Tomkins, G. M., Gelehrter, T. D., Granner, D., Martin, D., Jr., Samuels, H. H., and Thompson, E. B. (1969). *Science* **166,** 1474.

Toyama, K. (1902). *Bull. Coll. Agr. Tokyo* **5,** 73.

Trost, B. M. (1970). *Accounts Chem. Res.* **3,** 120.

Truman, J. W. (1971a). *J. Exp. Biol.* **54,** 805.

Truman, J. W. (1971b). *Proc. Nat. Acad. Sci. U. S.* **68,** 595.

Truman, J. W., and Riddiford, L. M. (1970). *Science* **167,** 1624.

Truman, J. W., and Riddiford, L. M. (1971). *Biol. Bull.* **140,** 8.

Turkington, R. W., and Spielvogel, R. L. (1971). *J. Biol. Chem.* **246,** 3835.

Unnithan, G. C., Bern, H. A., and Nayar, K. K. (1971). *Acta Zool. (Stockholm)* **52,** 117.

Van der Kloot, W. G. (1960). *Annu. Rev. Entomol.* **5,** 35.

Van der Kloot, W. G. (1962). *Annu. Rev. Physiol.* **24,** 491.

Van Tamelen, E. E., Storni, A., Hessler, E. J., and Schwartz, M. (1963). *J. Amer. Chem. Soc.* **85,** 3295.

Wajc, E., and Pener, M. P. (1971). *Gen. Comp. Endocrinol.* **17,** 327.

Waku, Y., and Gilbert, L. I. (1964). *J. Morphol.* **115,** 69.

Wall, B. J. (1965). *Zool. Jahrb., Abt. Allg. Zool. Physiol. Tiere.* **71,** 702.

Wall, B. J., and Ralph, C. L. (1962). *Biol. Bull.* **122,** 431.

Weir, S. B. (1970). *Nature (London)* **228,** 580.

Weirich, G., and Karlson, P. (1969). *Wilhelm Roux' Arch. Entwicklungsmech. Organismen* **164,** 170.

White, A. F. (1972). *Life Sci., Pt. II* **11,** 201.

White, D. F. (1968). *J. Insect Physiol.* **14,** 901.

White, D. F. (1971). *J. Insect Physiol.* **17,** 761.

Whitmore, D., Whitmore, E., and Gilbert, L. I. (1972). *Proc. Nat. Acad. Sci. U.S.* **69,** 1592.

Whitmore, E., and Gilbert, L. I. (1972). *J. Insect Physiol.* **18,** 1153.

Whitten, J. M. (1964). *Gen. Comp. Endocrinol.* **4,** 176.

Whitten, J. M. (1969a). *Chromosoma* **26,** 215.

Whitten, J. M. (1969b). *J. Insect Physiol.* **15,** 763.

Whitten, J. M. (1972). *Annu. Rev. Entomol.* **17,** 373.

Wicks, W. D. (1970). *In* "Problems in Biology: RNA in Development (E. W. Hanly, ed.), pp. 154–162. Univ. of Utah Press, Salt Lake City.

Wiedbrauck, H. (1953). *Biol. Zentralbl.* **72,** 530.

Wiens, A. W., and Gilbert, L. I. (1965). *Science* **150,** 614.

Wiens, A. W., and Gilbert, L. I. (1967a). *J. Insect Physiol.* **13,** 779.

Wiens, A. W., and Gilbert, L. I. (1967b). *Comp. Biochem. Physiol.* **21,** 145.

Wigglesworth, V. B. (1934) . *Quart. J. Microsc. Sci.* **77,** 191.

Wigglesworth, V. B. (1936). *Quart. J. Microsc. Sci.* **79,** 91.

Wigglesworth, V. B. (1940). *J. Exp. Biol.* **17**, 201.
Wigglesworth, V. B. (1952). *J. Exp. Biol.* **29**, 561.
Wigglesworth, V. B. (1955). *J. Exp. Biol.* **32**, 485.
Wigglesworth, V. B. (1959). "The Control of Growth and Form." Cornell Univ. Press, Ithaca, New York.
Wigglesworth, V. B. (1963). *J. Insect Physiol.* **9**, 105.
Wigglesworth, V. B. (1969). *J. Insect Physiol.* **15**, 73.
Williams, C. M. (1946). *Biol. Bull.* **90**, 234.
Williams, C. M. (1947). *Biol. Bull.* **93**, 89.
Williams, C. M. (1948). *Biol. Bull.* **94**, 60.
Williams, C. M. (1951). *Fed. Proc., Fed. Amer. Soc. Exp. Biol.* **10**, 546.
Williams, C. M. (1952a). *Harvey Lect.* **47**, 126.
Williams, C. M. (1952b). *Biol. Bull.* **103**, 120.
Williams, C. M. (1956). *Nature (London)* **178**, 212.
Williams, C. M. (1959). *Biol. Bull.* **116**, 323.
Williams, C. M. (1961). *Biol. Bull.* **121**, 572.
Williams, C. M., and Slāma, K. (1966). *Biol. Bull.* **130**, 247 (and references cited therein).
Willig, A., Rees, H. H., and Goodwin, T. W. (1971). *J. Insect Physiol.* **17**, 2317.
Willis, J. H. (1969). *J. Embryol. Exp. Morph* **22**, 27.
Willis, J. H., and Brunet, P. C. J. (1966). *J. Exp. Biol.* **44**, 363.
Willis, J. H., and Lawrence, P. (1970). *Nature (London)* **225**, 81.
Wobus, U., Panitz, R., and Serfling, E. (1970). *Mol. Gen. Genet.* **107**, 215.
Wobus, U., Serfling, E., and Panitz, R. (1971). *Exp. Cell Res.* **65**, 240.
Woolever, P., and Pipa, R. (1970). *J. Insect Physiol.* **16**, 251.
Wright, J. E. (1969). *Science* **163**, 390.
Wright, J. E., Chamberlain, W. F., and Barrett, C. C. (1971). *Science* **172**, 1247.
Wyatt, G. R. (1968). *In* "Metamorphosis: A Problem in Developmental Biology" (W. E. Etkin and L. I. Gilbert, eds.), pp. 143–184. Appleton, New York.
Wyatt, G. R. (1972). *In* "Biochemical Actions of Hormones" (G. Litwack, ed.), Vol. 2, pp. 385–490. Academic Press, New York.
Wyatt, S. S., and Wyatt, G. R. (1971). *Gen. Comp. Endocrinol.* **16**, 369.
Yagi, S., Kondo, E., and Fukaya, M. (1969). *Appl. Entomol. Zool.* **4**, 70.
Zalokar, M. (1968). *J. Insect Physiol.* **14**, 1177.
Zdarek, J., and Fraenkel, G. (1969). *Proc. Nat. Acad. Sci. U.S.* **64**, 565.
Zdarek, J., and Fraenkel, G. (1970). *Proc. Nat. Acad. Sci. U.S.* **67**, 331.
Zlotkin, E., and Levinson, H. Z. (1968a). *J. Insect Physiol.* **14**, 1195.
Zlotkin, E., and Levinson, H. Z. (1968b). *J. Insect Physiol.* **14**, 1719.
Zurflüh, R., Wall, E. N., Siddall, J. B., and Edwards, J. A. (1968). *J. Amer. Chem. Soc.* **90**, 6224.

Supplementary References

Books, Monographs, and Symposia Proceedings
"Insect Juvenile Hormones" (J. J. Menn and M. Beroza, eds.). Academic Press, New York, 1972.
"The Biology of Imaginal Disks" (H. Ursprung and R. Nöthiger, eds.). Springer-Verlag, Berlin and New York, 1972.

"Developmental Studies on Giant Chromosomes" (W. Beermann, ed.). Springer-Verlag, Berlin and New York, 1972.

Proc. 6 Int. Symp. Comp. Endocrimol.: Gen. Comp. Endocrinol., 1972, Suppl. 3.

"Developmental Systems—Insects" (S. J. Counce, ed.). Academic Press, New York, 1973.

Berridge, M. J., and Prince, W. T. The role of cyclic AMP and calcium in hormone action. *Advan. Insect Physiol* 9, 1 (1972).

Selected Papers
Control

Goldsworthy, G. J., Johnson, R. A., and Mordue, W. *J. Comp. Physiol.* **79**, 85 (1972). The authors suggest that a double innervation of the glandular lobes of the locust corpus cardiacum controls release of the adipokinetic hormone and that a single innervation controls diuretic hormone release.

Schlein, Y. *Nature (London)* **236**, 217 (1972). Ligature and cytological studies on *Sarcophaga* indicate that a secretion (possibly neurosecretion) from the ocellar nerve initiates postemergence growth (deposition of endocuticle and growth of skeletal muscles).

Fraenkel, G., Zdarek, J., and Sivasubramanian, P. *Biol. Bull.* **143**, 127 (1972). In what may be a classical study, a series of experiments on *Sarcophaga* suggest that ecdysone causes the appearance and/or accumulation of X factors (protein?) in body tissue(s) and that these are released by a neurosecretory product from the nervous system. It is these X factors that induce pupariation. Alternatively, the X factors may originate as neurosecretion stored in the periphery of neurons and ecdysone may elicit their release into the hemolymph. In both cases, it is the proteinic X factors rather than ecdysone that induce pupariation.

Molting Hormone

Borst, D. W., and O'Connor, J. D. *Science* **178**, 418 (1972). Development of a radioimmunoassay for ecdysone, reproducible at the 200-pg level.

Ellis, P. E., Morgan, E. D., and Woodbridge, A. P. *Nature (London)* **238**, 274 (1972). Studies on the locust lend further credence to the postulate that β-ecdysone is not synthesized by the prothoracic glands. Prothoracic glands produce two substances which may trigger β-ecdysone production at another body site.

Kaplanis, J. N., Thompson, M. J., Dutky, S. R., Robbins, W. E., and Lindquist, E. L. *Steroids* **20**, 185 (1972). 22, 25-Bisdeoxyecdysone is metabolized by the tobacco hornworm principally by hydroxylation and conjugation.

Zdarek, J. and Sláma, K. *Biol. Bull.* **142**, 350 (1972). Excessive doses of β-ecdysone elicit formation of perfect supernumery larvae in flies.

Alonso, C. *Develop. Biol.* **28**, 372 (1972). Studies on isolated salivary gland nuclei of *Drosophila* with β-ecdysone lead the author to conclude that the stimulation of RNA synthesis observed after β-ecdysone treatment is due to an increased rate of transcription of derepressed sites rather than to derepression of new sites.

Doenecke, D., Marmaras, V. J., and Sekeris, C. E. *FEBS Letters* **22**, 261 (1972). β-Ecdysone increases the hybridase (ribonuclease) activity of *Calliphora* epidermis.

Marmaras, V. J., and Sekeris, C. E. *Exp. Cell Res.* **75**, 143 (1972). Polysone formation is stimulated in *Calliphora* epidermis by β-ecdysone. This and other observations lead the authors to conclude that molting hormone acts at the transcriptional level.

Emmerich, H. *Gen. Comp. Endocrinol.* **19**, 543 (1972). Studies on *Drosophila* reveal the presence of ecdysone associated with salivary gland chromatin (most in nonhistone fraction) after incubation of isolated salivary glands with labeled hormone. Additional data are presented on ecdysone binding proteins.

Juvenile Hormone

Reddy, G., and Krishnakumaran, A. *Life Sci.* 11, 781 (1972). β-Ecdysone acts to enhance the morphogenetic activity of juvenile hormone when the two hormones are applied simultaneously.

Riddiford, L. M. *Biol. Bull.* 142, 310 (1972). The viscera of Cecropia pre-pupae are susceptible to juvenile hormone even after cessation of DNA synthesis. In this case, the hormone may be interfering with the degradation and reorganization of the tissue at the metamorphic molt.

Madhaven, K. *Wilhelm Roux' Archiv. Entwicklungsmech. Organismen* 169, 345 (1972). Juvenile hormone appears to induce melanotic pseudotumors in *Drosophila*.

Dyte, C. D. *Nature (London)* 238, 48 (1972). Insects can acquire resistance to the juvenile hormone.

Nair, K. K. and Menon, M. *Experientia* 28, 577 (1972). Investigations on the cockroach colleterial gland using [³H]actinomycin further support the premise that juvenile hormone acts at the transcriptional level.

Holderegger, C., and Lezzi, M. *J. Insect Physiol.* 18, 2237 (1972). Further studies on the effects of juvenile hormone on chromosome puffing reveal the possibility of hormone induction of a juvenile hormone degradative mechanism.

Cyclic AMP

Rensing, L., and Hardeland, R. *Exp. Cell Res.* 73, 311 (1972). Studies of the effects of dibutyryl cyclic AMP on puffing in *Drosophila* salivary gland chromosomes do not support the hypothesis that ecdysone may act via cyclic AMP. However, dibutyryl cyclic AMP did affect specific puffs.

Rojakovick, A. S., and March, R. B. *Comp. Biochem. Physiol.* 43B, 209 (1972). Adenyl cyclase activity was demonstrated in cockroach brain and β-ecdysone appears to inhibit its activity.

Whitmore, D., Applebaum, S. W., and Gilbert, L. I. *J. Insect Physiol.* 19, 349 (1973). Cyclic Amp phosphodiesterase activity has been demonstrated in the midgut of the tobacco hornworm.

Vedeckis, W., and Gilbert, L. I. *J. Cell Sci.* (1973) (submitted for publication). The prothoracic glands of the tobacco hornworm show the highest adenyl cyclase activity of any of the tissues or glands studied. The brain hormone is postulated to stimulate the prothoracic glands via adenyl cyclase.

In Vitro Studies

Shibuya, I., and Yagi, S. *Appl. Entomol. Zool.* 7, 97 (1972). *Galleria* ovaries *in vitro* develop only in the presence of β-ecdysone.

Oberlander, H., and Tomblin, C. *Science* 177, 441 (1972). Juvenile hormone inhibits the cuticle deposition elicited by β-ecdysone in *Plodia* wing discs. This is a further example of the antagonism between molting hormone and juvenile hormone.

Marks, E. P. *Biol. Bull.* 142, 293 (1972). Cuticle deposition in cockroach leg regenerates *in vitro* is elicited by β-ecdysone. Multiple cuticles were produced in the presence of large, multiple doses.

White, M. R., Amborski, R. L., Hammond, A. M., and Amborski, G. F. *In Vitro* 8, 30 (1972). Juvenile hormone is required for maintenance of the integrity of a lepidopteran sex pheromone gland *in vitro*.

Chapter 6

AGING IN INSECTS

Morris Rockstein and Jaime Miquel

I.	Insects in the Study of Aging	371
	A. Definitions of Aging	371
	B. Insects as Experimental Animals in Aging Studies	374
II.	Adult Life Span of Insects	377
	A. Life-Span Records	377
	B. Analysis of Duration of Life	381
III.	Factors Influencing Life Span	391
	A. Intrinsic Factors	391
	B. Extrinsic Factors	404
IV.	Manifestations of Senescence	424
	A. Structural and Histochemical Aspects	424
	B. Biochemical Aspects	443
	C. Physiological Aspects	450
V.	Evolution of Aging	468
VI.	Summary	470
	References	471

I. Insects in the Study of Aging

A. DEFINITIONS OF AGING

With very few exceptions, the life span of all metazoan animals can be subdivided into three major stages. Beginning with the climactic moment when the spermatozoon meets the ovum in successful fertilization, a new generation begins with the initial period of embryonic development, to be

371

followed by one of growth and maturation and, finally, by a period of progressive and increasing failure to cope with the environment, i.e., senescence.

Accordingly, for every complex organism there is a persistent alternating of cell death with cell regeneration and new cell growth, beginning with the embryo, continuing through mature life and, finally, into old age. Nevertheless, this overall economy of life in the existence of any organism eventually becomes unbalanced, ultimately yielding to the environmental assaults and insults, with the result of failure to survive that which is to become its final trimester of existence. Indeed, it is during this final period of both cell and organism existence that the regressive (if not retrogressive) aspects of the cellular, organ, and total body structure and function become manifest. This is particularly true in the case of postmitotic tissues, such as nervous tissue and striated muscle, in which a progressive decline both in mass and function proceeds with advancing age in virtually all animals in which studies of such systems have been made.

In its broadest sense, the process of aging can be defined as the sum total of those time-dependent reproducible changes both in structure and/or function for a given organism, species, or strain, during its total life span. As for *senescence,* the definition of aging can be modified more specifically to include the sum total of those changes in structure and function which, by virtue of their deleterious and degradative nature, result ultimately in the failure of the individual to survive and, therefore, result in its death (from "old age").

A number of theories of aging have been variously proposed by experimental gerontologists (Child, 1915; Lansing, 1947, 1952; Comfort, 1956, 1961; Bjorksten, 1958, 1963; Szilard, 1959a,b; Shock, 1960; Strehler and Mildvan, 1960; Strehler, 1962; Maynard-Smith, 1962; Kohn, 1965; Lloyd, 1967; Curtis, 1966, 1971). These theories can be grouped into two major categories based on the factors governing or regulating the course of senescence, as well as the mean and maximum life span of different animal (or human) populations, and of the individuals therein. These would include (1) those genetic factors which determine the time course of development and maturation as well as the onset of senescence, its duration and, finally, its termination, and (2) the environmental physical and biotic factors (assaults and insults) which, individually, but more likely cumulatively, reduce the probability of the organism to survive and, therefore, to die of "old age." Since "aging" and, in particular, "senescence" represent a complex of time-dependent changes involving one or many organs, and since death usually represents an event resulting from the interaction of both genetic and environmental factors, it is highly unlikely that such theories are mutually exclusive. This must be true despite the demonstrable, statistical probability of such aging processes occurring according to a reproducible time schedule, and death, similarly, occurring at a species-specific average of maximum time of existence, for any given species or strain.

Nevertheless, for each of these two major groups of theories of aging, there *have* been proposed specific or discrete mechanisms by which the likelihood to survive diminishes as time progresses, i.e., by which the time-course of senescence and life span are determined. Theories based on the concept of genetic basis for aging in senescence include the following: (1) the concept of aging as a consequence of programmed cessation (or slowing down) of growth, especially in the postmitotic tissues, specifically brain and muscle, manifested in such phenomena as decreasing metabolic rate, irreversible age-related changes in fibrous proteins, e.g., progressive cross-linkage in collagen and possibly elastin (see Lansing, 1952; Kohn, 1965) ; (2) programmed decline and/or failure of juvenile or growth substance responsible for maintenance of the young as well as the mature, nonsenescing state; (3) time-correlated depletion of essential substances within the cell, whether they be DNA at the nuclear level, or RNA, enzymes, coenzymes, or even substrates at the cytoplasmic level; these may be due, more specifically, to the programmed failures, at one or more points within the molecular genetic nexus of biochemical events (beginning with the originally encoded DNA to the final translation into the synthesized product within the cytoplasm) of such biochemical components as are involved in the normal functioning of the cell at its optimal level, within the environment in which it lives; (4) the scheduled, increasing production or accumulation of an aging factor or hormone; and (5) the scheduled accumulation of substance (s) which may be chemically or mechanically harmful to the organism with advancing time, programmed to reach its acme at a statistically probable point in the life of the individual.

As to theories of aging in which the proposed dominant controlling factor is environmental in nature, each of the following has been proposed as being the prime factor in aging in general and, in particular, *senescence:* (1) the cumulative effects of extrinsic radiation, whether it is ionizing, infrared, etc.; (2) the cumulative effects of pathological insults, of an infectious nature, from viruses to bacteria; and (3) the cumulative effects of other physically traumatic influences of a changing environment, ranging from temperature extremes to mechanical injury.

One would find it most difficult to propose a unitary theory for the process of aging, in view of that fact that, whereas all metazoan animals do grow old, so many different organisms with different genetic constitutions may respond quite differently to different environmental conditions, whether they be physical or biotic. Therefore, it is equally unlikely to envision the operation of a single limiting factor as being involved in determining the rate of aging as well as its end point of death, i.e., its life span. Nevertheless, assuming a definite interrelationship between the rate of aging and life span, a logical attack upon this complex problem can best be made by studies of different species or strains (or between the two sexes within one species) with widely differing mean and maximum longevities. Such studies would include programmed, correlated observations on structural and functional changes both at the gross organismic, organ as well as cellular and subcellular levels, wherein both reproducibly programmed maturation as well as senescence are manifest, generation after generation, to occur at the same time in the life of the species or sex under examination.

B. Insects as Experimental Animals in Aging Studies

As Chapter 1 of this volume has indicated, the Insecta, having evolved successfully from a time long before man's most primitive origin, are made up of cells (which under the microscope would be) indistinguishable from those of higher animals including man and which cells, in turn, possess the full complement of biochemical systems involved in metabolism, in general, and in cellular functions, in particular. Moreover, insects grow old and die and manifest aging processes exactly like those of higher vertebrates, including aging of postmitotic tissues such as striated muscle and nervous tissue. In addition, this highly diversified and ubiquitous group of distinctive animals present an unusual combination of virtually all the desiderata uniquely suited to attacking most of the questions concerning the nature of the aging process.

1. Availability in Large Numbers

Unlike mammals, from man at one end to felids and rodents near the other, which have only one to relatively small numbers of offspring per litter, insect species generally exhibit an unusually high degree of fecundity. The queen honey bee, for example, with a life span of 4–8 years, will readily lay at least 2000 eggs a day during the height of the honey flow during the spring and summer season, following one single nuptial flight and insemination, from which at least approximately 6 million spermatozoa are readily available, as required, from the spermatheca in which they are stored throughout the lifetime of the queen honey bee. Similarly, a termite queen of some species of termites can lay as many as 8000 eggs per day or 6 eggs per minute, producing colonies of literally millions of individuals. In the case of the common house fly, *Musca domestica* L., a minimum of 125 eggs per day are laid by a 4- to 5-day-old impregnated female for which highly reproducible survival curves and life tables, as well as age-related structural, functional, and biochemical signs of aging can be obtained, generation after generation.

2. Short Life Span

In terms of the limited *productive* period of the human investigator's life, as well as his relatively short *total* life span, in relation to studying other humans and even mammals such as rats (with approximately 2–3 years of maximum longevity) and dogs (with a maximum longevity of approximately 12 to 18 years), short-lived species or strains of animals, such as insects, are highly desirable for such studies. In the case of insects, studies involving one generation of the house fly, for example, can be completed in less than 3 months and, indeed, several replicate generational studies can even be pursued by overlapping studies during the life span of the first generation. Accordingly, over a period of a few years, numerous replicate studies are possible. Similarly, spring and summer honey bees with a maximum longevity of approximately 3 months, as well, offer similar advantages for aging studies in insects. This is especially true since hundreds of thousands of such worker honey bees, resulting from the mating of one drone with a virgin queen bee, represents genetically a much more uniform population than multiple litters from various parents, as well as litters from successive generations of inbred but still relatively small populations of mammals.

3. Availability as Homogeneous or Genetically Pure Strains

Genetically pure strains of *Drosophila melanogaster,* in particular, have been used in classical studies by geneticists, beginning with Thomas Hunt Morgan and his colleagues in purely genetic studies on the one hand, and over a period of several decades by Pearl and his colleagues (Pearl and Parker, 1922a,b; Pearl and Miner, 1935), who isolated different mean-longevity specific strains of this species (Fig. 1) (Pearl, 1922). Highly inbred strains of the common house fly, *M. domestica,* as well as of the honey bee, *Apis mellifera,* and the confused flour beetle, *Tribolium confusum,* as well as the yellow meal worm, *Tenebrio molitor,* have been employed similarly in longevity as well as other studies and are similarly available for laboratory maintenance, breeding, and rearing under established, standardized condtions.

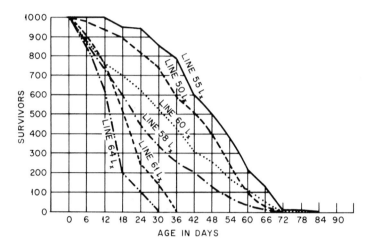

Fig. 1. Life lines for different inbred lines of descent in *Drosophila* (From Pearl and Parker, 1922a,b. University of Chicago Press).

4. Manageability

As poikilothermous animals, insects adjust their body activities to the external, physical environmental conditions of temperature in particular. As such, the duration of the total life span, as well as of individual stages of development and maturation, can be controlled by establishing the environmental temperature in which the particular strain or species has been raised and maintained. Thus in the NAIDM strain of the house fly employed in the laboratory, house flies maintained at 82°F (26.6°C) and a relative humidity of 45%, under continuous condition of lighting, the adult goes through a 2-week generation cycle, with the peak emergence of literally thousands of adult flies every 2 weeks between Wednesday evening and the following Thursday afternoon. In this way flies of known age can be isolated, within a very narrow margin of time (from 0 to 5 minutes of age, for example), and be available for both longevity and specific aging studies.

5. Small Size

The small size of insects, rather than being a handicap, has a number of distinct advantages. For example, since the cell size of insectan tissues is essentially that of higher animals such as man, the number of cells to be counted becomes reduced by thousands of times and makes a more feasible and accurate type of measurement. This is similarly true of chemical or electrical parameters under study, since the microtechniques

of today, including highly sensitive electronic instrumentation of high amplification, as well as gel electrophoresis techniques, have been developed
to handle micro-action-potentials, on the one hand, and the isolation of
small amounts of purified proteins such as enzymes, on the other. Moreover, the small size of insects means that extremely large numbers can be
housed in animal quarters normally capable of accommodating only
small numbers of mammals and at an extremely modest cost, in contrast
to that needed for mammals.

6. Models of Aging

Since insects represent a highly advanced, successful groups of animals
with many desirable features which make them highly suited to research
in aging, among other areas of investigation, it is not surprising to find
that increasing numbers of biologists, biochemists, and biophysicists continue to exploit insect species in their basic studies. The extensive radiation from a common primitive insect ancestor, characterizing the now
million or more species extant on the earth (see Chapter 1 of this volume), particularly favor gerontological studies involving insects as an experimental animal. This is especially true considering the wide variability
in their mode of development, feeding habits, and ability to survive wide
extremes of ecological conditions, both physical and biotic.

Thus, insects as experimental animals in gerontological research offer
a singular combination of properties which permit (1) the highest degree
of reproducibility of experimental data, through the availability of large
numbers of individuals from genetically similar, if not identical, strains
and of known age; (2) the ability to replicate experiments within relatively short periods of time, in view of their extremely short life spans, in
comparison to higher animals; and (3) their relatively limited space requirements and low maintenance cost because of their small size.

II. Adult Life Span of Insects

A. LIFE-SPAN RECORDS

In comparative studies of duration of life of different animals, there
are two kinds of records which define life span: the first is the extreme or
maximum longevity recorded for an individual member of a particular
strain or species, and the second, the determination, within a cohort or
population of individuals (of a particular species or strain) of the day-
to-day progress of death, and, ultimately, the average or mean life span
for the entire population. Of the two, life-span data of an entire popula-

TABLE I

MEAN ADULT LIFE SPAN OF INSECTS (IN DAYS)

Insect	Male (days)	Female (days)	Reference
Diptera			
Drosophila melanogaster			
Wild (line 107)	38.1	40.1	Gonzalez (1923)
Vestigial mutant	15.0	21.0	
Drosophila subobscura			
9 inbred lines (average)	40.0	36.4	Maynard-Smith (1959)
4 outbred populations			
(average)	56.8	60.0	
Musca domestica	17.5	29.0	Rockstein and Lieberman (1959)
Musca vicina	20.8	23.3	Feldman-Muhsam and
Calliphora erythrocephala	35.2	24.2	Muhsam (1945)
Aedes aegypti		15	Kershaw *et al.* (1953)
Lepidoptera			
Acrobasis caryae	6.5	7.3	Pearl and Miner (1936)
Bombyx mori (unmated)	11.9	11.9	Alpatov and Gordeenko (1932)
B. mori (mated)	15.2	14.2	
Fumea crassiorella (unmated)		5.5	Matthes (1951)
F. crassiorella (mated)		2.3	
Samia cecropia	10.4	10.1	MacArthur and Baillie (1932)
Samia californica	8.7	8.8	
Tropea luna	5.9	6.0	
Philosamia cynthia	5.9	7.1	
Telea polyphemus	8.1	10.0	
Callosamia promethea	4.6	7.0	
Pyrausta nubilalis	13.0	17.4	
Pyrausta penitalis	6.8	7.7	
Carpocapsa pomonella	9.4	10.2	
Hymenoptera			
Apis mellifera			
Summer bees		35	Ribbands (1952)
Winter bees		350	Maurizio (1959)
Habrobracon juglandis			
Wild type	24	29	Georgiana (1949)
Small wings, white eyes,			
mutant	20	24	
Habrobracon serinopae	62	92	Clarke and Rubin (1961)

(continued)

TABLE I *(continued)*

Insect	Male (days)	Female (days)	Reference
Orthoptera			
Blatta orientalis	40.2	43.5	Rau (1924)
Periplaneta americana	200	225	Griffiths and Tauber (1942)
Schistocerca gregaria	75	75	Bodenheimer (1938)
Coleoptera			
Tribolium confusum	178	195	Park (1945)
Tribolium madens	199	242	
Procrustes	374	338	Labitte (1916)
Carabus	323	386	
Necrophorus	232	291	
Dytiscus	854	740	
Hydrophilus	164	374	
Melolontha vulgaris	19	27	
Cetonia aurata	57	88	
Lucanus cervus	19	32	
Dorcus	327	375	
Ateuchus	338	467	
Sisyphus	198	266	
Copris	497	623	
Geotrupes	700	642	
Oryctes	37	55	
Elaps mortisaga	848	914	
Blaps gigas	700	728	
Blaps magica	700	728	
Blaps edmondi	700	728	
Akis	854	951	
Pimelia	669	714	
Timarcha	135	182	

tion are much more useful for analysis, since life tables and survivorship curves can be constructed for such a cohort. However, mortality records are known for relatively few insect species; those available show that (1) each species has a characteristic life span under defined conditions, particularly where such information has been derived from laboratory-maintained species and strains; and (2) there is an extremely wide range in duration of life among different insect species, despite the relatively short mean life span of most of those insect species for which information of this kind is available. In this connection, it should be stressed that longevity data for insect populations, obtained under controlled laboratory conditions, may differ very widely from those obtained for populations of the same species in the wild state, for biotic as well as physical environmental reasons.

Maximum longevity data have been compiled by Rockstein (in Spector, 1956) and in a more abbreviated form by Comfort (1956, 1964) from records of various sources (some reliable and some questionable) for all phyla of animals from the Protozoa to the mammals. As for insects per se, Howard (1939) compiled then extant data for life spans for different orders of insects. The wide range of duration of life of insects was emphasized by Howard in reporting the longevity of adult mayflies as being 1 day, for some beetles as being more than 10 years, and, in the case of some termites, more than 25 years. However, since the life span of insects can be readily modified, particularly by physical environmental conditions, "normal life spans" must be obtained for stipulated conditions of breeding as well as maintenance. The adult life spans presented in Table I, are, therefore, definable for each species given only within the limitations of the laboratory conditions under which they were obtained (sometimes unstated, unfortunately). Indeed, experiments comparing the duration of life under different environmental conditions are obviously also desirable, since they might show both the mean and maximum life-span potential of a population, as well as permitting the assessment of the process of *senescence* under different experimental conditions. Similarly, different species within the same genus may show a considerable variation in mean and maximum longevity, presumably on purely genetic bases (e.g., *D. melanogaster* versus *Drosophila subobscura* and *M. domestica* versus *Musca vicina*—see Table I).

Similarly, different populations of the same species collected from different parts of the United States may show different life spans; for example, in *Samia cecropia*, the mean life span ranges from 7 to 15 days depending on the locale of each population (Rau and Rau, 1914). Variations in diet, as well as other factors involved in rearing and maintaining a particular population, may similarly produce pronounced differences in life span data for a given species. Thus, *Habrobracon serinopae* females live as long as 92 days when fed honey and water, but only 40 days when fed on *Ephestia* larvae (Clark and Rubin, 1961). Similarly Rockstein and Lieberman (1959) found that female house flies fed on sugar and water alone had a mean life span of only 19 days in contrast to 29 days for females fed on a complete diet of sugar, water, and powdered whole milk. Likewise, summer worker honey bees live approximately 35 days, in contrast to winter bees living approximately 6 to 8 months, owing in part to differences in brood-rearing responsibilities during different seasons. Longevity differences between the sexes for offspring from eggs laid by adults of different ages and between mated and unmated populations have also been reported (see Section III below).

B. ANALYSIS OF DURATION OF LIFE

1. Life Tables

Although the life span of a single individual in a given cohort population obviously cannot be predicted with accuracy; e.g., a newly emerged adult *Drosophila* may live for as few as 2 days or as many as 125 days,

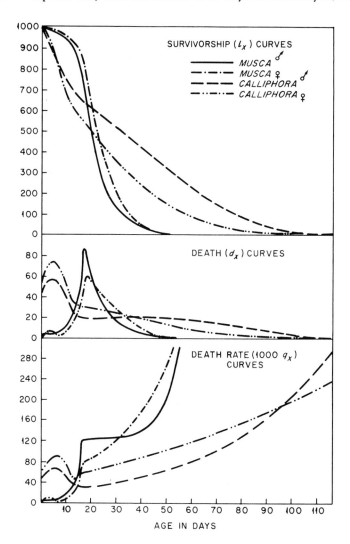

Fig. 2. Life table curves for *M. vicina* and *C. erythrocephala*. (Drawn from Feldman-Muhsam and Muhsam, 1945.)

TABLE II

LIFE TABLE FOR *Musca vicina* MACO[a]

Age in days (x)	Males			Females		
	Survivors (l_x)	Deaths per day (d_x)	Death rate per day ($1000\ q_x$)	Survivors (l_x)	Deaths per day (d_x)	Death rate per day ($1000\ q_x$)
0	1000	4	3.7	1000	0	0.1
1	996	4	4.2	1000	4	3.8
2	992	5	4.8	996	6	5.7
3	987	4	4.6	990	6	6.3
4	983	5	4.8	984	6	5.9
5	978	5	5.0	978	5	5.1
6	973	5	5.7	973	5	4.6
7	968	7	6.6	968	4	4.2
8	961	8	8.5	964	4	4.4
9	953	9	11.2	960	6	5.4
10	942	14	14.8	954	7	7.3
11	928	18	20.0	947	10	10.2
12	910	24	26.4	937	14	14.0
13	886	31	35.1	923	19	19.0
14	855	39	45.3	904	25	24.7
15	816	48	58.9	879	31	30.9
16	768	61	79.8	848	38	44.5
17	707	87	122.7	810	62	77.2
18	620	76	123.0	748	60	80.0
19	544	67	123.1	668	56	82.2
20	477	59	123.1	632	54	84.8
21	418	51	123.2	578	50	87.4
22	367	46	123.3	528	48	90.3
23	321	39	123.6	480	45	93.3
24	282	35	123.8	435	42	96.3
25	247	31	124.0	393	39	99.6
26	216	27	124.3	354	36	103.0
27	189	23	124.5	318	24	106.8
28	166	21	124.9	284	32	110.6
29	145	18	125.2	252	29	114.6
30	127	16	125.9	223	26	118.8
31	111	14	126.3	197	24	123.3
32	97	12	127.3	173	23	128.2
33	85	11	128.0	150	20	133.4
34	74	10	129.0	130	18	138.3
35	64	8	129.9	112	16	144.0
36	56	7	131.2	96	14	150.0
37	49	7	133.0	82	13	156.0
38	42	6	134.7	69	11	162.5
39	36	5	136.9	58	10	169.1
40	31	4	139.8	48	8	176.3

(continued)

TABLE II *(continued)*

Age in days (x)	Males			Females		
	Survivors (l_x)	Deaths per day (d_x)	Death rate per day $(1000q_x)$	Survivors (l_x)	Deaths per day (d_x)	Death rate per day $(1000q_x)$
41	27	4	142.6	40	8	183.9
42	23	3	146.2	32	6	191.6
43	20	3	150.3	26	5	200.0
44	17	2	155.2	21	4	208.5
45	15	3	161.1	17	4	217.6
46	12	2	167.7	13	3	226.9
47	10	2	175.7	10	2	236.9
48	8	1	184.8	8	2	247.3
49	7	2	195.5	6	2	258.1
50	5	1	208.0	4	1	269.6
51	4	1	222.2	3	1	280.8
52	3	0	239.1	2	0	293.4
53	3	1	254.6	2	1	305.7
54	2	1	280.2	1	0	319.2
55	1	0	305.3	1	1	335.2
56	1	0	333.6			
57	1	1	360.9			

[a] From Feldman-Muhsam and Muhsam (1945).

depending on cultural conditions. Nevertheless, accurate predictions of *mean* or *maximum* life spans for individuals of given populations can be made for specific environmental conditions of rearing and maintenance. However, neither mean life span nor (certainly) maximum life span alone are adequate parameters for evaluating the progress of death, either from the fundamental academic standpoint or from the practical point of view, for laboratory research studies of various kinds. That is because the rate of death throughout the life span of most populations is not constant, as shown by the existence of survivorship curves of different shapes for different populations of animals possessing similar, if not identical mean longevities (see Section II, B, 2, below and Fig. 2).

Nevertheless, with increasing chronological age, there is generally an increase in the probability of death owing to the decreased ability of older organisms to withstand the stresses which younger individuals of the same species are able to survive. Therefore, life tables (and survivorship curves derived therefrom) enable one to measure the extent of this age-related, increasing vulnerability or "force of mortality." Detailed reports have been made by Pearl and Parker (1922a,b), Pearl and Miner (1935), Pearl (1940), Allee *et al.* (1949), Rockstein and Lieberman (1959), and,

TABLE III

LIFE TABLE FOR 4627 MALE HOUSE FLIES, *Musca domestica* L. (NAIDM strain)

Age in days (x)	Death per day (d_x)	Survivors (l_x)	Death rate per day ($1000\, q_x$)	Life expectancy (e_x)
0–1	1.5	1000.0	1.5	16.88
1–2	2.8	998.5	2.8	15.90
2–3	3.7	995.7	3.7	14.94
3–4	2.8	992.0	2.8	14.00
4–5	2.6	989.2	2.6	13.04
5–6	5.6	986.6	5.7	12.07
6–7	8.6	981.0	8.8	11.14
7–8	14.0	972.3	14.4	10.23
8–9	19.5	958.3	20.3	9.37
9–10	48.0	938.8	51.1	8.56
10–11	46.5	890.9	52.2	7.99
11–12	57.5	844.4	68.1	7.40
12–13	94.9	786.9	120.6	6.91
13–14	69.8	692.0	100.9	6.79
14–15	77.8	622.2	125.0	6.49
15–16	64.2	544.4	117.9	6.35
16–17	62.0	480.2	129.1	6.13
17–18	61.8	418.2	147.8	5.96
18–19	52.7	356.4	147.9	5.91
19–20	49.9	303.7	164.3	5.85
20–21	41.7	253.7	164.4	5.90
21–22	31.8	212.0	150.0	5.97
22–23	28.1	180.2	155.9	5.93
23–24	22.9	152.2	150.5	5.93
24–25	16.6	129.2	128.5	5.90
25–26	14.0	112.6	124.3	5.69
26–27	14.9	98.6	151.1	5.43
27–28	18.8	83.6	165.1	5.32
28–29	12.3	69.8	176.2	5.27
29–30	8.4	57.5	146.1	5.29
30–31	8.4	49.1	171.1	5.11
31–32	5.6	40.6	137.9	5.07
32–33	6.7	35.0	191.4	4.80
33–34	4.3	28.3	151.9	4.82
34–35	5.0	24.0	208.3	4.59
35–36	3.0	19.0	157.9	4.66
36–37	2.6	16.0	162.5	4.44
37–38	1.5	13.4	111.9	4.21
38–39	2.4	11.9	201.7	3.67
39–40	2.6	9.5	273.7	3.47
40–41	2.8	6.9	405.8	3.59
41–42	1.1	4.1	268.3	4.71
42–43	0.6	3.0	200.0	5.23

(continued)

TABLE III *(continued)*

Age in days (x)	Death per day (d_x)	Survivors (l_x)	Death rate per day $(1000\ q_x)$	Life expectancy (e_x)
43–44	0.2	2.4	83.3	5.42
44–45	0.2	2.2	90.9	4.86
45–46	0.4	1.9	210.5	4.53
46–47	0.4	1.5	266.7	4.60
47–48	0.0	1.1	0.0	5.09
48–49	0.0	1.1	0.0	4.09
49–50	0.4	1.1	363.6	3.09
50–51	0.2	0.6	333.3	4.17
51–52	0.0	0.4	0.0	5.00
52–53	0.0	0.4	0.0	4.00
53–54	0.2	0.4	500.0	3.00
54–55	0.0	0.2	0.0	4.50
55–56	0.0	0.2	0.0	3.50
56–57	0.0	0.2	0.0	2.50
57–58	0.0	0.2	0.0	1.50
58–59	0.2	0.2	1000.0	0.50

more recently, by Nowosielski and Patton (1965), for a number of different insects, including *Drosophila, Musca,* and *Acheta.* Table II (Feldman-Muhsam and Muhsam, 1945) describes age–mortality relationships within an aging population of *M. vicina.* Thus, beginning with a population of newly emerged adults, i.e., a cohort of known size, the mortality for each interval of time is recorded until the death of its last member. The nomenclature of Pearl (1940) is given below.

x = the age interval, in units of hours or days in the case of insects is given below

d_x = the number of individuals dying within the age interval (x)

l_x = the number of individuals surviving to age interval (x)

q_x = the rate of mortality (d_x/l_x) ; the number of individuals dying in the age interval (x) divided by the number alive at the onset of that interval (usually expressed as a rate per 1000 or a 1000 q_x)

e_x = expectation of life at any given age; not shown in Table II but shown in Table III for *M. domestica* L. (NAIDM strain; Rockstein and Lieberman, 1959)

The significance of such life tables is at least twofold:

1. This permits the preparation of survival curves from the life tables and therefore analysis of the changing "force of mortality on the one hand.

TABLE IV

Life Table for 3875 Female House Flies, *Musca domestica* L. (NAIDM strain)

Age in days (x)	Deaths per day (d_x)	Survivors (l_x)	Death rate per day ($1000\ q_x$)	Life expectancy (e_x)
0–1	1.3	1000.0	1.3	28.74
1–2	1.8	998.7	1.8	27.77
2–3	6.5	996.9	6.5	26.82
3–4	6.2	990.5	6.3	26.00
4–5	5.4	984.3	5.5	25.15
5–6	6.5	978.8	6.6	24.29
6–7	8.0	972.4	8.2	23.45
7–8	12.1	964.4	12.5	22.64
8–9	9.5	952.3	10.0	21.92
9–10	15.2	942.7	16.1	21.14
10–11	16.8	927.5	18.1	20.48
11–12	17.5	910.7	19.2	19.85
12–13	16.3	893.2	18.2	19.23
13–14	19.9	876.9	22.7	18.57
14–15	20.4	857.0	23.8	17.99
15–16	17.3	836.6	20.7	17.42
16–17	16.5	819.4	20.1	16.77
17–18	21.2	802.8	26.4	16.11
18–19	16.5	781.7	21.1	15.53
19–20	17.3	765.2	22.6	14.86
20–21	18.3	747.9	24.5	14.19
21–22	19.1	729.5	26.2	13.53
22–23	22.7	710.5	31.9	12.88
23–24	25.5	687.7	37.1	12.29
24–25	31.0	662.2	46.8	11.75
25–26	24.8	631.2	39.3	11.30
26–27	23.5	606.5	38.7	10.74
27–28	27.9	583.0	47.9	10.15
28–29	28.1	555.1	50.6	9.64
29–30	30.2	527.0	57.3	9.12
30–31	43.9	496.8	88.4	8.65
31–32	33.5	452.9	74.0	8.44
32–33	33.3	419.4	79.4	8.07
33–34	28.1	386.1	72.8	7.72
34–35	31.2	357.9	87.2	7.29
35–36	30.2	326.7	92.4	6.94
36–37	32.3	296.5	108.9	6.60
37–38	31.2	264.3	118.0	6.34
38–39	30.2	233.0	129.6	6.13
39–40	26.8	202.8	132.1	5.96
40–41	27.6	176.0	156.8	5.80
41–42	20.4	148.4	137.5	5.78
42–43	17.3	128.0	135.2	4.06
43–44	13.2	110.7	119.2	5.42

(continued)

TABLE IV *(continued)*

Age in days (x)	Deaths per day (d_x)	Survivors (l_x)	Death rate per day ($1000\ q_x$)	Life expectancy (e_x)
44–45	14.7	97.5	150.7	5.09
46–47	12.6	70.7	178.2	4.65
47–48	10.1	58.1	173.8	4.55
48–49	7.5	48.0	156.3	4.41
49–50	6.7	40.5	165.4	4.13
50–51	6.5	33.8	192.3	3.85
51–52	8.0	27.4	292.0	3.64
52–53	5.2	19.4	268.0	3.93
53–54	3.4	14.2	239.4	4.18
54–55	1.8	10.8	166.7	4.34
55–56	1.3	9.0	144.4	4.11
56–57	2.3	7.7	298.7	3.71
57–58	0.3	5.4	55.6	4.07
58–59	0.8	5.2	153.8	3.21
59–60	1.5	4.4	340.9	2.70
60–61	0.5	2.8	178.6	2.96
61–62	0.5	2.3	217.4	2.48
62–63	0.8	1.8	444.4	2.00
63–64	0.3	1.0	300.0	2.20
64–65	0.3	0.8	375.0	1.63
65–66	0.3	0.5	600.0	1.20
66–67	0.3	0.3	1000.0	.67

2. On the other hand, it permits the prediction of the expectation of life at any given age of the particular species under consideration.

Thus, in the case of Tables III and IV (Rockstein and Lieberman, 1959), one can predict that, upon emergence, the life expectancy of a male house fly is approximately 17 days and that of a female imago is approximately 29 days. Similarly, a male house fly surviving to 29 days following emergence may be expected to live an additional 5½ days, whereas a female surviving to 29 days may be expected to survive an additional 9 days. Data of this kind are commonly used by professional actuaries in evaluating life expectancy of the adult humans in establishing life insurance premium charges for different age groups.

2. Survival or Mortality Curves

Although the survivorship curve is an important species- or mutant-associated characteristic, only few such data are available, especially for insect species. Moreover, such information requires the stipulated environmental conditions under which each such curve is derived. Figure 1

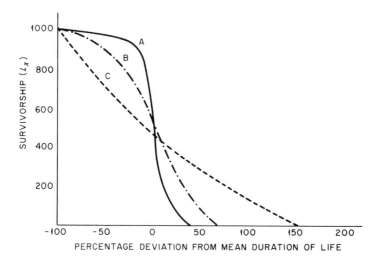

Fig. 3. Classes of survivorship curves. A, rectangular type; B, intermediate type; C, diagonal type. (Adapted from Pearl, 1940.)

(discussed briefly above) and Fig. 2 both show survivorship curves for several species of insects. Pearl and Miner (1935) and Pearl (1940), upon analysis of data of different population of different species, described survivorship curves as falling into three categories (see Fig. 3), as follows:

1. The rectangular curve (Fig. 3, curve A): This is a distribution in which a few deaths occur for the greater part of the life span, but once dying begins, death occurs at a rapid rate so that most of the members of the population die within a relatively short space of time. The rate of death or slope in such a curve is quite steep, and the life span of the last surviving individual is about 40% greater than the mean longevity. This situation is approached in starved *Drosophila* (Pearl and Miner, 1935), *Drosophila* kept at 21°C (Fig. 4), and in honey-fed *H. serinopae* (Clark and Rubin, 1961; Clark, 1963). A population whose survival is delineated by such a curve may truly be described as manifesting senescence.

2. The diagonal curve (Fig. 3, curve C): The death rate for such a population is constant for the greater part of the population's existence, but with the oldest individuals having a life span of almost three times the mean life span of the population. Such a pattern is shown by the mutant vestigial of *D. melanogaster* (Pearl, 1940), by *Calliphora* males and females (Fig. 2), and by the house cricket, *Acheta domesticus* L. (Nowosielski and Patton, 1965). Such a population is said to exhibit no real senescence but

is exposed only to a random overall mortality, and individuals die, presumably, of any age.

3. The intermediate curve (Fig. 3, curve B) : Generally, real survival curves tend to be intermediate in form between the two extremes of the theoretical curves described above. Here the death rate is slow in the young population, gradually increasing during the middle part of life and finally slowing down again. Such curves, as shown in Figs. 2 and 5 for *M. vicina* and for *M. domestica,* respectively, are typical of many species of animals for which life tables and survival curves have been obtained (see Allee *et al.,* 1949) . In such a population, the rate of dying is slow (i.e., the curve is flattened) at the beginning; it gradually increases so that the slope becomes more steep during the major part of the duration of the cohort, and finally slows down once more during the later portion of cohort existence (i.e., the curve flattens out once more and slope diminishes remarkably) . Thus, dying off is spread out over a longer period of time, so that in the case of the intermediate curve, the last few individuals tend to attain a life span of about twice the *mean* life span of that population (e.g., *Blatta orientalis,* Pearl, 1940) .

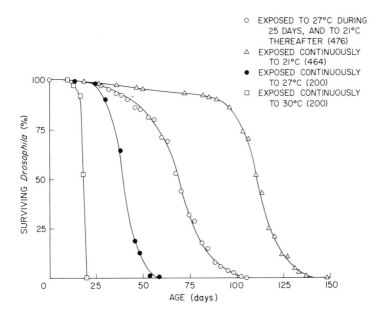

Fig. 4. Survival curves for male *D. melanogaster* imagoes exposed to various temperatures (21° and 27°C). (The numbers in parentheses indicate the number of flies used in each experiment.) (J. Miquel and P. R. Lundgren, unpublished.)

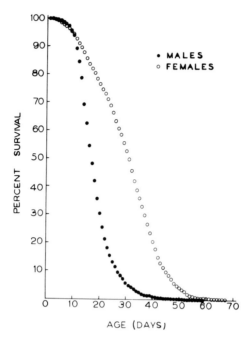

Fig. 5. Survival curves for male and female house flies. (From Rockstein and Lieberman, 1958, 1959.)

The significance and usefulness of the various classes of survivorship curves described by Pearl must certainly await further investigation, although the rectangular curve or an intermediate form thereof represents the situation in which populations die of senescence, whether this senescence is spread out over a longer or shorter period of time. The diagonal curve, on the other hand, which is said not to involve senescence per se, may be more significant where a particular deleterious gene or specific adverse environmental factor may be acting throughout the adult life of the population involved. Certainly this raises a further question of the need for investigation of the significance of the survivorship curve in relation to the genetic makeup of the particular strain or species population being investigated. In such cases, genetic crossing of different strains of the same species, in which different gene-controlled survivorship traits are suspected from their respective survivorship curves, would be called for. Survivorship curves obtained for offspring from such crosses can then be compared with the form of the survivorship curves of their respective parents; they can also be employed in attempting to correlate the rate of dying, i.e., mortality, with the rate of aging (viz., structural and physiological changes occurring with passage of time).

III. Factors Influencing Life Span

A. INTRINSIC FACTORS

1. Genetic Constitution

A strong case has been made before of the role of the genotype of an organism in determining not only its life span but its rate of aging as well (Rockstein, 1958). This has been reinforced in part by studies of Clarke and Maynard-Smith (1955), Lints (1961, 1962), and Clark (1964).

There has been work on *D. melanogaster* in particular by Gonzalez (1923) and numerous studies have been done by Pearl and his co-workers (Pearl and Parker, 1922a,b), by Gowen (1934), by Doane (1960), and, most recently, by Lints (1971). They have reviewed the numerous, possible contributory factors which might determine the longevity of poikilothermous animals, especially *D. melanogaster* and *D. subobscura*.

Gene action must certainly be involved in the ontogeny of all stages in the life cycle of insects. In fact, lethal genes have been demonstrated which cut off life at any stage in the development of the insect beginning with the egg, including the larval, pupal, and adult stages. In the case of some genes, their effect may be through the onset of a particular pathological condition leading to death, as in the case of focal melanosis, a disease associated with an autosomal, recessive gene, characterized by localization of melanosis in the leg-muscle joints of adult *D. melanogaster,* resulting in death soon after eclosion (Doane, 1960). *Adipose,* an autosomal recessive gene in *Drosophila,* in which the fat body hypertrophies in the adult female, results in a decrease in life span in homozygous females from 49 days in the wild type to 28 days in the *Adipose* adult. Thus, pathological genes producing a decrease in life span may do so through mechanisms quite different from those responsible for normal "senescence" as such.

a. Strain Differences. Pearl and Parker (1922a) clearly demonstrated that the "duration of life" is a phenotype for which genetically definitive and workable characters must exist. Thus, by cross-breeding of a long-lived (wild-type) stock and a short-lived stock homozygous for five mutants, including *vestigial wing,* they found they produced a slightly longer lived progeny in the F_1 generation than either parent stock. However, in the F_2 generation, a clear-cut segregation of life span, short life had been

TABLE V

DURATION OF LIFE OF DIFFERENT STRAINS OF *Drosophila melanogaster* ADULT[a]

Strain	Mean duration of life (days)			Sex with longer life span
	Both sexes	Males	Females	
Wild	39.47 ± .28	38.08 ± .36	40.62 ± .42	Female
Black	40.68 ± .50	41.03 ± .53	40.33 ± .51	—
Purple	24.54 ± .18	27.42 ± .27	21.83 ± .23	Male
Vestigial	18.22 ± .29	14.98 ± .28	20.93 ± .40	Female
Arc	26.81 ± .29	25.20 ± .33	28.40 ± .37	Female
Speck	42.66 ± .47	46.63 ± .63	38.91 ± .65	Male

[a] After Gonzalez (1923) *Amer. Naturalist* © Univ. of Chicago Press.

associated with the vestigial-winged flies and longer life with winged wild-type individuals, and, moreover, the duration of life for the F_2 wild type and the vestigial-winged flies, respectively, was identical with that of their parent stocks. Moreover, the decreased life span of the vestigial flies was not due simply to wing length, since wild-type flies whose wings had been surgically removed did not show any significant decrease in their life span. However, studies by Pearl and his colleagues (Pearl, 1922; Pearl and Miner, 1935, 1936; Pearl and Parker, 1922a,b; Pearl *et al.,* 1927) have emphasized the role of the genome in determining the longevity of a particular strain. Thus, by Pearl's brother–sister matings of short- and long-lived strains of *D. melanogaster* (1922) in which, by outbreeding and then inbreeding he was able to isolate five distinct strains (Fig. 1) with varying average longevities from 14 to 44 days, each strain bred true for that particular longevity. In general, similar data confirm the role of the genome in longevity where data are available for different species as well as for different strains within other animal species, particularly for such strains (employed in laboratories) for which there are already established life tables or mortality values (see Rockstein, 1958). Similar work by Gowen and Johnson (1946) (see below) and by Gonzalez (1923) demonstrate examples of race-specific longevities for different mutants of *D. melanogaster.* Indeed, Gonzalez (Table V) concluded the following from his studies.

1. Each mutant has a characteristic effect upon adult life span.

2. Each mutant has a characteristic effect upon the life span of each sex. Thus, for *Black,* a body-color factor, the life span of males and females are equal; for *Purple,* eye color, and *Speck* (black spot in the axil of each wing), males live longer than females; and for *Wild, Vestigial,* and *Arc* (wings bent forward) females live longer than males.

3. Duration of life does not depend as much upon the number of mutations in a strain as the type of mutation. Thus, the mean life span for flies homozygous for the quadruple mutant type *Black, Purple, Arc,* and *Speck* (with a mean life span of 22.9 days) was greater than for *Vestigial* flies with a mean life span of 18.22 days.

4. Certain mutant combinations diminish while others prolong adult life span, as in the case homozygous *Black* or *Speck,* each of which has a life span similar to the wild type, but which, in combination, have a mean life span of only 31.09 days. Similarly, the double-mutant type *Purple* and *Arc* have a longer life span (33.71 days) than either *Purple* or *Arc* individually.

It is obvious, therefore, that although there is hereditary basis for longevity, it is an indisputable fact that life span is a reflection of the complex interaction of genetic factors related to disease susceptibility, including acute, lethal as well as relatively long-term life-shortening factors, all interacting with the environment.

b. Hybrid Vigor. Hyde (1913) first demonstrated that hybridization of *Drosophila* lengthened its life span so that an inbred stock with a mean life span of 37 days when crossed with a truncate stock (mean life span of 21 days) produced hybrid progeny with a mean life span of 47 days. Similarly, Clarke and Maynard-Smith (1955) doubled the life-span values of both sexes of the inbred parent lines B and K (see Table VI) in the hybrid lines B/K and K/B. As Clark (1964) indicated, such hybrid populations are less likely to occur at any given point in the life of the hybrid offspring owing to the "dilution" of deleterious genes normally expected to occur in either of the homozygous parents, purely as a matter of Mendelian chance. However, as Gonzalez (1923) has emphasized, and Lints (1971) more recently has reiterated, mutant combinations are extremely important, especially in determining the adult phase of life

TABLE VI

AVERAGE LIFE SPANS FOR INBRED AND
HYBRID LINES OF *Drosophila subobscura*[a]

| Line | Life span (days) | |
	Females	Males
B	35.12 ± 1.82	27.68 ± 1.86
K	25.04 ± 1.52	39.20 ± 2.12
B/K	70.56 ±2.39	63.36 ± 2.36
K/B	62.00 ±3.23	67.28 ± 2.90

[a] After Clarke and Maynard-Smith (1955).

span and, accordingly, the concept of "hybrid vigor" is one that must be interpreted with some reservations, especially in view of the fact that mutant combinations may, in one case, result in enhancement of life span over the wild type, whereas other such combinations may, in other instances, result in a diminution in life span over the wild or single mutant type per se.

2. Sex

Although, in general, males of many species of animals studied have been shown to manifest a shorter life span than the females, which suggests that duration of life is a secondary sex character, many exceptions, especially in insects, have been demonstrated even in the case of XY males versus XX females. Nevertheless, a number of hypotheses have been proposed to account for the predominently widespread age-related longevity favoring the female (see Rockstein, 1958). These have included (1) differences in chromosome number and (2) differences in rates of metabolism of each sex.

a. Chromosome Number. In most orders of insects, the male is indeed heterogametic (XY or XO) and the female homogametic, as in the vertebrates. Among the Lepidoptera, however, the female is indeed the heterogametic sex (WZ), whereas in the Hymenoptera there are no special sex chromosomes, but ploidy differences may exist in which the male is usually haploid and the female diploid (as in the case of the honey bee). Indeed, if the differences in life span between males and females are due to the presence of subvital recessive genes, one would expect that the heterogametic or haploid sex would be more vulnerable than the homogametic or diploid sex. Conversely, a deleterious gene would be more likely to be expressed phenotypically for organisms that are haploid for a chromosome set or for a particular chromosome and, similarly, masked by a normal allele in diploid heterozygous organisms.

For heterogametic males and homogametic female species, among many strains of *Drosophila,* the males have a shorter life span than females. However, as has been indicated above, both in *D. melanogaster* (Gowen and Johnson, 1946) and in *D. subobscura* (Maynard-Smith, 1959) some races showed a longer-lived male than female and, in others, the female life span was longer than that of the male. Moreover, in still other races, both males and females show no difference in duration of adult life (see Tables I and V). In the house fly, Rockstein and Lieberman (1959) showed a consistently shorter life span in males than in females. In *Calliphora erythrocephala,* males have a longer life span (Feldman-Muhsam and Muhsam, 1945). In the order Coleoptera, both *Tri-*

bolium madens and *T. confusum* males showed a shorter life span than comparable females (Park, 1945). However, in only three of nineteen other species of beetle, males had a longer life span than females (see Table I; Labitte, 1916).

In heterogametic female–homogametic male strains, where one would expect longer-lived males on the basis of arguments presented earlier, MacArthur and Baillie (1932) (see Table I, above) found relatively little difference in life span between males and females in the case of all but three species, but in the case of the three remaining species mentioned, the females, unexpectedly, show a greater life span than the males.

Finally, as regards the difference in life span between haploid and diploid individuals, in the wasps, *H. juglandis* and *H. serinopae,* both haploid and diploid males can be obtained and the females of the diploid as well. Since the factor of sex can be separated from that of ploidy, experiments dealing with life span could be especially significant in relation to the possible contributory role of chromosomal number to longevity. Georgiana (1949) thus reported that wild-type haploid males of *H. juglandis* have a shorter life span than diploid females (shown in Table I, above). However, for *H. serinopae,* the life spans of both haploid and diploid males were identical (62 days) but shorter than that of the diploid females (mean life span of 92 days), when all individuals were fed honey and water for the duration of life. When the females were fed on *Ephestia* larvae, their life span was reduced to only 40 days. However, the radiation studies of Clark and his students (Clark and Rubin, 1961; Clark *et al.,* 1963) (indicated above, i.e., extrinsic factors) strongly suggest a relationship between ploidy and life span, since adult diploid males exposed to X rays showed a decrease in life span from 62 days to 37 days in the case of diploid males and from 62 days to only 18 days in the case of haploid males, following administration of 50 kR. Moreover, the survival curves show that haploid experimentals also start to die at a much earlier age than the diploids. Thus, the decreased life span resulting from ionizing radiation suggests that if, indeed, longevity is related in some way to external environmental "hits" the number of chromosomes on the polyploid individual is greater, such as in the case of XX females or WW males. However, as indicated earlier, Clark and Cole (1967) concur with Lamb (1965) in the view that radiation-induced reduction in longevity, as well as in the shift of the normal survival curve to the left, must be different from the factor(s) involved in "natural aging."

Flemings and Ludwig (1964) similarly showed there was no appreciable difference between male and female life span in the human body louse, *Pediculus humanus,* when reared and maintained at a temperature range of 29°–32°C. On the other hand, Lambremont and Earle (1961) found that the mean as well as maximum life span of the male boll weevil, *Anthonomus grandis,* reared on artificial diets under controlled conditions, was greater than those of the female in the case of both the Mexican and Louisiana strains. Crystal (1967) similarly found that the longevity of the female screwworm fly, *Cochliomyia hominivorax* (Coquerel), showed a greater longevity when both sexes were segregated or when flies were kept isolated in solitary fashion, but not when living in a bisexual population, when both males and females had similar longevities. T. J. Crovello and C. S. Hacker (unpublished, 1972) showed that in lab stocks of thirteen strains of *A. aegypti,* the longevities of the female (or male, respectively) varied from one order to another, but that all females had a greater life span than the male of the same species. Sondhi (1964, 1967) reported higher male than female life span in the Samarkand wild type of *D. melanogaster,* but the reverse for the Swedish B[6] wild type.

Thus, from the literature reviewed, the duration of life cannot be correlated with either the heterogametic or homogametic state in all cases.

b. Metabolic Rate. Heilbrunn (1952) has stated that males have a higher rate of metabolism than females in most species. This appears to be true in only some cases among insect species, and, indeed, it is doubtful if metabolic rate differences can be used as an underlying factor in the sex-related longevity differences favoring the female in most species (see Edwards, 1953). Thus, the male pupae of *Ephestia kühniella* and *Galleria mellonella* have a greater oxygen consumption throughout the major portion of the pupal stage than do female pupae (Taylor and Steinbach, 1931).

Similarly, the adult male house fly has a higher oxygen consumption than the female on a body-weight basis (Edwards, 1953). Raffy (1934) similarly found the oxygen consumption and CO_2 liberation to be greater for males than for females in four butterfly species. In *T. confusum,* on the other hand, the newly emerged adult female has a higher oxygen consumption rate than males, whether expressed on a per animal or body-weight basis (Park, 1936). Other metabolic differences between the sexes have been shown for specific tissues or total body homogenates. Thus, the leg muscles of the adult male cockroach, *P. americana,* show a higher oxygen uptake, glycogen content, DPN (NAD), diphosphothiamine, cytochrome c, total iron, and total solid content than those of females (Barrón and Tahmisian, 1948). In the female cockroach muscle, Edwards (1953) found that total dehydrogenase and succinic dehydrogenase is greater for the male than for the female muscle. In *H. juglandis,* total body homogenates of males show higher succinic dehydrogenase activity than females (most of the activity being found in the thorax) according to Griggs (1960). Acid phosphatase activity is higher for total body homogenates from female than from male *H. juglandis* (Herr, 1953) and for the female adult house fly, *M. domestica* (M. Rockstein, unpublished, 1950; Barker and Alexander, 1958). On the other hand, wing-beat frequency for *D. melanogaster, Schistocerca* species, and *A. aegypti,* which may be in turn used as an index of metabolic activity according to Williams *et al.* (1943), is less for females than for males (Chadwick, 1953). Rockstein and Bhatnagar (1966) later found that the wing-beat frequency of male and female house flies was essentially identical both during the first day of adult life and particularly from the third day onward, when the peak, initial wing-beat frequency of approximately 9700–9800 beats/minute was recorded. However, the ability to fly for extended periods of time was considerably less in the case of males, both initially as well as on a day-to-day basis, from 2 days to "old age" (see Section IV, C, below). From these data it appears as if there is little, if any, unequivocal basis in observations or experimental fact to explain differences in sex-related longevity in terms of metabolic rate or on the basis of metabolic differences measured by any criteria, at the present time.

3. Parental Age

Lansing (1954), in what is now a classical study, showed that offspring from younger rotifers, parthenogenetically have a longer life span than offspring from older parents. Moreover, in selected lines from young, middle-aged, and senile mothers over successive generations, those selected from young mothers increased their life span in a cumulative fashion while that of progeny from older mothers, similarly selected, progressively decreased. Furthermore, the shortened life span of the line from older mothers could be reversed (increased) by further selection from young parents from within this narrow short-lived line. This suggested that, at least in rotifers, there is a cumulative, reversible, nongenic aging factor which is presumed to be transmitted through the maternal cytoplasm.

Since that time, a number of attempts have been made to demonstrate unequivocally the operation of a "Lansing" factor in a number of species, including insects. In the house fly, *M. domestica,* over a single generation involving many thousands of the NAIDM strain, Rockstein (1957, 1959b) produced offspring of decreasing longevity by selecting the eggs from mothers inseminated at an early age, but whose fertilized eggs were

TABLE VII

Effect of Parental Age on the Longevity of Adult House Flies[a]

Parental age (days)	Males	Females	
	30-day mortality (%)	30-day mortality (%)	Average longevity (days)
4	95	50	32
6	93	52	29
9	97	70	28
15	92	82	25
23	97	80	24
27	96	90	22

[a] Data from Rockstein (1959b).

collected as late as 4 weeks of age (Table VII). However, the 30-day mortality for male offspring appears to be unaffected, although unfortunately no records were available of male mean life span for each age group. Nevertheless, in a series of follow-up experiments (M. Rockstein, unpublished) this anticipated "Lansing" factor did not obtain and the successive selection of three generations of eggs from older mothers actually produced longer-lived males without extending the longevity of the female offspring. This unanticipated but not necessarily anomalous effect might very well be the result of a selection of a sex-limited genetic factor for longer-lived males from (presumably genetically longer-lived) mothers still able to produce viable eggs at 27 days of age, but which effect is exerted only on the male offspring.

Callahan (1962), in a later study, actually *reduced* the longevity of offspring from "first eggs" laid, selected for over 18 generations, in the case of the CSMA strain. However, in the Wilson strain (unfortunately reared on a different rearing medium) only the female (and not the male) descendants showed a decreased longevity after the twelfth generation of "first egg" selection. Moreover, the use of the "last viable eggs" in the CSMA strain also resulted in *decreased longevity* as well as *reduction in reproductive* capacity. However, offspring from eggs laid by CSMA parents at 9–11 days of age, and as late as 18 days, showed no significant difference in longevity from that of the P_1 generation after six consecutive generations. These data, albeit based on different larval rearing media as well as being complicated by different results obtained for different relative humidities of adult maintenance, appear to reject the involvement of a "Lansing" factor in these strains of house fly.

Comfort (1953) found no "Lansing" factor, as regards parental age affecting the duration of life, for *D. subobscura,* for progeny selected from 30-day-old females over eight generations. O'Brian (1961), on the other hand, reported that both male and female offspring from old *D. melanogaster* parents had a shorter life span from those of younger flies, for three successive generations, after which further selection had no additional, similar effect. To indicate how complex this particular factor (if indeed it is a *single* factor) must be, an interesting study involving selection in longevity in *D. melanogaster* has been performed by Glass (1960). Two lines were started from the Oregon-R strain, an "early line" from males and females paired immediately after eclosion and a "late line" derived from males and females that were isolated for 21 days before being paired. Selection was continued in successive generations for early and late lines. These lines were then compared for longevity under conditions of (1) immediate and (2) deferred mating. The progeny from the early line lived longer than those from the late line when parents within each group were mated immediately after eclosion, but flies from the late line lived longer when such mating was deferred. Thus, "each line seems to demonstrate a longer life span under conditions of mating to which it was subjected during previous generations" (Glass, 1960).

Wattiaux (1968a,b) in another study reported that flies from older *D. pseudobscura* parents (6–8 weeks old) had increased longevity and fecundity, whereas eggs seeded from parents 10 days of age produced shorter-lived offspring. This appears to coincide with Rockstein's experimental results (1959b) in which longer-lived descendants were produced by selection of eggs from the heartier and longer-lived parents.

A number of studies have been made on the effect of parental age on offspring in the mealworm, *T. molitor,* particularly by Ludwig and his students. Tracey (1958) reported that offspring from older mealworms had a significantly shorter life and a higher growth rate than those from young parents. Ludwig and Fiore (1960), in verifying Tracey's work, reported that age-related factors were not operating until the parent beetles were at least one month of age. Moreover, for *T. molitor,* the yellow mealworm, Ludwig and Fiore (1960) found that the duration of the total larval stage was reduced and the rate of larval growth greater for progeny from older mothers, at all temperature ranges studied (20°, 25°, and 30°C), although only at 20° and 25°C was the adult life span of progeny from older mothers less than that of progeny from younger mothers; in other words, at 30°C, although the rate of larval growth was greater from older mothers and the duration of total larval stage was less, the mean life span of the resulting adults from such mothers at 30°C was not significantly different from that of adult beetles from younger mothers.

More recently, Ludwig and Fiore (1961), studying offspring from isolated pairs of parents, could produce *no* effect of shortening of adult life, although other effects like higher growth rate were so obtained by selection of eggs from the same pair of adults over various periods in the life of the adult parents.

Howe (1967), on the granary weevil *(Sitophilus granarius),* found no evidence of a definite trend related to parental age and offspring characteristics including longevity. He also reported his inability to duplicate the data of Raychaudhuri and Butz (1965a) on *T. molitor,* namely, that single pair crosses showed any effect on the role of parental age at the time of mating and egg laying and the longevity of the offspring. Indeed, Howe (1967) has raised serious questions concerning the significance of their data in relation to their methodology, in view of his own conflicting data on the same species. Blest (1962) observed that neither depletion of metabolic reserves nor the consumption of essential substances by their incorporation into the eggs (which are well developed in the newly emerged female) appear to be the mechanisms involved in this mating-accelerated "senescence," in *Automeris aurantiaca.*

In the cockroach, *P. americana,* an increased egg production seems to be correlated with decreased life span, since females (which were kept continuously with males) producing about 20 capsules per 8 days had a life span of 181 days, whereas virgin females producing about 7 capsules per 26 days had a life span of 295 days (Griffiths and Tauber, 1942).

Liles and DeLong (1960), on the other hand, found that the mated female *A. aegypti* mosquito lived just as long as the unmated ones, in spite of greater egg production by the mated adult females. They attempted to explain this on the basis of a beneficial "male effect," a concept derived from results obtained on rearing males with females and on rearing males and females separately, in which males living alone lived longer, whereas females living with males lived longer than when living alone. A possible complication, however, was the fact that only fifty individuals were used in the separate sex cages, whereas fifty males and fifty females were used in the cages where both sexes were reared together. Again, the question of population density on the one hand, and the advantage of mating and egg production to the female per se, on the other, cannot be ignored in what now is obviously a rather complex set of several to many interacting intrinsic and extrinsic environmental factors, all which must contribute to the ultimate rate of aging and the mean as well as maximum longevity of a particular strain and species.

In *Ephestia kühniella,* Norris (1933) showed that successfully mated females produced more eggs in the ovaries, and laid more eggs than un-

TABLE VIII

EGG PRODUCTION AND FEMALE LONGEVITY IN *Ephestia kühniella*[a]

Condition of female	No. of eggs produced in ovaries	Percentage of eggs laid	Adult life span (days)
Successfully paired	310	100	6.8
Unsuccessfully paired	188	67	11.6
Unmated	167	65	10.5

[a] After Norris (1933).

successfully mated or virgin females. Moreover, in this species, *virgin* females showed a much greater life span and a smaller number of eggs produced than the successfully mated group (see Table VIII). Considerable variation in the relationship between egg production and adult longevity has been reported by Gowen and Johnson (1946) when this criterion was applied to eight inbred strains and one hybrid race of *D. melanogaster*. They found that, in general, both male and female parents with the longer life span produced more eggs and at a greater rate (Table IX). Interestingly, in this connection, they found that for homozygous 42, low egg production was correlated with shorter duration of life for both male and female adults, whereas for the hybrid (Ames I × Inbred 92) producing a high number of eggs, the adult duration of life was similarly higher. However, similarity of life span for males and females *within each race* clearly indicates that egg production per se is not of primary importance in the aging process or longevity of these races, but rather that egg

TABLE IX

RELATION OF EGG PRODUCTION TO LONGEVITY IN *Drosophila melanogaster*[a]

Race	Total egg production	Days of egg laying	Eggs/day	Mean life span (days) Females	Males
Hybrid	2034	43.4	46.9	50.0	55.4
Ames II	1701	46.0	37.4	56.1	58.7
Ames II	1511	40.0	37.8	51.5	53.6
Ames I	1000	38.4	26.0	50.9	49.6
Princeton	814	35.4	23.0	48.4	46.7
Florida-45	610	22.4	27.2	28.5	32.6
Oregon R-C-44	413	28.7	14.4	36.4	35.5
Swede-b-40	398	16.5	24.1	26.7	35.7
Inbred 92	389	17.2	22.6	33.4	44.0
Homozygous 42	263	16.7	15.7	22.7	27.9

[a] After Gowen and Johnson (1946), *Amer. Naturalist*. © Univ. of Chicago Press.

production, in these cases, may itself be a concomitant advantageous characteristic related or even linked to greater longevity of both parents.

In a very recent study, Gray and Berberian (1971) and Berberian *et al.* (1971) repeated an earlier study by Rockstein (1957) in which supplementation of a sugar and water diet with powdered whole milk produced longer-lived females than those fed on sugar and water alone. At the same time, Berberian *et al.* (1971) demonstrated that there was a direct relationship between maximum longevity and rate of egg laying of the adult female house fly, *M. domestica;* i.e., longevity was maximum for a programmed 4-day interval of egg laying. Moreover, Rockstein *et al.* (1971) further showed that feeding, egg-laying and, inferentially, longevity were related to the control of the time sequence of brain neurosecretory events, such as hormonal development and subsequent release of neurosecretory substance from the brain of the female house fly in relation to egg-laying and longevity. However, these data are not concerned with longevity per se, unlike the report of Adams and Hintz (1969), who discussed ovarian development as a marker of physiological age, in particular relation to the time of mating and, in some species, of pheromone production.

4. Fecundity and Egg Laying

Although the exact cause-and-effect relationship is not clear, longevity in a number of cases appears to be related either directly or inversely to fecundity and egg-laying on the part of the female. However, no clear-cut relationship between this factor and the course and rate of *senescence* has been established per se. Maynard-Smith (1959) (Table

TABLE X

EXPECTATION OF LIFE OF *Drosophila subobscura* FEMALES
KEPT AT 20°C[a]

Female	N	e_x at age 10 days
Mated		
Kept continuously at 20°C	48	33.1 ± 1.6
Exposed to 31°C for 5 days	23	61.2 ± 5.7
Virgin		
Kept continuously at 20°C	89	58.7 ± 2.7
Ovariless		
Kept continuously at 20°C	28	67.6 ± 4.7
Exposed to 31°C for 3 days	22	64.2 ± 5.6

[a] Data from Maynard-Smith (1959).

X) has shown that life span of *D. subobscura* females is prolonged when the rate of egg laying is reduced. Thus, mated females (with a high egg production) had a shorter life expectancy than either virgin females (low egg production) or females without ovaries (no eggs laid). Moreover, exposure of mated females to a high temperature (31°C) for 5 days decreased egg production of the resulted injury to the ovaries, but more significantly, it resulted in an increased expectation of life. This was in contrast to no such increase in life span for females without ovaries exposed to those high temperatures. Bielewicz (Comfort, 1956) similarly showed a greater longevity of virgin over mated females in *D. melanogaster*.

Virgin female hemileucine saturniid moths *(Automeris aurantiaca)* have a life span of 9–10 days in contrast to mated females, which may mate within 24 hours after emergence, lay their eggs compulsively 24 hours after mating, and may be dead within 48 hours from the moment of eclosion (Blest, 1962).

In a recent study by Sondhi (1968a), the transplantation of corpus allatum complex into aging female *D. melanogaster* (Swedish-b[8]) showed no increase in egg production, although a decrease in imaginal life span occurred, whether the transplantation took place on the third day or on the fourteenth day of adult female life. Unfortunately, this latter study throws little light on the possible interaction of longevity and fecundity, in view of the fact that in an earlier experiment Sondhi (1966) similarly did reduce the life span of young *Drosophila* receiving the hemolymph of older individuals, but without affecting the fecundity. In substance, Sondhi suggests very strongly that homeostatic mechanisms regulating the physiology of reproduction in *Drosophila* can be maintained even if the adult life span is shortened by external influences. Indeed, as before, such equivocal results raise the question of the role of genetic versus environmental factors in determining life span as well as the rate of aging.

These scattered reports with their variable, if not conflicting results, especially depending on the species employed, open the door to a new attack upon the problem of physiological aging and longevity in the female of the species, especially in relation to hormonal control of egg production.

Indeed, when one considers some of the reports discussed earlier, including that of Lambremont and Earle (1961), in which the question of isolated versus mixed sexes and longevity is discussed, the question of mating versus nonmating and (even more likely to be significant) the question of successful mating, egg production, and fecundity as an important complex of factors governing the adult female longevity, in particular, cannot be ignored.

5. Length of Metamorphosis

Several studies have been made to determine if there is a relationship between duration of adult life and the length of the preimaginal stages. Thus, Northrop (1917) found that increasing the larval period of *D. melanogaster* from 8 to 17 days by reduced food intake produced no effect on the adult life span. Moreover, similar prolongation of duration of larval life in *D. melanogaster* by rearing at lower temperatures of 18°C, likewise produced adults (reared at 28°C) only slightly longer-lived than comparable adults reared as larvae at 28°C (Alpatov and Pearl, 1929).

In several, scattered, more recent experiments, data concerning the relationship of longevity of the adult to length of development have proven equally inconclusive. Thus, Lints and Lints (1969a, 1971a,b,c) stated that the argument by Comfort (1968), that the total life span of an organism could be lengthened merely by lengthening the developmental period of the immature stages, could not be substantiated by their experiments involving several highly inbred as well as reciprocal hybrid strains of *D. melanogaster*. Indeed, they could prolong the life span of the adults either by increasing the preimaginal population density at constant temperature, or by decreasing the developmental temperature at constant population density. Moreover, where increased preimaginal population density extended adult life span, it also resulted in a decrease in size as well as in mean daily egg production of the resulting imagoes. Thus, the involvement of such factors as preimaginal population density, preimaginal temperature, as well as genotype per se, exerting as they do an effect both on fecundity as well as on the rate of aging of the resulting adults, led Lints and Lints to the conclusion that longevity cannot be determined solely by the duration of the preimaginal developmental period.

It is, therefore, obvious, at this point, that a number of factors, including genotype, may be involved in extending larval development, especially in relation to their individual as well as joint action in regard to the ultimate effects both upon the rate as well as age of maturation, the rate of aging, and, finally, the age at which death will occur in the adult form.

B. Extrinsic Factors

1. Temperature

Since insects are poikilothermal, their metabolic rate is greatly influenced by the temperature of the environment, i.e., within a range of temperature that permits survival, the higher the environmental temperature, the higher the rate of heat production and oxygen consumption (Edwards, 1953).

TABLE XI

Life Span and Temperature Coefficients
for *Drosophila melanogaster* Imagos[a]

Temperature (°C)	Duration of life (days)	Rate (100/time)	Q_{10}
10	120.5	0.83	
			1.7
15	92.4	1.08	
			5.2
20	40.2	2.49	
			2.0
25	28.5	3.51	
			4.4
30	13.6	7.35	

[a] From Loeb and Northrop (1917).

Loeb and Northrop (1917) demonstrated the existence of a definite temperature coefficient for duration of life for *D. melanogaster;* thus, populations of imagoes lived 120.5 days at 10°C but only 13.6 days at 30°C. In the range of 10°–30°C, the life span was inversely proportional to the ambient temperature (Table XI). (For more recent data on a longer-lived strain of *D. melanogaster,* see Fig. 4.) Loeb and Northrop (1917) concluded that the "duration of life is determined by the production of a substance leading to old age and natural death, or by the destruction of a substance which normally prevents age and natural death." In Loeb and Northrop's opinion, this substance was accumulated or lost according to a law relating temperature and rate similar to that of a chemical reaction, i.e., the temperature coefficient (Q_{10} or μ) would be between 1.5 and 3. On the other hand, Alpatov and Pearl (1929), on the basis of their own experiments, postulated that *Drosophila* has a shorter duration of adult life at higher temperatures simply because it is more active at these temperatures, i.e., has a higher "rate of living."

Data obtained by Shaw and Bercaw (1962) in an investigation of aging of *D. melanogaster,* suggested that, in agreement with Loeb and Northrop's views, aging is a result of the depletion of some longevity substance and that its rate is temperature dependent. This is in sharp disagreement with the opinions expressed by Maynard-Smith (1958, 1959, 1963), and by Clarke and Maynard-Smith (1961a,b), from their investigations of aging in *D. subobscura.*

Maynard-Smith (1958) prolonged the life of *D. subobscura* females by exposure to high temperature. Adult females, exposed to 30.5°C for 5–12 days and then returned to 20°C, lived up to 50% longer than did females kept continuously at 20°C. He suggested that the effect of this exposure is to reduce permanently the rate of metabolic processes at 20°C, since the rate of egg-laying for females kept continuously at 20°C is much higher, and he argued that the senescent changes occurring at 30.5°C temperature cannot be the same as the senescent changes occurring at 20°C, since a reduction in life span would be expected. Different processes of senescence are presumed to occur at 30.5°C than at 20°C. Direct measurements of metabolic rates in such studies would be desirable to confirm this hypothesis. In more recent studies, in confirmation of these findings, Clarke and Maynard-Smith (1961a,b) found that imagoes transferred to a temperature of 26°C, after 4–24 days at 20°C, lived as long as animals that spend their entire adult lives at 26°C. Conversely, imagoes kept first at a high temperature and then transferred to a lower one had the same life span as flies kept continuously at the lower temperature. These results contradict the rate of living theory, and Clarke and Maynard-Smith have proposed a new theory to explain them. According to the "threshold theory" of aging, the initial phase of the aging process is irreversible and proceeds at a rate which is independent of temperature between 15° and 30°C, and continues until the "vitality" of the individual has fallen to a threshold level below which it can no longer maintain a steady state. There is an increased threshold level at higher temperatures. Individuals able to maintain themselves at a low temperature may be unable to do so at some higher temperature. When "vitality" decreases below the threshold appropriate to the temperature at which the animal is living, a second process (dying) begins which is temperature dependent and can be reversed in flies transferred to lower temperatures. This theory is made plausible by the increasing number of demonstrations of biological clocks with good temperature compensation (Sacher, 1967).

Hollingsworth (1966a) demonstrated that the rate of aging of *D. subobscura* at 28.8°C was the same as at 18.5° and 24.8°C. Death in young flies occurred sooner than expected at 28.8°C, probably due to a breakdown in the homeostatic mechanism caused by the cumulative effects of some unknown metabolic imbalance. The flies went into a coma when heated to 37°C for 25 minutes in moist air, but were walking about 5 hours later. Death occurred if the 37°C exposure time was 35 minutes or longer.

The age-related decrease in ability to withstand high temperature in *D. subobscura* has also been investigated by Hollingsworth (1966b). At 34°C there was an age-related, rapid decline in the survival of the flies by the sixteenth day of imaginal life, falling to half the value at 1 day of age.

Hollingsworth suggests that his observations support the hypothesis of Medawar (1952) and of Williams (1957), suggesting that few, if any, individuals in a natural environment die in old age. Consequently, natural selection will favor vigor early in life at the expense of vigor in later life.

Hollingsworth (1968) has performed further experiments on the effects of temperature on the longevity of *D. melanogaster* on imagoes which were kept at (a) 25°C, (b) 30°C, and (c) alternating periods at 25° and 30°C, and he has found that the length of adult life in environment (c) was clearly intermediate between that in the low- and that in the high-temperature environments. The length of life in environment (c) greatly exceeded the expectation according to the "rate of living" theory. Accordingly, Hollingsworth suggested that the original form of the "threshold" theory requires modification because of the great influence of temperature on the prethreshold period.

Hollingsworth (1969a) has shown that death of the imagoes of *D. subobscura* was virtually instantaneous at 37°C, while estimation by extrapolation of the data predicted that flies would live 2.7 years if kept at 0°C. The critical point in the temperature–length-of-life relationship appears to be at 28°–29°C and indicates that the higher temperatures are life shortening because they cause events which do not occur at the lower temperatures. In a later study, Hollingsworth (1969b) exposed *D. melanogaster* adults to fluctuating temperatures (exposed to 20°C for given periods of time, but aged at 25°C) and confirmed that the life span of males approximated that expected according to Pearl's "rate of living" theory. Female flies, exposed to 30°C for only 3 hours and to 25°C for 21 hours/day, showed life spans expected according to the "threshold" theory with the ability to reverse life-shortening effects of daily high-temperature exposure completely.

When aged at 15°C versus exposure to 25° and 30°C, flies of both sexes live even longer than expected according to the "rate of living" theory of aging. From the latter experiments, the author concludes that aging at 15°C increases the adult fly's vitality.

Strehler (1961) exposed adult *D. melanogaster* to a 1-hour temperature shock at 38.5°C on the sixth day of life, and then returned them to 25°C for the duration of life. Within 3 days, 50% of the population was killed by the high-temperature exposure. The surviving flies showed an identical mortality behavior as control flies. Strehler (1962 demonstrated that when the food medium was regularly replaced, there is a significant effect of thermal shock on the long-term mortality of flies. In Strehler's view, although denaturative processes may mimic the effects of time on the aging of *Drosophila*, this does not mean that the mechanisms of the deleterious changes occurring are similar under the influence of both time and temperature.

The exact cause of heat-induced death is not known, although several possible mechanisms have been suggested; among them is protein denaturation (Abercrombie and Johnson, 1941; Maynard-Smith, 1957; Strehler, 1961; Bowler and Hollingsworth, 1965). Of particular relevance would be enzyme inactivation which may be detected at temperatures as low as 30°C (Sizer, 1943). As pointed out by Hollingsworth (1969a), another possible cause of heat-death might be the melting of lipid-containing structures such as cell membranes, with the consequent loss of organization within the cells. This hypothesis is supported by the observation that blowflies raised at higher temperatures have phospholipids which are more saturated and therefore have higher melting points than those raised at low temperatures (Fraenkel and Hopf, 1940). In this same connection, Beament (1959) has stressed the role of water loss by alteration of the permeability of the cuticle in *Rhodnius, Tenebrio,* and *Pieris* in high temperature-related death (see Chapter 2 by Locke, Volume VI of this treatise for a detailed discussion of water loss from death in relation to critical temperatures for such water loss in relation to alteration of natural, water-barrier wax layers of the cuticle).

Sacher (1967) has analyzed data on the temperature dependence of maturation rates, metabolic rates, and mortality rates of insects in an effort to determine if the experimental evidence supports the entropic hypothesis or the hypothesis of a temperature-independent primary aging process. Commenting on Maynard-Smith's threshold theory of aging, Sacher (1967) has suggested that the available information about temperature adaptations and circadian (and other) rhythms suggests a complex rather than a simplistic explanation for the effects of temperature on the rate of dying or aging. Sacher suggests instead that the mortality rate curve is a positively accelerated function of temperature, and that mutation, developmental anomaly, developmental failure, and aging are the result of the "increase in organizational entropy" as temperature is displaced from an optimum value. This increase would be the result of an irreducible heterogeneity of activation energies of enzyme-catalyzed reactions. In his words, "Aging can no longer be considered as simply a question of how much metabolic work, it is also a function of how well the work is done, in thermodynamic and informational terms."

2 Ionizing Radiation

A variety of insects have been used to investigate the effects of ionizing radiation on physiological activities, genetic factors, and developmental processes (Hasset and Jenkins, 1952; Grosch, 1962).

Adult insects are much more radioresistant than vertebrates (as shown in Fig. 6), presumably owing to the low level of mitotic activity in the imago. However, as noted by O'Brien and Wolfe (1964), generalizations about effective doses have only limited meaning in view of the large differences between sterilizing doses and acutely lethal doses, which, for example, for the wasp, *Bracon hebetor,* are 5 kR and 300 kR, respectively.

Ionizing radiation is basically a disorganizing agent, which produces damage to a variety of structures, particularly the genetic apparatus. It is therefore surprising that X rays are capable of increasing the life span of insects. Radiation-induced life prolongation was reported as long ago as 1917 by Davey, following exposure of *T. confusum* to low doses of X rays. More recently, Cork (1957) found an increase in life span in *Tribolium* exposed to a daily dose of 100 R or to a single dose of 3 kR of gamma rays. Increased longevity has also been reported for X-irradiated *Habrobracon* kept without food (Sullivan and Grosch, 1953; Grosch, 1956). This effect was probably due to the lowered energy consumption associated with radiation-induced lethargy. An earlier report by Gowen and Stadler (1952) had shown that the survival of the imagoes of *D. melanogaster* was not influenced by X irradiation at a dose as high as 12 kR. On the other hand, Strehler (1962) reported an increase in the survival of the fruit fly when exposed to a single dose of 5 kR. Since, under aseptic conditions, survival curves of the flies exposed to 5 kR or less were very similar to those of normal flies, Strehler attributed this increase to the culture conditions. Sacher (1963) reported that for *D. melanogaster* there is a 30% increase or more in the mean aftersurvival as a result of exposure to daily doses of 1.5–3.0 kR, but not if single, more massive doses are used. Radiation-induced life extension, in Sacher's view, would be due to a reduction in the effectiveness of deleterious environmental random variables. This reduced effectiveness might result from an inactivation of the environmental factor or from an increase in resistance induced in the flies by the radiation exposure.

On the other hand, Dauer *et al.* (1965) have shown that the average life span of those male house flies successfully emerging following exposure of *pupae* to 10–15 kR was increased, but remained unchanged at 20 kR, and declined significantly at 30-kR exposures. Wing loss, which is a normal concomitant of aging in male house flies up to 2 weeks of adult life at the most, was progressively diminished for these levels of exposure, so that at 30 kR normal wing loss was repressed to the extent of 96% of the males retaining their wings at death, in contrast to 6.5% of wing retention at death for untreated males and 17.8% for 10 kR exposed pupae.

In further investigations on *D. melanogaster,* Sonnenblick and Grodis

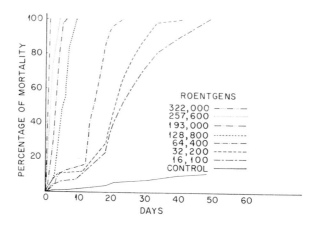

Fig. 6. Mortality rates of adult *Rhyzopertha* exposed to X rays. (From Hassett and Jenkins, 1952.) Reprinted with special permission from *Nucleonics* © 1952 by McGraw-Hill.

(1963) and Atlan *et al.* (1970) have been unable to detect a radiation-induced increase in longevity. In *Drosophila,* according to Lamb (1964), there is an interaction between nutrition, egg production, and longevity, and X radiation will only increase the longevity of the females if they are kept in nutritionally suboptimal conditions.

Large doses of radiation (about 200 kR) can stun, paralyze, and cause the death of an insect within hours, probably because of irreversible injury to the central nervous system. Doses of this magnitude are therefore not useful for life span studies. Within a dose range of 5–25 kR, life span curves which can be constructed show orderly decreases with dose. In general, the survival curves for irradiated insects resemble those of the controls but the time at which death of the population occurs is earlier and the slope of the curve is usually steeper (Fig. 6). This has been well documented by a study of the influence of X rays at doses up to 125 kR on the longevity of *D. melanogaster* (Nothel, 1965). With increasing doses, the log mean survival time decreased linearly in both sexes. The LD_{50} was 46 kR in males and 96 kR in females. At doses above 90 kR, immediate death occurred. Similar results have been obtained by Atlan *et al.* (1970) in an investigation of the effects of low- and high-LET cyclotron accelerated particles on the longevity of *D. melanogaster.* Dose–mean longevity curves, as in Nothel's experiments, were exponential. The effect of low-LET particles was similar to that of ^{60}Co, whereas the high-LET α-particles were more effective than the two other types of radiation, with an RBE of 1.3. No dose–rate effect was observed in the range of 4–256 kR/minute.

Observations by Miquel *et al.* (1972) on the mating behavior of gamma-irradiated *D. melanogaster* suggest that exposure to 50 kR induces both a reversible damage and an irreversible, progressive injury which results in imaginal death.

In life span studies, it is of prime importance whether radiation is administered as single or fractionated doses, since total dose alone is an inadequate parameter. In *T. confusum*, for example, the life span is affected less by a total dose of 45 kR, delivered as a 100-R daily dose, than by 20 kR delivered as a single dose (Cork, 1957); *P. americana* males exposed to a single dose of 10 kR had a much shorter life span than those exposed to 5 doses of 2 kR each delivered at intervals of $1\frac{1}{2}$ hours (Wharton and Wharton, 1959). Also, *Drosophila* adults lived longer after fractionated doses giving the same total dose than after a series of single large doses (Baxter and Tuttle, 1957). These differences in killing efficiency indicate that recovery processes may be operating and suggest that postirradiation conditions may be manipulated to modify life span.

Whiting (1949) has shown that when radiation injury is strictly chromosomal it is not reduced by fractionation, but when cytoplasmic damage occurred, the effect was prevented or minimized by giving the radiation in smaller doses. More recently, Baxter and Blair (1969) have investigated recovery from radiation injury contributing to acute lethality. *Drosophila melanogaster* of various ages were exposed to a sublethal dose of X rays, followed after a variable interval by a second dose adjusted to permit determination of acute lethal dose. This study has shown that over-recovery (measured by increase of lethal dose above its normal value) may be as great or greater than the original injury and lasts for the remainder of life, which, however, is shortened by the initial dose. On the basis of this work, Baxter and Blair have postulated that life-shortening is determined by reversible injury to the cell nucleus and that acute lethality is determined by extranuclear injury.

It is generally assumed that insects capable of developing to the adult stage, after irradiation as embryos, larvae, or pupae, are free from injury and have a normal life span. It is unfortunate that in almost all such experiments, failure of adult emergence is used as the criterion of injury and the term "life span" is actually applied to preimaginal duration of life. *Habrobracon juglandis* (Clark, 1961) and *H. serinopae* (Clark and Rubin, 1961) were irradiated as larvae and pupae with doeses too small to arrest their development to the adult stage. Nevertheless, the adults, although apparently normal, showed a marked reduction in mean life span.

Erdman (1960) found a reduction in life span among adult *Habrobracon* surviving exposure to X irradiation as embryos. The mean life span of adult *H. juglandis* females exposed as white pupae to 20,000 R was likewise reduced from the control level of 29.0 days to 9.0 days, although no decrease in the incidence of adult emergence was observed. Exposure of white pupae to 5000 R similarly resulted in a reduction in mean adult life span to 21.5 days (Clark, 1961). Thus, when the adult life span is used as the criterion of damage, insects do not appear to be as resistant to radiation as is commonly thought. Moreover, the adult life span is a more sensitive criterion of radiation damage than adult emergence. Similarly, exposure to 10,000 R will shorten the mean life span of *P. americana* adults, from about 2 years to 3 weeks (Wharton and Wharton, 1959).

In other organisms, exposure to ionizing radiation generally results in a decrease in life span and a tendency to exhibit at an earlier age those diseases generally associated with advancing age. These observations suggest that the radiation may have accelerated aging (Upton, 1957). The possible relationship between radiation and aging has been considered in an early review by Strehler (1959).

On the basis of observations on irradiated *D. melanogaster,* Lamb (1966) and Lamb and Maynard-Smith (1969) favor the hypothesis that radiation accelerates the natural aging process. On the other hand, Baxter and Blair (1967a,b) suggest that, since according to their own data age of death of *Drosophila* does not depend on age of exposure, radiation injury does not accelerate the aging process but simply adds an equivalent of natural aging. Atlan *et al.* (1969a) have adopted a third position. In their experiments, age at irradiation influenced survival time only when the flies were irradiated 30–90 days after eclosion. When the imagoes of *D. melanogaster* were exposed to 50 kR of gamma radiation at 1–20 days of age, death occurred at a constant time after exposure. According to Atlan *et al.,* these results would be consistent with the view that death is the outcome of a radiation syndrome, which, at least for 1- to 20-day-old flies, is unrelated to aging. Further support for this concept is given by recent light and electron microscopic investigations showing that the degenerative changes present in the tissues of old flies are different from those shown by irradiated imagoes (Miquel *et al.,* 1972).

Another approach to the study of radiation-induced aging has been by comparison of the longevity of strains that differ in karyotype. Such studies have been reported for haploids and diploids of the wasp, *H. serinopae* (Clark and Rubin, 1961; Clark *et al.,* 1963).

Both haploid males of two genetic types, veinless and wild type, and diploid males, heterozygous for veinless, had a mean life span of 62 days. Adults exposed to X rays (50 kR) showed a marked decrease in life span; e.g., diploid males had a life span of 37 days, while haploid groups had a mean life span of 18 days. Moreover, the survival curves showed that the haploid experimentals started to die at an earlier age than the diploids. These results indicate that the decreased life span caused by ionizing radiation results from damage to the nuclear genetic material by such radiation. Moreover, the similarity between the controls and the marked differences found for the irradiated groups strongly suggest that the mechanisms leading to death in each case must be quite different. This indicates that damage to the nuclear genetic material caused by ionizing radiation results in a decreased life span. It does not seem likely that the same type of damage is involved in the normal aging process.

Similar results have been obtained by Clark and Cole (1967) for haploid and diploid males and diploid and triploid females of the wasp, *Mormoniella vitripennis*.

The problem has also been investigated in diploid and triploid *D. melanogaster* by Lamb (1965), who indicates that the results of her experiments do not support the hypothesis that radiation-induced life shortening is the result of mutations in somatic cells. Based on their own experiments on wasps, Clark and Cole (1967) concurred in that opinion and expressed the view that the types of injury leading to natural aging must be different from those leading to radiation-induced decrease in life span. This is in agreement with the original opinion expressed by Müller (1960, 1963) that permanent alterations in genes are not involved in natural aging and that the radiation-induced modification of life span is not comparable to the "spontaneous" aging process.

3. Nutrition

The work of McCay *et al.* (1939) and Ross (1959, 1961) on male rats has shown that nutrition is an important factor in modifying life span, altering metabolic conditions, and causing disease. The ease with which the duration of insect adult life can be modified by diet indicates that insects may be useful for nutritional studies related to aging. The subject of insect nutrition, as such, has been reviewed by House (Volume V, Chapter 1). The present discussion, therefore, deals primarily with nutritional influences on the duration of life of the adult insect.

In insects, diet may modify the rate of development, oviposition, fertility, and organ size, as well as life span. The following generalizations can be made.

1. The nutritional levels required for optimal growth and development during the preimaginal stages are different from those required for the adult.

2. Preimaginal stages are lengthened, whereas the imaginal duration of life is shortened, by inadequate diets.

3. Lengthening the duration of the preimaginal stages does not necessarily result in a lengthened adult life span.

4. Males and females may have different nutritional requirements. The resulting duration of life may, therefore, be a consequence of metabolic changes which are modified by nutritional state.

Significant studies must consider not only the effects of diet on life span per se, but also the more immediate effects on enzyme patterns, organ development, and accumulation of substances which are by-products of metabolism.

The simple fact that nutrition can modify the adult duration of life has been demonstrated in the investigations described below.

Drosophila adults fed yeast in addition to a basic medium lived longer than those deprived of yeast (Alpatov, 1930). Adult *Drosophila* fed various fractions of royal jelly showed that pantothenic acid was an important substance in increasing life span up to 46%. Addition of RNA, on the other hand, increased longevity about 10% (Gardner, 1948a,b).

Musca domestica adult females fed sugar and water alone had a mean life span of only 19.5 days, whereas females fed a powdered bovine whole-milk preparation (KLIM), in addition to sugar and water, had a mean life span of 32.7 days (Rockstein and Lieberman, 1959). The consistently shorter mean life span of males (16–17 days), however, was not significantly modified by a similar change in diet.

Haydak's study (1953) on cockroaches has correlated changes in duration of life with changes in internal structure at different protein levels. Haydak fed diets containing different levels of protein to three species of cockroaches and observed effects upon adult life span and on the duration of nymphal life. Marked decreases in adult longevity were observed with increasing levels of protein (Table XII), although for very low (0.5%) levels also there was a slight decrease in duration of life. Moreover, optimal levels required for nymphal development were not the same as for adult longevity. Autopsies of *P. americana* adults revealed a considerable increase in fat and urate material in animals maintained at higher protein levels. Thus, adults fed a diet of 91% protein showed swollen abdomens and deposition of large masses of fat in the head, legs, and antennal sockets. Indeed, the abdomens were so filled with fat that the internal organs were compressed. When such adults were transferred to a diet of pure dextrin, both fat and urate deposits diminished and longevity was increased in comparison with those kept on the high-protein diet.

TABLE XII

RELATION OF PROTEIN LEVEL TO ADULT LONGEVITY FOR COCKROACHES[a]

Species	Sex	N	Protein level (%)	Longevity (days)
Blattella germanica	F	27	11–24	270
		19	49–74	114
		21	79–91	74
	M	30	11–24	207
		8	49	123
		18	74–79	86
		15	86–91	68
Blatta orientalis	F	21	22–24	185
		6	49	151
		11	74–79	90
		8	86–91	63
	M	15	0–11	204
		18	22–24	233
		6	49	148
		7	74–79	109
		6	86–91	56
Periplaneta americana	F	13	0–5	618
		20	11–49	726
		20	74–79	613
		10	86–91	474
	M	6	2.5–11	791
		19	22–24	825
		5	49	790
		9	74–79	560
		11	86–91	516

[a] After Haydak (1953).

Other experiments indicate that the protein level in the diet may modify adult life span in insects. Male and female *A. aegypti* lived longer when fed only 10% sucrose than when fed citrated hemolyzed beef blood containing 10% sucrose (Liles and DeLong, 1960). *Mormoniella vitripennis* adults live longer on 10% sucrose alone than on 10% sucrose plus bovine serum albumin, milk albumin, or egg albumin (A. M. Clark and K. W. Cole, unpublished, 1963) *Habrobracon serinopae* adults live longer on 10% sucrose than on bovine serum albumin in a 10% sucrose solution. In addition, urate material accumulates with age in adults fed the bovine serum albumin, but not the sucrose (A. M. Clark, unpublished, 1963).

A complex relationship involving life span, nutritional state, brood-rearing, season, and physiological state is seen in the case of the honey bee worker (Maurizio, 1959; see Section IV, A, 3). The bee colony contains, at different seasons, summer bees and winter bees. Summer bees have a minimal life span of 25–35 days and a maximal life span of 60–70 days and are involved in brood rearing. Winter bees live for 6–8 months and are free from brood-rearing responsibilities. In summer bees, the pharyngeal glands and wax glands attain full development and then degenerate. The fat body, however, remains undeveloped throughout life. In winter bees, the pharyngeal glands and fat body remain fully developed for 6–7 months.

The life span of summer worker bees can be increased by feeding them pollen early in adult life and by freeing them from brood-rearing responsibilities. Such bees not only possess fully developed pharyngeal glands but also form a winter fat body which stores proteins, carbohydrates, and fat and live as long as 166 days. Reduced demands upon such food reserves results in extended maintenance of the fat body and a concomitant prolongation of adult life.

The implications of such dietary influences on both the physiological state and longevity, in terms of development or failure of specific endocrine structures, are such as to suggest the need for a critical attack upon this very challenging problem at the endocrine level.

In this connection, Standifer et al. (1960) suggested serious discrepancies between their findings on the role of pollen in promoting gland development and longevity in worker bees. They reported that caged honey bees, when fed different percentages of egg albumin, showed a decreased adult life span of the following order: 10% albumin, 18.3 days; 5%, 16.3 days; 2.5%, 12.6 days; 15%, 8.0 days; and 20%, 7.3 days. However, interpretation of their results is difficult in view of the conditions of their experiments, involving 75 bees caged in the limited space of 6 × 6 × 3 inches and the use of the "half-life" of such a small population, rather than the mean or maximal longevity, as a measurement of longevity.

Different dietary requirements may obtain not only for different species and different sexes but also for different mutants of the same sex and species. Adult females of *Habrobracon* normally feed upon the larvae of *Ephestia kühniella* but can also be kept alive on honey and water. Some strains of *Habrobracon females,* when fed white-clover honey, lived much longer than *Ephestia*-fed females, while for other strains the adult life span was identical for females on either diet (Clark, 1963). The response to diet is thus genetically determined. Moreover, optimal conditions of diet for some mutant types may be different from those for others.

It is obvious that nutritional studies can be of great importance in elucidating the factors involved in life span. There are a great number of nutritional variables to consider, viz., different levels of protein, fat, and carbohydrate; variation in specific amino acids fed singly and in combination; differential caloric intake; and qualitative and quantitative differences in specific vitamins and mineral trace substances. Great versatility in such studies are obtained because of the possibility for specific action of individual dietary substances upon organ growth and metabolic patterns. The consequences of such more immediate effects of nutrition should yield information needed to understand the aging process.

Various authors have investigated the effects of starvation on the longevity of *D. melanogaster*. According to Kopec (1928), the injurious influence of longer, less frequent fasting intervals was more pronounced than that of shorter more frequent periods of inanition, which could even produce significant increases in the longevity of imagoes. In Alpatov's (1930) opinion, duration of life for different grades of intermittent starvation followed a logistic curve. In an investigation by Greiff (1940), starvation acted as an externally administered poison. More recently, David *et al.* (1971) have studied the effects of quantitative underfeeding on the longevity and fertility of *Drosophila*. By dilution of an axenic medium, it was possible to reduce the quantity of foodstuff ingested by the imagoes. Dilution resulted in a progressive reduction of fertility. However, no important changes in longevity were seen for concentrations ranging from 4 to 16%. At lower concentrations, striking decreases in longevity occurred. Highly diluted media were much better tolerated by larvae than by adults. This could correspond to higher carbohydrate requirement in imagoes.

The effect of limited milk feeding on the longevity of the house fly, *M. domestica,* has been studied by Gray and Berberian (1971). Female flies live as long on a 3-day powdered whole-milk supplement beginning 12 hours after emergence as they do on a constant milk supplement throughout their entire life span. Male house flies are not so affected. The beneficial effects on the female's longevity are indicative that utilization of milk is intimately related to egg development, and this in turn related to increased longevity. Female flies on either constant or 3-day milk regimes ingest enough milk shortly after emergence for the maturation of a batch of eggs and, owing to lack of suitable oviposition site, do not lay their eggs. Instead they harbor a fully developed batch of eggs, and do not ingest more milk (cf. Rockstein and Lieberman, 1959).

The effects of axenic culture conditions on the longevity of *D. melanogaster* have been investigated by Steinfeld (1928). Aseptic larval–pupal life followed by standard conditions during the imaginal stage, increased the expectation of life of the adult flies by 13.7% in comparison with the controls. Furthermore, on adequate food, banana agar and 10% yeast, *Drosophila* reared through under aseptic conditions had a mean duration of life greater than that of controls by 18.04 days, 69% of the life span. The life curves of the aseptic flies were closer to the right-angle type than the mortality curves of *Drosophila* kept under nonaseptic conditions.

4. Other Factors

a. Ultraviolet Radiation. Doses of 3,000 J/m² have a definite life-shortening effect on the imagoes of *D. melanogaster*. It appears that UV radiation at both 2600 and 2800 A resulted in similar reduction of the life span. Whereas exposure to ionizing radiation shortens life and reduces the variability of longevity of the various flies of a group, UV irradiation shortened life with a marked increase in variability; i.e., the plateau phase of the control mortality curve was sharply shortened in the irradiated groups, while the maximum life span was much less reduced. Because of the similarity of the effects of the two different wavelengths used and because of the strong absorptive properties of the pigmented superficial layers of the flies, it is likely that sensitive superficial structures, particularly the eyes, are responsible for the life shortening (Atlan *et al.*, 1969b).

b. Light Intensity. Drosophila which had been grown previously in the dark for 200 generations were exposed to different light intensities from a Mazda bulb of 150, 500, and 1000 W. The adult duration of life was rapidly shortened by exposure above 1000 meter candles when the flies were kept at 20°C. On the other hand, if the flies were kept at 30°C, the adult life span was not affected by the light (Northrop, 1926). Greenberg (1960) reported that house flies, when kept in total darkness and given only water, lived longer than flies kept in constant light. Such a difference is apparently due to the decreased activity of the flies kept in the dark.

In view of the dramatic effects of different wavelengths of light upon biological systems, further research along such lines may be fruitful, especially in relation to aging and longevity.

c. Magnetic Fields. Continuous exposure to uniform magnetic fields of 10 G of newly eclosed *Drosophila* imagoes did not influence life span (Close and Beischer, 1962). Further unpublished work by Kitzman and Miquel (1971) has failed to detect any influence of exposure to low magnetic fields (i.e., 50 G) on *Drosophila* mating, fertility, or longevity. In the house fly, *M. domestica,* L. D. Baker and M. Rockstein (unpublished, 1972) found that exposure for 3½ days to low magnetic fields (40 G), of pupae less than 1 hour old, had no effect upon the mating, fertility, or longevity of the resultant, emerging adult male or female flies.

M. Rockstein, G. J. Farrell, and G. T. Baker, III, (unpublished, 1972) also found that exposure of *M. domestica* pupae 2 days following pupation, at 5000 G for up to 4 hours, and of pupae, from 0 to 72 hours following pupation, to 10,000 G for up to 24 hours of exposure, produced no significant effect on emergence, longevity, or fecundity, as well.

d. Acceleration and Clinostat Exposure. Wunder (1955, 1963) has investigated the effects of acceleration on *Drosophila*. The larvae survived exposure to 3000 g for 48 hours, but their growth rate decreased linearly with increased g to about 1000 g. On the other hand, an acceleration of 500 g caused an increase in growth of about 25%.

Unpublished data by J. Miquel and P. R. Lundgren (1971) have shown that the mating behavior and embryonic development of *D. melanogaster* were apparently not affected by rotation of the eggs, larvae, and pupae in clinostats. On the other hand, the longevity of the imagoes kept continuously in clinostats was reduced by about 15%. Increased ambulatory activity, with a correspondingly higher energy utilization, was the probable cause of the shortening of life span.

Current studies by M. Rockstein, S. M. Losa, and C. Place (unpublished, 1972) on clinostat rotation, in a vertical plane, of pupae immediately upon, as well as up to 17 hours following pupation, at a rotation rate of 15 turns per hour, produced no significant effect upon emergence, breeding, or longevity, in comparison with normal, untreated male or female flies.

e. Humidity. *Drosophila* (wild-type) adults when reared in vials

TABLE XIII

LENGTH OF LIFE (IN DAYS) OF THE LEVANT HOUSE FLY UNDER
DIFFERENT CONDITIONS OF TEMPERATURE AND HUMIDITY[a]

Temperature (°C)	Life in days at relative humidities of				
	30%	40%	60%	73%	80%
14.5				47.0 ± 14.4	
19	56.0 ± 1.9	52.4 ± 1.7	39.0 ± 1.8		28.0 ± 0.9
24			27.4 ± 1.8	29.3 ± 2.0	19.5 ± 1.1
27 (series A)		19.5 ± 0.7	23.0 ± 1.3		19.5 ± 0.8
27 (series B)		25.3 ± 1.0	27.0 ± 1.5		19.5 ± 0.6
30		20.3 ± 0.7	18.9 ± 0.9		17.1 ± 0.5
35			17.6 ± 0.8		

[a] From Feldman-Muhsam (1944).

plugged with cotton have a duration of life of 43.66± 0.39 days; when reared in vials covered by a layer of silk bolting cloth with a mesh of 48 strands per inch, they lived 47.92± 0.40 days, a 10% increase in life span. Flies in the well-ventilated vials tended to congregate at the mouth of the bottle and moved to the bottom of the vial only to feed, while flies in plugged vials had no preference for the top of the vial (Pearl and Parker, 1922a,b). The precise role played by humidity (and other factors) remains to be clarified in this case.

Feldman-Muhsam (1944) observed life span differences for the Levant house fly, *M. domestica vicina* Macq., reared at different temperatures and humidities. Cages containing 100 flies were placed in closed glass jars containing various concentrations of H_2SO_4 to maintain the required relative humidities. A clear effect of humidity was shown (Table XIII). At lower temperatures, life span was prolonged with lower humidities. For 19°C, the life span at 30% relative humidity (RH) was 56 days, while at 80% RH it was 28 days. With increasing temperatures, there was a decrease in life span for all relative humidities, but at high humidities this temperature effect was less striking. At 40% RH, for example, the range in duration of life for 19° to 30°C was 52.4 to 20.3 days, while at 80% RH the range was 28 to 17.1 days, respectively.

f. Oxygen Tension. Continuous exposure of *Drosophila* imagoes to low oxygen tensions (oxygen at 1–2% in nitrogen) apparently increased

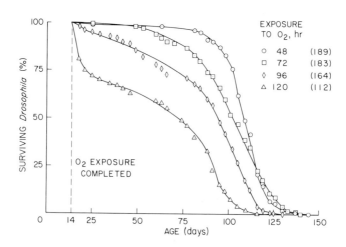

Fig. 7. Longevity of male *D. melanogaster* imagoes exposed to 1 atm of 100% O_2. The survival curve for flies exposed to 48 hours is practically identical to the survival curves of control populations. (The numbers in parentheses indicate the number of flies used in each exposure to the gas.) (J. Miquel and P. R. Lundgren, unpublished.)

the longevity of *Drosophila* by about 20% (Strehler, 1962). In further experiments by J. Miquel and P. R. Lundgren (unpublished), the longevity of the imagoes of *D. melanogaster* was reduced by exposure times of 48 hours or longer to 1 atm of pure oxygen (Fig. 7). Exposure to ⅓ atm of oxygen or to oxygen-nitrogen (1:1) produced decreases in mean longevity of about 10 and 50%, respectively. Preliminary histopathological investigation of the oxygen-poisoned flies show marked sponginess of the brain. Therefore, specific nervous-system injury, rather than accelerated aging, seems most likely cause of the decrease in life span. At higher pressures, *Drosophila* survival in oxygen is reduced to a few hours [for example, as shown by Williams and Beecher (1944), survival is only 6.75 hours at 5 atm]. More recently, Thomas *et al.*, (1966) have shown that X irradiation can remarkably potentiate the acute neurological effects of oxygen at high pressure (7.8 atm). Also, shortening of the life span of young male *Drosophila* by doses of 30–75 kR was augmented significantly by a concurrent 40-minute exposure to oxygen at high pressure (which alone did not significantly decrease life span). In the opinion of Thomas *et al.* (1966), these results support the concept that oxygen exerts its toxic effects via free radical intermediates.

g. *Toxic Agents.* Economically important insects have been exposed to insecticides and other toxic agents, but the effectiveness of these agents is usually measured by immediate knockdown and 24-hour kill. However, a few studies have been made in which the effects over longer periods of time with lower concentrations of such substances are observed. Moffett (1952) found that a dose of 100 ppm reduced life span from 31 to 15 days for caged honey bees fed iodine mixed with syrup, for a concentration range of 1–1000 ppm.

Also, in a study by Kuenen *et al.* (1957), time-mortality curves for the granary weevil and house fly were constructed for control and DDT-treated groups. Although a sharp increase in mortality occurred for the experimental groups soon after treatment, the death rate among the survivors was less than that for the controls. This indicated that the insects with a shorter life expectancy from natural causes were more susceptible to DDT than those with a long life expectancy. Were DDT mortality independent of natural mortality, one would expect the death rates to be identical. Thus, Kuenen *et al.* (1957) suggest that insecticidal and natural mortality are not independent. This report is also valuable in showing the usefulness of probit log-time mortality curves in the analysis of life span data; indeed, this type of analysis has been employed in evaluating factors involved in longevity differences between male and female house flies by Rockstein and Lieberman (1959).

Adult house flies treated topically with o-isopropyloxyphenyl methyl-carbamate, 6-chloro-3,4-xylylmethylcarbamate, and carbanyl were most resistant to these chemicals when 5 days old. It seemed that accumulation of the toxicant at the site of action varied in insects of different ages (Green and Dorough, 1968). Further, when *M. domestica* were injected thoracically with 1 μl of various concentrations of mtepa, the amount of chemosterilant necessary to kill or sterilize the imago generally decreased as the age of the fly increased, particularly for females. Treated flies usually had a shorter life span than untreated flies (Kung and La Brecque, 1971).

The mutagenic agent, ethyl methane sulfonate (EMS), when injected in doses of 0.62 ml of a 25% solution dissolved in $10^{-3}M$ $CuSO_4$ solution, reduced the life span of virgin female *H. juglandis* Say [now *Bracon hebetor* (Ashmead)] adults (Hoffman, 1968). Egg production and hatchability were reduced in a dose-related manner, indicating disruption of mitosis and differential destruction of mitotic cells. In further experiments by the same author (Hoffman, 1970), a synergistic effect of copper sulfate with EMS was observed. Egg hatchability for day 1 and fertility, fecundity, and life span over a period of fifteen days were decreased following injection of the wasps with 0.2% EMS in $CuSO_4$ (10^{-3} M).

The effects of the heat-stable toxin produced by *Bacillus thuringiensis* were studied upon *Drosophila* adult longevity. Chronic intoxication was obtained by incorporating the toxin in the medium. This resulted in a reduction of longevity approximately proportional to the log of the concentration. However, it was assumed that the physiological alterations produced by the toxin were largely independent from those due to senescence (Van Herrewege and David, 1970).

h. Pharmacological Agents. In laboratory tests conducted in Honolulu, Hawaii, from 1964 to 1968 (unpublished), oriental fruitflies, *Dacus dorsalis,* and Mediterranean fruitflies, *Ceratitis capitata,* sexually sterilized with tepa, lived longer than untreated flies of both sexes; moreover, longevity increased with higher dosages of tepa until the chemosterilant acted as a toxicant (Keiser and Schneider, 1969).

The effect of ionol on the duration of life of *D. melanogaster* was studied by Nikoforova (1971). In contrast to earlier data on the duration of life in mice, these experiments revealed an unfavorable effect on the duration of life of adult flies, which was more evident with an increase in dose from 0.031 to 0.125% (of the diet by weight).

Thirty-eight membrane-stabilizing drugs were added to the nutrient medium to investigate their effect on the longevity of *D. melanogaster.* Significant extensions of mean and maximal life span in flies of both sexes were produced by cortisone, hydrocortisone, triamcinolone, aspirin, and several other drugs (Hochschild, 1971).

Work in progress on the effect of antioxidants (J. Miquel, 1971; unpublished) suggests that vitamin C is without effect on *Drosophila* longevity. On the other hand, addition of 0.25 or 0.50% of vitamin E to the food medium resulted in significant extension of life span (Fig. 8).

i. Population Density. Pearl *et al.* (1927) reared *D. melanogaster* in 1-oz bottles at initial densities of 2–500 flies. The curve for life span as a function of density was not linear. The longest life spans were obtained when groups of 30–40 flies were used. Only slight decreases in life span were observed for population densities over 200. The fact that minimal densities are not optimal indicates some type of interaction and interdependence in the population.

More recently, the effects of larval crowding on the longevity of *D. melanogaster* were investigated by Miller and Thomas (1958). With an adequate adult nutrition and with the adults kept under uncrowded conditions, larval crowding and corresponding decreases in adult body size tend to increase expectation of life and maximum longevity. Miller and Thomas suggest that the increased activity and metabolic rate of smaller

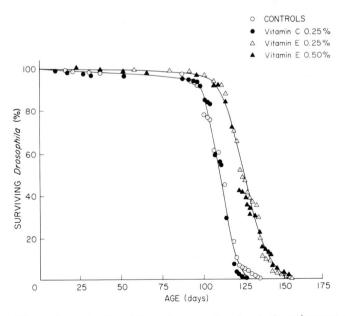

Fig. 8. Effects of vitamins C and E on the longevity of male *D. melanogaster* imagoes. (J. Miquel, unpublished).

flies may increase longevity under certain conditions, possibly through a more efficient mobilization of glycogen and more prompt recovery from carbohydrate depletion. These results have been confirmed by Lints and Lints (1969b) who have studied the effects of preimaginal density on reciprocal hybrids of two highly inbred lines of *D. melanogaster,* Gabarros 4 and Abeele. When the density increased, the longevity of the emerging imagoes, isolated by pairs, increased as well. This increase in imaginal life span was not a simple prolongation of the egg-laying period, since at high density the length of the final period without egg production is larger by a factor of 6 or 7 than at low density. Moreover, the imaginal age at which the maximal egg production occurs is considerably delayed with increasing density. This can be really considered as an effect of delayed maturity and the imaginal life span prolongation as a stretching of the development program as a whole.

j. Sexual Activity. Beetles of the genus *Carabus* do not attain as advanced an age when they reproduce as when prevented from reproducing (Krumbiegel, 1930). In *Drosophila,* a delay in breeding results in longer-lived imagoes of both sexes (Krumbiegel, 1929). More recently, similar results have been obtained by Bilewicz (1953) in a study of the effects of mating on the longevity of *D. melanogaster.* In both males and females copulation resulted in a significant decrease in life span. In the females, the decreased longevity was accompanied by an earlier onset of oviposition, an increase in the daily rate of eggs laid, and an increase in the number of fertile days.

IV. Manifestations of Senescence

A. STRUCTURAL AND HISTOCHEMICAL ASPECTS

1. Cuticle and Wings

The external appearance of old insects, including a "shiny" appearance of the integument of older, worker honey bees (Hodge, 1894) or the fraying and loss of wings in male house flies, have been variously ascribed to (1) senescence (Hodge, 1894; Rockstein, 1957), (2) disease (Rockstein, 1950), or (3) the resistance of the once-mated female house fly to second mating attempts by the male (Patterson, 1957). Nevertheless, as in higher animals which show definite age-related alterations in the outward appearance of the skin, the "old" appearance of the external cuticle, especially the abrading of setae and wings, may be considered a structural signpost of senescence in old insects, worthy of further study from a basic chemical standpoint.

In a more recent investigation, Sondhi (1967) found that the sternal pigment is lacking in very young imagoes of *D. melanogaster* and is always present in senescent flies. In individual imagoes, the rate of pigment accumulation, as determined by taking the time of appearance of pigment as a criterion, was observed to be related to the life span. This was confirmed by the finding that in flies undergoing a reduction in longevity at higher temperature the rate of pigment formation was increased. Moreover, inbred females, the life span of which was extended by injection of hemolymph from hybrid donors, showed a delayed appearance of the sternal pigment. Sondhi concluded that pigment accumulation is a true age-dependent phenomenon and that the rate of pigment formation is under genetic control.

2. Digestive System

In the honey bee, Haydak (1957) found that the pharyngeal glands develop rapidly to fullness in a turgid, milky-white state by the fourth day of adult life. This condition persisted until the ninth day, following which degeneration, marked by a change in color to a yellowish cast, set in and was complete by 43 days. Among overwintering bees, even at 69 days, some still-active bees showed a persistence in the pharyngeal glands (Maurizio, 1954). Most caged bees without queens showed a similar persistence of functional (fully active) pharyngeal glands at 57 days and, in the case of a small number of bees, even at 185 days. Since the reinitiation of brood-rearing in queenless and overwintering colonies is a known observation, the persistence of the pharyngeal glands in older animals under such hive conditions can be linked to the potential for such brood-rearing. The hormonal influences implicit in such interdependent functional-structural changes and corresponding behavioral alterations suggest an important new area of likely experimental investigation.

Haydak (1957) also observed what appeared to be a reciprocal effect of age as regards the postcerebral salivary glands and the pharyngeal glands. Thus, the filling of the acini of the salivary glands is associated with the degeneration of the pharyngeal glands in short-lived summer bees; in winter bees, with pharyngeal glands active throughout the winter period, flattened, undeveloped postcerebral salivary gland acini were observed. The mandibular glands, which have been associated with alteration of the consistency of the pharyngeal secretion in the formation and presentation of royal jelly in its final form by the nurse bee to the feeding larvae, first attain a milky-white and turgid appearance and then become increasingly vacuolar with advancing age after the fifth day of adult life. In winter bees, even at 90 days of age, the mandibular glands (together with

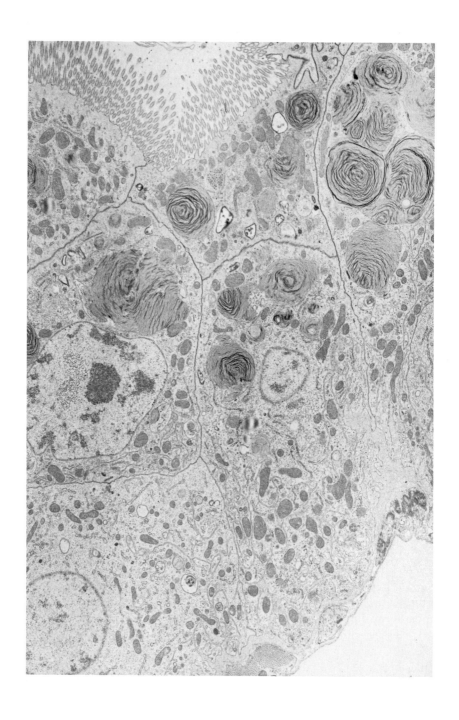

the persistent pharyngeal glands) were turgid and full of milky secretion and free from vacuoles. Haydak (1957) also cites Kratky (1931) as having observed that prolongation of the activity of the pharyngeal glands was accompanied by a slower degeneration of the mandibular glands. The thoracic salivary glands, apparently functional throughout adult life, showed no changes from opaque at 16 days through 69 days, in both a queenright colony and for wintering bees as well.

In *D. melanogaster,* Miquel (1971) reported that the esophagus, crop, anterior intestine, and rectum of old imagoes (70–100 days old) usually appeared normal. However, in some instances the digestive cells of the ventricular epithelium were not so basophilic and its "brush border" was not so conspicuous as in the young individuals. Another time-related change was an increase in the number and size of the vacuoles present in the cardia cells.

Furthermore, electron microscopic investigations by Miquel *et al.* (1972) have shown that the most striking change in the midgut of old *Drosophila* was the accumulation of numerous, large, lamellated cytoplasmic inclusions (Fig. 9) which closely resemble so-called myeloid figures and, to a certain extent, osmiophilic cytoplasmic bodies of human ceroid storage disease. Lipid droplets were also more prominent in these cells than in normal cells.

3. Circulatory System

a. Hemocytes. In the cockroach, *Blaberus giganteus,* the wing vein hemocytes were observed daily during the insect's adult life. Blood circulation, which was constant and vigorous in young adults, declined and was variable with increasing age. All the veins became occluded to a certain extent, but the main ones supported blood circulation until the insect's death. In old insects, gas hemocyte accumulations formed around many tracheae, with the hemocytes surrounding and engulfing gas bubbles that escaped from the tracheae (Arnold, 1959).

b. Oenocytes. According to Haydak (1957), an age-related accumulation phenomenon is very prominent in the worker honey bee. Beginning with the eighth day, the previously clear oenocytes showed greenish-brown granules around the nuclei of the cells. This continued to increase, with age, both as regards accumulation per cell and the number of bees exhibiting such age-related increase in green-pigmented oenocytes. In-

Fig. 9. Midgut cell of an 84-day-old imago of *D. melanogaster* containing numerous lamellated cytoplasmic inclusions. Viral particles are also present in the nuclei. × 9000. (Miquel *et al.*, 1972.)

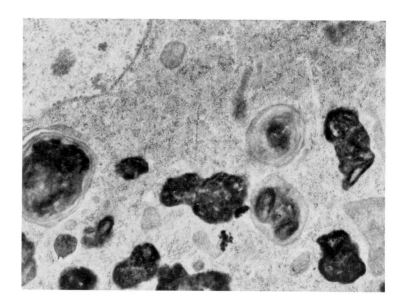

Fig. 10. Electron micrograph of oenocyte of an old imago (76 days) of *D. melanogaster*, showing abundant dense bodies, some of which are surrounded by lamellae of mitochondria. × 15,000. From Takahashi *et al.* (1970a) .

deed, Haydak (1929, cited by Haydak, 1957) once suggested that the age of bees can best be judged by the color of their oenocytes.

A similar accumulation of pigment has been observed by Takahashi *et al.* (1970a) and by Miquel (1971) in the oenocytes of aging *D. melanogaster.* In this insect, electron microscopic studies suggest that occasionally the pigment granules are surrounded by mitochondrial lamellae (Fig. 10) .

c. Fat Body. Age-related changes in the fat body of the honey bee worker have been described by Haydak (1957) . In young insects this tissue was in continuous development to a maximum by the sixth day and a gradual decline to medium-rich to poor appearance after 10–25 days of adult life. In overwintering colonies, however, all bees showed only rich to medium-rich fat bodies throughout the study.

Comfort (1956) cites evidence by Norris for the depletion of the fat body as part of the process of senescence in *Ephestia elutella, Carabus* sp., *Drosophila* sp., and *Sitodrepa panicea,* with complete exhaustion thereof occurring in *Ephestia* which had died of "old age."

As far back as 1929, the fat body of *Drosophila* was the object of an histological investigation by Krumbiegel. He observed that in freshly emerged individuals the fat bodies were filled with flaky inclusions, which within a few days became less abundant. In older flies the nuclei were small and poor in chromatin. In general the cells of the old imagoes were smaller, had a withered and collapsed appearance, and showed a decrease in fat content. The shrinkage of the cells was responsible for the narrow and wrinkled abdomen of the senescent fly.

More recently, histological, histochemical, and fine structural observations on the fat body of *D. melanogaster* have been performed by Miquel (1971) and by Miquel *et al.* (1972). Maximal development of this tissue was shown by 5- to 15-day-old imagoes. At a later age, some shrinkage of the fat body was apparent in most flies. Histochemical staining showed abundant glycogen uniformly distributed in the cytoplasm of the fat body of young *Drosophila*. On the other hand, most senescent flies (70 days and older) showed glycogen concentrated in clumps while some areas were devoid of it. Changes in lipid distribution also seemed to occur with age, since recently emerged flies had very large fat droplets which were no longer present in flies 7 days and older. The lipid droplets were more abundant in 30 than in 7-day-old individuals and they had a tendency to coalesce in senescent *Drosophila*. The amount of fat ranged widely in old flies, some having abundant deposits, whereas in other individuals, histochemically demonstrable lipids were almost nonexistent.

Investigations on the fat body of other insectan species have focused in the storage–excretion phenomenon of urate accumulation (Cuénot, 1895; Philiptschenko, 1907a). Urate deposits were also observed in the fat body of the adult moquito, *Culex* sp. (de Boissezon, 1930), of *Bombyx mori* (Metchnikoff, 1915), and of insects without Malpighian tubules (Philiptschenko, 1907b).

More recently, Clark and Smith (1967) found that some of the fat cells of the parasitic wasp, *H. juglandis,* accumulate urates with advancing age in adult females fed on either honey or on their host, *Ephestia (Anagasta).* Females of the species *H. serinopae* accumulated less urate when fed on honey and were longer lived than those fed on *Ephestia* (see Section II, A). Moreover, *H. serinopae,* accumulating urates when fed on *Ephestia,* do so at a lower rate and live longer than *Ephestia*-fed *H. juglandis* females.

The effects of temperature were also investigated on females reared on a diet of *Ephestia* larvae. When the wasps were raised at 22°C the life spans were longer and the rates of urate accumulation were less than for comparable groups at 30°C.

Another observation by Clark and Smith (1967) is that the longevity of individual *H. juglandis* was related to the amount of urate which could be seen through the abdominal wall. The females that showed a high urate level on day 5 died sooner than females which showed no urate at that age. Clark and Smith concluded that urate accumulation in fat cells of certain insects is an aging (i.e., time-dependent) phenomenon, the rate of which formation is inversely related to life span. As in the case of many observed age-related structural and functional changes, however, urate formation may be a useful measure of the rate of aging rather than a direct cause of senescence.

4. Excretory System

Haydak (1957) has reported that the Malpighian tubules of aging worker bees begin to show a yellowish-green tint at 10 days, which persists through old age.

More recently, electron microscope studies by Miquel *et al.* (1972) have shown large numbers of electron-opaque granules in the mitochondria of Malpighian tubules in old *D. melanogaster*. Other time-associated

TABLE XIV

NUMBER AND SIZE OF SARCOSOMES IN THE FLIGHT MUSCLE OF AGING HOUSE FLIES[a]

	Number		Size	
Age	Males	Females	Males	Females
4 hours	13.71	12.02	1.92	1.88
24 hours	14.41	12.73	1.91	1.94
3 days	14.63	20.10	2.04	2.12
4 days	14.56	20.04	2.08	2.13
5 days	—	—	—	—
6 days	16.01	20.06	2.10	2.18
7 days	17.43	20.14	2.11	2.28
8 days	19.78	20.20	2.28	2.37
9 days	—	—	—	—
11 days	19.31	19.88	2.12	2.23
12 days	19.32	19.89	—	—
14 days	16.45	19.40	2.06	2.26
15 days	15.44	19.44	1.96	2.24
16 days	—	—	—	—
19 days	14.24	19.14	1.96	2.25
20 days	—	18.74	—	—
21 days	13.23	15.24	1.95	1.95
24 days	—	15.32	—	1.92
25 days	—	—	—	—
27 days	—	12.76	—	1.89

[a] From Rockstein and Bhatnagar (1965).

changes observed in the Malpighian tubules were a decrease in ribosomes and in rough endoplasmic reticulum and an increase in myeloid figures, which apparently originate through autophagocytosis.

5. Muscular System

a. *Flight Muscle.* Hylton (1966) has shown histological changes which occurred with age in the flight muscle of the African mosquito, *Eretma-podites chrysogaster.* There was a loss of nuclei and of cross striation in the muscle fibers, a loosening of the sarcostyle network, and an increase in the fiber diameter. These changes were first observed in 25-day-old mosquitoes, and increased in frequency and severity with age.

In *M. domestica,* age changes in size and number of giant mitochondria have been investigated by Rockstein and Bhatnagar (1965) (see Table XIV). In the male fly, both mean size as well as total number of mitochondria per fly increased up to the beginning of the second week and then, at the end of the second week, a decline in number began. In the female, the maximum size and number were also reached by the third day and remained unchanged until the end of the third week, at which time both size and number showed a dramatic decline. Rockstein and Bhatnagar (1965) postulate that multiplication, growth, and lysis of mitochondria are continuous processes throughout the life span of the flies, but that their rates differ with age. In the male fly, these changes in number and size of mitochondria are preceded by the loss of wings and decline in ATPase and α-glycerophosphate dehydrogenase activities, whereas in the female fly such mitochondrial changes occur concomitant with the decline in the locomotor function of flight (see Section IV, C below).

More recently, Simon et al. (1969) have performed an electron microscopic study of mitochondrial changes in the flight muscle of aging house flies. In all the specimens examined, two kinds of mitochondria were recognized: type A, with simple folded cristae and a light matrix, and type B, with complex multicristae surrounded by a dense matrix. In newly emerged flies, A and B types were equally represented. They were loosely arranged between the muscle fibers and were surrounded by large quantities of glycogen. About 12 days after emergence, the population of type-B mitochondria increased in some individuals and the multicristae developed fenestrations or became arranged in whorls resembling myelin figures. The amount of glycogen was reduced and the mitochondria were more closely packed between the muscle fibers. After 20 days, the structural complexity of the mitochondria began to decrease and degeneration started. Type A degenerated by swelling due to nonuniform increase of their intracristal spaces, whereas type B degenerated by developing structureless areas in place of a dense matrix. The outer membrane in both types of mitochondria loosened up and acquired a fuzzy appearance. Along with the mitochondrial degeneration, the muscle substance also decreased in old flies.

Further electron microscopic studies on the flight muscle of houseflies have been performed by Sohal and Allison (1971). In 7- to 11-day-old flies, these authors have shown fusion and degeneration of mitochondria, dissolution of myofibrils, and condensation of chromatin. Fusion oc-

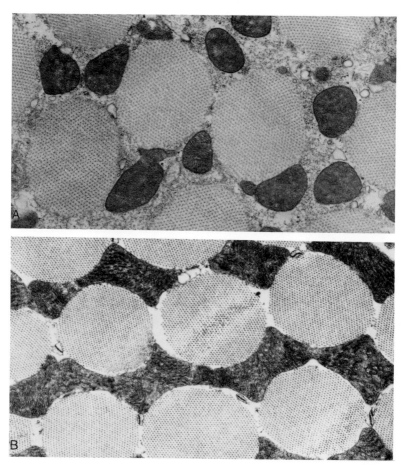

Fig. 11. (A) Transverse section through the flight muscle of a 1-day-old house fly showing isolated mitochondria. $\times$ 19,300. (B) Transverse section of the flight muscle of a 9-day-old house fly showing mitochondrial fusion. $\times$ 19,300. (Courtesy of Dr. R. S. Sohal.)

curred between the mitochondria aligned end to end in a single file as well as laterally between those lying parallel to each other (Fig. 11). As many as sixteen mitochondria may fuse to form a single mitochondrion and the fusing mitochondria are often enclosed within a common outer mitochondrial membrane. Although lysosomes are frequently involved in cellular autophagy and structural degeneration, in the flight muscle of the house fly they were infrequently encountered. Sacktor and Shimada (1972) have recently completed an excellent comparative study on the age-dependent degenerative changes in the mitochondria from flight muscle of aging blowflies, *Phormia regina,* by electron microscopy. They found that the normal cristae conformation showed an age-related increasing reorganization of the inner membranes into "myelinlike" whorls, which increased in size and number with advancing age.

Histochemical and electron microscopic investigations on aging changes in the flight muscle of *D. melanogaster* by Miquel (1971) and by Takahashi *et al.* (1970b) show that histochemically demonstrable glycogen reached its maximum in 2- to 30-day-old imagoes, decreased in older individuals, and in some 84- to 100-day-old flies was practically nonexistent. Fine structural alterations observed in senescent imagoes included myofibrillar degeneration, membrane pools, and mitochondrial densification (Fig. 12).

b. Heart. A comparison of the heart of young (7-day-old) and old (4-month-old) *Drosophila repleta* showed an increase in the size of many mitochondria in the old flies. Glycogen particles were seen either in a single aggregate mass or several isolated masses at different loci within the mitochondria (Sohal, 1970).

Further electron microscopic studies by Sohal and Allison (1971) have demonstrated focal degenerative changes of the myofibers in the heart of *M. domestica,* with fragmentation usually occurring at the level of the A band. Mitochondria also showed a variety of alterations such as irregular shapes, reduction in matricial density, and loss and fragmentation of cristae. Another change involving the mitochondria was their close association with lipidlike droplets. Autophagic vacuoles with segments of the sarcoplasm enclosed within a single smooth membrane were also seen. Cellular components such as degenerating myofilaments, mitochondria, and membranes of the tubular system could be identified inside autophagic vacuoles and membranous whorls. Lysosomes and lipofuscinlike structures were also frequently found in the cytoplasm. Since similar structural alterations can be induced in experimental animals by a variety of physiological and pathological stimuli, Sohal and Allison (1971) do not consider the fine structural changes present in the heart of *Musca* as specific to aging.

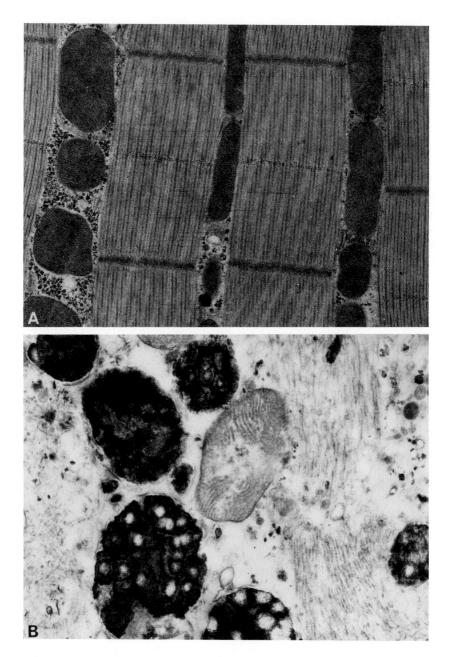

Fig. 12. Longitudinal sections of flight muscle of *D. melanogaster.* (A) 7-day-old imago showing A, I, M, and Z bands. Note also the myofibrils and the abundant

6. Nervous System

Histochemical studies by Rockstein *et al.* (1971) have shown that the neurosecretory material from the medial neurosecretory cells of the brain of the house fly increases rapidly from a minimum to a peak level, from emergence to approximately 48 hours of adult life. This peak level persists through advanced age. Thus, it appears that aging is not correlated with a depletion of neurosecretory material per se, but with a failure to cause the release of the hormone from the cells so that it is unavailable to initiate physiological reactions in the old fly. Ingestion of milk by the female releases the neurosecretory material into the axons just prior to the initiation of vitellogenesis. The availability of oviposition sites stimulates the female to lay eggs up to 45 days of age and is accompanied by the persistence of neurosecretory substance in the axons of the median neurosecretory cells at that late date as well. This indicates that the neurosecretory substance is either directly or indirectly involved (probably via the corpus allatum) with the regulation of protein and carbohydrate metabolism and concomitantly with the rate of aging of female house flies in relation to their oviposition capacity and life span.

The neurons of several species of higher animals (Hatai, 1902; Ellis, 1919, 1920; Inukai, 1928; Andrew, 1938, 1939; Gardner, 1940) have been shown to decrease in number with age in a gradual involutionary fashion. Comparative data on the honey bee brain have also been reported in three different papers. Hodge (1894) made a study of both human males (a newborn infant, a 47-year-old and a 72-year-old man) and on the brains of worker honey bees, *A. mellifera*. There is, however, serious question of whether his so-called "old bees," which he so described as having worn and frayed wings, abraded "hairs," and lack of activity—a description strongly suggestive of a diseased rather than a senile state—were truly "normal" old bees. Nevertheless, Hodge reported that (1) the neurons in the antennal lobe of the brains of old bees showed a loss of two out of three cells compared with those of newly emerged worker honey bees, and that (2) their cytoplasm was all but absent and the nuclei shriveled. Hodge concluded that death occurs when the original "superabundance" of cells, which furnish the animal energy to maintain the vital process, is reduced beyond the number just barely able to support processes requisite for life.

---

mitochondria surrounded by glycogen granules. $\times$ 20,800. (B) 84-day-old imago. Note myofibrillar degeneration and various stages in mitochondrial densification. $\times$ 25,700. Takahashi *et al.* (1970b) .

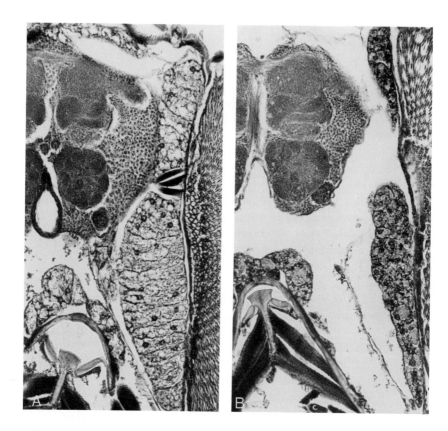

Fig. 13. Vertical transections of the head of *D. melanogaster.* (A) 5-day-old, showing normal appearance of the cortical layers, neuropil, and 2 giant nerve cells located immediately dorsal to the esophagus. The fat body situated between the brain and the eye has the structure usually found in young flies. (B) 70-day-old. Both the brain and the fat body are shrunken, the cortical layers are reduced in thickness, and the neuropil shows moderate "sponginess." Basic fuchsin-amido black satin. × 225. (From Miquel, 1971.)

Smallwood and Phillips (1916) reported no detectable changes in nuclear size of neurons in the antennal lobe of the worker bee brain from the young to overwintering adult. Pixell-Goodrich (1919) did not count cell numbers, but confirmed the vacuolar, cytoplasm-deficient character of honey bee brain cells previously reported by Hodge (1894) for aged worker bees. Moreover, no change was seen in the nuclear size of such senile brain cells. She also observed that the "signs of old age," which Hodge had employed as a basis for selecting old bees, are not necessarily a reliable index of biological age.

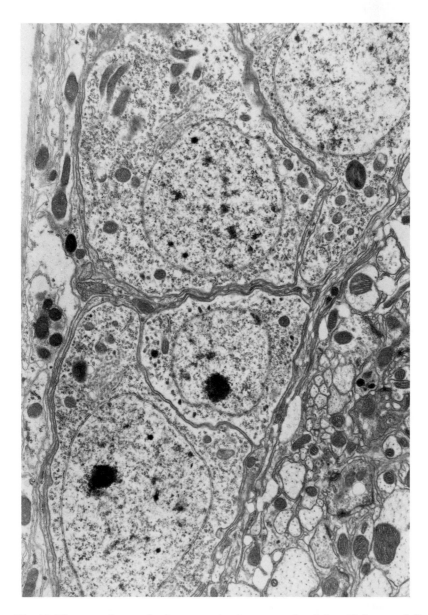

Fig. 14. Electron micrograph of neurons in the cortex of a 7-day-old imago of *D. melanogaster*. Note the abundant ribosomes in the cytoplasmic area. × 11,040. (Courtesy of Dr. Mary M. Herman, cited in Miquel, 1971.)

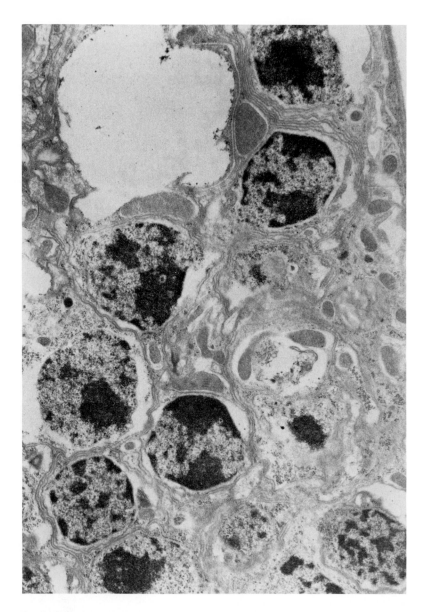

Fig. 15. Electron micrograph of neurons in the cortex of an 85-day-old imago of *D. melanogaster*. As compared to the 7-day-old fly (Fig. 14), there is a striking reduction in the amount of neuronal cytoplasm and a corresponding decrease in ribosomes. Nuclear size also appears decreased. Cystic spaces surrounded by glial lamellae are also present. $\times$ 9280. (Courtesy of Dr. Mary M. Herman, cited in Miquel, 1971.)

In a later, more extended study, Rockstein (1950) explored the relationship of change in cell number to brain enzyme activity (acetylcholinesterase) in the aging worker honey bee. The number of brain cells in the middle antennal and posterior antennal lobe and in the anterior subesophageal regions declined steadily to the extent of a total of 33% loss in cell number from emergence to old age, but was more marked for bees in "queenright" hives than for bees maintained in queenless cages indoors.

In the brain of senescent *D. melanogaster,* nerve-cell degeneration has been shown by light (Miquel, 1971) and electron microscopy (Herman *et al.,* 1971). Aging resulted in a sponginess of the neuropil first noticeable in approximately 50% of 70-day-old flies and present in almost all 84- to 100-day-old *Drosophila* (Fig. 13). The most striking fine structural change observed in the brain of the old flies was a loss of free ribosomes and granular endoplasmic reticulum in neurosecretory cells (Figs. 14 and 15). There was also an increase in autophagic vacuoles and lipid

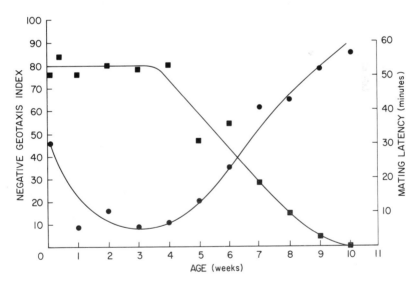

Fig. 16. Effects of aging on negative geotaxis and on mating latency of male *D. melanogaster.* The squares represent the percentage of flies that reached the 250-ml line in a volumetric cylinder 20 seconds after shaking them to the bottom. Each point is the mean of 10 consecutive readings. The circles represent the average mating latency (time to the first mating when 1 male is left in a vial with 3 virgin 7-day-old females). To calculate the mating latency, all the observations in which no matings occurred were assigned a value of 61 minutes. The total number of male flies used at each age was 20. (Herman *et al.,* 1971, *Acta Neuropath.* © 1971 by Springer-Verlag, Berlin and New York.)

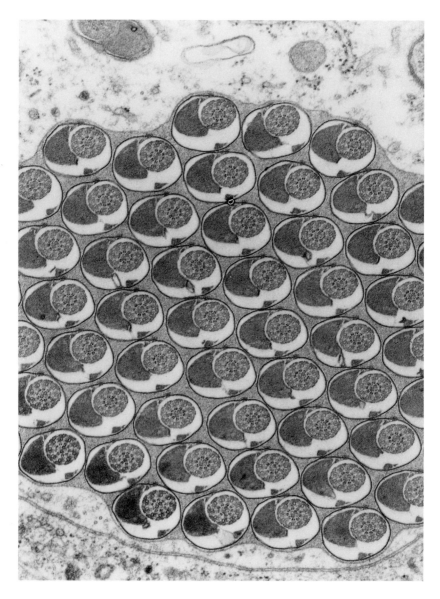

Fig. 17. Spermatozoa in the vas deferens of a 7-day-old *D. melanogaster.* The flagellar and mitochondrial rods appear in cross sections. $\times$ 44,000. (From Miquel *et al.,* 1972.)

bodies in the cytoplasm, which was reduced in size. Pale processes were also observed and numerous dense bodies were present in the neuropil. The involutive changes in the brain of *Drosophila* began at approximately 30 days of age, and therefore correlated well with the onset of degradation of behavior observed in flies at 28–35 days (Fig. 16).

7. Reproductive System

In *D. melanogaster*, the most obvious time-related histopathological changes were seen in the testes, accessory gland, and anterior ejaculatory duct. In the testes, there was a decrease in the number of spermatogonia

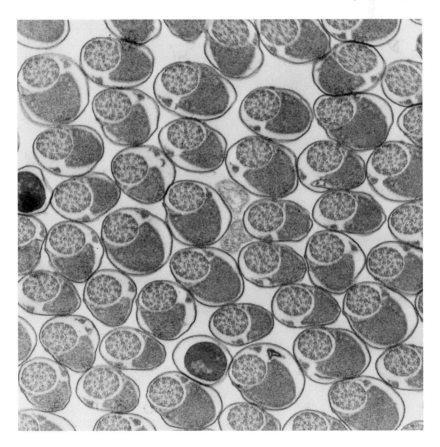

Fig. 18. Cross section of spermatozoa in the vas deferens of an 84-day-old imago. The interstitial fluid is not electron dense and the spermatozoa have lost their orderly arrangement. Also, occasionally, the spermatozoa lack their axial filament complex. × 45,000. (From Miquel *et al.*, 1972.)

and spermatocytes. Also, in senescent flies the epithelium of the anterior ejaculatory duct showed loss of the nuclei and ballooning of the cytoplasm. In light microscopic sections there was also a change in the fluid content of the accessory glands. The coagulated fluid, which was rather homogenous in young *Drosophila,* had a coarse appearance in senescent flies (Miquel *et al.,* 1972).

As demonstrated by electron microscopy, in young *Drosophila* the spermatozoa showed a remarkable orderly arrangement in the vasa deferentia (Miquel *et al.,* 1972). Usually, groups of approximately 50 were clustered in a cytoplasmic invagination, with the interstices between the individual sperm cells filled with a moderately electron opaque fluid which was much lighter in the old flies (Figs. 17 and 18). In addition, in old *Drosophila,* the symmetry of the arrangement of the cells was also disturbed and some spermatozoa had lost their axial filament complex.

8. Firefly Lantern

Aging of this specialized organ has been the object of an exhaustive histochemical investigation by Press *et al.* (1966). Appreciable decreases in ATPase, ADPase, and succinoxidase activities were seen in the tracheolar system, whereas changes in DPN diaphorase and alkaline phosphatase were less marked. The photogenic layer of the old firefly lantern showed moderate declines in ATPase and ADPase activities and a large decrease in leucine aminopeptidase activity. There were also marked decreases in the concentration of RNA, free sulfhydril groups, glycogen, choline-containing lipids, neutral fat, and phospholipids in the photogenic layer. Basic proteins, free α-amino groups, and acid mucopolysaccharides similarly decreased in the photogenic layer. In the reflector layer a considerable decline in acid mucopolysaccharides, glycogen, and calcium was also observed. Structural alterations were also noticed. The nuclei of the aging lantern were pycnotic, whereas the thickness of the photogenic layer decreased during aging.

9. Summary

In regard to mammalian aging, Alexander (1966) has emphasized the fact that even very old mice (e.g., more than $2\frac{1}{2}$ years of age), which have been sacrificed and examined while still fit, showed remarkable absence of pathology and, indeed, were virtually indistinguishable from young animals. In insects, the picture seems strikingly different since practically all the species investigated showed abundant degenerative changes in their tissues, with advancing age. This may be explained (as has been suggested earlier) by the fact that adult insects show few mitoses except in the gonads. It is conceivable that in the absence of cellular replacement, the whole insect does indeed deteriorate with the passage of time to a higher degree than the mammals.

One common characteristic of both vertebrate and insect aging seems to be the accumulation of "age pigment" and, indeed, in vertebrate (including human) heart and brain tissue, such accumulated pigments are proposed to be a manifestation of biochemical aging (Bondareff, 1957; Strehler et al., 1959; Brody, 1960; Duncan et al., 1960).

In Miquel's (1971) view, the granules observed in the oenocytes of senescent flies are true "age pigment," since they increase continuously with age and are similar in color and size to mammalian lipofuscin. Moreover, fluorescent molecular damage similar to the lipofuscin age pigment found in many senescent mammals, including man, has been demonstrated in extracts of senescent flies (Hochschild, 1971). Often, mammalian lipofuscin originates with the intervention of lysosomal enzymes localized in autophagic vacuoles. That lysosomal enzymes may play some role in the nervous tissue of insects, as well, has been postulated by Pipa et al. (1962) and by Waku and Gilbert (1964).

Until the mechanisms involved in insect aging are better known, the relative importance of the various tissues in producing senescence can only be conjectured. Histological studies by Miquel (1971) suggest that fat-body degeneration may play an important role. However, insect death could result as well from starvation, because of a failure of the digestive system, or from poisoning associated with failure in normal function of the excretory organs. Nevertheless, the severity of the pathological changes observed in the brain of senescent honey bees and flies suggests that at least for these two species, failure of the CNS may be a major contributory factor to, if not the ultimate cause of death in old age.

B. BIOCHEMICAL ASPECTS

In general, only a relatively small number of biochemical studies have been made in insects directly involving maturation or senescence of a particular body function and/or observable age-dependent relevant structural changes (see Section IV, C, 2 below). On the other hand, there have been a considerable number of studies on total body composition, as regards one or more chemical components of insects, by a number of biologists and biochemists interested primarily in such phenomena as protein synthesis, mechanisms of hormonal control of differentiation and, in a number of important studies involving genetic considerations.

1. Nucleic Acids

Studies of the nucleic acids, particularly DNA and RNA, have as their ultimate objective an understanding of the molecular genetic basis for a programmed development, maturation, and senescence. Such studies should eventually permit the pinpointing of the site or sites of genetic control for enzyme or coenzyme synthesis or decline, which have been observed in relation to advancing age in any tissue or organ showing other more obvious signs of such aging.

Lang *et al.* (1965), in pursuit of the concept that aging at the molecular level should be reflected in a decrease in overall biosynthesis, found that, during growth, total body weight and total body RNA and DNA all rose, whereas during aging, total body DNA and protein as well as RNA to DNA ratios all remained constant in the mosquito *A. aegypti.* They therefore concluded that physiological aging in the mosquito is *not* accompanied by a significant decrease in either cell number or level of protein synthesis.

The one insect species employed both in classical as well as in continuing and recent genetic studies, *D. melanogaster,* has been studied variously for DNA and RNA content of adults. Balazs and Haranghy (1965) reported an increase in the DNA and RNA content in the female, and increase in the DNA content of the male during the first days of imaginal life, following which the DNA content remained constant throughout the remainder of the imaginal life. On the other hand, the RNA to DNA level of postmaturation adults remained unchanged throughout the remainder of imaginal life.

More recently, Samis *et al.* (1971), studying the DNA as well as other chemical composition (see below) in total body homogenates of *D. melanogaster* from 8 to 77 days of age, found that there were no age-related changes in DNA content in males, but that the DNA content of females was lowered during the middle life of the adult, possibly related to egg production, with the young and old females showing high DNA levels. Moreover, in males the RNA to DNA ratio was constant with age, but again was different from females, for reasons suggested above.

In contrast to the reports mentioned above involving whole insect preparations, Krueger and Ballard (1965) determined the DNA content of the "heart and associated tissues," specifically of adult *M. domestica* male and female, to be fairly constant throughout adult life, which is essentially equal for both sexes. In 1966, Yale and Ballard, similarly determined the RNA levels in the heart tissue of adult male and female house flies again to be relatively constant with respect to both age and sex, and when expressed in grams per gram of dry tissue, but RNA content was reduced in very old male flies when expressed in grams per whole organ. They concluded that the heart of old male flies, due to tissue loss, has undergone a reduction in potential for protein synthesis on a per organ, but not on a tissue mass basis, and, therefore, that total cell number remains unchanged in spite of the decrease in the dry weight of the heart or "associated tissues."

In one of a number of important studies on hormonal control of growth and differentiation, Schneiderman and his co-workers (Krishnakumaran and Schneiderman, 1964) found that there was no DNA synthesis in adult *Cecropia* and other saturniid moths, but that RNA synthesis does occur in the adult at a considerably reduced rate, compared with that of the preimaginal stage. Moreover, grafting the pupae to adults resulted not only in increase in RNA synthesis but also in restoration of DNA synthesis and a manyfold prolonged life span of the adult moths. Accompanying such extension of life span, as well, was the "sparing" of the fat body, which is normally consumed early in the adult life of this as well as other species.

2. Protein Synthesis

Baumann and Chen (1968) found that ^{14}C-labeled lysine, α-alanine, and glycine decreased distinctly, both as regards rates of turnover and incorporation into protein, from 3 to 50 days of age, in adult *D. melanogaster*. Moreover, for 30 amino acids tested, incorporation rates per mg of protein in 50-day-old flies amounted to only 37–42% of that obtained in 3-day-old flies.

In the closely related species *D. subobscura,* Clarke and Maynard-. Smith (1966) concluded that, since the rate of incorporation of labeled L-leucine into proteins in males 60 days of age was twice that of young male flies (20 days of age), the rate of synthesis of proteins was twice as great in old flies as in young flies. However, Baumann (1969), studying protein turnover in *D. melanogaster,* reported that both lysine and glycine showed a *decrease* of approximately 45% over 50 days of age, following emergence, and that of β-alanine showed an *increase* (by about 24%) in turnover. Moreover, the oxidation of lysine, glycine, and β-alanine in adult males, estimated by $^{14}CO_2$ release, showed a *reduction* in ranges of 5–15% during the same 50 days of aging of the adult.

Maynard-Smith *et al.* (1970) fed labeled amino acids to *D. subobscura* axenic larvae and then determined the radioactivity of the protein fraction in the adult. They found that total body protein activity declined rapidly over the first four days after emergence and then remained constant. It is interesting, in this connection, that the changes which they reported for the immediately postemergent adult were directly related to the disappearance of the protein-rich pupal fat body, another fragmentary datum bearing upon the phenomenon of metachemogenesis (see Section IV, C, 2 below).

Thayer and Terzian (1970), likewise found that, in the aging female mosquito *A. aegypti,* the titers of threonine-serine, valine, isoleucine, leucine, tyrosine, phenylalanine, lysine, tryptophan, histidine, and arginine all decreased during the first week following emergence and did not change significantly thereafter (see Section IV, C, 2 below).

Similarly, Levenbook and Krishna (1971) reported that the turnover rates and rates of incorporation of both alanine and lysine into proteins were significantly lower in 37- to 40-day-old adults than in the 5- to 6-day-old adult blowfly, *Phormia regina.*

Ludwig and Jones (1964) found that methionine, phenylalanine, tryptophan, and tyrosine all decreased markedly from time of emergence to as many as 12 weeks of age in the yellow mealworm, *T. molitor* L.; such changes ranging from 80% reduction in the case of methionine to approximately 50% reduction in the case of phenylalanine and tryptophane and 33⅓% in the case of tyrosine. Similar data were obtained for offspring from old as well as from younger parents, although changes in general were greater in beetles from old rather than from young parents. Alanine, lysine, proline, threonine, and valine, however, did not show any changes with age in adults of the first generation or differences for offspring from young versus old parents.

Heslop (1967) likewise found that in the locust *Schistocerca gregaria* there was no significant increase in protein synthesis in the wings of older insects, which do age and break off (as in the house fly). Indeed, after 14 weeks, they found a *reduction,* by 45%, in protein synthesis, over that of newly emerged adults. These data indicated that there is *no* net synthesis of protein by wings of this species during adult life.

Finally, Harrison and Holliday (1967) attempted to test Orgel's hypothesis that cellular senescence might be the result of failure to maintain error-free protein synthesis by treating *D. melanogaster* with amino acid analogues and streptomycin, known to induce errors of protein synthesis via action upon the ribosomes. Thus, larvae administered canavanine, ethionine, *p*-fluorophenylalanine, 2-phenylalanine, 4-methyl tryptophan, and streptomycin showed a considerably shorter longevity than the imagoes. However, the apparent absence of any specific evidence for incorporation into proteins and, even more significantly, the absence of any data concerning protein synthesis, specifically enzymes, etc., indicates the need for more extensive study along this line of attack before any further substantiation of Orgel's theory of aging can be attempted.

However, the studies of Krishnakumaran and Schneiderman (1964; see above) do suggest very strongly, at least in the saturniid moth, a direct relationship between the ultimate failure to survive and the inability of the adult to synthesize DNA completely and to synthesize RNA at a sufficiently high rate, something which can be altered by grafting the adult to the pupal stage.

3. Enzymes

A considerable number of isolated studies on enzyme distribution with age have been made, but in connection with no specific aging phenomenon per se. In the house fly, *M. domestica* L., however, Rockstein and his colleagues *have* studied the age-related changes of a considerable host of enzymes concerned with the intermediary metabolism of carbohydrates, particularly as it relates to the aging of the locomotor ability of flight (see Section IV, C, 2).

In the mosquito, *A. aegypti,* also, Lang (1967) selected NADP- and NADPH-linked enzymes, instead of representative enzymes of each major metabolic pathway, to study aging. Lang rationalized that the co-enzyme could be a key biochemical factor in the regulation of biosynthesis, since the NADPH-linked enzymes are frequently involved in several metabolic pathways, ultimately leading to biosynthesis of nucleic acids, amino acids, and fatty acids. Lang (1959) and Lang and Stephan (1967) showed that the NADPH-cytochrome c reductase decreased with advancing age, whereas the NADP-linked enzymes, glucose-6-phosphate, 6-phosphogluconate, and isocitrate dehydrogenases, increased with advancing age. Moreover, the specific activity levels of the NADP enzymes attain their maximal values in the pupal or very early adult stages. From these maxima, there then occur declines, so that at the end of the tenth day of adult life there is an 81% decrease in glucose-6-phosphate dehydrogenase and a 67% decrease in 6-phosphogluconate dehydrogenase activities, with a 77% decrease in isocitrate dehydrogenase activity before the fifth day.

Raychaudhuri and Butz (1965b) reported that alkaline phosphatase activity in females rose sharply during the first few days of adult life in the flour beetle, *T. confusum,* with very little detectable age-related changes in males. Acid phosphatase activity varied considerably, but males showed maximal activity in the early part of adult life, and the females two maxima, interpreted as being related to egg production.

Hall (1969) attempted to confirm the genetic basis for senescence by relating enzyme changes of a qualitative and quantitative nature in crude extracts of total body homogenates in *D. melanogaster*. Hexose-P-isomerase isolated by starch-gel electrophoresis from very old females lacked two of the five bands, characteristic of extracts from young females, on starch gels. Esterase from old males also isolated by starch-gel electrophoresis showed several additional electrophoretic bands not seen in assays from young males. Glucose-6-phosphate dehydrogenase determined quantitatively *in toto* from the gel extracts showed a decrease in function with age, after the peak activity of the male enzyme occurred at 25 days of age and that of females at 49 days of age. However, the author admits that these peaks might be the result of more enzymes being produced, on the one hand, or of a new, more active enzyme being synthesized in the same amount as in very young individuals. [This is in contrast to the findings of Rockstein and Farrell (1972) who found that the age-related changes in α-glycerophosphate dehydrogenase in the aging male house fly were not due to changes in enzyme species, inasmuch as no isozymes were found for this enzyme either at any given age, or from one age level to another, in the male fly thoracic flight muscle.] They also found that alkaline phosphatase activity (diphenyl phosphate procedure) increased to a peak at 25 days for females continuing until 49 days of age and declining thereafter, with males showing a peak at 49 days. Unfortunately, no direct relevancy of such changes to gross aging or senescence phenomena has been implicated by Hall in his study, something which could best be accomplished by the isolation of such enzymes on a quantitative basis from specific organs or tissues.

4. Lipids, Fats, Hormones, and Vitamins

The age-related distribution of glycogen has been studied in a number of insects, particularly in relation to postemergent maturation, as well as senescence of functions such as flight (see Section IV, C, 2, below). Samis *et al.* (1971) found that the glycogen content in both sexes of *D. melanogaster* decreases with advancing age (when expressed on a DNA basis) by about 50% from young to old male flies, the DNA itself showing no age-related changes between young and old flies, especially in aging males. Babers (1941) has shown that the glycogen content of the southern armyworm *Prodenia eridania*, rising to a maximum at pupation, fell steadily during pupation and then rose sharply during the 24 hours after adult emergence. However, the adult peak was maintained for only approximately 4–4½ days, following which there is a dramatic fall once more. Since this study was not carried beyond the seventh day of adult life, these data are more significant in relation to postemergence bio-chemical maturation, discussed below.

Nettles and Betz (1965) found that adult boll weevils, *Anthonomus grandis* Boh., have the highest glycogen content at 6–15 days of age, decreasing thereafter.

In this connection, Butterworth and Bodenstein (1968) found that the larval adipose tissue of *D. melanogaster* begins to break down during the first two days after adult emergence, with a gradual increase in adult fat body (primarily concerned with storage and metabolism of both glycogen and lipids) to a maximum size at 7 days of age. The development of this important organ of intermediary metabolism is also controlled by the ovaries in the female, at least in part.

Rockstein and Srivastava (1967) found that the nonreducing disac-charide trehalose reaches a peak in the thoracic flight muscle of the adult male house fly within 4 hours after emergence, then falling precipitously to a minimum by the end of 24 hours, at which level it remains un-changed for 12 days. This age-related distribution of trehalose appears to be related to the utilization by the house fly of trehalose from an endogen-ous pool of carbohydrates, rather than as a primary source of energy in the energizing of contraction of flight muscle.

5. *Accumulation of Storage–Excretion Substances*

Haydak (1957) reported the accumulation of a yellowish-green pig-ment in the Malpighian tubules of the aging worker honeybee, at 10 days of age, which persisted throughout old age. Beginning with the eighth day, the previously clear oenocytes began to show granular matter of a greenish-brown hue in the region of the nuclei of the cells, which contin-ued to increase with age, both as regards accumulation per cell and the number of bees exhibiting such age-related, green-pigmented oenocytes. Other workers have also reported age-dependent accumulation of pig-ments, especially in the oenocytes and in the pericardial cells (referred to as nephrocytes) (Wigglesworth, 1950; Fox, 1953). In vertebrate (in-cluding human) heart and brain tissue, such accumulations of pigments are thought by some to be true manifestations of functional senescence (Bondareff, 1957; Strehler *et al.*, 1959; Brody, 1960; Duncan *et al.*, 1960). As indicated above, Miquel (1971) described similar age-related changes in the oenocytes of *D. melanogaster* in the accumulation of a true age pigment, which increases continuously with age and which is similar in color and size to mammalian lipofuscin. However, in *Drosophi-la*, Miquel notes that these pigments are uncommon to absent in those tissues showing the heaviest deposits in mammals, namely, muscle and nerve tissue. Moreover, the pigment granules seen in the oenocytes of *Drosophila*, according to Miquel, exhibit a dull orange fluorescence instead of the brilliant orange characteristic fluorescence of the mammalian lipofuscin. Miquel concludes that, whereas the lipofuscin granules are generally agreed upon to have a lysosomal origin, the pigment in the oenocytes appears to be more closely related to the mitochondrial pigment previously reported by Rudzinska (cited by Miquel, 1971).

In another connection, Sondhi and Turoczi (1966) related the reduction in melanin formation on the sternites of the Canton inbred line of *D. melanogaster*, by erythrobic acid administered in the food medium, to the higher life span of this particular strain.

Urate accumulation as a storage–excretion phenomenon has been described above (see Section IV, A, 3,c, above) [Cuénot (1895) and Philiptschenko (1907a) for the fat body of the adult cockroach; de Boissezon (1930) for the fat body of the adult cockroach; de Boissezon (1930) for the adult mosquito, *Culex* sp.; Metchnikoff (1915) for *Bombyx mori*; and Philiptschenko (1907b) for insects without Malpighian tubules]. As has also been mentioned earlier, Clark and Smith (1967) found that some of the fat cells of the parasitic wasp, *H. juglandis*, accumulate urates with advancing age in adult females fed on either honey or on their host *Ephestia (Anagasta)* and moreover, females fed on either of these diets showed similar life spans. On the other hand, *H. serinopae*, accumulating urates when fed on either honey or on *Ephestia*, do so at a lower rate and live longer than *Ephestia*-fed *H. juglandis* females. The clear inference from their findings is that urate accumulation in fat cells or certain insects is an aging (i.e., time-dependent) phenomenon, the rate of which formation is inversely related to life span. As in the case of many observed age-related structural and functional changes, however, urate formation may be a useful measure of the rate of aging, rather than a direct or predisposing cause of senescence. As Clark and Smith emphasized in that report (1967), although their experiments include the findings that ionizing radiation decreases adult life span, while increasing the rate of urate accumulation, data for different strains of *H. juglandis*, obtained since the publication of the first edition of the present volume, weakens any such hypothesis when applied to *H. juglandis*, depending on the strain involved; indeed, many females of this species with high urate accumulation as young adults had a very long life span!

C. PHYSIOLOGICAL ASPECTS

If one considers the role of the adult insect as a reproductive stage, especially in the Holometabola, it is not unexpected to find that the two major systems concerned with reproduction, namely, flight and reproduction itself, have been most extensively studied from the standpoint not only of senescence per se, but also as regards maturation in the immediately postemergent adult. However, since, aside from developing gametes, the cells of holometabolous adult insects are essentially postmitotic, it is not surprising to find that the body of literature concerned with flight muscle and the physiology of flight represents the majority of the still relatively sparse scientific literature on this subject.

1. Reproduction

It has been shown above (Section III, A, 2) that parental age appears to have an effect on the offspring longevity. However, parental age may also influence the reproductive potential of the mating pair, not only through mating behavior, but also in terms of fecundity as well as fertility of the gametes of each of the parents. In general, the existing literature covering this subject indicates that older females lay smaller numbers of eggs and that these eggs possess a higher percentage of nonviability than those laid by younger mothers. For example, in *A. aegypti,* Woke *et al.* (1956) reported that the age of the mosquito at the time of the blood meal was a significant factor in the number of eggs laid. Thus, at 5 days of age, they obtained a mean value of 89 eggs per female. This remained essentially unchanged through the second week of adult life, so that a 14-day-old female gave a mean value of 86 eggs per mosquito. However, 4-week-old females gave a considerably reduced number of eggs—56 per mosquito. Richards and Kolderie (1957) similarly recorded a decline in egg production in a mass culture of the milkweed bug, *Oncopeltus fasciatus,* in the later days of the culture existence. However, the above-mentioned authors could give no actual figures for egg production on a per animal basis, as such. Nevertheless, they did report that the fewer eggs laid by the older females in the culture weighed less, took longer to develop, and had a much lower hatching percentage. Ludwig and Fiore (1960), on the other hand, found that parental age made no difference in the mass of the individual egg nor in the duration of the egg stage in the mass culture of *T. molitor.* However, they did find that the number of eggs produced fell from about 3800 for parents in the range of 1–10 weeks of age, 300 eggs for parents of the age group of 15–21 weeks. In addition, the hatchability of such eggs, regardless of the temperature at which both parents and eggs were maintained—20°, 25°, or 30°C—was reduced from 90% for ova from the youngest, to 50% for eggs from the oldest parental groups, respectively. In a later study, however, (involving only four pairs of adult beetles of these species), the number of *larvae* produced showed no clear-cut relationship to parental age for six different ranges of parental age groups, varying from 1 to 11 weeks (Ludwig and Fiore, 1961).

In *D. melanogaster,* Butz and Hayden (1962) showed that the number of adults emerging from eggs laid by parents 35 days old was considerably lower than those from parents 24 hours of age. Moreover, a series of experiments involving parents of (1) the same age, (2) young males and old females, and (3) young females and old males, showed that the reduction in viability of the emerging adults was directly related to the age of the maternal parent, i.e., the older the mother the fewer the number of adult flies emerging. Furthermore O'Brian (1961) similarly observed that offspring from older parents of *D. melanogaster* produced fewer viable eggs and for a shorter period of time (25 days) than offspring from younger parents, which continued to lay eggs over a 46-day period. This reduction in numbers of viable eggs, for offspring derived from older parents, could be enhanced by continued selection over several generations. Sondhi (1966), found that removal of 0.02 μl of hemolymph from freshly emerged *D. melanogaster* females Swedish-b inbred strain, maintained in brother-sister matings for over 60 generations) produced a striking life-shortening effect without a decrease in egg production. The substitution of hemolymph from younger animals into older animals of the same strain had no effect on longevity or fecundity. In a later study (1967), Sondhi found that removal of a greater volume of hemolymph from Canton-S inbred *D. melanogaster* females, i.e., 0.10 μl, compared with 0.02 μl in his earlier studies (1966), reduced the life span of the female by 30% and the fecundity (total number of eggs per female) by approximately 37%; however, the peak of egg-laying was reached on the twelfth day in both control and experimental groups. Sondhi interprets these effects as being related to the depletion of proteins and other reserves and possibly the decrease in immunity from infected organisms due to loss of hemocytes.

Gray and Berberian (1971) and Berberian *et al.* (1971) confirmed the dietary basis for enhanced female longevity when fed an enriched diet, originally described by Rockstein (1957). They found that feeding female parents milk for three days has the same beneficial effect on the longevity of the female as a constant milk-imposed regimen of egg-laying and so regulates the periodic release of neurosecretory material from the medial neurosecretory cells, which extends even further the life span of the adult female. This clearly supports the concept that longevity of the adult female depends upon the interaction of egg production and available nutrient reserves, suggested both by the work of Sondhi (1968a,b) as well as some of the temperature studies by Maynard-Smith (1958, 1959, 1962).

In one study on mosquitoes, Liles (1961) reported that offspring from the first batch of eggs laid by females *A. aegypti* had lower fertility than those from 15- to 20-day-old parents.

2. Flight

a. Behavioral Aspects. Blest's interesting studies (1960, 1962, 1963) on flight behavior in relation to age in adult hemileucine saturniid moths suggest an area of insect biology—behavior—which deserves further exploration in the field of aging in general, especially as it might involve aging of the nervous system. Such adult moths normally settle into position after flight and perform a rocking action involving the legs, thorax, and abdomen. This motion is subject to ready quantitation as to the number of side-to-side oscillations. In some species, it is related directly to the duration of the immediately previous flight, as well as inversely to the excitability of the insect. Interestingly too, flight excitability in the males of two palatable, cryptic species increases with advancing age, to a maximum at the third to fourth day for *Automeris junionia,* and at 4–5 days for *Lonomia cynura.* In the distasteful *Dirphia cumemide,* there is no such age-related change in flight excitability (Blest, 1963).

In *Automeris aurantiaca,* particularly, the strength of the rocking response is a linear function of the preceding flight duration for moths of a given age. In older moths, moreover, the excitability rises and, with it, the rocking response conversely declines. Thus, at 9–9.5 days after emergence, the rocking response declines to a minimum for each of various durations of previous flight, varying from 0–10 to 20–30 minutes. Indeed, as the male grows older, the excitable nature of flight increases to one of a violent nature in the terminal phases of life, with a minimal rocking motion following each such flight, whereas in virgin females, at least, no such changes are manifest. Moreover, since high excitability is associated with soft scaling of the cryptic species, in older males this results in the acceleration of obliteration of color patterns by mechanical damage to the wings and, therefore, increased vulnerability to predators.

b. Physiological–Biochemical Aspects. 1. Maturation–Metachemogenesis. From his first study on physiological aging, Rockstein (1950) concluded (1956, 1959a) that maturation of flight ability, particularly of the holometabolous adult, was actually initiated (especially in the case of the Diptera) at some time during the late pupal stage, probably at the pupal–adult apolysis (see Hinton, 1971) which continued for some time well into the postemergent life of the imago.

Rockstein (1950) found a direct relationship between duration of flight ability, by the end of the first week to 10 days of adult life, and brain cholinesterase; however, despite the progressive loss in cell number,

TABLE XV

Time Sequence of Aging of Flight Ability in the Male House Fly

Biological parameter	Maximum	Reference
Acid phosphatase	Emergence[a]	Clark and Rockstein, 1964
Trehalose content	4 hours	Rockstein and Srivastava, 1967
Brain cholinesterase	1 day	Babers and Pratt, 1950
Duration of flight	1 day	Rockstein and Bhatnagar, 1966
Arginine phosphokinase	2 days	Baker and Rockstein, 1971
Wing-beat frequency	4–9 days	Rockstein and Bhatnagar, 1966
Thiamine content	4 days	Rockstein and Hawkins, 1970
α-GDH	4 days	Rockstein and Brandt, 1963
Arginine phosphate	5 days	Rockstein, 1971
Alkaline phosphatase	5 days	Clark and Rockstein, 1964
% wing loss	6 days[b]	Rockstein and Brandt, 1963
Mg-ATPase	6 days	Rockstein and Brandt, 1963
ATP content	8 days	Rockstein and Gutfreund, 1961
Number of mitochondria	8–12 days	Rockstein and Bhatnagar, 1965
Cytochrome c oxidase	11 days	Rockstein, 1967

[a] Minimum at 5 days.
[b] Onset.

the brain cholinesterase per worker bee continued at a high level throughout the adult life of the worker, which then continues to fly effectively virtually up to the very last day of postemergent life. [This is in contrast to the housefly, which Babers and Pratt (1950) found to show a peak level of brain cholinesterase in the male at exactly 1 day postemergence, in keeping with other data in Table XV.] This concept of postemergence biochemical maturation was termed "metachemogenesis" by Rockstein (1959a). In two important studies (Herold and Borei, 1963; Herold, 1965), this concept, in a study of the biochemical as well as structural changes in the worker honeybee flight muscle, was confirmed, particularly in relation to development. They found that late pupal and early adult life was characterized by a progressive increase in cytochrome $a + a_3$ as well as the appearance and progressive increase in cytochrome $b + c_1$ and cytochrome c content. These changes parallel quite coincidentally the growth of the specialized wing-muscle giant mitochondria (sarcosomes) according to Herold (1965), whose electron micrographic study of the developing structure of honey bee flight muscle showed that these sarcosomes increase both in size and in volume (a twelvefold increase) from immediately postemergence to 20 days of adult life. These recent reports of age-related structural changes are in keeping with the time of maximal, field-foraging, flight activity of the adult worker honey bee. Moreover, these data are also in agreement with the important, earlier report by Levenbook and Williams (1956) on the aging of the flight ability in *P. regina,* in which the dry weight of the sarcosomes, the cytochrome c titer and the wing-beat frequency *all* show a rising trend from emergence of the adult to a peak level at exactly 7 days postemergence.

Accordingly, Rockstein (1959b) had inferred that such metachemogenesis could be related directly to the maturation of flight ability, in all holometabolous insects, from evidence for adult maturation of four species of holometabolous insects representing the orders Hymenoptera *(A. mellifera)* and Diptera *(M. domestica, P. regina,* and *Drosophila funebris).* This conclusion was also based on the data by Williams *et al.* (1943) whose pioneer study on aging of flight ability indicated a direct relationship between the glycogen availability and flight ability (as measured by wing-beat frequency and duration of flight) in *D. funebris,* in which maximum flight ability as well as glycogen concentration of the adult reached their peak levels by the second week following adult emergence.

In two early reports (Lennie and Birt, 1967; Gregory *et al.,* 1968) postemergence maturation of the adult blowfly, *Lucilia sericata,* involves a rapid increase in the number of thoracic flight-muscle mitochondria, concomitant with an increase in synthesis of relevant respiratory enzymes. Walker and Birt (1969) in a follow-up experiment on the same species showed that emergence of the adult is accompanied by a twofold increase in the mitochondrial α-glycerophosphate oxidase, but by a marked decrease in respiratory control by ADP in relation to α-glycerophosphate oxidation. However, they found no comparable, age-related changes in ADP control over mitochondrial oxidation of pyruvate. These reported postemergence, maturational biochemical changes, i.e., metachemogenesis, related by Walker and Birt (1969) to the maturation of flight ability during the several days immediately following emergence of the adult flying insect, precede similar, very recent important confirmatory studies by Sacktor and his colleagues (Sacktor and Shimada, 1972; Bulos *et al.,* 1972) combining ultrastructural with biochemical studies, in the postemergence adult flight-muscle mitochondria of *P. regina* into the senile state. [Also see references to a similar, combined ultrastructural-biochemical study on flight muscle mitochondria in *C. erythrocephala,* below, by Tribe and Ashhurst (1972) , Section IV,A,2,b.]

Numerous other scattered reports have appeared since the first edition of this treatise (Clark and Rockstein, 1964) involving biochemical changes in the developing pupa and the postemergent adult. Cheng and

Cutkomp (1972), for example, reported that, in the adult worker honey bee brain, total ATPase activity rose sharply from emergence to a peak at seven days of age; both Mg^{2+} ATPase as well as $Na^+–K^+$ ATPase, the two competent ATPase systems, individually paralleled in age-related distribution the above-mentioned observation for total ATPase activity in the brain of the worker honeybee. In partial confirmation of the earlier study by Rockstein (1950) on brain cholinesterase activity changes with age, Cutkomp and Cheng reported essentially little change in the peak activity of their enzyme systems thereafter until the sixth week of adult life, when a high percentage of the worker population was dying or had died.

Similarly, in the confused flour beetle, *T. confusum*, Raychaudhuri and Butz (1965b) reported that the peak activities at the age of 6 weeks in the case of the female, and 10 weeks in the case of the male, for acid phosphatase, and at 6 weeks in the case of the female for alkaline phosphatase, but with little significant change in alkaline phosphatase from emergence to old age in the case of the male. Chaudhary and Lemonde (1963) found evidence of new synthesis of phospholipids and nucleic acids in the newly emerged adult *T. confusum* in contrast to earlier reports by Levenbook (1953) and Khouvine and Grégoire (1940), who found *no* major changes in the phospholipid or nucleic acid phosphorus content during the pupal period of *Calliphora erythrocephala*. Crone (1964), studying the phospholipid content of the sarcosomes of the flight muscle of *M. domestica*, similarly found that the lipid phosphorus content of sarcosome extracts increased from 0.59 to 1.02 μg from the first to fifth day postemergence. Pearincott (1960), in a study on lipid metabolism during development of the house fly, *M. domestica*, reported that the cholesterol content per insect increased by 50% from the 4-day-old pupa to the newly emerged adult, and by almost 100% in the seventh to tenth day of adult life; the fatty acid content by approximately 33⅓% from the 4-day-old pupa to the newly emerged adult (which level may not change to the seventh day of adult life. The lipid phosphorus content, on the other hand, fell by 50% from the third to fourth day of pupal life, remained unchanged at adult emergence, but then increased almost tenfold by the seventh to tenth day of adult life.

Most recently, Butler and co-workers have described several aspects of postemergence maturation in the black carpet beetle, *Attagenus megatoma*, in the form of the reversal from negative to positive phototaxis as well as enzyme (acid phosphatase) changes in the flight muscle in the postemergent, ovipositing female. They also reported concomitant structural maturation in the development of a double convex lens following emergence (Butler *et al.,* 1970), together with postemergent ultrastructural maturation of the flight and leg muscles, in the 5–9 day postemergent adult (Butler and Nath, 1972), all in relation to maturation of the function of female reproduction. This ongoing study will, without doubt, produce significant additional data confirming not only the existence of metachemogenesis, but most likely as well an integrated pattern of adult, age-related changes at the biochemical, as well as functional level, related to senescence of reproduction as well as of flight in this species.

Other scattered studies involving postemergence, adult changes in chemical composition, related most probably to the maturation of flight ability, have been those by Crompton and Birt (1967) on *Lucilia cuprina,* by Carey and Wyatt (1963) on the silkmoth and *Hyalophora Cecropia* (L.) and by Stephen and Gilbert (1970) on the same species. In other holometabolous insects, Jones (1964) observed changes in respiratory enzyme activity from various organs of *T. molitor* as undergoing pronounced changes, particularly in the case of cytochrome oxidase in the gut, heart, and nerve cord, as well as the ovary of the adult female, from the 8-day-old pupa to the newly emerged adult and reaching a peak at 1 week of adult age. Similarly, malic dehydrogenase in the gut, testis, and ovary showed sizable increase particularly from the 8-day-old pupa to the 1-week-old adult. Finally, isocitric dehydrogenase in the gut of this insect showed a pronounced increase particularly from the newly emerged adult to 1 week postemergence, with a 40% increase in the same enzyme both in the testis of the male and the ovary of the female from newly emergent adult to 1-week-old adult insect.

As has been indicated in part (above), a number of scattered studies involving protein synthesis and distribution of proteins and amino acids have been made in various tissues in a variety of insects, with the several workers being concerned with an equal number and variety of biological phenomena. For example, *D. melanogaster* has been studied by Wattiaux and Lamborot (1967) and Chen and Buhler (1970). Chen (1971) has studied saturniid and *Cecropia* moths. Schneiderman and his co-workers have studied the relationship of protein synthesis, and particularly RNA and DNA synthesis, in relation to hormonal control of development and metamorphosis [see Schneiderman and Gilbert (1964), Krishnakumaran *et al.* (1965), Berry *et al.* (1967), and Patel and Schneiderman (1969); for a more thorough coverage of this entire subject, one is referred to the recent books by Chen (1971) and Rockstein and Baker (1972)].

In the mosquito, *A. aegypti,* Thayer and Terzian (1970) found that taurine, proline, and β-alanine all increased with advancing age in the female mosquito to a peak at 21 days, whereas the titers of threonine, serine, asparagine, and/or glutamine, valine, isoleucine, leucine, tyrosine, phenylalanine, lysine, tryptophan, histidine, and arginine were significantly lower 7 days after emergence. This was in agreement with the data by Chen (1958) who noted, however, an increase in methionine sulfoxide with advancing age in the female mosquito, *C. pipiens,* and a similar increase in β-alanine in males.

Chen and Levenbook (1966), in a study on ontogenetic patterns of hemolymph proteins of the blowfly, *P. regina,* found a rapid decline in the total concentration of proteins from larva to white pupa and at adult emergence, so that in the newly emerged adult flies the total protein concentration amounts to 3.5% (w/v), only about one-sixth of that in the mature larva (a reduction from 6.01 mg per insect in the last instar larva to 0.43 mg in the newly emerged adult fly). The significance of these and similar data cited by Chen and Levenbook for a wide variety of insects, including the *Cecropia* moth, the Japanese beetle, and the silkworm, appears to be in relation to the presence of a large number of enzymes in the hemolymph, probably concerned with the larval–pupal ecdysis as well as the pupal–adult apolysis.

Johnson, in his chapter on insect migration (Volume III, Chapter 4 of this treatise), discusses in some further detail the biochemical maturation of migrant and nonmigrant insect forms concomitant with the development of the flight muscle and, hence, flight capacity, during the first days to weeks following emergence of the adult, both in holometabolous insects and those with gradual metamorphosis.

As we have seen immediately above, and shall see in our discussion below, concerning physiological aging of flight, some enzymes are replaced by others concerned primarily with the metabolic release of energy in the contraction of thoracic flight muscle during the postemergent maturation of such flight ability, as at least several enzyme systems including acid phosphatase, continue to fall, well into the adult stage, after the onset of decline during the late larval and early pupal stage.

Metachemogenesis is not a phenomenon unique to the Holometabola since it is also seen in some of the findings on insects with incomplete or gradual metamorphosis. Thus, McShan and co-workers (1954) reported a significant increase in the succinoxidase activity of the pink thoracic muscles of the Madeira roach, *Leucophaea maderae,* from ½ hour of age to the fifth day after the final molt into the adult form. Moreover, this elevated activity then persisted for 30 days following which there is another rise (by 50% more) to a maximum at 40 days of age. A more recent study by S. Kramer and W. H. McShan (personal communication, 1955) on *P. americana* showed that succinoxidase activity of the basal leg–thoracic muscles of the cockroach increased by about 60% from 12 hours to the tenth day following adult emergence from the last nymphal stadium. Brooks (1957) correlated the age-related changes in succinoxidase activity with maturation of the pink leg and wing muscles in the American cockroach in terms of such changing succinoxidase activity. Thus, in the nymphs of both sexes, all wing and leg muscle are white and the succinoxidase activity is at a minimum. However, in the male cockroach, the final molt is marked by a rapid increase in pigmentation, i.e., pink color, which in itself is accompanied by a rise in succinoxidase activity in the muscles primarily concerned with flight, which reaches its peak by the third week of adult life both with regard to pink pigmentation, as well as succinoxidase activity in the flight muscle of the thorax. In the case of the female cockroach, on the other hand, both pigmentation and associated succinoxidase activity do not show any principal changes for at least 2 months after adult emergence. At that time (when the male muscle pigmentation and enzyme activity have been at maxima for well over 1 month), the muscles of the females show only a faint pigmentation and possess a succinoxidase activity equal to only $1\frac{1}{2}$ times that of the younger female and less than $\frac{1}{3}$ of that of the corresponding muscles from males of the same age.

More recently, Brosemer (1967) has demonstrated, in the paurometabolous, Lubber grasshopper, *Romalea microptera* (Beauvois), a similar postemergent chemical maturation (metachemogenesis) in the form of a fourfold increase in the "glycero-P-dehydrogenase" equally both in the bifunctional wing–leg thoracic muscle as well as in the monofunctional jumping muscles, by the fifteenth–eighteenth day after the final nymphal ecdysis.

In summary then, in *Drosophila* sp., *P. regina*, in the honey bee, *A. mellifera* and in the house fly, *M. domestica*, there appears to be a well-coordinated complex of chemical changes accompanying maturation and development of the thoracic flight-muscle sarcosomes, all in relation to the maturation of flight ability occurring at different ages in the postemergent adult. In insects with incomplete metamorphosis, there appears to be not only differences in degree of maturation of flight ability upon emergence, but also differences between the two sexes within one species of such postemergent state or degree of maturation. This may be under the control of the corpus allatum, an endocrine organ which itself shows considerable variation in degree of maturation at adult emergence, from species to species (see Rockstein, 1950; Rockstein *et al.*, 1971).

2. Chemosenescence of Flight. Williams *et al.* (1943) pioneered the first really significant contribution to our knowledge of the physiologi-

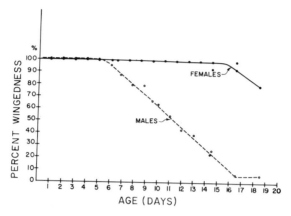

Fig. 19. Wing loss in aging male and female house flies. [Rockstein and Brandt (1963), *Science* © 1963 by the Amer. Assoc. Advance. Sci.]

cal aging of flight in relating the virtually precise coincidence of flight ability, as measured by wing-beat frequency and duration of flight, to glycogen content in *D. funebris.* These workers found that flight ability reaches its peak at approximately 2 weeks of adult life, which is exactly the same time at which glycogen concentration of the adult reaches its maximum level, as well, following which both glycogen content of the

TABLE XVI

CHOLINESTERASE ACTIVITY OF NORMAL FLIES AND THOSE RESISTANT TO DDT[a,b]

Age (days)	Normal flies		Resistant flies	
	Males	Females	Males	Females
Just emerged	0.187	0.187	0.130	0.142
1	0.475	0.350	0.307	0.212
2	0.437	0.207	0.412	0.187
3	0.545	0.287	0.382	0.187
4	0.512	0.400	0.487	0.200
5	0.612	0.312	0.325	0.207
6	0.427	0.225	0.525	0.482
7	0.645	0.357	0.512	0.350
8	0.502	0.307	0.717	0.337
9	—	0.262	0.537	0,362
10	—	0.267	—	0.255
11	—	0.317	—	0.287

[a] After Babers and Pratt (1950), *Physiol Zool.* © 1950 Univ. of Chicago Press.
[b] Rates in ml of 0.02 *N* NaOH added in 20 minutes.

adult as well as flight ability concomitantly fall, first precipitously and then more gradually in an almost precisely parallel fashion.

Several later studies involving the biochemical, histological, and histochemical changes with age in *D. melanogaster* by Delcour (1968) and by Samis *et al.* (1971) have added little to the original report by Williams *et al.* (1943). Most recently Takahashi *et al.* (1970b) confirmed the earlier report by Williams *et al.* of the decrease in glycogen content (in this case in *D. melanogaster*) both as regards densification of mitochondria, myofibrillar disintegration, and considerable age-related reduction in the glycogen content of the flight muscle of this species. These data correspond to those by Simon *et al.* (1969) on changes in the flight muscle of aging house flies, *M. domestica* (for further details concerning these histological, histochemical, and biochemical changes with age in relation to function, see Section IV, A and B, above).

M. Rockstein (unpublished, 1951) first observed that male houseflies showed a pronounced tendency to early abrading and loss of their wings,

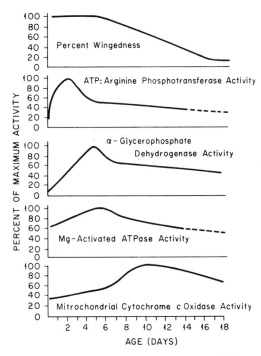

Fig. 20. Sequence of age-dependent changes in the male house fly (**M. Rockstein,** unpublished).

beginning with the fourth to fifth day postemergence and reaching, by the middle of the third week, a level of wing loss to the extent of 90–95% of the population (Fig. 19). Accordingly, for well over a decade, Rockstein and his co-workers have been exploring the details of both the physiological and biochemical aspects of aging in the male house fly, *M. domestica*, in relation to the gross structural and functional changes which accompany the manifest senescence of flight ability.

Their data indicate a well-integrated pattern of interrelated biochemical changes, preceding, accompanying, and following the onset of failure of flight, which is climaxed by the total loss of wings in virtually all male house flies by the end of the third week (Rockstein, 1966). Table XV summarizes the data for the time sequence of the aging of flight ability in the male house fly, in indicating the points in postemergent adult life when the various enzymes and substrates concerned either with the energizing of flight or, in the case of brain cholinesterase (Table XVI), the control of locomotor ability at the central nervous system level (Babers and Pratt, 1950) begins to decline.

Figures 20 and 21 illustrate in graphic form the remarkable biochemical nexus of the step-by-step onset of decline of four major enzyme systems, namely the extramitochondrial enzymes ATP: arginine phosphotransferase and α-glycerophosphate dehydrogenase, and the intramitochondrial Mg-activated ATPase and cytochrome c oxidase activities, peaking at 2 days, 4 days, 6 days (which is also the point of actual onset

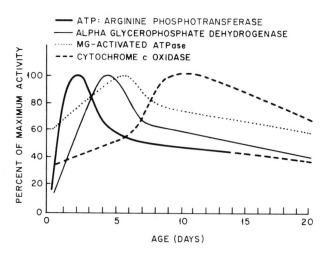

Fig. 21. Sequence of enzyme activity changes in the flight muscles of the male house fly.

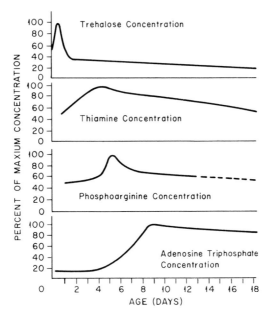

Fig. 22. Sequence of substrate concentration changes in the flight muscle of the male house fly.

of wing loss in male postemergent adult life), and 11 days, respectively. The change in the last-mentioned enzyme occurs coincident with the onset of decline in the number of sarcosomes or giant mitochondria in the flight muscle of the male house fly.

Figures 22 and 23, moreover indicate that, whereas trehalose, the non-reducing disaccharide, is utilized at a very rapid rate during the first few minutes of flight as the major source of energy, it is comparatively unimportant after the first few hours following emergence of the adult male fly. On the other hand, thiamine content and phosphoarginine (arginine phosphate) content reach their peaks *prior to* the actual onset of aging of flight in terms of wing loss as well as the onset of failure of Mg-activated ATPase. As described by Clark and Rockstein (1964) and Rockstein (1966, 1967), this represents one of the most detailed studies on the various biochemical components within the flight muscle as a function of age, in direct relation to the onset of *failure* of locomotor function.

In an attempt to pinpoint levels of control of such senescence of flight function in the male house fly, Rockstein (1966) investigated the possible cause-and-effect relationship between wing loss and decline in activity of

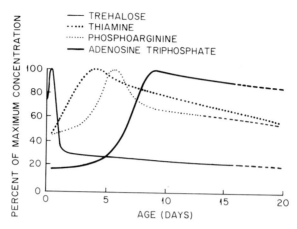

Fig. 23. Composite picture of sequence of substrate concentration changes in the flight muscle of the male house fly.

α-glycerophosphate dehydrogenase (GDH) occurring *prior to* the onset of wing loss, and of Mg-activated ATPase activity decline virtually *simultaneously* with the onset of wing loss, by surgical removal of the wings from immediately postemergent adult males. As shown in Figs. 24 and 25, removal of the wings before the normal onset of senescence (i.e., in the newly emerged house fly) produces virtually no change in the age-related pattern of Mg-activated ATPase (Fig. 24), whereas such de-alation of the very young male fly (i.e., prior to its actual attainment of maturity of flight ability) blocks the otherwise normal decline of α-glycerophosphate dehydrogenase activity (Fig. 25). Thus, the peak level attained at 36 hours of age for this last-mentioned enzyme persists to the fourteenth day

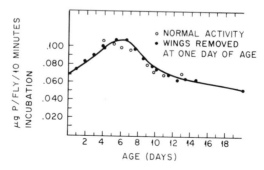

Fig. 24. Mg-activated ATPase activity in normal and de-alated male house flies. (From Rockstein, 1966.)

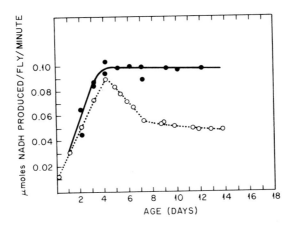

Fig. 25. α-Glycerophosphate dehydrogenase activity in normal and de-alated house flies. [Rockstein (1960), © Cambridge Univ. Press.]

of adult life in the case of the males, a point where normally 90% of the males will have lost their wings in the otherwise normal untreated adult. This observation suggests very strongly that the very presence of the intact wing in the normal fly in some (direct or indirect) fashion, perhaps endocrine-mediated (see Rockstein *et al.,* 1971), is responsible for the ultimate failure of the important DPN reoxidizing enzyme (GDH) found primarily in the flight muscle of flying insects (see Fig. 26, from Gilmour, 1960). The remarkable coincidence of wing retention and Mg-activated ATPase activity in relation to the aging of house fly flight ability is further

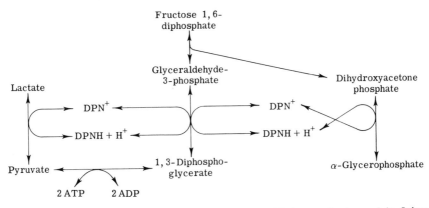

Fig. 26. Pathways of oxidation of reduced NAD (DPN) in vertebrates and in flying insects (Gilmour, 1960).

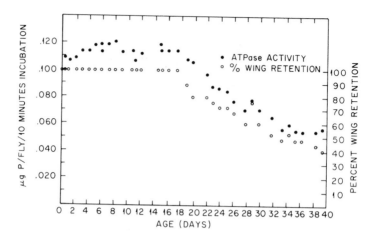

Fig. 27. Mg-activated ATPase activity in relation to wing retention in aging female house flies. (M. Rockstein, unpublished.)

confirmed by Fig. 27, from Clark and Rockstein (1964), in which Mg-activated ATPase activity parallels almost precisely the wing retention pattern of females from emergence to over almost 6 weeks of age.

Recently, Simon *et al.* (1969) studied the fine structure of the mitochondria of flight muscle of aging house flies, *M. domestica,* in an attempt to define more precisely the nature of the age-related changes in diameter and number of such giant mitochondria (previously reported by Rockstein and Bhatnagar, 1965). This more recent study supports to a considerable extent the details of Rockstein and Bhatnagar's report (1965) concerning the various sizes in mitochondria ranging from 1 to 6 μm in diameter, but adds considerable details as to the relationship of the type of mitochondria and age, in relation to the aging of flight ability. Thus, type-A mitochondria with simple cristae and light matrix are characteristic primarily of newly emerged flies and these mitochondria are loosely arranged between the muscle fibers and surrounded with a large amount of glycogen. [*N.B.* this is the time when most of the enzyme systems (see Table XV, above) concerned with energizing of flight are at their minimal adult level]. With advancing age, however, type-B mitochondria containing complex cristae (usually fenestrated) and with dense matrix increase in number to a peak level by the fifteenth day postemergence. (*N.B.* no distinction between the sexes was made in the isolation of these mitochondria, perhaps unfortunately from the standpoint of attempting to relate this directly to aging of flight ability, particularly in the *male* house fly).

Sohal and Allison (1971) explored this matter further by examining the fine structure of the flight muscle in aging adult male house flies, confirming in part the findings of Simon *et al.* (1969) but describing the degenerate changes of myofilaments particularly the focal degeneration of the myofibrils in 25- to 30-day-old flies (discussed above; Section IV, A).

Moreover, Rowley and Graham (1968) found that flight performance of virgin female *A. aegypti* mosquitoes, as measured by the distance flown, was maximal during the first 14 days of adult life, decreasing by 42% at the beginning of the fifteenth day and dropping off sharply during the fourth week as well. Rowley and Graham also related the failure in flight ability to the degree of glycogen *utilization* rather than glycogen *content* per animal. The question is raised by the authors as to whether this means that flight ability declines in the older mosquito because it loses its ability to utilize glycogen present or does the glycogen remain unused because the mosquito is no longer capable of flying, or for some other reason? In any case, their data suggest the possibility of direct biochemical or indirect (endocrine) changes with age limiting flight ability in some programmed fashion.

One known study of senescence of flight in blowflies (Tribe, 1966) involved *C. erythrocephala* under conditions of rest, free movement, and flight in adult males in relation to age (cf. Levenbook and Williams, 1956). He reported that the mean oxygen consumption for young blowflies at rest was 1.6 μl of O_2 per mg wet weight per hour, which rose significantly in old flies to 2.0 μl of O_2. In free-moving flies, oxygen consumption ranged from 2.4 μl of O_2 on the day of adult emergence to 8.9 μl of O_2 at 7 days of age, following which there was a progressive fall with age to a minimum of 3.9 μl of O_2 at 80 days of age. These oxygen consumption values were correlated closely with the degree of activity of young and old flies, respectively. On the day of emergence, flies flew for only a short period of time, with low wing-beat frequencies (100 cycles/second); these rose progressively with increasing age, both as regards wing-beat frequency and oxygen consumption, to a maximum at 50 days of age of 184 cycles/second and 60 μl of O_2 per mg wet weight, both falling thereafter to a minimum at 60 days. Duration of flight of 6–7 minutes, at 4 days of age following adult emergence, then fell to 2–3 minutes for flies 60 days of age. The author concluded that oxygen consumption in very old flies at rest suggests a loss of efficiency and that both the decline in efficiency and physiological performance marked advancing age.

It is apparent from these limited data (physiological, histochemical, and biochemical), available for several species of insects, that one may infer a programmed age-related maturation, as well as decline, in various functions but, most particularly, in the function of flight, a universally distributed aging phenomenon both in vertebrates as well as invertebrates. Accordingly, where, in the case of the house fly, *M. domestica,* such a pattern has been fairly extensively established, there is the need for pinpointing the site or sites within the genome, from DNA to RNA transcription and, finally, to protein synthesis in the translation of the genetic code, particularly of the decline in activity of enzymes with advancing age (in keeping with decline of flight ability). Current studies by M. Rockstein and G. T. Baker (unpublished) are aimed at such a genetic explanation for the programmed senescence of one of the several known manifestations of aging.

Thus, it is anticipated that future research on the aging process of this species will not only entail the explanation of the facts of aging, but also the biochemical and, ultimately, the genetic basis for the aging process.

V. Evolution of Aging

A wide range in the duration of metamorphosis and adult life-span is found within the class Insecta. Whatever the conditions of life, however, there has been, as in the cases of all successful species, a selection for those genotypes which enable the species to perpetuate itself within its particular habitat. In part, evolutionary success is therefore measured in terms of reproductive success. To achieve full reproductive potential, selection should favor not only a genotype required for optimum fertility and fecundity, but also for the ability of sexually immature insects to develop into reproductively functional adults and, furthermore, for such adults to remain alive until they have reproduced. How important is it to the species, however, for individuals which have completed their reproductive function to continue to live? In fact, is aging a biological phenomenon that has undergone evolution? Difficult as they may be, studies relating to the origin of total life span, as well as duration of each of the different stages of development, furnish an important approach for the understanding of senescence.

Interesting speculations on the evolution of aging are found in papers by Medawar (1957), Williams (1957), Dobzhansky (1958), as well as in Comfort's books (1956, 1961), Strehler (1962), and in the "Gatlinburg Conference on Aging Proceedings" (edited by Strehler, 1960).

Medawar (1957) has called senility "an artifact of domestication." In the laboratory, old insects demonstrate the deterioration of reproductive processes, the loss of vigor, or the accumulation of useless or harmful materials. In natural, wild populations, however, insects like other animals may not die because of senescence but rather from accidents, thus preventing most species in natural populations from achieving their potential life span. Moreover, some adults die soon after reproduction; in the one notable case of the praying mantis, the males may be destroyed by females with copulation.

August Weisman (Medawar, 1957) supposed that senescence was beneficial to the species, that the death of older organisms was necessary in order to make room for the younger and reproductively functioning organisms. Thus, he assumed, senescence is directly affected by natural selection. It is more likely, however, that senescence is as much a by-product of evolution, rather than being one aspect of the general program of natural selection, and moreover, that the efficiency and effectiveness of natural selection declines with increasing age.

Genes are pleiotropic in their action. They affect different processes and exert their effects at different times during life. A gene with beneficial effect during the preimaginal stage, but with a detrimental effect during the postreproductive stage, will be favored over one that is beneficial for long life but detrimental to the young. There would, therefore, tend to be an accumulation of those genes which are beneficial for embryos, larvae, pupae, and fertile adults, regardless of whether or not they might be harmful to older adults. It may therefore be that, if one were to select for longevity in laboratory populations, it might be accomplished at the expense of mortality during youth. Accumulation of periodic mortality records and survival curves, requisite for other, earlier-stated reasons, will serve to permit critical evaluation of such an hypothesis.

Delayed senescence may likewise be a direct consequence of continued fecundity, such that adults with a longer period of reproduction would tend to produce more offspring. Thus, genotypes, for a longer period of reproductive capacity, could become established and the duration of the adult existence would consequently be lengthened.

Medawar (1957) has suggested three factors which may have been important in the evolution of senescence These are that (1) genes which affect very old organisms cannot be eliminated by natural selection, (2) postponement of the time of action of a deleterious gene is equivalent to its elimination and may sometimes be the only way in which elimination can be achieved, and (3) natural selection may actually enforce such a postponement and expedite the age of onset on the action of favorable genes. These suggested factors point to the kind of experiments needed to test the concept of senescence as an evolutionarily derived phenomenon characteristic of all metazoan organisms.

VI. Summary

Insects possess characteristics which make them especially useful as experimental animals in aging studies. Since mean life span alone is an inadequate index of aging in its total sense, investigations in the field of physiological aging should, at the outset, obtain life tables and survival curves under carefully controlled conditions. The significance of these survival curves for aging populations likewise needs further study, especially since the life span of adults can be modified by extrinsic and intrinsic factors. Indeed, probit analysis of longevity data may prove additionally useful. Moreover, it is not sufficient simply to demonstrate that the life span has been altered. Since the duration of life of an organism must be the consequence of age-related structural and physiological changes, duration of life must be related to those processes in specific animals, for which reproducible life tables have been or can be obtained. In the same connection, it is equally important to distinguish between those age-related changes which do modify life span and those which do not.

Life span is a genetically controlled trait since the inherited genotype determines the life span (see Rockstein, 1958); however, it is also a biological characteristic that can be considerably modified by the environment. This is indeed an area of investigation in which more studies are needed, viz., the detailed genetic aspects of aging as a process, longevity as an inherited trait, and the extrinsic factors controlling or altering the process of aging and duration of life. Such genetic experiments should, therefore, select not only for long- and short-lived lines, but also for the processes themselves which may influence life span. The role of parental age, especially the maternal influence, is important, since separate nuclear and cytoplasmic factors may be involved in the determination of life span.

One can suggest that aging is a biological phenomenon which has undergone evolution and that the possession of a finite life span is an essential feature of species survival. There are indeed hypothetical inferences yet to be substantiated by critical observation and experimental data in studies which are peculiarly well suited and designed to resolve such difficult quesions. Such studies are particularly notable by their absence from the current scene of biological gerontological studies.

There is likewise at present no general theory of aging which can be applied to a significant range of different species of organisms or which can be employed to plan experiments and, more hopefully, by which to predict results. The study of physiological aging has both the challenge and charm of any classical biological problem with both theoretical and practical implications. Only through the continued attraction of critical workers in all areas of the biological and physical sciences can the expectation of the formulation of a sound, acceptable, invulnerable theory of aging be realized. With the wealth of versatile living material at our disposal in the form of insects, with the many attributes making them admirably suitable for gerontological study, scientists employing insects as experimental animals should be making major strides in the direction of clarifying some of the still ill-defined characteristics of the aging process in *all* metazoan animals, as well as the underlying mechanisms thereof.

Acknowledgments

The work reported on by Dr. Rockstein and his colleagues in this chapter, was supported in part, by funds from Research Grants HD 00571 and GM 09680 from the U.S. Public Health Service, National Institutes of Health, and from the U.S. Atomic Energy Commission Contract No. At-(40-1)-3862. The authors acknowledge with appreciation the contribution by Ricki Davidson, who was primarily responsible for the preparation of this manuscript. Acknowledgment is also due to Dr. George T. Baker, III and to Marvin Sussman, for their editorial assistance in the final preparation of this manuscript, without which this major revision could not have been possible.

References

Abercrombie, M., and Johnson, M. L. (1941). *Proc. Zool. Soc. London* **111**, 87.

Adams, T. S., and Hintz, A. M. (1969). *J. Insect Physiol.* **15**, 201.

Alexander, P. (1966). *In* "Perspectives in Experimental Gerontology" (N.W. Shock, ed.), Chapter 20, p. 266. Thomas, Springfield, Illinois.

Allee, W. C., Emerson, A. E., Park, O., Part, T., and Schmidt, K. P. (1949). "Principles of Animal Ecology." Saunders, Philadelphia, Pennsylvania.

Alpatov, W. W. (1930). *Amer. Natur.* **64**, 37.

Alpatov, W. W., and Gordeenko, N. A. (1932). *Zool. Zh.* **11**, 60

Alpatov, W. W., and Pearl, R. (1929). *Amer. Natur.* **63**, 37.

Andrew, W. (1938). *Z. Zellforsch. Mikrosk. Anat.* **28**, 294.

Andrew, W. (1939). *J. Comp. Neurol.* **70**, 413.

Arnold, J. W. (1959). *Ann. Entomol. Soc. Amer.* **52**, 229.

Atlan, H., Miquel, J., and Binnard, R. (1969a). *J. Gerontol.* **24**, 1.

Atlan, H., Miquel, J., and Jennings, B. (1969b). *Drosophila Inform. Serv.* **44**, 88.

Atlan, H., Welch, G., and Miquel, J. (1970). *Int. J. Radiat. Biol.* **18**, 423.

Babers, F. H. (1941). *J. Agr. Res.* **62**, 509.

Babers, F. H., and Pratt, J. J., Jr. (1950). *Physiol. Zool.* **23**, 58.

Balazs, A., and Haranghy, L. (1965). *Acta Biol. (Budapest)* **15**, 343.

Baker, G. T., and Rockstein, M. (1971) . unpublished.

Barker, R. J., and Alexander, B. H. (1958). *Ann. Entomol. Soc. Amer.* **51**, 255.

Barrón, E. S. G., and Tahmisian, T. N. (1948). *J. Cell. Comp. Physiol.* **32**, 57.

Baumann, P. A. (1969). *Z. Vergl. Physiol.* **64**, 212.

Baumann, P. A., and Chen, P. S. (1968) . *Rev. Suisse Zool.* **75**, 1055.

Baxter, R. C., and Blair, H. A. (1967a). *Radiat. Res.* **30**, 48.

Baxter, R. C., and Blair, H. A. (1967b). *Radiat. Res.* **31**, 287.

Baxter, R. C., and Blair, H. A. (1969). *Radiat. Res.* **39**, 345.

Baxter, R. C., and Tuttle, L. W. (1957). *Radiat. Res.* **7**, 303.

Beament, J. W. L. (1958). *J. Exp. Biol.* **35**, 494.

Beament, J. W. L. (1959). *J. Exp. Biol.* **36**, 391.

Berberian, P. A., Rockstein, M., and Gray, F. H. (1971). *J. Gerontol.* **26**, 485.

Berry, S. J., Krishnakumaran, A., Oberlander, H., and Schneiderman, H. A. (1967). *J. Insect Physiol.* **13**, 1511.

Bilewicz, S. (1953). *Folia Biol. (Warsaw)* **1**, 177.

Bjorksten, J. (1958). *J. Am. Geriatrics Soc.* **6**, 740.

Bjorksten, J. (1963). *Gerontologia* **8**, 179.

Blest, A. D. (1960). *Behaviour* **16**, 188.

Blest, A. D. (1962). *In* "Biological Aspects of Aging" (N. W. Shock, ed.), pp. 12–16. Columbia Univ. Press, New York.

Blest, A. D. (1963). *Nature (London)* **197**, 1183.

Bodenheimer, F. S. (1938). "Problems of Animal Ecology." Oxford Univ. Press, New York and London.

Bondareff, W. (1957). *J. Gerontol.* **12**, 364.

Bowler, K., and Hollingsworth, M. J. (1965). *Genet. Res.* **6**, 1.

Brody, H. (1960). *J. Gerontol.* **15**, 258.

Brooks, M. A. (1957). *Ann. Entomol. Soc. Amer.* **50**, 122.

Brosemer, R. W. (1967). *J. Insect Physiol.* **13**, 685.

Bulos, B., Shukla, S., and Sacktor, B. (1972). *Arch. Biochem. Biophys.* **149**, 461.

Butler, L., and Nath, J. (1972). *Ann. Entomol. Soc. Amer.* (in press).

Butler, L., Roppel, R., and Zeigler, J. (1970). *J. Morphol.* **130**, 103.

Butterworth, F. M., and Bodenstein, D. (1968). *J. Exp. Zool.* **167**, 207.

Butz, A., and Hayden, P. (1962). *Ann. Entomol. Soc. Amer.* **55**, 617.

Callahan, R. F. (1962). *J. N.Y. Entomol. Soc.* **70**, 150.

Carey, F. G., and Wyatt, G. R. (1963). *J. Insect Physiol.* **9**, 317.

Chadwick, L. E. (1953). *In* "Insect Physiology" (K. D. Roeder, ed.), Chapter 22, p. 577. Wiley, New York.

Chaudhary, K. D., and Lemonde, A. (1963). *Comp. Biochem. Physiol.* **9**, 343.

Chen, P. S. (1958). *J. Insect Physiol.* **2**, 128–136.

Chen, P. S. (1971). "Biochemical Aspects of Insect Development." Karger, Basel.

Chen, P. S., and Buhler, R. (1970). *J. Insect Physiol.* **16**, 615.

Chen, P. S., and Levenbook, L. (1966). *J. Insect Physiol.* **12**, 1595.

Cheng, E. Y., and Cutkomp, L. K. (1972). *J. Insect Physiol.* (in press).

Child, C. M. (1915). "Senescence and Rejuvenescence." Univ. of Chicago Press, Chicago, Illinois.

Clark, A. M. (1961). *Radiat. Res.* **15**, 515.

Clark, A. M. (1963). *Ann. Entomol. Soc. Amer.* **56**, 616.

Clark, A. M. (1964). *Advan. Gerontol. Res.* **1**, 207–255.

Clark, A. M., and Cole, K. W. (1967). *Exp. Gerontol.* **2**, 89.

Clark, A. M., and Rockstein, M. (1964). *In* "The Physiology of Insecta" 1st. ed. (M. Rockstein, ed.), Vol. I, Chapter 6, p. 227. Academic Press, New York.

Clark, A. M., and Rubin, M. A. (1961). *Radiat. Res.* **15**, 244.

Clark, A. M., and Smith, R. E. (1967). *Exp. Gerontol.* **2**, 217.

Clark, A. M., Bertrand, H. A., and Smith, R. E. (1963). *Amer. Natur.* **97**, 203.

Clarke, J. M., and Maynard-Smith, J. (1955). *J. Genet.* **53**, 172.

Clarke, J. M., and Maynard-Smith, J. (1961a). *J. Exp. Biol.* **38**, 679.

Clarke, J. M., and Maynard-Smith, J. (1961b). *Nature (London)* **190**, 1027.

Clarke, J. M., and Maynard-Smith, J. (1966). *Nature (London)* **209**, 627.

Close, P., and Beischer, D. E. (1962). Proj. MR-005-13-9010 Subtask 1, Rep. No. 7. Bureau of Medicine and Surgery.

Comfort, A. (1953). *Nature (London)* **172**, 83.

Comfort, A. (1956). "The Biology of Senescence." R. Holt, New York.

Comfort, A. (1961). *Amer. Heart J.* **62**, 293.

Comfort, A. (1968). *Nature (London)* **217**, 320.

Comfort, A. (1964). "Ageing." R. Holt, New York.

Cork, J. M. (1957). *Radiat. Res.* **7**, 551.

Crompton, M., and Birt, L. M. (1967). *J. Insect Physiol.* **13**, 1575.

Crone, H. D. (1964). *J. Insect Physiol.* **10**, 499.

Crystal, M. M. (1967). *J. Med. Entomol.* **4**, 479.

Cuénot, L. (1895). *Arch. Biol.* **14**, 293.

Curtis, H. J. (1966). "Biological Mechanisms of Aging." Thomas, Springfield, Illinois.

Curtis, J. J. (1971). *Advan. Genet.* **16**, 305.

Dauer, M., Bhatnagar, P. L., and Rockstein, M. (1965). *J. Gerontol.* **20**, 219.

Davey, W. P. (1917). *J. Exptl. Zool.* **22**, 573.

David, J., Van Herrewege, J., and Fouillet, P. (1971). *Exp. Gerontol.* **6**, 249.

de Boissezon, P. (1930). *Arch. Zool. Exp. Gen.* **70**, 281.

Delcour, J. (1968). *Exp. Gerontol.* **3**, 247.

Doane, W. W. (1960). *J. Exp. Zool.* **145**, 1.

Dobzhansky, T. (1958). *Ann. N.Y. Acad. Sci.* **71**, 1234.

Duncan, D., Nall, D., and Morales, R. (1960). *J. Gerontol.* **15**, 366.

Edwards, G. A. (1953). In "Insect Physiology" (K. D. Roeder, ed.), Chapter 5, p. 55. Wiley, New York.

Ellis, R. S. (1919). *J. Comp. Neurol.* **30**, 229.

Ellis, R. S. (1920). *J. Comp. Neurol.* **32**, 1.

Erdman, H. E. (1960). *J. Econ. Entomol.* **53**, 971.

Feldman-Muhsam, B. (1944). *Bull. Entomol. Res.* **35**, 53.

Feldman-Muhsam, B., and Muhsam, H. V. (1945). *Proc. Zool. Soc. London* **115**, 296.

Flemings, M. B., and Ludwig, D. (1964). *Ann. Entomol. Soc. Amer.* **57**, 560.

Fox, D. L. (1953). "Animal Biochromes and Structural Colours," Chapter 13. Cambridge Univ. Press, London and New York.

Fraenkel, G., and Hopf, H. S. (1940). *Biochem. J.* **34**, 1085.

Gardner, E. (1940). *Anat. Rec.* **77**, 529.

Gardner, T. S. (1948a). *J. Gerontol.* **3**, 1.

Gardner, T. S. (1948b). *J. Gerontol.* **3**, 9.

Georgiana, M. (1949). *Amer. Natur.* **83**, 39.

Gilmour, D. (1960). "Biochemistry of Insects," p. 76. Academic Press, New York.

Glass, B. (1960). *Amer. Inst. Biol. Sci., Publ.* **6**, 185.

Gonzalez, B. M. (1923). *Amer. Natur.* **57**, 289.

Gowen, J. W. (1934). *Cold Spring Harbor Symp. Quant. Biol.* **2**, 128.

Gowen, J. W., and Johnson, L. E. (1946). *Amer. Natur.* **80**, 147.

Gowen, J. W., and Stadler, J. (1952). *Genetics* **37**, 586.

Gray, F. H., and Berberian, P. A. (1971). *Exp. Gerontol.* **6**, 205.

Green, L. R., and Dorough, H. W. (1968). *J. Econ. Entomol.* **61**, 88.

Greenberg, B. (1955). *J. Econ. Entomol.* **48**, 654.

Greenberg, B. (1960). *Ann. Entomol. Soc. Amer.* **53**, 125.

Gregory, D. W., Lennie, R. W., and Birt, L. M. (1968) . *J. Roy. Microsc. Soc* [3] **88**, 151.

Greiff, D. (1940). *Amer. Natur.* **74**, 363.

Griffiths, J. T., and Tauber, O. E. (1942). *Physiol. Zool.* **15**, 196.

Griggs, R. C. (1960). *Bios* **30**, 202.

Grosch, D. S. (1956). *J. Econ. Entomol.* **49**, 629.

Grosch, D. S. (1962). *Annu. Rev. Entomol.* **7**, 81.

Hall, J. C. (1969). *Exp. Gerontol.* **4**, 207.

Harrison, B. J., and Holliday, R. (1967). *Nature (London)* **213**, 990.

Hasset, C. C., and Jenkins, D. W. (1952). *Nucleonics* **10**, 42.

Hatai, S. (1902). *J. Comp. Neurol.* **12**, 107.

Haydak, M. H. (1953). *Ann. Entomol. Soc. Amer.* **46**, 547.

Haydak, M. H. (1957). *Bee World* **38**, 197.

Heilbrunn, L. V. (1952) . "An Outline of General Physiology." Saunders, Philadelphia.

Herman, M. M., Miquel, J., and Johnson, M. (1971) . *Acta Neuropathol.* **19**, 167.

Herold, R. C. (1965). *Develop. Biol.* **12**, 269.

Herold, R. C., and Borei, H. (1963). *Develop. Biol.* **8**, 67.

Herr, E. B. (1953). *Anat. Rec.* **117**, 546.

Heslop, J. P. (1967). *Biochem. J.* **104**, 5.

Hinton, H. E. (1971). *Proc. Roy. Entomol. Soc. London* **35**, 55.

Hochschild, R. (1971). *Exp. Gerontol.* **6**, 133.

Hodge, C. F. (1894). *J. Physiol. (London)* **17**, 129.

Hoffman, A. C. (1968). Thesis submitted to the North Carolina State University, Raleigh.

Hoffman, A. C. (1970). Thesis submitted to the North Carolina State University. Raleigh.

Hollingsworth, M. J. 1966a) . *Exp. Gerontol.* **1**, 259.

Hollingsworth, M. J. (1966b) . *Exp. Gerontol,* **1**, 251.

Hollingsworth, M. J. (1968) . *Nature (London)* **218**, 869.

Hollingsworth, M. J. (1969a). *Exp. Gerontol.* **4**, 49.

Hollingsworth, M. J. (1969b). *Exp. Gerontol.* **4**, 159.

Howard, L. O. (1939). *In* "Problems of Ageing" (E. V. Cowdry, ed.). Baillière, Tindall, and Cox, London.

Howe, R. W. (1967). *J. Stored Prod. Res.* **3**, 371.

Hyde, R. R. (1913). *Indiana Acad. Sci. Rep.* p. 113.

Hylton, A. R. (1966). *J. Invertebr. Pathol.* **8**, 75.

Inukai, T. (1928). *J. Comp. Neurol.* **45**, 1.

Jones, C. R. (1964). *J. Cell. Comp. Physiol.* **63**, 65.

Keiser, I., and Schneider, E. L. (1969). *J. Econ. Entomol.* **62**, 663.

Kershaw, W. E., Lavoiepierre, M. M. T., and Chalmers, T. A. (1953). *Ann. Trop. Med., Parasitol.* **47**, 207.

Khouvine, Y., and Grégoire, I. (1940). *Bull. Soc. Chim. Biol.* **22**, 506.

Kohn, R. R. (1965). *In* "Reproduction: Molecular, Subcellular and Cellular" (M. Locke, ed.), p. 291. Academic Press, New York.

Kopec, S. (1928). *Brit. J. Exp. Biol.* **5**, 204.

Kratky, E. (1931). *Z. Wiss. Zool.* **139**, 120.

Krishnakumaran, A., and Schneiderman, H. A. (1964). *J. Exp. Zool* **157**, 293.

Krishnakumaran, A., Oberlander, H., and Schneiderman, H. A. (1965). *Nature (London)* **205**, 1131.

Krueger, H. S., and Ballard, R. C. (1965). *Comp. Biochem. Physiol.* **16**, 13.

Krumbiegel, I. (1929). *Zool. Jahrb., Abt. Anat. Ontog. Tiere* **51**, 111.

Krumbiegel, I. (1930). *Forsch. Fortschr.* **6**, 85.

Kuenen, D. J., Den Boer, P. J., and De Melker, J. (1957). *Physiol. Comp. Oecol.* **4**, 313.

Kung, K., and La Brecque, G. C. (1971). *J. Med. Entomol.* **8**, 45.

Labitte, A. (1916). *Bull. Mus. Hist. Natur. Paris* **22**, 105.

Lamb, M. J. (1964). *J. Insect Physiol.* **10**, 487.

Lamb, M. J. (1965). *Exp. Gerontol.* **1**, 181.

Lamb, M. J. (1966). *In* "Radiation and Ageing" (P. J. Lindop and G. A. Sacher, eds.), pp. 163–174. Taylor & Francis, London.

Lamb, M. J., and Maynard-Smith, J. (1969). *Radiat. Res.* **40**, 450.

Lambremont, E. N., and Earle, N. W. (1961). *J. Econ. Entomol.* **54**, 964.

Lang, C. A. (1959). *Exp. Cell Res.* **17**, 516.

Lang, C. A. (1967). *J. Gerontol.* **22**, 55.

Lang, C. A., and Stephan, J. K. (1967). *Biochem. J.* **102**, 331.

Lang, C. A., Lau, H. Y., and Jefferson, D. J. (1965). *Biochem. J.* **95**, 372.

Lansing, A. I. (1947). *J. Gerontol.* **2**, 228.

Lansing, A. I. (1952). "Cowdry's Problems of Aging," 3rd ed. Williams & Wilkins, Baltimore, Maryland.

Lansing, A. I. (1954). *Ann. N.Y. Acad. Sci.* **57**, 455.

Lennie, R. W., and Birt, L. M. (1967). *Biochem. J.* **102**, 338.

Levenbook, L. (1953). *J. Cell. Comp. Physiol.* **41**, 313.

Levenbook, L., and Krishna, I. (1971). *J. Insect Physiol.* **17**, 9.

Levenbook, L., and Williams, C. M. (1956). *J. Gen. Physiol.* **39**, 497.

Liles, J. N. (1961). *Bull. Entomol. Soc. Amer.* **7**, 168 (abstr.).

Liles, J. N., and DeLong, D. M. (1960). *Ann. Entomol. Soc. Amer.* **53**, 277.

Lints, F. A. (1961). *Genetica* **32**, 177.

Lints, F. A. (1962). *Acta Biotheor.* **16**, 1.

Lints, F. A. (1971). *Gerontologia* **17**, 33.

Lints, F. A., and Lints, C. V. (1969a). *Exp. Gerontol.* **4**, 81.

Lints, F. A., and Lints, C. V. (1969b). *Exp. Gerontol.* **4**, 231.

Lints, F. A., and Lints, C. V. (1971a). *Nature (London), New Biol.* **229**, 86.

Lints, F. A., and Lints, C. V. (1971b). *Exp. Gerontol.* **6**, 417.

Lints, F. A., and Lints, C. V. (1971c). *Exp. Gerontol.* **6**, 427.

Lloyd, J. B. (1967). *Brit. J. Geriat. Pract.* **4**, 133.

Loeb, J., and Northrop, J. H. (1917). *J. Biol. Chem.* **32**, 103.

Ludwig, D., and Fiore, C. (1960). *Ann. Entomol. Soc. Amer.* **53**, 595.

Ludwig, D., and Fiore, C. (1961). *Ann. Entomol. Soc. Amer.* **54**, 463.

Ludwig, D., and Jones, C. R. (1964). *Ann. Entomol. Soc. Amer.* **57**, 210.

MacArthur, J. W., and Baillie, W. H. T. (1932). *Quart. Rev. Biol.* **7**, 313.

McCay, C. M., Maynard, L. A., Sperling, G., and Barnes, L. L. (1939). *J. Nutr.* **18**, 1.

McShan, W. H., Kramer S., and Schlegel, V. (1954). *Biol. Bull.* **106**, 341.

Matthes, E. (1951). *Z. Vergleich. Physiol.* **33**, 1.

Maurizio, A. (1954). *Landwirt. Jahrb. Schweiz* **68**, 115.

Maurizio, A. (1959). *Ciba Found. Colloq. Ageing* **5**, 231.

Maynard-Smith, J. (1957). *J. Exp. Biol.* **34**, 85.

Maynard-Smith, J. (1958). *Nature (London)* **181**, 496.

Maynard-Smith, J. (1959). *Nature (London)* **184**, 956.

Maynard-Smith, J. (1962). *Proc. Roy. Soc., Ser. B* **157**, 115.

Maynard-Smith, J. (1963). *Nature (London)* **199**, 400.

Maynard-Smith, J., Bozcuk, A. N., and Tebbutt, S. (1970). *J. Insect Physiol.* **16**, 601.

Medawar, P. B. (1952). "An Unsolved Problem of Biology." Lewis, London.
Medawar, P. B. (1957). "The Uniqueness of the Individual." Basic Books, New York.
Metchnikoff, E. (1915). *Ann. Inst. Pasteur, Paris* p. 477.
Miller, R. S., and Thomas J. L. (1958). *Ecology* **39**, 118.
Miquel, J. (1971). *Advan. Gerontol. Res.* **3**, 39.
Miquel, J., Bensch, K. G., Philpott, D. E., and Atlan, H. (1972). *Mech. Aging Develop.* **1**, 71.
Moffet, J. O. (1952). *J. Econ. Entomol.* **45**, 135.
Müller, H. J. (1960) . *Int. J. Radiat. Biol.* **1**, 321.
Müller, H. J. (1963) . *In* "Cellular Basis and Aetiology of Late Somatic Effects of Ionizing Radiation" (R. J. C. Harris, ed.), pp. 235–245. Academic Press, New York.
Nettles, W. C., and Betz, N. L. (1965). *Ann. Entomol. Am.* **58**, 721.
Nikoforova, T. L. (1971). *Byull Eksp. Biol. Med.* **71**, 81.
Norris, M. J. (1933). *Proc. Zool. Soc. London* **103**, 33.
Northrop, J. H. (1917). *J. Biol. Chem.* **32**, 123.
Northrop, J. H. (1926). *J. Gen. Physiol.* **9**, 81.
Nothel, H. (1965). *Strahlentherapie* **126**, 269.
Nowosielski, J. W., and Patton, R. L. (1965). *J. Insect Physiol.* **11**, 201.
O'Brian, D. M. (1961). *Ann. Entomol. Soc. Amer.* **54**, 412.
O'Brien, R. D., and Wolfe, L. S. (1964). "Radiation, Radioactivity, and Insects," pp. 23–54. Academic Press, New York.
Park, T. (1936). *J. Cell. Comp. Physiol.* **7**, 313.
Park, T. (1945). *Amer. Natur.* **79**, 436.
Patel, N. G., and Schneiderman, H. A. (1969). *J. Insect Physiol.* **15**, 643.
Patterson, R. S. (1957). *J. Econ. Entomol.* **50**, 104.
Pearincott, J. V. (1960). *J. Cell. Comp. Physiol.* **55**, 167.
Pearl, R. (1922). "The Biology of Death." Lippincott, Philadelphia, Pennsylvania.
Pearl, R. (1940). "Introduction to Medical Biometry and Statistics." Saunders, Philadelphia, Pennsylvania.
Pearl, R., and Miner, J. R. (1935). *Quart. Rev. Biol.* **10**, 60.
Pearl, R., and Miner, J. R. (1936). *Mem. Mus. Hist. Natur. Belg.* **3**, 169.
Pearl, R., and Parker, S. L. (1922a). *Amer. Natur.* **56**, 174.
Pearl, R., and Parker, S. L. (1922b). *Amer. Natur.* **56**, 385.
Pearl, R., Miner, J. R., and Parker, S. L. (1927). *Amer. Natur.* **61**, 289.
Philiptschenko, J. (1907a). *Rev. Russe Entomol.* **7**, 188.
Philiptschenko, J. (1907b). *Z. Wiss. Zool.* **88**, 99.
Pipa, R. L., Nishioka, R. S., and Bern, H. A. (1962). *J. Ultrastruct. Res.* **6**, 164.
Pixell-Goodrich, E. L. M. (1919). *Quart. J. Microsc. Sci.* **64**, 191.
Press, G. D., Raychaudhuri, A., and Strehler, B. L. (1966). *J. Gerontol.* **21**, 13.
Raffy, A. (1934). *Ann. Physiol. Physiochim. Biol.* **10**, 437.
Rau, P. (1924) . *Trans. Acad. Sci. St. Louis* **25**, 57.
Rau, P., and Rau, N. (1914). *Trans. Acad. Sci. St. Louis* **123**, 1.
Raychaudhuri, A., and Butz, A. (1965a). *Ann. Entomol. Soc. Amer.* **58**, 535.
Raychaudhuri, A., and Butz, A. (1965b). *Ann. Entomol. Soc. Amer.* **58**, 541.
Richards, A. G., and Kolderie, M. Q. (1957). *Entomol. News* **68**, 57.
Rockstein, M. (1950). *J. Cell. Comp. Physiol.* **35**, 11.
Rockstein, M. (1956). *Science* **123**, 534.
Rockstein, M. (1957). *J. Gerontol.* **12**, 253.
Rockstein, M. (1958). *J. Gerontol.* **13**, Suppl., 7.
Rockstein, M. (1959a). *Smithson. Misc. Collect.* **137**, 263.

Rockstein, M. (1959b). *Ciba Found. Colloq. Ageing* 5, 247.

Rockstein, M. (1966). *In* "Topics in the Biology of Aging" (P. L. Krohn, ed.), p. 43. Wiley (Interscience), New York.

Rockstein, M. (1967). *Symp. Soc. Exp. Biol.* 21, 337.

Rockstein, M. (1971) . unpublished.

Rockstein, M., and Baker, G. T., III (eds.) (1972). "Molecular Genetic Mechanisms in Development and Aging." Academic Press, New York.

Rockstein, M., and Bhatnagar, P. L. (1965). *J. Insect Physiol.* 11, 481.

Rockstein, M., and Bhatnagar, P. L. (1966). *Biol. Bull.* 131, 486.

Rockstein, M., and Brandt, K. (1963). *Science* 139, 1049.

Rockstein, M., and Farrell, G. J. (1972). *J. Insect Physiol.* 18, 737.

Rockstein, M., and Gutfreund, D. C. (1961) . Science 133, 147.

Rockstein, M., and Hawkins, W. B. (1970). *Exp. Gerontol.* 5, 187.

Rockstein, M., and Lieberman, H. M. (1958). *Nature (London)* 181, 787.

Rockstein, M., and Lieberman, H. M. (1959). *Gerontologia* 3, 23.

Rockstein, M., and Srivastava, P. N. (1967). *Experientia* 23, 1.

Rockstein, M., Gray, F. H., and Berberian, P. A. (1971). *Exp. Gerontol.* 6, 211.

Ross, M. H. (1959). *Fed. Proc., Fed. Amer. Soc. Exp. Biol.* 18, 1190.

Ross, M. H. (1961). *J. Nutr.* 75, 197.

Rowley, W. A., and Graham, C. L. (1968). *J. Insect Physiol.* 14, 719.

Sacher, G. A. (1963). *Physiol. Zool.* 36, 295.

Sacher, G. A. (1967). *Ann. N.Y. Acad. Sci.* 138, 680.

Sacktor, B., and Shimada, Y. (1972). *J. Cell Biol.* 52, 465.

Samis, H. V., Jr., Erk, F. C., and Baird, M. B. (1971). *Exp. Gerontol.* 6, 9.

Schneiderman, H. A., and Gilbert, L. I. (1964). *Science* 143, 325.

Shaw, R. F., and Bercaw, B. L. (1962). *Nature (London)* 196, 454.

Shock, N. W., ed. (1960). "Aging—Some Social and Biological Aspects," Publ. No. 65. Amer. Ass. Advan. Sci., Washington, D.C.

Simon, J., Bhatnagar, P. L., and Milburn, N. S. (1969). *J. Insect Physiol.* 15, 135.

Sizer, I. W. (1943). *Advan. Enzymol.* 3, 35.

Smallwood, W. M., and Phillips, R. L. (1916). *J. Comp. Neurol.* 27, 69.

Sohal, R. S. (1970). *Exp. Gerontol.* 5, 213.

Sohal, R. S., and Allison, V. F. (1971). *Exp. Gerontol.* 6, 167.

Sondhi, K. C. (1964). *Amer. Zool.* 4, 45.

Sondhi, K. C. (1966). *J. Exp. Zool.* 162, 89.

Sondhi, K. C. (1967). *Exp. Gerontol.* 2, 233.

Sondhi, K. C. (1968a). *Exp. Gerontol.* 3, 235.

Sondhi, K. C. (1968b). *Proc. Nat. Acad. Sci. U.S.* 59, 785.

Sondhi, K. C., and Turoczi, L. J. (1966). *Proc. Nat. Acad. Sci. U.S.* 56, 1743.

Sonnenblick, B. P., and Grodis, J. (1963). *Drosophila Inform. Serv.* 37, 130.

Spector, W. S. (ed.) (1965). "Handbook of Biological Data," p. 182. Saunders, Philadelphia, Pennsylvania.

Standifer, L. N., McCaughey, W. F., Todd, F. E., and Kemmerer, A. R. (1960). *Ann. Entomol. Soc. Amer.* 53, 618.

Steinfeld H. M. D. (1928). *Univ. Calif., Berkeley, Publ. Zool.* 31, 131.

Stephen, W. F., and Gilbert, L. I. (1970). *J. Insect Physiol.* 16, 851.

Strehler, B. L. (1959). *Quart. Rev. Biol.* 34, 117.

Strehler, B. L. (1960). *Amer. Inst. Biol. Sci., Publ.* 6.

Strehler, B. L. (1961). *J. Gerontol.* 16, 2.

Strehler, B. L. (1962). "Time, Cells, and Aging." Academic Press, New York.

Strehler, B. L., and Mildvan, A. S. (1960). *Science* **132**, 14.
Strehler, B. L., Mark, D. D., Mildvan, A. S., and Gee, M. V. (1959). *J. Gerontol.* **14**, 430.
Sullivan, R. L., and Grosch, D. S. (1953). *Nucleonics* **11**, 21.
Szilard, L. (1959a). *Proc. Nat. Acad. Sci. U.S.* **45**, 30.
Szilard, L. (1959b). *Nature (London)* **184**, 956.
Takahashi, A., Philpott, D. E., and Miquel, J. (1970a). *J. Gerontol.* **25**, 210.
Takahashi, A., Philpott, D. E., and Miquel, J. (1970b). *J. Gerontol.* **25**, 222.
Taylor, I. R., and Steinbach, H. B. (1931). *Physiol. Zool.* **4**, 604.
Thayer, D. W., and Terzian, L. A. (1970). *J. Insect Physiol.* **16**, 1.
Thomas, J. J., Baxter, R. C., and Fenn, W. O. (1966). *J. Gen. Physiol.* **49**, 537.
Tracey, K. M. (1958). *Ann. Entomol. Soc. Amer.* **51**, 429.
Tribe, M. A. (1966). *J. Insect Physiol.* **12**, 1577.
Tribe, M. A., and Ashhurst, D. E. (1972). *J. Cell Sci.* **10**, 443.
Upton, A. C. (1957). *J. Gerontol.* **12**, 306.
Van Herrewege, J., and David, J. (1970). *Exp. Gerontol.* **5**, 131.
Waku, Y., and Gilbert, L. I. (1964). *J. Morphol.* **115**, 69.
Walker, A. C., and Birt, L. M. (1969). *J. Insect Physiol.* **15**, 305.
Wattiaux, J. M. (1968a). *Exp. Gerontol.* **3**, 55.
Wattiaux, J. M. (1968b). *Evolution* **22**, 406.
Wattiaux, J. M., and Lamborot, M. (1967). *Curr. Mod. Biol.* **1**, 5.
Wharton, D. R. A., and Wharton, M. L. (1959). *Radiat. Res.* **11**, 600.
Whiting, A. R. (1949). *Biol. Bull.* **97**, 210.
Wigglesworth, V. B. (1950). "Principles of Insect Physiology," p. 228. Methuen, London.
Williams, C. M., and Beecher, H. K. (1944). *Amer. J. Physiol.* **140**, 566.
Williams, C. M., Barness, L. A., and Sawyer, W. H. (1943). *Biol. Bull.* **84**, 263.
Williams, G. C. (1957). *Evolution* **11**, 398.
Woke, P. A., Ally, M. S., and Rosenberger, C. R., Jr. (1956). *Ann. Entomol. Soc. Amer.* **49**, 435.
Wunder, C. C. (1955). *Proc. Soc. Exp. Biol. Med.* **89**, 544.
Wunder, C. C. (1963). *J. Aerosp. Med.* **34**, 5.
Yale, T. H., and Ballard, R. C. (1966). *Comp. Biochem. Physiol.* **19**, 29.

AUTHOR INDEX

Numbers in italics refer to the pages on which the complete references are listed.

A

Abercrombie, M., 408, *471*
Aboim, A. N., 62, *88*
Achazi, R. K., 186, *233*
Achtelig, M., 192, 206, *233*
Adams, T. S., 109, 121, 125, *150*, 323, *354*, 402, *471*
Adelung, D., 287, *354*
Adiyodi, K. G., 30, *85*, 114, *150*
Adkisson, P., 132, *157*
Aggarwal, S. K., 25, 27, 28, 32, 36, 39, *89*, 163, *240*, 258, *360*
Aggarwal, U., *89*
Agrarval, H. C., 179, *243*
Agrell, I., 167, 168, 169, 170, 171, 172, 174, 203, 204, 211, 212, 217, 219, 220, 221, 223, 224, 225, 226, 227, 228, 229, 230, *234*
Agui, N., 332, 333, *354*
Ajami, A., 299, *354*
Akai, H., 216, *234*
Alexander, B. H., 397, *471*
Alexander, J., 179, *237*
Alexander, P., 442, *471*
Alfert, M., 210, *234*, 353, *354*
Allais, J. P., 176, 177, *234*
Allee, W. C., 383, 389, *471*
Allegri, G., 179, *236*
Allen, E. R., 22, 23, *85*, *87*
Allen, T. H., 175, 185, 187, *234*, *235*
Allfrey, V. G., 344, *354*
Allison, V. F., 432, 433, 467, *477*
Ally, M. S., 451, *478*
Alpatov, W. W., 404, 405, 417, *471*
Alumot, E., 30, *90*
Ambrosioni, J. C., 219, *237*

Ammon, H., 272, *358*
Anderson, D. S., 46, *85*
Anderson, D. T., 172, 188, 191, 197, 198, 200, 202, 204, 206, *234*
Anderson, E., 16, 18, 29, 32, 34, 42, *85*, *92*
Anderson, J. F., 84, *85*, *89*
Anderson, L. M., 27, 37, *85*, *88*
Anderson, R. J., 294, 299, *354*, *365*
Anderson, W. A., 27, *85*, 119, *156*
Andrew, W., 435, *471*
Anglas, M. J., 218, *234*
Ankersmit, G. W., 131, 132, *150*
Applebaum, S. A., 304, 351, *354*, *357*
Arai, T., 327, *358*
Arking, R., 335, *354*
Arnaud, M., 351, *354*
Arnold, J. W., 427, *471*
Arvy, L., 117, *150*
Ashburner, M., 208, 210, *234*, 282, 283, 343, 344, *354*
Ashhurst, D. E., 455, *478*
Atlan, H., 410, 411, 412, 418, 427, 429, 430, 440, 441, 442, *471*, *476*

B

Baard, G., 127, *152*
Babcock, K. L., 178, *234*
Babers, F. H., 213, 223, *234*, 448, 454, 460, 462, *471*
Babu, T. H., 317, *354*
Baillie, W. H. T., 378, 395, *475*
Baird, M. B., 444, 448, 461, *477*
Baker, G. L., 176, 177, *245*
Baker, G. T., III, 454, 457, *471*, *477*

Baliga, B. S., 230, *234*
Ballard, R. C., 444, *475, 478*
Balazs, A., 444, *471*
Balzam, B., 188, *234*
Bantock, C. R., 165, 205, 206, *234*
Barker, K. R., 65, *86*
Barker, R. J., 397, *471*
Barnes, L. L., 413, *475*
Barness, L. A., 397, 455, 459, 461, *478*
Barrett, C. C., 328, *368*
Barrón, E. S. G., 396, *471*
Barsa, M. C., 214, 226, *241*
Bartel, A. H., 179, *239*
Barth, R. H., 116, 141, *150, 152*, 325, *354*
Barton, D. H. R., 276, *354*
Barton-Browne, L., 309, *354*
Basile, R., 32, 36, *85*
Bassurmanova, O. K., 123, 136, *155*
Baumann, G., 346, *354*
Baumann, P. A., 445, *471*
Baumhover, A. H., 285, *360*
Baxter, R. C., 411, 412, 421, *472, 478*
Bayreuther, K., 23, *85*
Beament, J. W. L., 43, 46, 57, *85*, 408, *472*
Beams, H. W., 34, 35, 42, *85, 89*
Beaudoin, A. R., 213, 221, *234*
Beaulaton, J., 261, *354*
Beck, S. D., 328, *354*
Becker, E., 274, *354*
Becker, M., 221, *234*
Beckmann, R., 70, *86*
Beecher, H. K., 397, 421, 455, 459, 461, *478*
Beenakkers, A. M. T., 324, *364*
Beermann, W., 202, 208, *234*
Beetsma, J., 314, *354*
Beetsma, Y., 150, *157*
Beischer, D. E., 418, *473*
Beklemishev, V., 58, *85*
Bell, J., 219, *234*
Bell, W. J., 27, 29, 47, *85*, 92, 116, *150*, 325, *354*
Bellas, T. E., 72, *93*
Bellini, L., 176, *246*
Belyaeva, T. G., 136, *155*
Benassi, C. A., 179, *236*
Bender, H. A., 207, *244*
Benjamin, W. B., 344, *354*
Bensch, K. G., 411, 412, 427, 429, 430, 440, 441, 442, *476*
Bentley, R. M., 163, *240*

Bentz, F., 30, *85*
Benz, G., 143, 146, 147, *150*, 213, 223, *234*
Berberian, P. A., 402, 417, 435, 452, 459, 465, *472, 473, 477*
Bercaw, B. L., 405, *477*
Berendes, H. D., 343, 344, 348, 350, *354, 358, 361, 364*
Berger, C. A., 210, *234*
Bergerard, J., 81, 84, *85*, 176, 177, *234*
Berkoff, C. E., 293, *354*
Berlese, A., 17, *85*
Bern, H. A., 252, 254, 257, *354, 367*, 443, *476*
Bernard, G. R., 223, *234*
Bernstein, M. H., 41, *89*
Berreur, P., 327, 328, *354*
Berridge, M. J., 310, *354, 363, 364*
Berry, S. J., 32, *89*, 230, *240*, 322, 325, 336, *354, 361, 363*, 457, *472*
Bertrand, H. A., 395, 412, *472*
Betz, N. L., 449, *476*
Beyerinck, M. W., 56, *85*
Beziat, Y., 351, *354*
Bhakthan, N. M. G., 309, 322, 324, *355*
Bhandari, K. G., 38, *85*
Bhatnagar, P. L., 397, 409, 431, 454, 461, 466, 467, *473, 477*
Bhuiyan, N. I., 206, *234*
Bieber, M. A., 295, *355*
Bier, K., 20, 31, 32, 33, 34, 36, 41, *85, 86, 88*, 149, *150*, 182, 205, 206, *234, 235, 240*
Biesele, J. J., 65, *86*
Bilewicz, S., 424, *472*
Binnard, R., 412
Birt, L. M., 213, 221, 223, 224, 226, 227, 228, 230, *235, 236, 237, 239, 241*, 455, 457, *474, 475, 478*
Bishop, G. H., 66, 67, 68, 73, 74, *86*
Bjorksten, J., 372, *472*
Blair, H. A., 411, 412, *472*
Blaustein, M. P., 229, *235*
Blest, A. D., 400, 403, 453, *472*
Blickenstaff, C. C., 130, *150, 152*, 268, *355*
Bliss, D. E., 209, *235*
Bloch, B., 117, *150*, 254, *355*
Block, B. C., 71, *93*
Blum, M. S., 66, 68, 69, 70, 71, 72, *86*, 92
Blumenfeld, M., 30, *86*, 325, *355*
Bock, E., 188, 199, *235, 245*
Boctor, I. Z., 326, *356*

Bode, C., 287, *360*
Bode, H. J., 172, *242*
Böden, E., 314, *364*
Bodenheimer, F. S., 379, *472*
Bodenstein, D., 101, 103, 104, 110, 120, 123, 124, 130, 135, 138, *150, 154, 156, 157,* 188, 209, 210, 215, 226, *235,* 252, 258, 260, 326, *355, 360, 365,* 449, *472*
Bodine, J. H., 173, 174, 175, 176, 178, 179, 180, 181, 183, 185, 186, 187, 219, 220, *235, 241, 243, 245, 246*
Bodnaryk, R. P., 28, 30, *86,* 214, 235, 341, 342, *355, 361*
Boell, E. J., 174, 175, 176, 185, 187, *235, 243*
Bohijn, W., 29, 37, *87*
Böhm, G.-A., 310, *357*
Bombosch, S., 144, *150*
Bondareff, W., 443, 449, *472*
Bongers, W., 143, *150*
Bonhag, P. F., 15, 17, 18, 21, 23, 25, 31, 32, 35, 36, 39, 41, 50, 64, 68, 74, *86, 93, 94,* 163, *244*
Bonnemaison, L., 131, *150*
Borch, E., 230, *234*
Borden, J. H., 315, 324, *355*
Borei, H., 454, *474*
Borgna, J. L., 351, *354*
Boughton, D. C., 147, *150*
Bounhiol, J. J., 30, *88,* 104, *150,* 252, *355*
Bowers, B., 230, *235,* 256, 264, *359*
Bowers, W. S., 120, 130, *150,* 268, 291, 296, 308, 353, *355*
Bowler, K., 408, *472*
Boyd, H., 227, *235*
Boyd, J. B., 227, *235*
Boyette, M., 294, 295, *362*
Bozcuk, A. N., 445, *475*
Brandenburg, J., 58, *86,* 136, *150*
Brandt, A., 16, *86*
Brandt, H., 147, *150*
Brandt, K., 454, 460, *477*
Brauer, A., 179, 196, *235*
Breland, O. P., 65, *86*
Bresslau, E., 74, *86*
Breuer, M. E., 79, *86, 92*
Bridges, C. B., 79, 82, *86, 91*
Briegel, H., 179, *236*
Briggs, R., 202, *235*
Brighenti, A., 223, *235*

Brindley, T. A., 71, *89*
Britten, R. J., 353, *355*
Brody, H., 443, 449, *472*
Brookes, V. J., 30, *87,* 116, *151,* 325, 347, *355, 357*
Brooks, M. A., 459, *472*
Brosemer, R. W., 459, *472*
Brousse-Gaury, P., 108, *150,* 267, *355*
Brower, J., 72, *86*
Brower, L. P., 72, *86*
Brown, A. W. A., 214, 223, *235*
Brown, B. E., 309, *355*
Brown, D. D., 340, *366*
Brown, E. H., 18, *86*
Brown, N. M., 42, *87*
Browne, L. B., 57, *86*
Browne, L. E., 72, *93*
Brownlee, R. G., 72, *93*
Bruce, V., 263, *364*
Bruchovsky, N., 284, *355*
Brunet, P. C. J., 55, 56, *86,* 326, *368*
Brust, R. A., 84, *86, 89*
Bryan, J. H. D., 21, *86*
Bryant, P. J., 197, 217, *235,* 319, *355*
Buchner, P., 48, 49, 50, *86*
Buck, J. B., 219, 220, 221, 224, *235*
Buhler, R., 457, *472*
Bühlmann, G., 113, *154*
Bull, A. L., 192, 194, *235*
Bullock, M. W., 272, *355*
Bulos, B., 455, *472*
Bunde, D. E., 179, *235*
Burdette, W. J., 272, 327, *355*
Burkholder, J. R., 174, *235*
Burkholder, W. E., 71, *93*
Burnett, A. L., 345, *361*
Burroughs, N., 226, *246*
Burtt, E. T., 99, *150*
Bushland, R. C., 60, 61, *86, 90*
Bushnell, R. J., 147, *150*
Busnel, R. G., 213, *236*
Butcher, E. W., 350, *364*
Butenandt, A., 70, *86,* 271, 272, 280, *355*
Butler, C. G., 148, 149, *150*
Butler, L., 457, *472*
Butt, F. H., 160, *239*
Butterworth, F. M., 326, *355,* 449, *472*
Butz, A., 400, 447, 452, 456, *472, 476*
Buxton, P. A., 54, *95*
Bygrave, F. L., 345, *355*

C

Callahan, P. S., 68, *86*
Callahan, R. F., 398, *472*
Callow, R. K., 149, *150*
Calzada, M. C., 286, *358*
Camenzind, R., 53, *86*
Campbell, F. L., 165, *236*
Campbell, S. F., 293, 294, *359*
Candy, D. J., 309, *362*
Cannon, H. G., 64, 67, *87*
Cantacuzène, A. M., 66, *86*, 138, *150*
Cappe de Baillon, P., 44, 46, *86, 87*
Cappugi, G., 227, *246*
Carayon, J., 49, 50, 77, 78, *87*
Carey, F. G., 457, *472*
Carlisle, D. B., 265, *355*
Carlson, L. D., 186, 187, *235, 236*
Carr, C. A. H., 149, *150*
Cascio, T., 68, *86*
Caspari, E., 252, *355*
Cassaunel, C., 47, *87*
Cassier, P., 123, *151, 152*
Castillón, M. P., 213, 221, *236*
Catalán, R. E., 213, 221, *236*
Cave, M. D., 22, 23, *85, 87*
Caveney, S., 322, *355*
Cazal, M., 306, *355*
Cazal, P., 123, *151*, 260, *355*
Century, T. J., 346, *355*
Cerkasov, J., 131, *153*, 225, *236*
Cerny, V., 292, *355*
Chadwick, L. E., 260, 286, *355, 397, 472*
Chalmers, T. A., 378, *474*
Chamberlain, W. F., 328, *368*
Chambers, D. L., 116, *151*
Chandler, A. E. F., 144, *151*
Chang, M. L., 273, *362*
Chang, T. H., 65, *87*
Chase, A. M., 230, *236*, 346, *355*
Chaudhary, K. D., 327, *355, 361*, 456, *472*
Chefurca, W., 214, 227, *241*
Chellappah, W. T., 214, *247*
Chen, P. S., 144, *151*, 179, 213, 219, 223, *236*, 445, 457, 458, *471, 472*
Cheng, E. Y., 455, 456, *472*
Cherbas, L., 288, 304, *355*
Cherbas, P., 288, 304, *355*
Chihara, C. J., 283, 299, 339, *355*
Child, C. M., 372, *472*

Child, G. P., 197, *239*
Chino, H., 176, 177, 180, 181, 186, 187, 221, *236,* 301, 303, 304, *356*
Chippendale, C. M., 224, *236*
Chong, Y. K., 272, 285, *356*
Christenson, L. D., 60, *93*
Chrishan, B., 223, 228, *235*
Church, N. S., 42, 47, *88, 92*, 163, 166, 167, *243*
Clark, A. M., 378, 380, 388, 391, 393, 395, 411, 412, 413, 415, 416, 429, 450, 454, 455, 463, 466, *472*
Clark, J. K., 322, *366*
Clarke, J. M., 391, 393, 405, 406, 445, *472, 473*
Clarke, K. U., 133, *151*
Claycomb, W. C., 344, *356*
Clements, A. N., 135, *151*
Clever, U., 343, 344, 346, *356*
Cliff, A. D., 122, *151*
Close, P., 418, *473*
Cobben, R. H., 45, 46, 47, 57, 61, *87*
Cockayne, E. A., 82, 83, *87*
Cohen, C. F., 328, *364*
Cohen, E., 324, 334, 335, 351, *356*
Cole, K. W., 395, 413, *472*
Coleman, A. E., 186, *236*
Coles, G. C., 30, *87*, 113, *151*
Collatz, S., 172, *242*
Colombo, G., 179, *236*
Colucci, V., 303, *359*
Comeau, A., 71, *92*
Comfort, A., 372, 380, 398, 403, 404, 428, 468, *473*
Comstock, J. H., 4, *8*
Congote, L. F., 337, 338, 344, *356, 360*
Corey, E. J., 293, *356*
Cork, J. M., 409, 411, *473*
Couch, E. F., 123, *154*
Counce, S. J., 164, 165, 188, 195, 197, 202, 203, 206, 207, *236*
Cragg, F. W., 78, *87*
Craig, G. B., 84, *87*, 144, *154*, 315, *356*
Craig, R., 179, *239*
Cranston, F. P., 72, *86*
Crescitelli, F., 219, 221, *236*
Crompton, M., 221, 226, *236*, 457, *473*
Crone, H. D., 456, *473*
Cross, A. D., 276, *365*
Crossley, A. C., 216, 218, *236*

Cruikshank, W. J., 31, *87*
Crystal, M. M., 60, *90,* 396, *473*
Cuénot, L., 429, 450, *473*
Cummings, M. R., 28, 32, 36, 39, 42, *87*
Curtis, C. F., 60, *87*
Curtis, H. J., 372, *473*
Curtis, J. J., 372, *473*
Cutkomp, L. K., 455, 456, *472*
Cymborowski, B., 263, *356*
Czoppelt, C., 221, *236*

D

Da Cunha, A. B., 80, *87*
Dahm, K. H., 103, *156,* 289, 290, 291, 292, 293, 294, 295, 296, 297, 298, 299, *356, 362, 364, 365*
Daille, J., 180, 181, *242*
Dammeier, B., 278, *356*
Daneholt, B., 343, *356, 364*
Dapples, C. C., 32, *87*
D'Armiento, M., 342, *356*
Das, C. C., 184, 202, *236*
Das, N. K., 41, *89,* 353, *354*
Dauer, M., 409, *473*
Davenport, R., 34, 35, *95*
Davey, K. G., 30, 67, 74, *87, 89, 92,* 144, 145, 146, 147, *151,* 313, *356*
Davey, W. P., 409, *473*
David, J., 417, 422, *473, 478*
David, W. A., 57, *87*
Davidson, E. H., 353, *355*
Davis, C. W. C., 172, 191, 192, 193, 194, 197, 200, *236*
Davis, J. S., 350, *366*
Davis, J. W., 351, *359*
Davis, N. T., 103, *151*
Day, M. F., 98, 106, 108, 110, 120, 123, 124, 138, *151*
D'Costa, M. A., 221, *236*
de Boer, J. A., 47, *87,* 102, 106, 107, 110, 113, 115, 116, 117, 130, 134, *151, 156,* 268, 324, *356, 366*
de Boissezon, P., 429, 450, *473*
De Borde, D., 32, *93*
de Groot, A. P., 148, *151*
Dejmal, R. K., 30, *87*
de Jong, J. K., 135, *151*
de Kort, C. A. D., 110, 111, 113, 127, 130, *151, 152,* 324, *356*

Delcour, J., 461, *473*
Deleurance, E. P., 118, 141, *151*
De Long, D. M., 400, 415, *475*
de Loof, A., 24, 28, 29, 37, 38, 40, 42, 43, 48, 69, *87,* 102, 110, 111, 113, 116, 118, 126, 127, 128, 130, 138, 139, *151, 152,* 322, 348, *356, 364*
De Luca, H. F., 284, *358*
Del Vecchio, R. J., 221, 223, 224, *236*
De Melker, J., 421, *475*
Demyanovsky, S. Y., 213, 221, *236*
Den Boer, P. J., 421, *475*
Derr, R. F., 178, *243*
de Ruiter, L., 314, *354*
De Sombre, E. R., 303, 306, 352, *359, 362*
Dethier, V. G., 57, *87*
Detinova, T. S., 101, 135, *151*
Devi, A., 181, 183, 230, *236*
de Wilde, J., 21, 28, 37, 47, *87,* 102, 103, 106, 107, 110, 113, 115, 116, 117, 126, 127, 128, 130, 131, 132, 134, 135, *151, 152,* 268, 314, *354, 356*
Diem, C., 144, *151*
Dillon, J., 274, 294, *362*
Dinamarca, M. L., 223, 224, 230, *236, 241*
Dion, A. S., 180, *238*
Dixon, A. F. G., 123, *152*
Doane, W. W., 391, *473*
Dobrogosz, W. J., 182, 183, 187, *237*
Dobzhansky, T., 83, *87,* 468, *473*
Dodson, L. F., 309, *354*
Dogra, G. S., 254, *356*
Dolejš, L., 292, *355*
Doncaster, L., 64, 67, *87*
Dorn, A., 318, *356*
Dorough, H. W., 422, *473*
Downer, R. G. H., 227, *243,* 309, *356*
Drescher, W., 36, *88*
Du Bois, A. W., 196, *236*
Duchâteau-Bosson, G. H., 213, *237*
Dufour, D., 30, *87*
Duhman, L., 299, *358*
Duintjer, C. S., 21, 47, *87,* 130, 132, 134, *152*
Duncan, D., 443, 449, *473*
Dünnebeil, K., 281, *358*
Dupont-Raabe, M., 117, *152*
Du Praw, E. J., 188, 202, *237*
Durand, M., 35, *88,* 180, 181, *237*
Duspiva, F., 182, 186, *233, 237, 238*

Dutkowski, A. B., 39, *92*, 116, 118, *152*, 263, *356*
Dutrieu, J., 178, *237*
Duve, H., 99, *155*, 256, 308, *363*

E

Earle, N. W., 396, 403, *475*
Eastham, L., 165, *237*
Ebert, J. D., 353, *363*
Economopoulos, A. P., 332, *356*
Eddleman, C. D., 65, *86*
Edström, J.-E., 343, *356, 364*
Edwards, F. J., 324, *356*
Edwards, G. A., 173, 213, *237*, 396, 404, *473*
Edwards, J. A., 293, *368*
Edwards, J. S., 216, 218, *237*, 263, *356, 365*
Egarov, T. A., 38, *87*
Eguchi, M., 228, *237*
Egyházi, E., 343, *356, 364*
Eichembaum, D. M., 228, *245*
Eide, P. E., 323, *354*
Eidmann, H., 50, *87*
El-Ibrashi, M. T., 103, 130, *152*, 326, *356*
Ellis, P. E., 265, *355*
Ellis, R. S., 435, *473*
Emerson, A. E., 383, 389, *471*
Emmerich, H., 300, 301, 304, 344, *356*
Enders, E., 142, *152*
Endo, K., 105, *152*
Engelmann, F., 17, 30, 53, *87*, 103, 106, 107, 108, 109, 113, 114, 116, 117, 120, 123, 124, 125, 141, 143, 144, 146, 147, *152, 154*, 263, 266, 307, 325, *356, 362*
Engels, W., 32, 36, *87, 88*
Erdman, H. E., 412, *473*
Erickson, B. W., 293, *356*
Erk, F. C., 444, 448, 461, *477*
Etienne, J., 176, 177, *234*
Etkin, W., 218, *237*
Eudy, W. W., 182, 183, 187, *237*
Evans, A. C., 216, 221, 223, 224, *237*
Evans, T. C., 219, 220, *235*
Ewen, A. B., 103, *152*
Ewest, A., 163, 164, 189, 190, 191, 196, *237*

F

Fabbri, S., 280, 281, *359*
Fain-Maurel, M. A., 123, *152*

Fales, H. M., 271, 296, *355, 356*
Fan, S., 228, *241*
Farrell, G. J., 448, *477*
Fast, P. G., 219, *237*
Faulkner, D. J., 293, 294, 295, *355, 356, 359*
Faux, A., 271, 282, *356, 357*
Favard-Séréno, C., 35, 36, 37, 41, 42, 43, *88*, 180, *237*
Feakins, P. G., 276, *354*
Feder, N., 218, *239*
Feir, D., 30, *94*
Feldhege, A., 172, *242*
Feldherr, C. M., 346, *357*
Feldman-Muhsam, B., 378, 381, 383, 385, 394, 419, 420, *473*
Fenichel, I. R., 346, *355*
Fenn, W. O., 421, *478*
Fentiman, A. F., 72, *89*
Ferket, P., 135, *151*
Ficq, A., 32, 36, 79, *88*, 208, *237*
Finch, L. R., 213, 227, *224, 237*
Fink, D. E., 173, 227, *237*
Fiore, C., 399, 400, 451, 452, *475*
Fischer, L., 274, *357*
Fitzgerald, L. R., 178, 179, 187, *235, 237*
Fixler, D. E., 223, *234*
Flanders, S. E., 47, 58, 75, *88*, 135, *152*
Flemings, M. B., 395, *473*
Flesher, J. W., 303, *359*
Florkin, M., 213, *237*
Folsom, J. W., 4, *8*
Foltz, R. L., 72, *89*
Fordy, M. R., 31, 34, 42, *89*
Formigoni, A., 117, *152*
Forrest, H. S., 179, 181, 182, 183, 184, *237, 238, 240, 245*
Fouillet, P., 417, *473*
Fourche, J., 219, *237*
Fox, A. S., 195, *239*
Fox, D. L., 449, *473*
Fraenkel, G., 6, *9*, 252, 256, 327, 328, 347, *354, 357, 368*, 408, *473*
Fraser, D. R., 284, *361*
Frelinger, J. A., 32, *93*
Frew, J. G. H., 219, 223, *237*
Fried, J. H., 276, *358, 365*
Friedman, S., 307, 308, *355, 360*
Fristrom, J. W., 283, 299, 339, *355, 357, 363, 364*
Frontali, N., 308, 310, *362*

Frost, J. N., 83, *88*
Frühauf, E., 56, *88*
Fujioka, S., 273, 274, 287, *359, 362, 365*
Fukaya, M., 331, 332, 333, *354, 368*
Fukuda, S., 103, 104, *152*, 260, 328, 357, *363*
Fukuda, T., 213, *237*
Fulco, L., 333, *363*
Fung, S. F. C., 83, *88*
Furlenmeier, A., 276, 278, *357, 360*
Furneaux, P. J. S., 178, *237*
Fürst, A., 276, 278, *357, 360*
Fyhn, H. J., 226, *237*

G

Gabe, M., 106, 117, *150, 152*, 252, *357*
Gadallah, A. I., 183, 184, 185, *237*
Gaeta, I., 186, *237*
Galbraith, M. N., 272, 278, 281, 282, 284, 285, 286, 288, *356 357, 359, 366, 367*
Ganagarajah, M., 123, *152*
Ganti, Y., 213, *237*
Garcia Bellido, A., 144, *152*
Gardiner, B. O. C., 57, *87*, 310, *361*
Gardner, E., 435, *473*
Gardner, T. S., 414, *473*
Gassner, G., 65, *86, 88*
Gauss, U., 194, *237*
Gawlik, S., 228, *243*
Gay, H., 184, 202, *236*
Gee, M. V., 443, 449, *478*
Geigy, R., 62, *88*, 197, *237*
Geldiay, S., 103, 115, 130, 132, *152*
Gelehrter, T. D., 353, *367*
Georgiana, M., 378, 395, *473*
Georgiev, G. P., 230, *237*
Gerrity, R. G., 42, *88*
Gersch, M., 252, 265, 287, 310, *357*
Gershfeld, N. L., 352, *357*
Geyer-Duszynska, I., 165, 202, 205, *237, 238*
Gibbons, S. A., 149, *150*
Gier, H. T., 49, *88*
Gilbert, L. I., 105, *156*, 218, 219, 221, 227, *236, 237, 238, 239*, 250, 251, 254, 257, 258, 259, 263, 265, 268, 269, 270, 271, 291, 294, 295, 300, 301, 302, 303, 304, 305, 306, 307, 308, 309, 311, 312, 313, 314, 318, 319, 321, 322, 323, 324, 325, 326, 328, 332, 334, 335, 342, 343, 345,

346, 348, 349, 351, *354, 355, 356, 357, 358, 360, 361, 362, 365, 366, 367*, 443, 457, *477, 478*
Gill, K. S., 161, 163, *238*
Gillett, J. D., 101, 135, *152*
Gillot, S., 35, 36, *91*, 180, 181, *242*
Gillott, C., 133, *151, 152*
Gilman, N. W., 293, *356*
Gilmour, D., 230, *238*, 465, *473*
Gingell, D. J., 310, *358*
Girardie, A., 103, 107, 115, 117, 141, *152*, 258, 266, 269, *359*
Glass, B., 399, *473*
Gloor, H., 197, 204, *238*
Glowska, Z., 66, 68, 69, 70, 72, *86*
Goldman, A. S., 198, 201, *238*
Goldschmidt, R., 79, 82, 83, *88*
Goldsworthy, G. J., 133, *153*, 211, 214, *239*, 308, *357, 358*
Gomes, F. P., 80, *90*
Gonzalez, B. M., 378, 391, 392, 393, *473*
Goodman, R. M., 344, *354*
Goodwin, T. W., 284, 287, *368*
Gordeenko, N. A., 378, *471*
Gordon, H. T., 133, *152*, 332, *356*
Gorell, T. A., 301, 304, 305, 335, *357, 358*
Gorman, J. E., 71, *93*
Gorski, J., 303, *367*
Goryshin, N. I., 132, *152*
Gosbee, J. L., 254, *358*
Goss, R. J., 46, *88*
Goto, M., 273, 274, *359, 360*
Gowen, J. W., 82, 83, *88, 93*, 391, 394, 401, 409, *473*
Grace, T. D. C., 334, 351, *362*
Graham, C. L., 467, *477*
Granner, D., 353, *367*
Gray, F. H., 402, 417, 435, 452, 459, 465, *472, 473, 477*
Grebb, R. J., 82, *88*
Green, L. R., 422, *473*
Green, N., 71, *89*
Greenberg, B., 418, *473*
Greengard, P., 351, *361*
Greenslade, F. C., 123, *154*
Grégoire, I., 456, *474*
Gregory, D. W., 230, *241*, 455, *474*
Greiff, D., 417, *474*
Grellet, P., 171, 178, 202, *238*
Gresson, R. A. R., 32, 38, *88*

Griffiths, J. T., 379, 400, *474*
Griggs, R. C., 397, *474*
Grison, P., 58, *88*, 135, *153*
Grodis, J., 409, 410, *477*
Grosch, D. S., 58, *88*, 408, 409, *474, 478*
Grossbach, U., 348, *358*
Grosz, J., 16, 17, 25, *88*
Groulade, J., 30, *88*
Grützmacher, H. F., 272, 277, 281, *358*
Grzelak, K., 214, 228, *238*
Gueldner, R. C., 72, *94*
Guerrier, Y., 123, *151*
Guilleux, J. C., 351, *354*
Gunson, M. M., 344, *367*
Günthart, T., 22, 50, *88*
Günther, J., 206, *238*
Gupta, B. L., 39, *91*
Gupta, G. N., 303, *359*
Gupta, P. D., 76, *88*
Gurdon, J. B., 202, *238*
Gutfraund, D. E., 454, *477*
Gwadz, R. W., 119, 142, *153, 156*

H

Hachlow, V., 260, *358*
Hackney, R. J., 272, 284, 285, 288, *357*
Hadorn, E., 57, *88*, 99, *153, 156*, 209, 215, 217, *238*
Hafferl, W., 281, 283, 284, 285, 286, 288, 299, 301, 303, 304, *356, 357, 358, 362, 367*
Hagan H. R., 52, *88*
Haget, A., 167, 190, 196, 200, 201, *238*
Hagiwara, H., 278, 279, *360*
Halkka, L., 34, *88*
Halkka, O., 34, *88*
Hall, D. W., 80, *93*
Hall, J. C., 447, *474*
Haller, P. H., 218, *238*
Hallez, J., 56, *88*
Hallez, P., 39, *88*
Hamburger, K., 110, 116, *157*
Hamon, C., 30, *88*
Hampshire, F., 271, 272, 277, 280, 281, *358, 359*
Hanly, E. W., 339, *363*
Hänsel, R., 281, *358*
Hansen-Delkeskamp, E., 23, *88*, 182, 183, 185, 190, *238*
Hanström, B., 252, *358*

Hanzmann, E., 289, 290, 294, 295, *362*
Haranghy, L., 444, *471*
Harashima, K., 301, *356*
Hardee, D. D., 72, *94*
Harding, C., 71, *89*
Hardy, R. W., 65, *94*
Harker, J., 106, *153*
Harmsen, R., 256, *366*
Harris, S. E., 181, 182, 183, 184, *237, 238*
Harrison, B. J., 446, *474*
Harrison, I. T., 276, *358*
Hartmann, R., 120, 139, *153*
Harvey, W. R., 219, *238*
Hasegawa, K., 328, *365*
Haskell, P. T., 47, *88*, 117, 123, *153*
Hasset, C. C., 408, 410, *474*
Hatai, S., 435, *474*
Hattori, F., 281, *359*
Haub, J. G., 221, *238*
Hausman, S. J., 27, *88*
Hawkins, W. B., 454, *477*
Haydak, M. H., 414, 415, 425, 427, 428, 430, 449, *474*
Hayden, P., 452, *472*
Heby, O., 230, *238*
Hechter, O., 350, *358*
Hecker, E., 70, *86*
Hedin, P. A., 72, *94, 223, 242*
Hegdekar, B. M., 227, 228, *238*
Hegner, R. W., 189, 194, 196, 204, *238*
Heilbrunn, L. V., 396, *474*
Heinig, S., 191, 196, 201, *238, 240*
Heinrich, G., 288, *358*
Heller, J., 219, 220, 221, 223, 224, *238*
Helmsing, P. J., 344, *358*
Henke, K. E., 215, *238*
Hennen, S., 207, *242*
Henrick, C. A., 293, 294, 299, *354, 358, 365*
Henstra, S., 110, 113, *156*, 324, *366*
Herbst, E. J., 180, *238*
Herlant-Meeuwis, H., 117, *153*
Herman, M. H., 439, *474*
Herman, W. S., 254, 260, 261, 262, 264, 271, *358*
Herold, R. C., 454, *474*
Herout, V., 277, 281, *359*
Herr, E. B., 397, *474*
Herrebout, W. M., 144, *153*
Herth, W., 192, 196, 197, *244*
Herzfeld, A., 172, *292*

Heslop, J. P., 446, *474*
Hess, G., 148, *153*
Hessler, E. J., 291, *367*
Hesselhaus, F., 57, *88*
Heymons, R., 170, *238*
Heywood, R. B., 218, *239*
Highnam, K. C., 23, 47, *88,* 103, 106, 107, 113, 115, 116, 117, 118, 123, 125, 133, 138, 144, 147, *153,* 253, 308, 310, *358*
Hikino, H., 271, 288, 327, *358, 363*
Hikino, Y., 271, *358*
Hill, D. F., 353, *366*
Hill, D. L., 175, 176, 177, *239*
Hill, L., 30, *88,* 103, 113, 115, 133, *153,* 211, 214, *239,* 306, 310, *358*
Himeno, M., 227, *239*
Hinks, C. F., 254, *358*
Hinse, C., 327, *355, 361*
Hinton, H. E., 6, *9,* 42, 43, 44, 46, *89,* 161, 215, 216, *239,* 322, *358,* 453, *474*
Hintz, A. M., 402, *471*
Hintze, C., 251, *358*
Hintze-Podufal, C., 261, 300, 314, *358*
Hinz, A. M., 121, *150*
Hirano, C., 214, 225, 227, *239, 245*
Hirono, I., 327, *358*
Hitchcock, F. A., 221, *238*
Hochschild, R., 423, 443, *474*
Hocks, P., 272, 276, 277, 278, *357, 358, 360*
Hodek, I., 131, *153*
Hodge, C. F., 424, 435, 436, *474*
Hodgson, E. S., 309, *354*
Hoffman, A. C., 422, *474*
Hoffmeister, H., 272, 273, 274, 277, 278, 281, 284, 288, 327, *357, 358, 360, 366*
Hogan, T. W., 179, *241*
Hogben, L., 32, *89*
Hohorst, W., 76, *89*
Holick, M. F., 284, *358*
Holliday, R., 446, *474*
Hollingsworth, M. J., 406, 407, 408, *472, 474*
Hollingworth, R. M., *93*
Hollis, V. W., Jr., 221, *241*
Hollweg, G., 30, *89*
Holz, I., 141, *156,* 314, 321, *364*
Hopf, H. S., 408, *473*
Hopkins, D. E., 60, *86*
Hoppe, W., 271, 272, 276, 278, *356, 359, 360*

Hori, M., 281, *358*
Horie, Y., 186, *239,* 328, *359*
Horikawa, M., 195, *239*
Horn, D. H. S., 271, 272, 273, 277, 278, 280, 281, 282, 283, 284, 285, 286, 288, 328, 344, *356, 357, 358, 359, 365, 366, 367*
Horsfall, W. R., 84, *85, 86, 89*
Horowitz, S. B., 346, *355*
Howard, L. O., 380 *474*
Howe, R. W., 400, *474*
Howells, A. J., 213, 224, *239*
Howland, R. B., 197, *239*
Hoyle, G., 214, *239*
Hradec, J., 353, *360*
Hsiao, C., 328, *359*
Hsiao, T. H., 328, *359*
Hsu, H. Y., 273, *362*
Huber, F., 106, *153*
Huber, R., 271, 272, 276, *359, 360*
Hudson, A., 187, *244*
Hudson, B. N. A., 57, *89*
Hudson, B. W., 179, *239*
Hudson, V. W., 313, *366*
Huettner, A. F., 164, 169, *239*
Hufnagel, A., 218, *239*
Hughes, M., 32, 67, *89,* 339, *359*
Hughes-Schräder, S., 52, *89*
Huignard, J., 123, 144, 146, *153*
Humphrey, G. F., 69, *89*
Hüppi, G., 278, 279, *359*
Huxley, J., 211, *239*
Hyde, R. R., 57, *89,* 393, *474*
Hylton, A. R., 431, *474*

I

Ichikawa, M., 104, *153,* 267, *359*
Idris, B. E. M., 164, 190, 191, 192, *239*
Ikekawa, N., 281, *359*
Ilan, J., 313, 340, *359*
Ilan, J., 313, 340, *359*
Illmensee, K., 202, *239*
Imai, S., 273, 274, *359, 365*
Imaizumi, T., 206, *239*
Imms, A. D., 14, 15, 62, *89*
Imray, F. P., 344, *367*
Inukai, T., 435, *474*
Iperti, G., 144, *153*
Ishibashi, M., 281, *359*

Ishikawa, E., 351, *359*
Ishikawa, S., 351, *359*
Ishizaki, H., 218, *239*, 344, *359*
Ito, H., 97, *153*, 257, *359*
Ito, S., 347, *359*
Ito, T., 186, 213, 219, 226, 227, *239*, 328, *359*

J

Jacob, J., 36, *89*, 180, *239*
Jacobson, H. I., 303, *359*
Jacobson, M., 71, *89*
James, D. W., 352, *359*
Janda, V., 218, *239*
Jant, B. A., 345, *359*
Jarial, M. S., 310, *359*
Jarnicka-Stanios, H., 213, *239*
Jarraya, A., 30, 32, *90*
Javorsky, E. G., 214, *243*
Jazdowska-Zagrodzinska, B., 206, *239*
Jefferson, D. J., 230, *240*, 444, *475*
Jenkins, D. W., 408, 410, *474*
Jennings, B., 418, *471*
Jensen, E. V., 303, 306, 352, *359*, *362*
Jizba, J., 277, 281, *359*
Johansson, A. S., 47, 58, *89*, 107, 108, 117, 123, 124, 133, 135, 138, *153*
Johannsen, O. A., 160, *239*
Johnson, B., 256, 264, *359*
Johnson, G. S., 342, *356*
Johnson, J. D., 345, *359*
Johnson, L. E., 394, 401, *473*
Johnson, M., 439, *474*
Johnson, M. L., 408, *471*
Johnson, R. A., 123, 128, *153*
Johnson, W. S., 293, 294, 296, *359*, *361*
Johnston, N. C., 149, *150*
Joly, L., 103, *153*, 258, 266, 269, *359*
Joly, P., 100, 102, 103, 106, 110, 123, 125, 129, *153*, 258, 263, 266, 269, 314, *359*
Jones, B. M., 227, *239*
Jones, C. R., 226, *239*, 446, 457, *474*, *475*
Joseph, S. R., 176, *244*
Jost, E., 60, *90*
Joyner, S. C., 328, *364*
Judy, K. J., 218, *239*, 253, 323, 328, 331, *359*, *360*
Jung, E., 167, 192, 196, 200, *239*
Jungblut, P. W., 303, *359*

Jura, C., 164, 170, 178, 196, 200, 201, 206, *239*

K

Kafatos, F. C., 214, 218, *239*, *240*, 339, *360*
Kahle, W., 53, *89*, 169, 205, *239*
Kahn, I. L., 213, 219, 220, *240*
Kaiser, P., 109, 123, 138, *153*
Kalthoff, K., 174, 192, 194, 202, *240*
Kambysellis, M. P., 136, 137, *153*, 332, 339, *359*, *360*
Kaplanis, J. N., 272, 277, 279, 280, 281, 285, 286, 288, 327, 328, *360*, *364*, *366*
Karlinsky, A., 103, 116, *153*, *154*
Karlson, P., 70, *89*, 224, 230, *240*, 245, 271, 272, 274, 277, 280, 281, 284, 287, 327, 328, 337, 338, 341, 344, 346, *355*, *356*, *360*, *365*, *367*
Kater, S. B., 256, 306, 310, *360*, *365*
Katz, M., 281, *360*
Katzenellenbogen, B. S., 214, *240*
Katzenellenbogen, J. A., 293, *356*
Kaufman, S., 345, *359*
Kaufmann, B. P., 41, *89*, 184, 202, *236*
Ke, D., 259, *360*
Keeley, L. L., 307, *360*
Keilin, D., 83, *89*
Keiser, I., 472, *474*
Keister, M., 220, 221, *235*
Kemmerer, A. R., 416, *477*
Kerb, U., 276, 278, *357*, *360*
Kerr, W. E., 80, 84, *87*, *89*, *90*
Kershaw, W. E., 378, *474*
Kessel, R. G., 34, 35, 42, *85*, *89*
Khalifa, A., 76, 78, *89*
Khouvine, Y., 456, *474*
Kilgore, W. W., 182, 183, 184, 185, 186, *237*, *240*, *243*
Kimmel, E. C., 110, 113, *156*, 324, *366*
Kimura, A. K., 353, *366*
King, D. S., 278, 280, 283, 284, 285, 286, 287, 288, 299, 303, 339, *355*, *360*, *362*
King, P. E., 31, 32, 34, 42, *89*
King, R. C., 16, 18, 19, 20, 23, 25, 27, 28, 32, 36, 39, 42, 43, 46, *86*, *87*, *89*, *90*, *93*, 163, *240*, 258, *360*
King, T. J., 202, *235*
Kinsella, J. E., 176, 177, 178, *240*
Kinzer, G. W., 72, *89*

Kiraly, J. K., 309, *354*
Kislov, A. N., 347, *360*
Kjellberg, B., 228, *234*
Kláner, S., 179, 185, *246*
Klassen, W., 61, *92*
Kleinfeld, R., 68, 69, *94*
Klemm, N., 309, *360*
Klun, J. A., 71, *89*
Knytel, A., 80, *95*
Ko, J. H., 289, 290, 294, *362*
Kobayashi, M., 105, *157*, 328, *360*
Koch, A., 49, *89*
Koch, E. A., 16, 19, 20, 23, *90*
Koch, P., 185, 195, 201, *240*
Kodicek, E., 284, *361*
Kohn, R. R., 372, 373, *474*
Kolderie, M. Q., 451, *476*
Komárková, E., 353, *360*
Kondo, E., 331, *368*
Kopec, S., 252, *360*, 417, *474*
Koreeda, M., 273, 274, 278, 279, 287, 294, *360, 362*
Korschelt, E., 43, *90*
Kosminsky, P., 83, *90*
Kozhanchikov, I. V., 186, *240*
Kramer, S., 458, *475*
Kramer, V., 210, *240*
Kratky, E., 427, *474*
Krause, G., 161, 165, 166, 167, 172, 176, 188, 190, 192, 194, 195, 196, 198, 199, 200, 206, *233, 236, 239, 240, 245, 247*
Krause, J., 172, 176, 194, 195, 200, *236, 240*
Krieg, P., 218, *239*
Krishna, I., 446, *475*
Krishnakumaran, A., 230, *240*, 263, 265, 271, 273, 294, 296, 322, 325, 328, 332, 336, *354, 359, 360, 361, 363, 364*, 445, 447, 457, *472, 474*
Krishnan, N., 273, *364*
Kroeger, H., 345, 346, 347, *361*
Kroeger, M., 208 *240*
Krogh, A., 219, *240*
Krueger, H. S., 444, *475*
Krumbiegel, I., 424, *475*
Krzystofowicz, A., 32, *90*, 178, 201, 206, *239*
Kuenen, D. J., 421, *475*
Kühn, A., 223, *236*, 252, *361*
Kuk-Meiri, S., 186, *245*
Kulasekarapandian, S., 273, *364*
Kung, K., 472, *475*

Kunz, W., 30, 34, 37, *90*, 205, *240*
Kuo, J. F., 351, *361*
Kurichare, M., 32, *91*
Kurihara, M., 47, *91*
Kurland, C. G., 227, *240*
Kuroda, Y., 333, *361*
Kuske, G., 217, *240*
Küthe, H.-W., 191, 196, *240*

L

Laabs, A., 56, *90*
Labeyrie, V., 143, 145, *154*
Labitte, A., 379, 395, *475*
Lábler, L., 292, *355*
La Brecque, G. C., 60, 61, *90*, 422, *475*
LaChance, L. E., 59, 60, 61, *90*
LaFond, R. E., 344, *356*
Lagasse, A., 29, 37, 48, 69, *87*, 102, 110, 113, 116, 138, 139, *151*, 322, *356*
Lagowski, J. M., 184, *240*
Laidlaw, H. H., 74, 80, *90*
Lal, B., 39, *91*
Lal, D. M., 223, *243*
Lamb, M. J., 395, 410, 412, 413, *475*
Lambert, B., 343, *356, 364*
Lamborot, M., 457, *478*
Lambremont, E. N., 396, 403, *475*
Lamy, M., 30, *90*
Lamy, R., 30, *88*
Landa, V., 61, *91*, 120, *154*, 315, *362*
Lang, C. A., 230, *240*, 444, 447, *475*
Lang, N., 327, *358*
Langan, T. A., 344, *361*
Langemann, A., 276, *357, 360*
Langley, P., 133, *151*
Lansing, A. I., 372, 373, 397, *475*
Larsen, J. R., 101, 123, 135, *154*
Lassota, Z., 214, 228, *238*
Lau, H. Y., 230, *240*, 444, *475*
Laufer, H., 30, *90*, 224, 228, *240*
Laugé, G., 85, *90*
Laurinat, K., 144, *154*
Lauverjat, S., 54, *90*
Laven, H., 60, *90*
Laverdure, A. M., 30, *90*, 103, 119, *154*, 306, 528, *361*
Lavoiepierre, M. M. T., 378, *474*
Lavrova, N. P., 213, 219, 220, *240*
Lawrence, P. A., 209, 213, 215, *241*, 317, 322, *361, 368*

Lawson, D. E. M., 284, *361*
Lea, A. O., 101, 115, 117, 123, 125, *154*, 263, 264, 308, 315, *361*
Leahy, S. M. G., 144, *154*
Lebedeff, G. A., 83, *90*
Lee, H., 259, *361*
Lee, T., 228, *241*
Leenders, H. J., 350, *361*
Lees, A. D., 81, *90*, 132, *154*, 219, *241*, 318, *361*
Leloup, A. M., 119, *154*
Lemonde, A., 181, 183, 213, 221, 230, *234*, *236*, *246*, 456, *472*
Lender, T., 103, *154*
Lennie, R. W., 223, 224, 230, *241*, 455, *474*, *475*
Lensky, Y., 30, *90*, 281, *360*
Leonardi, M. C., 178, *241*
Leopold, R. A., 61, *90*, 332, *362*
Leroi, B., 147, *154*
Lesseps, R. J., 195, *241*
Leuckert, C. H., 281, *358*
Leuthold, R., 307, *361*
Levenbook, L., 180, 184, 223, 224, 226, 230, *236*, *241*, *246*, 341, *361*, 446, 455, 456, 458, 467, *472*, *475*
Leverich, A. P., 61, *90*
Levinson, H. Z., 324, 342, *368*
Lewerenz, G., 217, *241*
Lewis, E. B., 204, *241*
Lezzi, M., 208, *240*, 343, 345, 346, 348, 349, *361*
L'Hélias, C., 110, *154*
Li, T., 293, *359*
Lichtenstein, N., 186, *245*
Lieberman, H. M., 378, 380, 383, 385, 387, 390, 394, 414, 417, 421, *477*
Light, S. F., 149, *154*
Liles, J. N., 400, 415, 453, *475*
Lilienstern, M., 49, *90*
Lindh, N. O., 221, 223, 230, *234*, *241*
Lindroth, C. H., 81, *90*
Lints, C. V., 404, 424, *475*
Lints, F. A., 391, 393, 404, 424, *475*
Linzen, B., 230, *241*
Lipsitz, E. Y., 176, 177, 213, *241*
Lloyd, J. B., 372, *475*
Locke, D. R., 228, *245*
Locke, M., 262, *361*

Lockshin, R. A., 181, 182, 185, 216, 228, *241*
Loeb, J., 405, *475*
Loew, P., 294, 296, *361*
Loewenstein, W. R., 347, *359*
Loher, W., 115, 123, 125, 137, 138, 141, *154*, 314, *361*
Longo, E., 179, *236*
Lorkovic, Z., 58, 73, *90*
Loughton, B. G., 224, *241*
Louis, C., 30, 32, *90*
Louloudes, S., 272, 277, 280, 281, 327, *360*
Lowe, M. E., 271, 280, 281, *356*, *359*
Lowe, M. L., 144, *154*
Lu, K. H., 175, 176, 180, 181, 183, *241*
Ludwig, D., 173, 174, 176, 178, 214, 219, 225, 226, *241*, 395, 399, 400, 446, 451, 452, *473*, *475*
Ludwig, W., 74, *90*
Luizzo, J. A., 69, 71, *92*
Lukoschus, F., 123, *154*
Lumb, R. H., 213, *246*
Lupien, P. J., 327, *354*, *361*
Lüscher, M., 70, *89*, 103, 106, 108, 109, 113, 114, 118, 123, 149, *152*, *154*, 197, *241*, 307, 325, 327, *361*
Lusis, O., 47, *88*, *90*, 103, 113, 117, 147, *153*
Lusk, G. J., 30, *91*
Lynn, E. V., 274, *357*

M

Ma, W. C., 143, *154*
McAllen, J. W., 214, 227, *241*
MacArthur, J. W., 378, 395, *475*
McCarthy, C., 308, *364*
McCaughey, W. F., 416, *477*
McCay, C. M., 413, *475*
McDonald, M. P., 41, *89*
McFarlane, J. E., 43, *91*, 176, 177, 178, 179, 213, *237*, *241*
McGregor, H. G., 31, 32, *91*
Mackensen, O., 58, 66, 73, 80, *91*, *93*
Macklin, M., 345, *361*
McShan, W. H., 458, *475*
Maddrell, S. H. P., 256, 264, 310, *361*
Madhaven, K., 332, 333, 337, 338, *361*, *363*
Maeta, I. J., 47, *91*

Mahowald, A. P., 36, *91*, 163, 167, 180, 181, 201, 204, 206, 207, *241*, *242*
Mahr, E., 164, 172, 190, 191, *242*
Makings, P., 57, *91*
Mandaron, P., 333, *362*
Mandelstam, J. E., 228, *246*
Mandl, A. M., 60, *91*
Manning, A., *362*
Manning, F. J., 80, *91*
Mansingh, A., 176, 187, 228, *242*, *245*, 254, 335, *362*, *335*
Marei, N., 185, *237*
Mark, D. D., 443, 449, *478*
Marks, E. P., 331, 332, *360*, *362*
Marshal, J. P., 286, *358*
Martin, D., Jr., 353, *367*
Martoja, R., 54, *91*
Maruyama, K., 228, *242*
Maschlanka, H., 164, 189, 197, *242*
Masner, P., 61, 64, *91*, 120, *154*, 315, 323, *362*
Masuoka, M., 327, *362*
Mathur, M., 221, *244*
Matolín, S., 315, *362*
Matsuura, S., 218, 228, *242*
Matsuzawa, T., 327, *362*
Matthes, E., 378, *475*
Mattingly, E., 230, *242*
Maul, V., 200, *242*
Mauldin, J. K., 223, *242*
Maurizio, A., 378, 416, 425, *475*
Mayer, R. J., 309, *362*
Maynard, L. A., 413, *475*
Maynard-Smith, J., 372, 378, 391, 393, 394, 402, 405, 406, 412, 445, 452, *472*, *473*, *475*
Medawar, P. B., 407, 468, 469, *476*
Medler, J. T., 47, *91*
Mednikova, M. V., 101, 135, *154*
Meerovitch, E., 313, *365*
Mehta, D. R., 38, *91*
Mehrotra, K. N., 187, *242*
Meifert, D. W., *90*
Meinwald, J., 72, *91*
Meinwald, Y. C., 72, *91*
Melampy, R. M., 213, 219, 220, 221, *242*
Melander, Y., 205, *242*
Melius, E., 27, *91*
Mellanby, K., 144, 146, *154*
Melvin, R., 173, *242*

Menaker, M., 179, *237*
Meng, C., 30, *91*, 201, 204, 206, 207, 208, *242*
Menon, M., 29, 64, *91*
Menon, T., 350, *366*
Menusan, H., 132, *154*
Mer, G. G., 134, *157*
Merle, J., 144, 147, *154*
Metchnikoff, E., 51, *91*, 429, 450, *476*
Metzler, M., 290, 291, 294, 297, 299, *362*
Meyer, A. S., 268, 289, 290, 294, 295, 313, 314, 321, *359*, *362*, *365*
Meyer, D., 290, 291, 294, 297, 299, *362*
Meyer, H., 60, *90*, 319, 320, *364*
Mezger, J., 134, *156*
Middleton, E. J., 271, 272, 278, 281, 282, 283, 284, 285, 286, 288, *356*, *357*, *359*, *365*, *366*, *367*
Midgett, R. J., 284, *363*
Milburn, N. S., 431, 461, 466, 467, *477*
Mildvan, A. S., 372, 443, 449, *478*
Milkman, R. D., 287, *363*
Miller, A., 188, *243*
Miller, R. S., 423, *476*
Milligan, J. V., 254, *358*
Mills, R. R., 123, *154*
Miner, J. R., 375, 378, 383, 388, 392, 423, *476*
Minks, A. K., 113, 114, 117, 118, *154*
Minyard, J. P., 72, *94*
Miquel, J., 410, 411, 412, 418, 427, 428, 429, 430, 431, 433, 435, 436, 437, 439, 440, 441, 442, 443, 449, 450, 461, *471*, *474*, *476*, *478*
Misch, D. W., 329, 331, *364*
Missonnier, J., 131, *150*
Mitlin, H., 30, *91*
Mitlin, N., 223, *242*
Mitsuhashi, J., 332, 334, 351, *362*
Miya, K., 32, *91*
Miyazaki, H., 281, *359*
Moffet, J. O., 421, *476*
Mohan, P., 32, 34, 38, 39, *91*
Mohla, S., 306, 352, *362*
Möller, H., 116, 117, *157*
Møller, I., 306, *366*
Moloo, S. K., 178, *242*
Mook, L., 21, 47, *87*, 130, 132, 134, 152
Morales, R., 443, 449, *473*

Mordue, W., 103, 108, 115, 117, 124, 133, *153, 154,* 310, *362*
Morgan, E. D., 272, 281, *362*
Morgan, T. H., 82, *91*
Morgenthaler, H. M., 41, *91*
Mori, C., 281, *359*
Mori, H., 276, *362*
Mori, K., 314, *363*
Morimoto, T., 218, 228, *242*
Morishima, I., 227, *239*
Moriyama, H., 283, 284, 286, 287, 288, 303, *362*
Morris, H. R., 284, *361*
Morrison, P. E., 28, 30, *86*
Morton, L. J., 184, *237*
Mosbacker, G. C., 84, *91*
Moser, J. G., 172, 201, *242*
Moulinier, M. C., 177, *242*
Mousseron-Canet, M., 351, *354*
Mouton, J., 115, *154*
Muckenthaler, F. A., 36, *91,* 180, 181, *242*
Muftic, M., 273, *362*
Muhsam, H. V., 378, 381, 383, 385, 394, *473*
Mukerji, R. N., 34, *91,* 164, *242*
Müller, H. J., 49, 50, 60, *91,* 131, *154,* 413, *476*
Müller, H. P., 123, *154,* 307, *362*
Müller, K., 163, *242*
Mulnard, J., 32, 41, *91,* 161, 167, 201, *242*
Municio, A. M., 213, 221, *236*
Murakami, S., 301, *356*
Muramatsu, M., 352, *357*
Murata, E., 273, *359*
Murphy, R. C., 294, *362*
Murray, F. U., 165, 167, 218, *242, 245*
Musgrave, A. Y., 68, *91*
Müssbichler, A., 149, *154*
Myrtle, O. F., 284, *363*

N

Nabert, A., 257, *362*
Nabetani, S., 327, *358*
Nagata, S., 218, 228, *242*
Nair, K. K., 315, 324, *355*
Nair, M. K., 123, *154*
Naisse, J., 79, *91,* 139, 140, *155,* 311, *362*
Nakanishi, K., 273, 274, 278, 279, 281, 282, 283, 284, 286, 287, 288, 294, 295, 303, *360, 362, 365*

Nakayama, R., 327, *362*
Nall, D., 443, 449, *473*
Nassi, P., 227, *246*
Natalizi, G. M., 308, 310, *362*
Nath, J., 457, *472*
Nath, V., 32, 34, 38, 39, *85, 91*
Nation, J. L., 29, *94,* 325, *366*
Nayar, K. K., 107, 114, 117, 119, 121, 123, 142, *150, 155,* 254, 257, *367*
Needham, D. M., 219, 221, *242*
Needham, J., 176, 178, *242*
Nelsen, O. E., 67, *91*
Nettles, W. C., 449, *476*
Netzel, H., 161, 163, 201, *242*
Neufeld, G. J., 335, *363*
Neumann, H. G., 303, *359*
Newman, T., 179, *235*
Newsom, L. D., 132, *155*
Nicklas, R. B., 205, 206, *242*
Nicholson, A. J., 17, 46, *91*
Nielsen, R. A., 80, *89*
Niemierko, S., 214, *242*
Nigon, V., 35, 36, *91,* 180, 181, *242*
Nikoforova, T. L., 422, *476*
Nishimoto, N., 273, 277, 327, 328, *360, 363, 366*
Nishioka, R. S., 443, *476*
Nitschmann, J., 192, 197, *242*
Nitshiitsutsuji-Uwo, J., 104, *153,* 267, *359*
Noirot, C., 117, *155*
Nolte, H. W., 48, *91*
Nomoto, K., 327, *358*
Nonidez, J. F., 66, *91*
Nonnenmacher, T., 35, *91*
Norland, J. E., 61, *92*
Norman, A. W., 284, *363*
Normann, T. C., 99, *155,* 256, 257, 261, 308, *363*
Norris, M. J., 57, 68, 74, *91, 92,* 130, 131, 144, *155,* 400, 401, *476*
Northrop, J. H., 404, 405, 418, *475, 476*
Nothel, H., 410, *476*
Novak, A. F., 69, 71, *92*
Novák, V. J. A., 103, *155,* 210, *242,* 315, 321, *363, 365*
Nowicki, H. G., 284, *363*
Nowock, J., 332, *363*
Nowosielski, J. W., 385, 388, *476*
Nünemann, H., 172, 201, *242, 248*
Nussbaum, N. B., *92*

Nussbaum-Hilarowicz, J., 38, *92*
Nuttall, G. H. F., 83, *89*
Nutting, W. L., 286, *363*

O

Oberlander, H., 230, *240*, 265, 271, 322, 325, 333, 334, 336, *354, 361, 363, 364*, 457, *472, 474*
O'Brian, D. M., 399, 452, *476*
O'Brien, R. D., 409, *476*
Ochsé, W., 13, *92*, 218, *242*
Odhiambo, T. R., 69, *92*, 123, 139, 146, 147, *155*, 258, 266, 315, 325, 326, *363*
O'Farrell, A. F., 319, *363*
Ogawa, S., 273, 277, 327, 328, *360, 363, 366*
Ohizumi, Y., 288, *358*
Ohnishi, E., 227, *243*, 328, *363*
Ohtaki, T., 283, 287, 314, 326, 328, *363*
Okada, E., 163, 166, *243*
Okada, M., 176, 177, *243*
Okauchi, T., 283, 284, 286, 287, 288, 303, *362*
Okui, S., 327, *363*
Olsan, R. D., 213, 221, *242*
Onodera, K., 227, *239*
Orita, S., 327, *362*
Orr, C. W. M., 28, 30, *92*, 116, 123, *155*, 326, 353, *363*
Oschman, J. L., 310, *363*
Otaka, T., 327, *358, 363*
Oudemans, J. T., 141, *155*
Overton, J., 194, *243*
Ozeki, K., 271, *363*

P

Page, T. F., 72, *89*
Pain, J., 149, *155*
Painter, R. R., 181, 183, 184, 185, 186, *237, 240, 243*
Painter, T. S., 170, *243*
Palévody, C., 31, *92*
Palm, N. B., 58, *92*, 123, 136, *155*
Pan, M. L., 27, *92*, 325, *363*
Panelius, S., 20, *92*
Panitz, R., 348, *368*
Panov, A. A., 123, 136, *155*
Pant, R., 179, 221, 223, *243*

Pantelouris, E. M., 215, 227, *243*
Paquet, L., 117, *153*
Pardi, L., 47, *92*
Park, O., 383, 389, *471*
Park, O. W., 82, *93*
Park, T., 379, 383, 389, 395, 396, *471, 476*
Parker, C., 230, *242*
Parker, H. L., 47, *94*
Parker, S. L., 375, 376, 383, 391, 392, 420, 423, *476*
Passera, L., 149, *155*
Passhke, J. D., *93*
Pastan, I., 342, *356*
Patchin, S., 30, *92*
Patel, N. G., 224, *243*, 310, 337, 338, 340, 341, *354, 359, 363*, 457, *476*
Patterson, J. W., 315, *363*
Patterson, R. S., 424, *476*
Patton, R. L., 385, 388, *476*
Pauli, M. E., 189, 194, 197, *243*
Pavan, C., 79, *86, 88, 92*, 208, *237*
Payne, F., 38, *92*
Payne, M. A., 66, *92*
Peacock, W. J., 65, *94*
Pearincott, J. V., 456, *476*
Pearl, R., 375, 376, 378, 383, 385, 388, 389, 391, 392, 404, 405, 420, 423, *471, 476*
Pener, M. P., 103, 141, *155*, 186, *245*, 314, 315, *363, 367*
Penner, M. L., 217, *240*
Penney, D., 30, *87*, 113, 114, *152*
Pepper, J. H., 176, 177, 179, *235, 245*
Perez, C., 218, *243*
Perron, J. M., 30, *87*
Pesson, P., 30, 32, *90*
Petersen, M. R., 294, 295, *355, 356*
Petri, W. H., 283, 299, 339, *355, 357, 363*
Pettersson, I., 225, *243*
Petzelt, C., 30, 37, *90*
Pfeiffer, I. W., 326, *363*
Pflugfelder, O., 103, 119, 123, *155*, 188, *243*, 260, *363*
Philiptschenko, J., 164, 165, *243*, 429, 450, *476*
Phillips, R. L., 436, *477*
Philpott, D. E., 411, 412, 427, 428, 429, 430, 433, 435, 440, 441, 442, 461, *476, 478*
Piepho, H., 141, *156*, 217, *240*, 252, 260, 314, 319, 320, 321, *361, 363, 364*
Pilcher, D. E. M., 310, *361, 364*

Pipa, R. L., 263, *364, 368,* 443, *476*
Pitman, G. B., 72, *89*
Pixell-Goodrich, E. L. M., 436, *476*
Plagge, E., 252, *355*
Plough, H. H., 57, *95*
Poels, C. L. M., 324, 348, *364*
Polakis, S. E., 221, *236*
Polonovski, J., 176, 177, *234*
Pomonis, J. G., 121, *150*
Popják, G., 284, *363*
Porter, C. A., 214, *243*
Possompès, B., 103, 105, 115, *155,* 260, 265, *364*
Postlethwait, J. H., 217, *243,* 333, *364*
Poulson, D. F., 171, 174, 203, 219, *235, 243*
Pouvreau, A., 213, *243*
Poyarkoff, E., 6, *9,* 218, *243*
Poyser, J. P., 276, *354*
Pratt, J. J., Jr., 454, 460, 462, *471*
Press, G. D., 442, *476*
Price, G. M., 230, *243*
Price, R. D., 192, *243*
Priesner, E., 71, *93*
Prince, W. T., 310, *354, 364*
Pringle, J. A., 52, *92*
Proverbs, M. D., 58, *92*
Pryor, M. G. M., 56, *92*
Przelecka, A., 39, *92,* 116, 118, *152,* 263, *356*
Pyle, Z. P., 186, *235*

Q

Quatropiani, A. L., 42, *92*
Quickenden, K. L., 38, *92,* 176, 177, 178, *243*
Quo, F., 104, 105, 123, *157*
Quo, P., 123, *155*

R

Raab, M., 194, *243*
Raak, C. J., 324, *356*
Rabin, B. R., 352, *359*
Rabinowitz, M., 164, *243*
Radford, S. V., 329, 331, *364*
Raffy, A., 396, *476*
Raikow, R., 339, *357, 364*
Rainey, R. C., 213, *243*

Rajulu, G., 273, *364*
Rall, T. W., 350, *366*
Ralph, C. L., 308, 310, *364, 367*
Ramamurthy, P. S., 30, 37, *92*
Ramazzotto, L. J., 176, 178, *241*
Ramponi, G., 227, *246*
Randall, D. D., 178, *243*
Rao, R. M., 214, *243*
Rasch, E. M., 228, *243*
Rasmussen, H., 310, *364*
Ratcliffe, N. A., 31, 42, *89*
Rau, A., 49, *92*
Rau, P., 380, *476*
Rau, P., 379, 380, *476*
Raven, C. P., 17, 25, 36, 41, *92*
Ray, O. M., 187, 196, *235, 243*
Raychaudhuri, A., 400, 442, 447, 456, *476*
Rechsteiner, M. C., 214, 226, *243*
Reddy, G., 296, *364*
Reddy, S. R. R., 336, *364*
Rees, H. H., 284, 287, *368*
Regen, J., 76, *92,* 141, *155*
Reichenbach-Klinke, H. H., 329, *364*
Reinecke, J. P., 335, *364*
Reinecke, L. H., 61, *92*
Reith, F., 189, 190, 194, 196, 197, *243*
Rembold, H., 58, *92,* 221, *236*
Rempel, J. G., 42, 47, *88, 92,* 163, 166, 167, *243*
Rensch, B., 209, *243*
Rensing, L., 263, *364*
Retnakaran, A., 315, *364*
Ribbands, C. R., 378, *476*
Richards, A. G., 4, *9,* 188, 215, *243,* 451, *476*
Richards, J. G., 32, 34, *89*
Richards, R. C., 327, *355*
Richardson, C. D., 133, *157*
Richman, K., 334, *364*
Richter, K., 310, *357*
Ricklis, S., 313, *359*
Riddiford, L. M., 61, 73, *92,* 118, 120, *155, 157,* 299, 306, 311, 315, 316, 317, 318, *354, 364, 367*
Riemann, J. G., 65, *87, 90,* 167, 169, *243*
Ries, E., 38, 39, 50, 51, *92*
Riess, R. W., 65, *86*
Rimpler, H., 281, *358, 364*
Ringborg, U., 343, *356, 364*

Rinterknecht, E., 332, *364*
Ritter, F. J., 71, *92*
Robbie, W. A., 175, 185, *243*
Robbins, J. S., 335, *364*, 272, 277, 279, 280, 281, 285, 286, 288, 327, 328, *360, 364, 366*
Robert, M., 346, *364*
Robert, P., 135, *155*
Roberts, J. A., 353, *366*
Roberts, R. B., 179, *243*
Roberts, W. C., 66, 73, *91*
Robertson, C. W., 218, *244*
Robertson, J. G., 54, *92*
Robertson, M., 69, *89*
Robinson, A. C., 23, *89*
Robison, G. A., 350, *364*
Rockstein, M., 6, *9*, 219, 223, *244*, 378, 380, 383, 385, 387, 390, 391, 392, 394, 397, 398, 399, 402, 408, 409, 414, 417, 421, 424, 430, 431, 435, 439, 448, 449, 452, 453, 454, 455, 456, 457, 459, 460, 462, 463, 464, 465, 466, 470, *471, 472, 473, 476, 477*
Rodin, J. O., 71, *93*
Roeder, K. D., 73, *92*
Roelofs, W. L., 71, *92*
Roemhild, G., 171, 176, *244*
Rogers, D. C., 344, *367*
Rohdendorf, E., 103, *155*
Röller, H., 103, 105, 123, 141, *155, 156*, 289, 290, 291, 292, 293, 294, 295, 296, 297, 298, 299, *356, 362, 364, 365*
Roman, S. A., 293, *356*
Romaňuk, M., 291, *365, 366*
Romer, F., 119, *156*, 261, 262, 303, *365*
Roonwal, M. L., 46, *93*, 163, 164, 165, 171, *244*
Roppel, R., 457, *472*
Rosenberger, C. R., Jr., 451, *478*
Ross, H. H., 4, *9*
Ross, M. H., 413, *477*
Rossi, M., 186, *246*
Roth, L. M., 47, *93*, 144, 147, *156*
Roth, T. F., 32, *93*
Rothenbuhler, W. C., 80, 82, *93*
Rothstein, F., 176, 178, *241, 244*
Roubaud, E., 134, *156*
Rousell, P. G., 226, *244*
Rowley, W. A., 467, *477*

Roy, D. N., 144, 146, *156*
Royer, M., 31, *93*
Rubin, M. A., 378, 380, 388, 395, 411, 412, *472*
Rubio-Lightbourn, J., 281, *359*
Rudolfs, W., 221, *244*
Rufer, C., 272, *358*
Russo-Caia, S., 213, 214, 221, 223, 227, 228, *244*
Rutschky, C. W., 176, 178, *234, 244*
Rutter, W. J., 350, *365*
Ruttner, F., 66, 75, 80, *93*
Rydlander, L., 343, *364*

S

Sabrosky, C. W., 4, *9*
Sacher, G. A., 406, 408, 409, *477*
Sacktor, B., 226, *235*, 433, 455, *472, 477*
Saether, T., 226, *237*
Sägesser, H., 110, *156*
Saha, N. N., 303, *359*
Sahaaya, E., 120, *156*, 287, 326, 327, 335, 341, *354, 365*
Sahota, T. S., 116, 118, *156*, 335, *365*
Saitoh, K., 217, *247*
Sakai, F., 227, *239*
Sakai, M., 273, 274, *359, 365*
Sakurai, H., 328, *365*
Salkeld, E. H., 187, *244*
Salpeter, M. M., 43, *95*
Salt, R. W., 177, *244*
Samis, H. V., Jr., 444, 448, 461, *477*
Sammes, P. G., 276, *354*
Samuels, H. H., 353, *367*
Sander, K., 165, 170, 172, 188, 191, 192, 194, 196, 197, *237, 240, 244*
Sanderson, A. R., 80, *93*
Sang, J. H., 195, *245*, 319, *355*
Sarkar, N. K., 181, 183, 230, *236*
Sasaki, S., 273, *362*
Sasaoka, I., 327, *358*
Sato, Y., 273, 274, *359, 365*
Sauer, G., 196, 198, *244*
Sauer, H. W., 167, 170, 171, 179, 182, 185, 201, 202, *238, 244, 246*
Sauer-Löcher, E., 196, *244*
Sawai, M., 276, *362*
Sawant, V. A., 187, 214, 227, *246*

496

Sawyer, W. H., 397, 455, 459, 461, *478*
Schaaf, K. D., 281, *358*
Schäffer, K., 81, *93*
Schanz, G., 166, 170, 190, *244*
Scharrer, B., 99, 103, 108, 109, 120, 123, 124, 131, 132, 137, *156, 157,* 252, 254, 255, 256, 257, 258, 259, 260, 261, *265*
Scharrer, E., 252, *365*
Schatz, E., 215, *238*
Schaub, F., 293, *358*
Scheinert, W., 48, *93*
Scheurer, R., 114, *156*
Schlegel, V., 458, *475*
Schlottmann, L. L., 25, *93,* 163, *244*
Schmialek, P., 291, *365*
Schmidt, C. H., 61, *90*
Schmidt, E. L., 136, *156*
Schmidt, G. H., 221, *244*
Schmidt, K., 147, *150*
Schmidt, K. P., 383, 389, *471*
Schmieder, R. G., 252, *365*
Schneider, D., 71, *93*
Schneider, E. L., 422, *474*
Schneider, G., 48, *93*
Schneider, I., 333, *365*
Schneiderman, H. A., 30, *86,* 197, 202, 217, 219, 227, 229, *230, 235, 238, 240, 243, 244,* 258, 265, 268, 270, 271, 273, 289, 290, 294, 295, 302, 318, 321, 322, 325, 328, 332, 333, 336, 342, *354, 355, 357, 361, 362, 363, 364, 365,* 445, 447, 457, *472, 474, 476, 477*
Schnetter, M., 163, 164, 165, 166, 167, 169, 191, 196, 200, 201, *244*
Schnetter, W., 166, 167, 182, 183, 189, 196, 197, 202, 206, *244*
Schooley, D. A., 278, 279, 281, 282, 295, *360, 365*
Schooneveld, H., 104, 106, 107, 117, 130, 135, *152, 156*
Schoonhoven, L. M., 143, *151, 154*
Schröeder, C., 18, 63, *93*
Schubiger, M., 202, *244*
Schulz, G., 276, 278, 281, *357, 360, 361*
Schultz, J., 180, 184, *241, 246*
Schuves, H. K., 284, *358*
Schwalm, F. E., 167, 170, 196, 198, 202, 207, *244*
Schwan, H., 219, *244*
Schwartz, J. L., 324, *365*

Schwartz, M., 291, *367*
Schwenk, H., 215, *238*
Schwinck, I., 70, *93*
Scott, A. C., 52, *93*
Scriba, M. E. L., 203, *244*
Scudder, G. G. E., 310, *359*
Sehnal, F., 263, 321, 323, 325, *365*
Seidel, F., 164, 167, 170, 188, 189, 190, 191, 196, 199, *244, 245*
Sehl, A., 163, *244*
Seifert, J., 225, *236*
Seiler, J., 81, 85, *93*
Sekeri, K. E., 224, 230, *245*
Sekeris, C. E., 219, 224, 230, *240, 245,* 337, 338, 341, 344, *356, 360, 365*
Seki, M., 213, *239*
Selinger, R., 60, *90*
Seiler, B. J., 353, *366*
Sellier, R., 260, *365*
Selman, G. G., 188, 197, *236*
Serfling, E., 348, *368*
Setlow, R. B., 198, 201, *238*
Seugé, J., 84, *85*
Shafiq, S. A., 206, *234*
Shane, J. L., 328, *354*
Shanmugasundaram, E. R. B., 213, *237*
Shanta, C. S., 313, *365*
Shanun, V. P., *93*
Shappirio, D. G., 228, *245*
Sharma, S. C., 221, *243*
Shatoury, H. H., 211, *245*
Shaw, E. I., 179, *245*
Shaw, R. F., 405, *477*
Shibata, K., 276, *362*
Shieldo, G., 195, *245*
Shigematsu, H., 186, *239*
Shimada, Y., 433, 455, *477*
Shimizu, M., 327, *358*
Shino, A., 327, *362*
Shiplacoff, D., 303, *359*
Shock, N. W., 372, *477*
Shortino, T. J., 286, 328, *364*
Shukla, S., 455, *472*
Shulov, A., 186, *245*
Siddall, J. B., 276, 278, 279, 281, 283, 284, 285, 286, 288, 293, 294, 297, 299, 301, 303, 304, *354, 356, 357, 358, 359, 360, 362, 365, 366, 368*

Siew, Y. C., 123, 130, 132, *156*, 269, 304, *357, 365*

Silverstein, R. M., 71, 72, *93*

Simon, J., 431, 461, 466, 467, *477*

Simpson, J., 149, *150*

Simpson, R., 207, *244*

Singh, H. H., 265, *366*

Sirlin, J. L., 36, *89*, 180, *239*

Sizer, I. W., 408, *477*

Skillings, J. R., 214, *235*

Skinner, D. M., 224, *245*

Slade, M., 299, *366*

Slăma, K., 61, *91, 93*, 103, 119, 120, 123, *154, 156*, 213, 219, *245*, 291, 292, 296, 315, 317, 325, *354, 355, 362, 365, 366, 368*

Slater, C. E., 315, 324, *355*

Slifer, E. H., 43, *93*, 172, 175, 176, 177, 188, *245*

Smallman, B. N., 176, 187, 227, 228, *238, 242, 245*, 254, *358, 362*

Smallwood, W. M., 436, *477*

Smith, C. N., 60, *90*

Smith, D. S., 130, *157*, 254, 256, 257, 358, *366, 367*

Smith, H. W., 179, *243*

Smith, P. A., 16, 19, 20, 23, *90, 93*

Smith, R. E., 395, 412, 429, 450, *472*

Smith, R. F., 23, *89*

Smith, R. L., 179, 182, 183, 184, *245*

Smith, S., 303, *359*

Smith, U., 254, 256, 257, *366*

Smolin, A. N., 38, *87*

Smuckler, E. A., 306, *366*

Smyth, T. Jr., 176, 177, 178, *240*

Snodgrass, R. E., 3, 4, 6, 7, *9*, 62, 63, *93*, 215, 218, *245*

Sobels, F. H., 60, *93*

Sofer, W. H., 226, *246*

Sohal, R. S., 432, 433, 467, *477*

Soifer, D., 350, *358*

Sokoloff, L., 345, *359*

Sondhi, K. C., 396, 403, 425, 450, 452, *477*

Sonnenblick, B. P., 409, 410, *477*

Sorm, F., 120, *156*, 277, 291, 292, *355, 359, 365, 366*

Spande, T. F., 341, *361*

Spector, W. S., *477*

Spiecher, B. R., 82, *93*

Speicher, K. G., 82, *93*

Sperling, G., 413, *475*

Spielman, A., 27, *85*, 119, *156*

Spielvogel, R. L., 344, *367*

Spirin, A. S., 207, *245*

Squire, F. A., 219, *245*

Srinivasan, P. R., 230, *234*

Srivastava, K. P., 265, *366*

Srivastava, P. N., 449, 454, *477*

Srivastava, U., 181, 183, 230, *236*

Srivastava, U. S., 314, *366*

Sroka, P., 105, *156*, 325, *366*

Staal, G. B., 124, 127, 141, *152, 156*, 314, *366*

Stadler, J., 409, *473*

Stamm, D., 70, *86*, 224, *245*

Stamm, M. D., 272, 277, *366*

Stamm-Menéndez, M. D., 272, 328, *360*

Standifer, L. N., 416, *477*

Staudenmayer, T., 187, *245*

Stay, B., 27, 47, *93*, 144, 147, *156*, 322, *366*

Steadman, R. A., 353, *366*

Stebblings, H., 31, 32, *91*

Steel, C. G. H., 256, *366*

Steele, J. E., 308, 309, 345, *356, 366*

Stegwee, D., 110, 113, 130, *151, 156*, 324, *366*

Steinbach, H. B., 396, *478*

Steiner, L. F., 60, *93*

Steinfeld, H. M. D., 417, *477*

Stellwag-Kittler, F., 260, 286, *366*

Stephan, J. K., 447, *475*

Stephen, W. F., 326, *366*, 457, *477*

Stern, C., *93*

Stewart, D. J., 339, *357, 363*

Stock, A., 319, *363*

Stockdale, F. E., *366*

Storni, A., 291, *367*

Stowe, B. B., 313, *366*

Strambi, A., 117, *156*

Strangways-Dixon, J., 106, 108, 109, 114, 121, 123, 124, 133, *156*

Strasburger, E. H., 165, 166, *245*

Strauss, J., 213, 221, *245*

Strehler, B. L., 372, 407, 408, 409, 412, 421, 442, 443, 449, 468, *476, 477, 478*

Strong, L., 103, 107, 115, 117, 123, 130, 133, *156*, 315, *366*

Strübing, H., 54, *93*

Stüben, M., 60, *93*

Stumper, R., 149, *156*
Sturtevant, A. H., 83, *93*
Stürzebecher, J., 265, 287, 310, *357*
Suarez, A., 213, 221, *236*
Subrahmanyam, D., 214, *243*
Sulkowski, E., 226, *245*
Sullivan, R. L., 409, *478*
Suomalainen, E., 81, *93*
Sutherland, E. W., 350, 351, *359, 364, 366*
Suzuki, Y., 340, *366*
Svoboda, J. A., 176, 177, *245*, 285, 286, 288, *366*
Sweeley, C. C., 289, 290, 292, 295, *355, 365*
Swellengrebel, N. H., 128, *156*
Sweeny, P. R., 42, *88*
Sweetman, H. L., 147, *156*
Swift, H., 68, 69, *94*
Szego, C. M., 350, 353, *366*
Szilard, L., 372, *478*

T

Taber, S., 66, 68, 69, 70, 71, 72, *86, 92*
Taege, M., 202, *245*
Tahmisian, T. N., 187, *245*, 396, *471*
Takahashi, A., 428, 433, 435, 461, *478*
Takahashi, S., 230, *245*
Takami, I., 197, *245*
Takeda, M., 137, *156*
Takeda, N., 332, *366*
Takemoto, T., 273, 277, 327, 328, *358, 360, 363, 366*
Takeuchi, S., 314, *363*
Tange, F., 219, *245*
Tani, K., 105, *157*
Tanimura, I., 32, *91*
Tash, J., 301, 304, 305, *358*
Tashiro, Y., 218, 228, *242*
Taskar, S. P., 30, *87*
Tata, J. R., 306, 353, *366*
Tate, L. G., 221, *245*
Tates, A. D., 65, *94*
Tatsuyoshi, S., 228, *237*
Tauber, O. E., 379, 400, *474*
Tawfik, M. F. S., 206, *245*
Taylor, A. C., 196, *235*
Taylor, I. R., 219, 221, *236, 245*, 396, *478*
Tebbutt, S., 445, *475*
Teffert, W. A., 186, *235*

Telfer, W. H., 17, 27, 30, 32, 37, *85, 88, 91, 92, 94*, 181, *245*
Terando, M. L., 30, *94*
Terzian, L. A., 446, 457, *478*
Tessier, G., 211, *245*
Teunissen, J. H., 218, *245*
Thach, B., 263, *364*
Thayer, D. W., 446, 447, *478*
Theunissen, J., 60, *94*
Thomas, J. J., 421, *478*
Thomas, J. L., 423, *476*
Thomas, K. K., 29, *94*, 301, 303, 325, *366*
Thompson, A. C., 72, *94*
Thompson, E. B., 353, *367*
Thompson, M. J., 272, 277, 279, 280, 281, 285, 286, 288, 291, 296, 327, 328, *355, 360, 364, 366*
Thompson, V., 175, 180, *245*
Thompson, W. R., 47, *94*
Thomsen, E., 47, *94*, 98, 105, 106, 107, 108, 109, 110, 116, 118, 120, 121, 123, 124, 125, 138, *150, 154, 156, 157*, 254, 258, 259, 263, 264, 306, *355, 361, 366*
Thomsen, M., 116, 123, *150, 157*, 254, 258, 259, *355, 366*
Thomson, J. A., 272, 281, 282, 284, 285, 286, 328, 335, 344, *357, 359, 363, 366, 367*
Threadgold, L. T., 32, *88*
Tiegs, O. W., 165, 167, 218, *242, 245*
Toba, H. H., 71, *89*
Todd, F. E., 416, *477*
Toft, D., 303, *367*
Tojo, S., 214, 223, 225, *245*
Tokuyasu, K. T., 65, *94*
Tombes, A. S., 130, 132, *157, 258, 367*
Tomkins, G. M., 343, 353, *367*
Topper, Y. J., *366*
Torossian, C., 149, *157*
Toyama, K., 259, *367*
Toyosato, T., 273, *359*
Tozian, L., 73, *92*
Tracey, K. M., 399, *478*
Trager, E., 209, *246*
Travaglini, E. C., 180, 184, *241, 246*
Trepte, H.-H., 205, *240*
Treves, C., 227, *246*
Tribe, M. A., 455, 467, *478*
Trost, B. M., 289, 290, 292, 293, *356, 365, 367*

Trowbridge, C., 174, 175, 178, *246*
Truckenbrodt, W., 30, *94,* 202, *246*
Truman, J. W., 118, *157,* 306, 311, 318, *364, 367*
Tsiu-Ngun, W., 104, 105, 123, *157*
Tsuneda, K., 276, *362*
Tuft, P. H., 174, *246*
Tumlinson, J. H., 72, *94*
Turkington, R. W., 344, *367*
Turoczi, L. J., 450, *477*
Tuttle, L. W., 411, *472*
Tyshtchenko, V. P., 228, *246*

U

Uchiyama, M., 327, *358, 363*
Uebel, E. C., 291, 296, *355*
Uichanco, L. B., 51, *94*
Ullmann, S. L., 207, *246*
Ulrich, H., 53, *94*
Unnithan, G. C., 254, 257, *367*
Upton, A. C., 412, *478*
Urbani, E., 176, 186, *246*
Ursprung, H., 226, *246*

V

Vanderberg, J. P., 31, 35, *94,* 180, *246*
Van der Kloot, W. G., 252, *367*
Vanderplank, F. L., 83, *94*
Vanderzant, E. S., 133, *157*
Van Handel, E., 308, *361*
Van Herrewege, J., 417, 422, *473, 478*
Vanni, P., 227, *246*
Van Tamelen, E. E., 291, *367*
Varute, A. T., 187, 214, 227, *246*
Velthuis, H. J., 149, *157*
Veprintsev, B. N., 347, *360*
Verheyen-Voogd, C., 148, 149, *157*
Verma, G. N., 173, *246*
Villee, C. A., 344, *356*
Villeneuve, J. L., 213, 221, *234, 246*
Vinogradova, E. B., 129, *157*
Vité, J. P., 72, *89*
Vlasblom, A. G., 56, *94*
Vogel, A., 141, *152*
Vogt, M., 99, 101, 103, 110, 123, *157,* 215, *246*
Voinov, D. N., 38, *94*

Volk, S., 144, *150*
Vollmar, H., 170, 192, 196, 197, *244*
von Borstel, R. C., 41, *89,* 165, 167, 189, 201, 202, *246*
von der Crone-Gloor, U., 179, *246*
von Gast, R., 150, *157*
von Harnack, M., 109, 123, 124, *156, 157*
von Kraft, A., 41, *94,* 200, *246*
von Lengerken, H., 81, *94*
Voogd, C., 148, 149, *157*
Voogd, S., 148, *151*

W

Waddington, C. H., 163, 166, 211, 215, 217, *243, 245, 246*
Waddill, V. H., 307, *360*
Wajc, E., 315, *367*
Waku, Y., 220, *246,* 258, 259, *367,* 443, *478*
Waldvogel, G., 276, *357, 360*
Walker, A. C., 455, *478*
Walker, P. A., 218, *246*
Wall, B. J., 310, *367*
Wall, E. N., 293, *368*
Wallis, D. I., 57, *94*
Wardle, R. A., 4, *8*
Warthen, D., 71, *89*
Watanabe, K., 328, *359*
Wattiaux, J. M., 399, 411, 412, *399, 478*
Weber, H., 4, *9,* 13, 51, 56, *94*
Weed-Pfeiffer, I. G., 98, 110, 120, 124, 137, 141, *157*
Weel, P. B., 38, 39, *92*
Wegener, G., 179, 185, *246*
Weglarska, B., 178, 201, 206, *239*
Wehman, H. J., 217, *246*
Weiant, E. A., 73, *92*
Weidner, H., 67, *94*
Weir, S. B., 262, 286, *367*
Weirich, G., 344, *367*
Weiss, G., *365*
Weitzman, M., 253, 256, *365*
Welch, G., 410, *471*
Went, D. F., 52, 53, *94*
Wesenberg-Lund, C., 54, *94*
West, A. S., 224, *241*
West, M. W., 253, *358*
West, W. L., 186, *235*
Weyer, F., 47, *94*

Weygoldt, P., 171, *246*
Wharton, D. R. A., 144, *157*, 411, 412, *478*
Wharton, M. L., 144, *157*, 411, 412, *478*
Wheeler, W. M., 58, *94*
White, A. F., 299, *367*
White, D. F., 314, 318, *367*
White, M. J. D., 66, 81, *94*, 169, 205, *246*
White, R. H., 217, *246*
Whiting, A. R., *94*, 217, *246*, 411, *478*
Whiting, P. W., 80, *94*
Whitmore, D., 342, *367*
Whitmore, E., 302, 307, 342, *367*
Whitten, J. M., 212, 216, *246*, 256, 264, 322, 348, *367*
Whitten, M. J., 60, *94*
Wick, J. R., 50, 64, 68, 74, *86*, *94*
Wicks, W. D., 350, *367*
Wiechert, R., 272, 276, 277, 278, *357*, *358*, *360*
Wiedbrauck, H., 319, 320, *367*
Wiens, A. W., 307, 308, 309, 312, *367*
Wigglesworth, V. B., 8, *9*, 43, 47, 58, 61, *94*, *95*, 98, 103, 105, 116, 120, 123, 124, 133, 137, *157*, 209, 210, 211, 213, 215, 216, 218, *246*, *247*, 252, 258, 260, 267, 271, 296, 320, 322, 324, *367*, *368*, 449, *478*
Wilkens, J. L., 28, *95*, 98, 99, 105, 114, 115, 116, 117, 123, *157*
Willart, E., 348, *354*
Williams, C. M., 54, 61, 72, *92*, *93*, *95*, 104, 119, 120, 132, 136, 137, *153*, *156*, *157*, 216, 226, 228, 230, *235*, *241*, *246*, 252, 260, 268, 283, 287, 288, 292, 306, 315, 332, *360*, *361*, *363*, *364*, *366*, *368*, 397, 421, 455, 459, 461, 467, 477, *478*
Williams, D. H., 284, 352, *359*, *361*
Williams, G. C., 407, 468, *478*
Williams, M., 186, *246*
Williams, V., 284, *363*
Willig, A., 284, 287, *368*
Willis, E. R., 147, *156*, 213, 219, 220, *242*
Willis, J. H., 317, 324, 326, *368*
Wilson, E. B., 164, *246*
Wilson, J. D., 284, *355*
Wilson, R. S., 227, *239*
Wimer, L. T., 213, 221, *245*, *246*
Winter, G., 31, *95*
Wirtz, P., 150, *157*
Wiygull, G., 30, *91*
Wlodawer, P., 214, *242*

Wobus, U., 348, *368*
Wojtczak, A. F., 214, *242*
Wojtczak, L., 226, 227, *245*, *246*
Woke, P. A., 134, *157*, 451, *478*
Wolf, R., 164, 165, 166, 167, 205, 207, *246*, *247*
Wolfe, L. S., 409, *476*
Wolkin, J. E., 178, *235*
Wolsky, A. A., 174, 226, 227, *247*
Wolvekamp, H. P., 56, *94*
Wood, D. L., 72, *93*
Woodbridge, A. P., 272, 281, *362*
Woolever, P., 263, *368*
Woyke, J., 66, 74, 80, *95*
Wren, D. L., 286, *358*
Wright, J. E., 328, *368*
Wroniszewska, A., 214, 228, *238*
Wugmeister, M., 173, 174, 176, *241*
Wülker, W., 31, *95*
Wullems, G. J., 350, *361*
Wunder, C. C., 419, *478*
Wunderlich, J. A., 271, 272, *359*
Wyatt, G. R., 214, 219, 223, 229, 230, *241*, *247*, 282, 325, 335, 336, 351, *361*, *363*, *364*, *368*, 457, *472*
Wyatt, S. S., 336, *368*
Wyss-Huber, M., 113, *154*, 327, *361*

Y

Yabe, I., 214, 227, 228, *247*
Yagi, N., 217, *247*
Yagi, S., 331, 332, 333, *354*, *368*
Yajima, H., 192, 193, 200, *247*
Yale, T. H., 444, *478*
Yamaguchi, K., 333, *361*
Yamamoto, R. T., 272, 277, 279, 280, 281, 327, *360*, *366*
Yamashita, Y., 105, *157*
Yao, T., 187, 227, *247*
Yeoli, M., 134, *157*
Yoshikawa-Fukada, M., 353, *363*
Yosii, R., 215, *247*
Young, W. C., 57, *95*
Yuan, C., *361*
Yushima, T., 187, *236*, *247*

Z

Zalokar, M., 202, *247*, 326, *368*
Zaman, V., 214, *247*

Zappanico, A., 186, *237*
Zdarek, J., 256, 327, *368*
Zeigler, J., 457, *472*
Zeller, H., 57, *88*
Zeuthen, F., 174, *247*
Zibitt, C. H., 299, *366*

Zinsmeister, P. P., 34, 35, *95*
Zlotkin, E., 324, 342, *368*
Zubova, V. A., 213, 221, *236*
Zurflüh, R., 293, 294, 299, *354, 358, 368*
Zwicky, K., 213, *247*
Zwölfer, W., 132, *157*

SUBJECT INDEX

A

Acanthocephala, 35
Acanthoscelides, 32, 41, 143, 144, 145, 146, 147, 161, 167
Acheta, 34, 161, 163, 171, 180, 182, 183, 192
Acheta domesticus, 23, 37, 388
  egg, 41, 162–163
Achroia grisella, 57
Acrobasis caryae, 378
Actias selene, 143, 147
Activation center, 189–190
Adelphocoris, 103
Adelphocoris lineolatus, 64
Adoxophyes orana, 71
Aedes, 144, 230
  intersex, 84
Aedes aegypti, 27, 101, 115, 119, 142, 315, 378, 396, 397, 415, 441, 446, 447, 451, 452
Aedes taeniorrhynchus, 115, 117
Aeropylar filaments, 45
Aeschna, 42
Afrocimex, 78
Aging, 371–478
Agrotis, 53
Akis, 379
Alloeorhynchus, 78
Anabolia, 76
Anabolia nervosa, 75
Anacridium, 115, 130
Anacridium aegypticum, 103, 132
Anagasta kühniella, 31
Andrena vaga, 136
Androgenic hormone, 311
Anisolabis maritima, 17, 36
Anopheles, 20, 46, 57, 146
Anopheles atroparvus, 101

Anopheles maculipennis, 17, 101, 128, 129
Anopheles quadrimaculatus, 119
Antheraea, 38, 132, 261, 288
Anthereya eucalypti, 334, 351
Anthereya pernyi, 42, 272
Antheraea polyphemus, 30, 32, 72, 268
Anoplura, 50
Anthonomus grandis, 30, 61, 64, 396, 449
Anurida maritima, 4
Apanteles glomeratus, 31, 34, 135
Aphaniptera, 16
Aphid, 51, 318
Apion, 48
Apis, 20, 66, 68
Apis mellifera, 17, 30, 66, 70, 117, 123, 378, 435
Apterygota, 16, 75
Ateuchus, 379
Attagenus megatoma, 71, 456
Aulacara elliotti, 38
Aulocara, 177
Automeris aurantiaca, 400, 403
Automeris junionia, 453

B

Behavior, juvenile hormone effect on, 314–315
Biorrhiza pallida, 132
Blaberus, 101, 307
Blaberus giganteus, 427
Blaps edmondi, 379
Blaps gigas, 379
Blaps magica, 379
Blastoderm, 184, 189, 193, 201
  formation of, 166–170
Blatta orientalis, 379, 415
Blattella germanica, 133, 319, 415
Boll weevil, 396

502

Bombus, 123
Bombyx, 32, 105, 214, 227, 261, 277
Bombyx mori, 30, 53, 67, 70, 97, 104, 186,
   260, 272, 277, 286, 327, 340, 378, 429,
   450
Book louse, 46
Boreus hiemalis, 132
Bracon hebetor, 81, 409, 422
Brain activation, 263–264
Brain, prothoracotropic activity, 263
Brain hormone, 263, 265, 300, 308
Bruchidius, 192, 196
Bruchus, 196
Bruchus obtectus, 132
Bupalus, 50, 147
Bursa genitalis, 63
Bursae copulatrix, 12, 13
Byrsothria, 147
Byrsothria, fumigata, 141

C

Calandra granaria, 53
Calpodes, 286
Calliphora, 32, 46, 47, 105, 107, 108, 109,
   110, 114, 115, 116, 118, 119, 120, 124,
   125, 133, 138, 166, 167–168, 174, 178,
   192, 205, 221, 224, 227, 229, 230, 254,
   257, 261, 264, 282, 285, 287, 388
Calliphora erythrocephala, 98, 99, 117,
   123, 220, 222–223, 224, 229, 272, 378,
   394, 455, 456, 467
   egg, 44, 162–163
   life table curve, 381
Calliphora vicina, 272, 284
Callosamia promethea, 378
Campodea, 14
Camponotus, 49
Carabus, 379, 424, 428
Carabus catenulatus, 102
Carausius, 44, 104, 110, 117, 119, 123, 257
Carausius morosus, 39, 83, 103, 123, 310
Carbohydrate metabolism, 176–178, 307–309
Carcinus, 287
Carpocapsa pomonella, 378
Castration, 58, 135–136
Cecropia, 230, 253, 258, 259, 260, 262, 289,
   298, 301, 315, 336, 445
Cecropia JH, 292–293, 296, 312, 314, 317,
   325, 337, 339, 342, 351

Ceratitis capitata, 60
Cerura vinula, 251
Cetonia aurata, 379
Ceutorrynchus pleurostigma, 131, 132
Chemosenescence, 459–468
Chironomus, 20, 31, 193, 202
Chironomus tentans, 345
Chironomus thummi, 346
Cholesterol, 284
Chorion, 41, 43–47
Chortophaga, 68, 179
Chrotogonus, 39
Chromosome puffing, 343–352
Chromosomes, giant, 209–210
Chrysocoris purpureus, 123
Chrysopa, 199, 200
Cicadinae, 49
Cimex, 77, 103, 144
Circulatory system, senescence, 427–430
Clitumnus, 117
Clitumnus extradentatus, 80
Clytiomyia hellus, 136
Coccidae, 49
Coccinella septempunctata, 131
Cochliomyia, 169
Cochliomyia hominivorax, 60, 396
Cockroach, 213
Cocoon spinning, 327
Coelopa, 207
Coleoptera, 16, 17, 52, 53, 71, 164, 172,
   260, 379, 394
Coleoptera Polyphaga, 21
Collembola, 17, 211, 212
Colorado beetle, 102, 104, 111, 113, 118,
   125, 138
Copris, 379
Copulatory act, 72–78, 315
Corpora allata, 123, 124, 251, 289, 297, 314,
   318, 323, 459
   activation, 106–108
   diapause, 129
   feeding behavior, effect on, 114
   inhibition, 108–109
   male accessory glands, 137–139
   ovarion control, 97–106
   physiological action, 109–110
   prothoracic gland interaction, 267–271
   regulation of, 266–267
   sexual behavior, 141
   structure and function, 257–259

Corpus allatum hormone, metabolism relation, 110–114
Corpora cardiaca, 99, 105, 106, 107, 108, 118, 122, 142, 144, 251, 255, 264
    hormone effects, 306–312
    structure and function, 257
Courtship, pheromone role, 70–72
Crustecdysone, 273–277
Crysomyia, 187
Culex, 38, 128, 164, 179, 191, 192, 193, 213, 214
Culex fatigans, 39
Culex molestus, 101, 123
Culex pipiens, 60, 65, 101, 119, 123, 458
Cuticle
    formation of, 319, 320, 324, 328, 332, 334
    senescence of, 424–425
Cybister, 102
Cyclic AMP, 350–352
Cynthia, 269, 318, 338
Cytochrome system, 227

D

Dacus cucurbitae, 60
Dacus dorsalis, 60, 422
Dacus oleae, 60
Danais plexippus, 72
Dacus tryoni, 60
DDT, 421, 460
Dermaptera, 20
Dendroctonus frontalis, 72
Dendrolimus pini, 53
Dermestes, 196, 285
Determination, cytoplasmic agents of, 200–204
Development
    biochemical changes, 159–247
    endocrine aspects, 249–370
    postembryonic, 208–231
Diapause, 129–131, 132, 134, 174, 220, 268, 324
Diapause protein, 113
Dictyoptera, 75, 76
Differentiation center, 190–191
Digestive system, senescence, 425–427
Diploptera, 103, 108, 124, 125, 141, 144, 146, 147
Diploptera punctata, 123, 322

Diptera, 17, 18, 32, 46, 52, 53, 75, 99, 116, 161, 164, 166, 172, 206, 208, 216, 260, 378
Dirphia cumemide, 453
Diuresis, 115
Dixippus, 142
DNA, 176 *see also* Nucleic acids
    extrachromosomal, 22–23
    oogenesis, 33
    ooplasm, 35–36, 180–181
Dociotaurus maroccanus, 272
Dolichoderus quadripunctatus, 149
Dorcus, 379
Drepanosiphum platanoides, 123
Drosophila, 16, 32, 35, 36, 39, 42, 53, 57, 59, 60, 66, 81, 99, 101, 110, 103, 123, 124, 144, 147, 161, 163, 180, 181, 184, 192, 194, 195, 197, 201, 202, 205, 206, 207, 211, 213, 217, 219, 263, 299, 303, 304, 315, 319, 333, 339, 381, 388, 414, 419, 424, 428, 442
    embryogenesis, 161, 163, 164, 167, 169, 179
    life spans, 376, 378
    oocyte formation, 18–20, 23
Drosophila funebris, 455, 460
Drosophila hydei, 300, 347
Drosophila melanogaster, 33, 57, 65, 378, 409–411, 417, 419, 420, 422, 423, 425, 427, 428, 429, 430, 433, 441, 445, 446, 448, 449, 452, 457, 461
    egg production, 401, 403
    genotype and life span, 391–394, 396
    intersex, 82–85
    neuron aging, 436–439
    survival curves, 389
    temperature effect, 404–408
    yolk formation, 27–28
Drosophila pseudobscura, 399
Drosophila repleta, 433
Drosophila simulans, 83
Drosophila subobscura, 378, 394, 399, 402, 403, 405, 445
Drosophila virilis, 83
Dyar's law, 210
Dysdercus, 30, 38
Dysdercus fasciatus, 146
Dysdercus intermedius, 324
Dytiscus, 38, 50, 379
Dytiscus marginalis, 22, 32, 36, 123

E

Ecdysis, 214, 321
Ecdysone, 116, 137, 327
  arthropod, 273
  biosynthesis, 284–287
  chromosome puffing, 344, 346, 347
  enzyme induction, 341–342
  extraction and analysis, 280–282
  inactivation, 287–288
  macromolecular synthesis, effect on 335–341
  oogenesis, 119
  plant, 273–274
  structure-activity, 282–284
α-Ecdysone, 250, 271, 333, 338
  structure of, 274–277
  target cell recognition, 303–306
  transport, 300
β-Ecdysone, 268, 269, 270, 271, 328, 331, 332, 333, 336, 338, 344
  cyclic AMP interaction, 350–352
  structure of, 277–279
Ecdysone-dopa decarboxylase, 341–342
Eclosion hormone, 311–312
Egg
  mitosis and nuclear migration, 164–166
  organization of, 160–164
  pole cells, 204–208
Elaps mortisaga, 379
Embryogenesis,
  blastoderm formation, 166–170
  embryonic area formation, 170–173
  energy changes, 173–180
  juvenile hormone effect, 315–318
  structural changes, 160–173
Embryology
  enzyme development, 185–188
  induction, 198–200
  nucleic acid synthesis, 180–185
  nucleus–cytoplasm interaction, 200–204
  pole cell, fate and function, 204–208
  regulation and determination, 188–198
Encyrtidae, 46
Endoderm origin, 171
Endosymbiontic transfer, 48–50
Endrocrine control, gonotrophic dissociation, 128–129
Endocrine gland,
  interactions, 262–271

structure and function, 252–262
Enzyme development, embryonic, 185–188
Enzyme systems
  growth and molting, 213–215
  senescence and, 447–448
Eosentomon, 14
Ephestia, 68, 76, 147
Ephestia elutella, 428
Ephestia kühniella, 396, 400, 401
Epidermal cell, reversion, 321
Epidermis, larval, 216
Epinephrine, 309
Eretmapodites chrysogaster, 431
Eumenis semele, 72
Euscelis, 172, 192, 194
Eurygaster integriceps, 136
Euthystira brachyptera, 123
Exocytosis, 256

F

Farnesol, 291
Fat body, 113, 287, 288, 307, 308, 326, 428–430, 449, 450
  senescence of, 428–430
Fat utilization, 221–223
Fecundity, 53–54, 119, 134
Feeding, neuroendrocrine control, 133
Fertility, 57
Firefly lantern, 442
Flight
  chemosenscence, 459–468
  muscles of, 324, 431–433, 462
  senescence and, 453–468
Follicle cells, 43
Formica, 49, 206
Fulgoridae, 49
Fumea crassiorella, 378

G

Galleria, 76, 105, 127, 141, 263, 294, 296, 299, 323, 333
Galleria mellonella, 39, 116, 119, 123, 132, 314, 321, 396
Galeruca tanaceti, 130, 132
Gastrimargus, 285
Gastrulation, 171
Gelastocoris, 38
Genetics, life span, 391–394

Geotaxis, 314
Geotrupes, 379
Germ anlage, 170, 190, 196
Germ layers, 170–173
Glandulae sebaceae, 54
Glossina, 14, 60, 82, 144, 146
Glossina palpitans, 147
Glycogen, 36, 448, 460, 467
Glycoprotein, 28, 36
Golgi bodies, 38, 42, 259
Gomphocerus, 120, 125
Gomphocerus rufus, 115, 123, 139
Gonadotropic hormone, 117
Gonads, male, 61–62
Gonoduct, male, 61–64, 67–69
Gonopod, 14
Gonoporus, 13
Gonotropic dissociation, 128–129
Growth, 209–215
    endocrine aspects of, 249–370
    gradient of, 212
    metabolism during, 213–215
Grylloblatta, 4
Gryllodes, 39
Gryllus, 35, 42, 106, 123, 141
Gryllus capitatus, 36
Gryllus domesticus, 30, 33, 57
Gynandromorphs, 81–82
Gyrinus, 20

H

Habrobracon, 81, 409, 416
Habrobracon juglandis, 80, 378, 411, 412, 450
Habrobracon serinopae, 378, 380, 411, 412
Hemiptera, 17, 46, 51–52, 58, 76, 210, 260
Hemiptera-Heteroptera, 20
Hemocytes, 13, 427
Hesperoctenes fumarius, 52
Heteropeza pygmaea, 20, 52
Heteroptera, 56
Hibernation, 128
Hippobosca, 53
Histogenesis, 225, 228
Histolysis, 225, 228
Histones, 184
Holometabola, 450
Homoptera, 49, 53

Honey bee, 58, 81, 213, 220, 374, 380, 416, 424, 425, 428, 435, 454, 456
    insemination, 73–74
    ovary development, 148–149
Hormones, action of, 299–352
Humidity, longevity, effect on, 419–420
Hyalophora, 32, 39, 104, 120, 302
Hyalophora gloveri, 290
Hyalophora cecropia, 37, 61, 118, 136, 260, 267, 268, 270, 290, 457
    development summary, 316
    yolk formation, 26–27
Hydrophilus, 56, 123, 379
Hydroporus, gonoducts, 13
Hydropyles, 46
Hylemya antiqua, 64, 65
Hymenoptera, 17, 57, 58, 74, 75, 76, 81, 141, 148, 164, 172, 216, 260, 378, 394, 455
Hymenoptera juglandis, 395, 397, 429, 430
Hymenoptera serinopae, 395, 429
Hypera postica, 130
Hyperglycemic factor, 308–309
Hypoblast, 171
Hypolipemic factor, 309

I

Icerya purchasi, 31, 53
Imaginal buds, 211
Imaginal disc, 217, 299, 333, 339
Imaginal reproduction, 50–51, 52
Imago, 216, 217, 230
Insemination, 72–78
Intersex, 82–85
Iphita, 107, 117, 119
Iphita limbata, 119, 121, 123, 142
Ips confusus, 324
Ischnodemus sabuleti, 48

J

Juvabione, 61, 296
Juvenile histone, 184
Juvenile hormone, 61, 103, 113, 120, 126, 251, 258, 259, 266, 267, 268, 269, 271, 328
    behavior effect, 314–315
    biosynthesis, 297–298
    chromosome puffing, 344–346

effects of 312–327
embryogenesis, effect on, 315–318
enzyme induction, 342–343
extraction and analysis, 295–296
inactivation, 298–299
macromolecular synthesis, effect on, 335–341
occurrence, 288–292
postembryonic effect of, 319–324
structure, 292–294
structure-activity, 296–297
transport, 301–303
tumor induction, 319

K

Kalotermes, 117, 149
Kalotermes flavicollis, 30

L

Labidura, 39
Labidura riparia, 47
Lampbrush chromosome, 34
Lampetia equestris, 53
Lampyris noctiluca, 79, 139–140, 311
Lansing factor, 398–399
Laspeyresia, 146
Lepidoptera, 13, 17, 50, 53, 66, 71, 73, 74, 76, 103, 119, 141, 161, 164, 172, 217, 220, 257, 260, 321, 378, 394
Leptinotarsa, 42, 58, 106, 107, 108, 110, 114, 115, 127, 129, 130, 131, 134, 135, 139, 146, 166, 182, 183, 196, 200, 206
Leptinotarsa decemlineata, 28–29, 104, 134
Leucania, 104
Leucania separata, 105, 123
Leucophaea, 103, 109, 110, 113, 116, 117, 120, 124, 125, 126, 137, 141, 144, 147, 257, 261, 325
Leucophaea moderae, 30, 123, 255, 326, 458
Life span
extrinsic factors, other, 418–424
genetic constitution, 391–394
intrinsic factors, 391–404
ionizing radiation, 404–413
nutrition effect, 413–418
parental age factor, 397–402
record, 377–380

sex, effect of, 394–397
survival curves, 387–391
temperature and, 404–408, 429
Life tables, 381–387
Liogryllus, 76
Lipochondria, 39
Liposcelis divergens, 46
Listroderes obliquus, 132
Locusta, 30, 54, 107, 113, 124, 125, 128, 133, 308, 314, 315
Locusta migratoria, 33, 46, 68, 69, 103, 115, 117, 118, 132, 141, 266
Locusta migratoria manilensis, 123
Locusta migratoria migratorioides, 123
Lonomia cynura, 453
Lucanus cervus, 379
Lucilia, 110, 120, 124, 192, 197, 221
Lucilia cuprina, 122, 457
Lucilia sericata, 98, 108, 455
Luciola, 38
Lycia, 82
Lycorea, 72
Lyctus linearis, 48
Lygaeus, 73
Lymantria, 141
Lymantria dispar, 30, 83, 84
Lysosomes, 228, 330–331, 433
Lytta viridana, 42, 46

M

Macrodytes, 102, 129
Macrosiphum tanaceti, 51
Malacosoma pluviale, 116, 119
Mallophaga, 20, 50
Malpighian tubule, 310, 311, 430–431, 449
Manduca, 279, 284, 285, 288, 291, 294, 298, 299
Manduca sexta, 105, 253, 272, 277, 290
Mantid, 73
Mealworm, 214
Mecoptera, 260
Melanoplus, 68, 110, 120, 124, 137, 141, 326
Melanoplus differentialis, 67, 69, 98, 175
Meloë, 53, 54
Melolontha vulgaris, 379
Melophagus ovinus, 123
Membrane permeability, 346, 351
Mesadenia, 68

Metabolism
    embryogenesis, 173–188
    hormonal control, 306–310
    intermediate, 226–231
    juvenile hormone effect, 325–327
    metamorphosis, 219–231
Metamorphosis 215–231, 250–251, 319, 322–
        324, 404
    biochemistry of, 218–231
    energy utilization, 219–226
Miastor, 52, 66, 81, 169, 205, 207
Miastor metroloas, 52
Microhymenoptera, 17
Micromalthus debilis, 52
Milkweed bug, 214
Mimas tiliae, 314
Mitochondria
    aging, 431–433
    type B, 466
Mitosis, 323
    egg, 164–166
    gradients, 203–204
Molting, 250–251
    growth during, 210–213
    metabolism during, 213–215
    neurosecetory cell effect, 252–253
    supranumary, 263–264, 313
Molting hormone, 251, 260, 265
    bioassay, 328
    biosynthesis, 284–287
    extraction and analysis, 280–282
    inactivation, 287–288
    in vitro effects, 331–335
    in vivo effects, 327–331
    macromolecular synthesis, effect on, 335–
        341
    mammals, effect on, 327
    occurrence, 271–274
    structure, 274–280
    structure-activity, 282–284
    target cell recognition, 303–306
    transport, 300–301
Monema flavescens, 137
Mormoniella vitripennis, 413
Mortality curves, 387–391
Mosquito, 134–135
Musca, 20, 31, 183, 187, 214, 282
Musca domestica, 28, 30, 53, 109, 121, 125,
        375, 378, 397, 414, 417, 418, 444, 447,
        455, 456, 461

    flight muscle aging, 430, 431–433
    life tables, 384–387
    longevity, 397–398, 402
    survival curves, 390
    wing loss, 460, 461–466
Musca domestica vicina, 420
Musca vicina, 378, 381, 382–383
Mycetome, 48, 49

N

Nasonia, 42
Nasonia vitripennis, 32, 34
Nauphoeta, 103, 114, 147
Nauphoeta cinerea, 30, 118
Nebria brevicollis, 123
Necrophorus, 379
Nepa, 46
Nervous system, senescence, 435–441
Neuroptera, 17, 172
Neurosecretion, 106–107
Neurosecretory cells, 130, 251, 266
    activation, 263–264
    significance of, 114–118
    structure and function, 252–256
    water regulation, 310–311
Neurosecretory factor, 109
Neurosecretory material, 122, 256, 261, 300,
        435
Neurosecretory system, 306
Nitrogen metabolism, 178–179, 223–224
Noctuidae, 71
Nomadacris, 130
Nomadacris septemfasiata, 131, 141
Notonecta glauca, 31, 32
Nucleic acid, *see also* DNA, RNA
    embryonic synthesis, 180–185
    hormone effect on synthesis, 333–334,
        335–341
    metabolism, 229–230
    senescence and, 444–445
Nutrition
    life span effect, 413–418
    longevity and, 452
    oogenesis, 133–135

O

Ocellus, 267
Odonata, 164, 170, 172, 260
Odontotermes, 188

Oecanthus, 76
Oenocytes, 262, 427–428, 449, 450
Oligarces, 52
Oncopeltus, 20–21, 31, 35, 36, 38, 47, 50, 58, 64, 68, 106, 107, 108, 117, 124, 133, 135, 138, 178, 179, 181, 182, 183, 184, 187, 257, 317
Oncopeltus fasciatus, 30, 73, 123, 451
Oocyte
  membrane formation, 41–47
  polarity, 39–41
Oogenesis, 323
  adult diapause, 129–131
  carbohydrate yolk, 36–38
  copulation effect, 144–146
  DNA content, 33
  endrocrine control, 97–120
  fecundity, 53–54
  follicle cells, 25–26
  gonadotropic dissociation, 128–129
  lipid yolk, 38–39
  longevity effect, 401–403
  neurosecretory cell role, 114–118
  nutrition, 133–135
  pheromone, male effect, 147–148
  oocyte formation, 17–24
  photoperiod, 130, 131–132
  postembryonic development, 50–53
  rebound effects, 121–128
  RNA supply, 31–34
  senescence and, 451–453
  symbiont transfer, 48–50
  temperature, 132
  yolk formation, 23, 24, 25, 26–31
Ooplasm, DNA occurrence, 35–36
Oosorption, 47–48
Oostatic hormone, 121
Ootheca, 54
Operophtera brumata, 132
Ophion luteus, 34
Orthoptera, 16, 53, 76, 141, 164, 170, 172, 259, 262, 379
Oryctes, 379
Oryzaephilus, 147
Oryzaephilus surinamensis, 30, 32
Otiorrhynchus, 81
Ovarian transplantation, 101
Ovarioles
  panoistic, 16, 18, 32, 39
  polytrophic, 16–17, 18–20, 22–24, 26–28

  regions, 14–15
  telotrophic, 17, 20–21, 28–29, 47
Ovary, 12
Oviposition
  accessory glands, 54–57
  copulation effect, 146–147
  endocrine effects on, 142
  environmental control, 143–144
Ovitubus, 56
Oxygen tension, 420–421

P

Paedogenesis, 51–53
Pagasa, 78
Panolis, 50
Panolis flammea, 132
Panorpha communis, 37
Paper factor, 61, 120, 292
Parthenogenesis, 78–85
Pediculus, 38, 64, 82
Pediculus capitis, 50
Pediculus corporis, 67
Pediculus humanus, 396
Pediculus vestimenti, 50
Periplaneta, 16, 18, 23, 32, 34, 36, 38, 67, 101, 103, 106, 114, 144, 147, 177, 308
Periplaneta americana, 29, 53–54, 121, 123, 264, 379, 396, 400, 414, 415, 458
Phallus, 63
Pharyngeal gland, 425
Pheromones, 70–72, 141, 144
  oogenesis effect, 147
  reproduction inhibition, 148–150
Philosamia, 104, 230, 301
Philosamia cynthia, 30, 136, 290, 378
Philosamia cynthia ricini, 267
Phobaeticus, 44
Phormia, 182, 183, 187
Phormia regina, 28, 30, 57, 117, 123, 433, 446, 455, 458
Phospholipids, oogenesis, 21
Phosphorus metabolism, 180, 224–225
Photoperiod, 125, 130, 131–132, 311
Phryganida, 104
Phyllopertha horticola, 53
Pieris, 147, 408
Pieris brassicae, 30, 57, 116, 143
Pimelia, 379
Pimpla, 76, 192, 206

Pimpla turionella, 30
Pineus pineoides, 53
Plagiolepis pygmaea, 149
Platycnemis, 191
Plodia, 68, 76
Poecilopis, 82
Pole cells, fate and function, 204–208
Polistes, 117, 141
Polygonia c-aureum, 105
Ponasterone, 283, 334
Population density, 423–424
Porthetria dispar, 82, 252
Poststerone, 283
Primicimex cavernius, 78
Procrustes, 379
Prodenia eridania, 448
Prostemma, 78
Protein bodies, 322
Protein synthesis, 185, 229
    senescence and, 445–448
Prothoracic gland, 251, 253, 256, 286, 300
    activation, 265–266
    corpora allata interaction, 267–271
    maintenance, 270–271
    stimulation, 267–270
    structure and function, 259–262
Protophormia, 192
Przibram's rule, 210–211
Psocoptera, 56
Psylla pyri, 131
Psyllidae, 49
Psyllioides, 131
Pteromalid, 135
Pupatation, 260
Pyralidae, 71
Pyrausta penitalis, 378
Pyrausta peritalis, 378
Pyrrhocoris, 61, 103, 120, 184, 296, 315, 318, 323
Pyrrhocoris apterus, 123, 292, 300

R

Radiation, sterilization, 58–60
Reifungsfrass period, 134
Reproduction
    courtship, 70–72
    female system, 12–17
    fertility, 57
    insemination, 72–78

    male system, 61–64
    oogenesis, 17–54
    oviposition, 54–57
    parthenogenosis, 79–81
    pheromone role, 70–72
    senescence and, 441–442, 451–453
    sex determination, 78–85
    social control of, 144–150
    sperm and seman, 64–70
    sterility, 57–61
Respiration, 213–307
    embryogenesis, 173–176
    inhibitors, 226–227
    metamorphosis, 219–221
Respiratory enzymes, developmental
    changes, 186
Respiratory quotient, 176, 220
Rhodnius, 30, 31, 35, 46, 47, 57, 58, 76, 103, 113, 116, 120, 124, 137, 145, 146 147, 174, 180, 210, 211, 213, 216, 258, 259, 263, 264, 296, 299, 310, 320, 324, 408
Rhodnius prolixus, 30, 43, 98, 123
Rhynchophorus palmarius, 53
Rhynchosciara angelae, 36, 79
Rhynchosciara milleri, 79
Rhyssa, 56
Rhyzopertha, 410
Ring gland, 99, 100, 105, 119, 257, 260
RNA, 176, *see also* Nucleic acid
    embryonic, 181–184
    metabolism, 229–230
    oocyte, 30, 31–34
    synthesis, 265
    transport, 32, 34
Romalea microptera, 459
Rynchosciara, 230
Rynchosciara angelae, 32

S

Sabinia, 48
Sarcophaga, 107, 110, 114, 115, 118, 120, 282, 285, 287, 288
Sarcophaga bullata, 28, 98, 106, 117, 123, 304, 322, 329, 341
Sarcophaga securifera, 98, 108, 123
Salivary gland, 346, 425
Samia, 287
Samia californica, 378

Samia cecropia, 378, 380
Samia cynthia, 268
Samia walkeri, 136, 137
Sarcosomes, 454
Schistocerca, 34, 47, 107, 113, 116, 123, 125, 133, 137, 139, 141, 144, 397
Schistocerca gregaria, 30, 103, 115, 123, 132, 272, 314, 379, 446
Schistocerca paranensis, 103, 115, 117
Screwworm fly, 60
Scrobipalpa ocellalella, 135
Seminal vesicle, 66, 67
Semen, 69–70
Semen production, 136–139
Senescence
    biochemical aspects, 443–450
    circulatory system, 427–430
    cuticle, 424–425
    digestive system, 425–427
    enzyme systems, 447–448, 453–468
    evolution of, 468–469
    excretory system, 430–431
    flight and, 453–468
    nervous system, 435–441
    nucleic acid and, 444–445
    physiological aspects, 450–468
    protein synthesis, 445–448
    reproduction and, 441–442, 451–453
    structural aspects, 424–443
    theories of, 372–374
    wings, 424–425
Sex determination, 78–85
Sex differentiation, 139–140, 311
Sexual behavior, corpora allata effect, 141
Sheep blowfly, 213
Silkworm, 42, 213, 214
Siphunculata, 20
Sipyloidea sipylus, 103
Sisyphus, 379
Sitodrepa panicea, 428
Sitona, 196
Sitona lineata, 53
Sitophila, 48
Sitophilus granarius, 400
Smittia, 194, 202
Solenobia triguetella, 81, 85
Spermathecae, 12, 13
Spermatogenesis, 64–67, 136–137, 331
Spermatophore, 75–76, 144, 145
Spermatozoa, 440–442

Spermiodesms, 66
Sphaerularia bombi, 136
Stenocranus minutus, 131
Steraspis, 54
Sterility, 57–61
Sterilization, 120
    chemical, 60–61
    radiation, 58–60
Strepsiptera, 52
Stylops, 136
Subesophageal ganglion, 261
Survival curves, 387–391

T

Tachycines, 41
Tanytarsus, 52
Telea polyphemus, 378
Temperature, 57, 429
    gene function balance, 83–85
    life span, effect on, 404–408
    oogenesis, 132
Tenebrio, 21, 25, 41, 103, 108, 115, 117, 119, 124, 163, 196, 230, 286, 291, 296, 297, 299, 322, 340, 408
Tenebrio molitor, 30, 64, 176, 399, 400, 446, 451
Termite, 30, 49
Testis, 311
    spermatogenesis, 64–67
    structure and origin, 61–62
Tetradontophora bielanensis, 32
Thermobia, 103, 147
Thermobia domestica, 132
Thysanura, 106
Timarcha, 379
Tineola, 197
Tipula lateralis, 23
Tortricidae, 71
Tribolium, 181, 183, 229
Tribolium confusum, 379, 395, 396, 409, 411, 447, 456
Tribolium madens, 379, 394–395
Trichoptera, 76
Trichopterus, 123
Tropea luna, 378
Trophocyte, 18, 20, 26, 27, 30, 32, 34, 36, 37, 39, 50
Tsetse fly, 60
Tumor induction, 319

U

Ulogra reticulata, 30
Ultrasound, 197
Ultraviolet light, 62
  irradiation 193, 194, 197, 201, 418
Urate, 429, 430, 450
UV irradiation, *see* Ultraviolet light

V

Vagina, 12, 13
Vasa deferentia, 61–62, 67–68
Vesculae seminales, 61
Vitamin C, 423
Vitamin E, 423
Vitellarium, 15, 16, 17, 25
Vitelline membrane, 41–43, 46
Vitellogenesis, 26, 30, 38, 117, 322, 435
Vitellogenin, 27

W

Wachtiella, 164, 166, 167, 207
Water regulation, 310–311
Weismann's ring, 99, 100
Wing bud, 318
Wings
  loss of, 460, 461–466
  senescence of, 424–425

X

X-ray irradiation, 197, 409–413

Y

Yolk deposition, 98, 101, 103, 326

Z

Zeiraphera, 146, 147
Zeiraphera diana, 146, 147
Zoothermopsis, 149
Zophobas rugipes, 64